INTRODUCTION TO

Theoretical Physics

By

LEIGH PAGE, Ph.D.

Professor of Mathematical Physics in Yale University

THIRD EDITION—SECOND PRINTING

D. VAN NOSTRAND COMPANY, INC.

PRINCETON, NEW JERSEY

TORONTO LONDON

NEW YORK

D. VAN NOSTRAND COMPANY, INC.

120 Alexander St., Princeton, New Jersey
250 Fourth Avenue, New York 3, New York
25 Hollinger Rd., Toronto 16, Canada
Macmillan & Co., Ltd., St. Martin's St., London, W.C. 2, England

All correspondence should be addressed to the principal office of the company at Princeton, N. J.

Published simultaneously in Canada by
D. VAN NOSTRAND COMPANY (Canada), LTD.

Library of Congress Catalogue Card No. 52–10481

First Edition 1928

Three Reprintings

Second Edition 1935

Twelve Reprintings

Third Edition, August 1952

Reprinted September 1955

PRINTED IN THE UNITED STATES OF AMERICA

PREFACE

This book, designed as a text for first-year graduate students and advanced undergraduates who are specializing in physics, attempts to provide the student in an elementary way with a survey of the whole field of classical theoretical physics. Since so much of the subject can be treated in the most elegant manner by the use of vector methods, the book opens with an introductory chapter on vector and tensor analysis. Throughout, the endeavor is to provide a clear and logical presentation of the subject rather than to impart information.

In the chapter on Origin of Spectra a number of applications of the Bohr theory are given. However, no attempt has been made to include more than an introductory article on wave mechanics, since an adequate exposition of this important subject would make the book altogether too long.

The chief change which appears in the current third edition is the use of Gaussian units in the theoretical part of the chapter on Electric Currents and of m.k.s. units in the numerical problems. A very complete discussion of units is given in the next to last article of this chapter.

Fourteen articles have been added and three deleted. In order, however, to avoid resetting the many pages on which no changes have been made, the article numbering of the second edition has been retained.

L. P.

Yale University, March 1952.

CONTENTS

INTRODUCTION

Vector Analysis

PART I. DYNAMICS

CHAPTER I

Dynamics of Particles

CHAPTER II

Dynamics of Rigid Bodies

CHAPTER III

Dynamics of Deformable Bodies

CHAPTER IV

Advanced Dynamics

CHAPTER VIII

Statistical Mechanics

CHAPTER IX

Kinetic Theory of Gases

PART IV. ELECTROMAGNETISM

CHAPTER X

Electrostatics and Magnetostatics

CHAPTER XI

Electric Currents

CHAPTER XII

Electromagnetic Theory

PART V. OPTICS AND SPECTROSCOPY

CHAPTER XIII

Geometrical Optics

CHAPTER XIV

Physical Optics

CHAPTER XV

Origin of Spectra

INTRODUCTION

VECTOR ANALYSIS

1. **Definitions.** — Elementary physical quantities fall into two classes, *vectors* and *scalars*. A vector is a quantity such as displacement, velocity, force, momentum, which has both magnitude and direction. It is represented by a straight line drawn in the direction of the vector and provided with an arrowhead to indicate its sense. The length of the representative line is made proportional to the magnitude of the vector. The end A (Fig. 1) is called the *origin* and the end B the *terminus* of the vector **P**. A scalar, on the other hand, is a quantity such as density, mass, work, volume, which has magnitude but no direction. A vector is denoted by a letter in **black face** type, the scalar magnitude of the vector being indicated by the same **black face** letter between vertical bars, or simply by the same letter in *italics*. Thus the scalar magnitude of the vector **P** is designated by either $|\mathbf{P}|$ or P. In the case of a vector denoted by a single letter the second of these notations is the simpler, and therefore the one that is generally employed. In the case of a vector represented by a combination of letters, however, the second is usually unavailable and recourse must be had to the first. Thus the scalar magnitude of the vector $\mathbf{P} \times \mathbf{Q}$ is designated by $|\mathbf{P} \times \mathbf{Q}|$, and that of the vector $\frac{d\mathbf{P}}{dt}$ by $\left|\frac{d\mathbf{P}}{dt}\right|$.

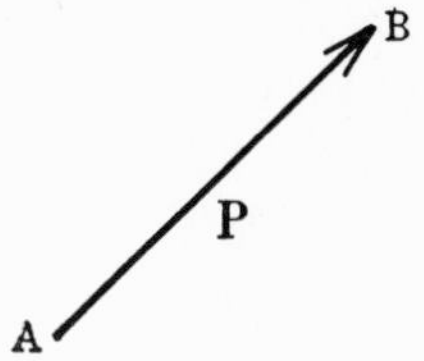

Fig. 1.

To multiply a vector **P** by a positive scalar m multiply the magnitude of the vector by m, leaving its direction unaltered. The product is designated by either $m\mathbf{P}$ or $\mathbf{P}m$.

The negative of a vector **P** is the vector taken in the opposite sense, that is, with the arrowhead pointing the opposite way on the representative line.

The product of a vector by a negative scalar $-m$ is the product of the negative of the vector by m.

A *unit vector* is one whose magnitude is unity. The unit vectors of most importance are the three unit vectors, **i**, **j**, **k** parallel respectively to the X, Y, Z rectangular axes. Rectangular axes are always taken so as to constitute a right-handed set, that is, the positive direction of the Z axis is determined by the sense of advance of a right-handed screw rotated in the XY plane from the positive direction of the X axis to that of the Y axis through the right angle between them.

Occasionally it is convenient to specify the direction of a vector by its three direction cosines l, m, n with the axes X, Y, Z. The student is reminded of the geometrical relations

$$l^2 + m^2 + n^2 = 1,$$
$$\cos\theta = l_1 l_2 + m_1 m_2 + n_1 n_2.$$

In the second of these θ is the angle between two lines whose direction cosines are l_1, m_1, n_1, and l_2, m_2, n_2, respectively.

Certain laws of combination which are valid in scalar algebra require justification when we are dealing with vector quantities. These are the *commutative law of addition*,

$$a + b = b + a,$$

the *associative law of addition*,

$$(a + b) + c = a + (b + c),$$

the *commutative law of multiplication*,

$$ab = ba,$$

the *distributive law of multiplication*,

$$(a + b)c = ac + bc,$$

and the *associative law of multiplication*,

$$(ab)c = a(bc).$$

The distributive law is of particular importance. For only if this law holds may we write

$$\begin{aligned}(a + b)(c + d) &= (a + b)c + (a + b)d \\ &= ac + bc + ad + bd.\end{aligned}$$

In the articles on vector addition and multiplication the validity of these laws for vector sums and products will be investigated.

Problem 1*a*. Show that if the distributive law of multiplication is valid

$$(a + b + c)(d + e + f) = ad + ae + af + bd + be + bf + cd + ce + cf.$$

2. Addition of Vectors. — To add two vectors **P** and **Q** place the origin of **Q** at the terminus of **P**. Then the vector **R** extending from the origin of **P** to the terminus of **Q** (Fig. 2) is defined as the *sum* or *resultant* of **P** and **Q**. Reversing the order of addition gives rise to the same sum, as is clear from the figure. Therefore the commutative law holds in addition. The magnitude of the resultant **R** is given by

$$R^2 = P^2 + Q^2 + 2PQ \cos \alpha, \tag{2–1}$$

where α is the angle between the positive directions of **P** and **Q**.

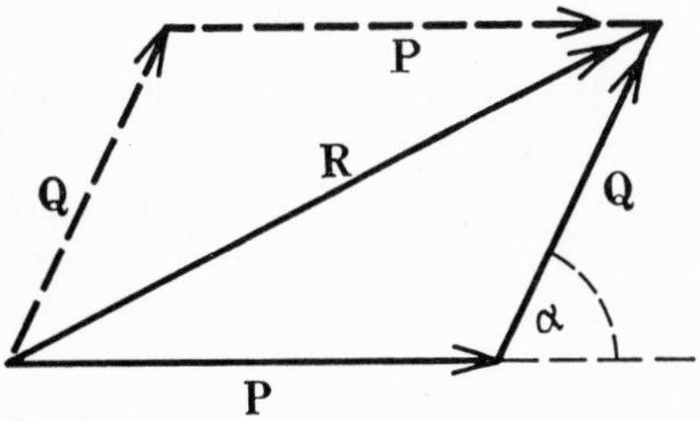

FIG. 2.

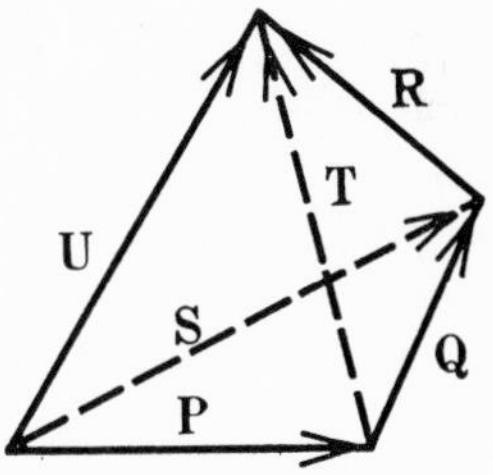

FIG. 3.

To add several vectors **P, Q** and **R,** find first the sum **S** of **P** and **Q** (Fig. 3) and then the sum **U** of **S** and **R**. The manner in which the vectors are grouped is immaterial. Thus if **Q** and **R** are added first the sum is **T**, and the sum of **P** and **T** is again **U**. Consequently the associative law of addition is valid for vectors.

To subtract **Q** from **P**, add − **Q** to **P**.

The *components* of a vector **P** are any vectors whose sum is **P**. The components most frequently used are those parallel to the axes X, Y, Z. These are called the *rectangular components* of the vector. If P_x, P_y, P_z are the projections of **P** on the axes X, Y, Z, respectively, the rectangular components of **P** are $\mathbf{i}P_x$, $\mathbf{j}P_y$, $\mathbf{k}P_z$. It is customary, however, to speak of the scalar magnitudes P_x, P_y, P_z as the components of **P**, since the subscript on each is sufficient to indicate its direction. Clearly

$$P^2 = P_x^2 + P_y^2 + P_z^2. \tag{2–2}$$

Equal vectors have the same magnitude and the same direction. Therefore if two vectors are equal it follows that each rectangular component of the one is equal to the corresponding rectangular component of the other.

Consider two vectors

$$\mathbf{P} = \mathbf{i}P_x + \mathbf{j}P_y + \mathbf{k}P_z,$$

and

$$\mathbf{Q} = \mathbf{i}Q_x + \mathbf{j}Q_y + \mathbf{k}Q_z,$$

expressed as the sums of their rectangular components. Since addition is commutative and associative,

$$\mathbf{P} + \mathbf{Q} = \mathbf{i}(P_x + Q_x) + \mathbf{j}(P_y + Q_y) + \mathbf{k}(P_z + Q_z), \quad (2\text{-}3)$$

showing that each rectangular component of the sum is equal to the sum of the corresponding rectangular components of the two vectors.

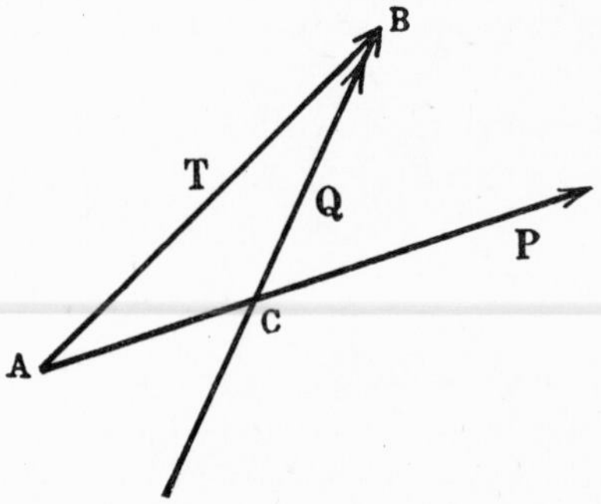

FIG. 3.1.

Any vector **T** (Fig. 3.1) can be expressed in terms of any two non-collinear vectors **P** and **Q** lying in a plane passing through **T**. All that is necessary is to lay off the vector **P** with its origin at the origin A of **T**, and the vector **Q** with its terminus at the terminus B of **T**. Then **T** is the sum of the vectors $\overline{AC}$ and $\overline{CB}$. But the vector $\overline{AC}$ equals $m\mathbf{P}$ and $\overline{CB}$ equals $n\mathbf{Q}$, where m and n are scalars. Hence

$$\mathbf{T} = m\mathbf{P} + n\mathbf{Q}.$$

Finally, any vector **T** can be expressed in terms of any three non-coplanar vectors **P**, **Q** and **R**. Let **S** be a vector having the direction of the line of intersection of the plane of **T** and **P** with the plane of **Q** and **R**. Then, as **P** and **S** are coplanar with **T**, **T** can be expressed in terms of **P** and **S**. But, as **S** is coplanar with **Q** and **R**, **S** can be expressed in terms of **Q** and **R**. Therefore **T** can be expressed in terms of **P**, **Q** and **R**. Note that, if **P**, **Q** and **R** are coplanar, **P** and **S** are collinear and the construction of Fig. 3.1 fails.

3. **Vector Representation of Surfaces.** — Although a directed segment of a straight line is the most obvious type of directed quantity, other geometrical forms possess the property of direction in addition to the property of magnitude. Of particular importance is the bounded plane surface such as is illustrated by ABC (Fig. 4). It has a magnitude represented by its area and a direction specified by its orientation in space. Since its orientation is determined by the direction of its normal, it may be characterized vectorially by a directed segment of a straight line having the direction of its normal and a length proportional to its area. However an ambiguity exists as to the positive sense of the normal. To remove this ambiguity the following conventions are adopted: (*a*) if the surface is part of a closed surface the outward drawn normal is taken as positive; (*b*) if the surface is not part of a closed surface the positive sense of describing the periphery is connected with the positive direction of the normal by the rule that a right-handed screw, rotated in the plane of the surface in the positive sense of describing the periphery, advances along the positive normal. Thus in Fig. 4, if the periphery of the surface is described in the sense ABC, the positive sense of the normal and therefore the direction of the vector $\boldsymbol{\sigma}$ representing the surface is upward.

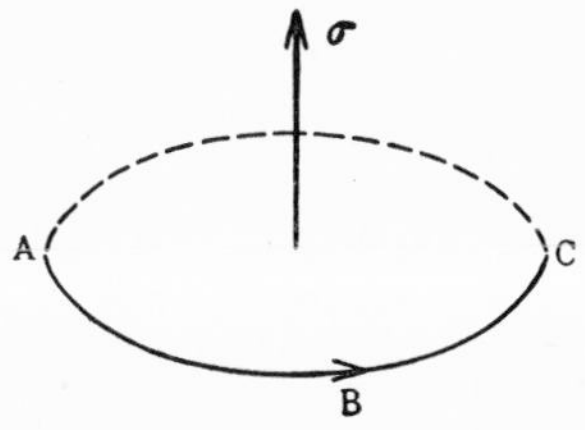

FIG. 4.

If a surface is not plane, it may be divided into a number of elementary surfaces each of which is plane to any desired degree of approximation. Then the vector representative of the entire surface is the sum of the vectors representing its elements.

Two surfaces, considered as vectors, are equal if their representative vectors are equal. Therefore two plane surfaces are equal if they have equal areas and normals in the same direction even if they have different shapes. Furthermore a curved surface may be replaced by a plane surface perpendicular to its representative vector having an area equal to the magnitude of this vector.

Let $ABCD$ (Fig. 5) be a plane rectangle, the edges AB and CD being parallel to the plane determined by the normal $\boldsymbol{\sigma}$ and the

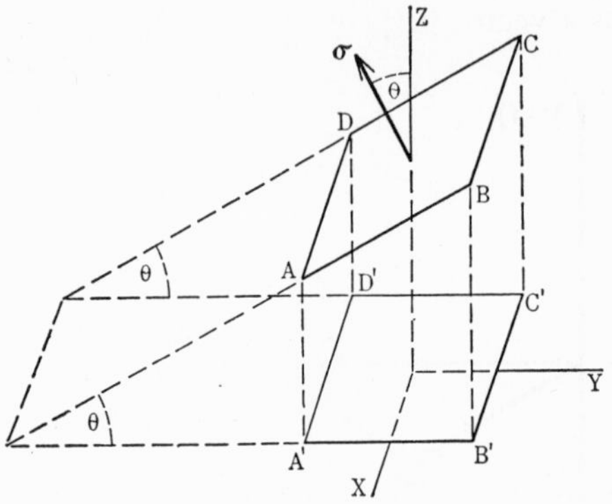

Fig. 5.

Z axis. If $A'B'C'D'$ is the projection of the rectangle on the XY plane,

$$A'D' = AD,$$

$$A'B' = AB \cos \theta,$$

and therefore

$$A'B'C'D' = ABCD \cos \theta.$$

But if $\boldsymbol{\sigma}$ is the vector representing the surface,

$$\sigma_z = \sigma \cos \theta = ABCD \cos \theta.$$

Therefore σ_z is the projection of the surface on a plane perpendicular to the Z axis. Note that if the angle θ is greater than 90° the projection is negative.

A plane surface whose shape does not conform to that of Fig. 5 may be divided by a network of straight lines into elementary surfaces for each of which the preceding conclusion holds. Hence σ_x, σ_y, σ_z represent the projections of any plane surface on planes perpendicular to the X, Y, Z axes respectively. This statement is also valid for a curved surface since the elements of such a surface may be treated as if they were plane.

The vector representing a closed surface is zero. For the projection of the entire surface on any plane is zero since as much of the projected area is negative as positive. Therefore the vector representative of the entire surface has zero components along the three axes X, Y, Z and consequently it vanishes.

4. Vector Product of Two Vectors. — The *vector* or *cross product* of two vectors is a vector perpendicular to their plane in the sense of advance of a right-handed screw rotated from the first to the second of these vectors through the smaller angle between their positive directions. It has a magnitude equal to the product of the magnitudes of the two vectors by the sine of the angle α between them. The vector product of $\mathbf{P}$ and $\mathbf{Q}$ is denoted by $\mathbf{P} \times \mathbf{Q}$. As is clear from Fig. 6 the commutative law does not hold, but instead the *anti-commutative law*

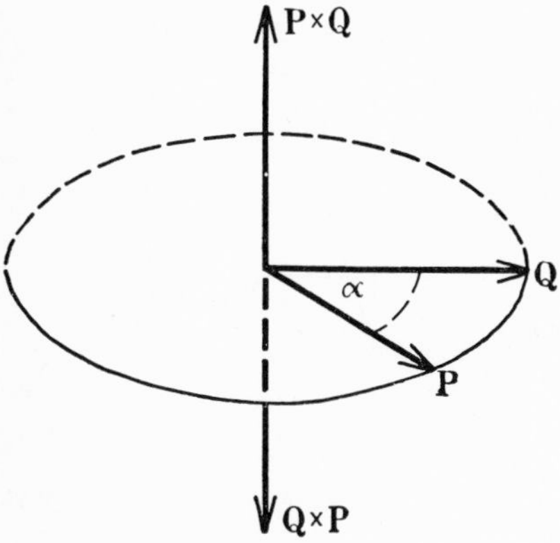

FIG. 6.

$$\mathbf{Q} \times \mathbf{P} = -\mathbf{P} \times \mathbf{Q}, \quad \mathbf{P} \times \mathbf{P} = 0. \tag{4-1}$$

It follows from the definition that the magnitude of the vector product of $\mathbf{P}$ and $\mathbf{Q}$ is equal to the area of the parallelogram of which $\mathbf{P}$ and $\mathbf{Q}$ are the sides. Therefore $\mathbf{P} \times \mathbf{Q}$ is the vector representing the surface of this parallelogram.

To prove that the distributive law holds for the vector product consider the prism (Fig. 7) whose edges are the vectors $\mathbf{P}$, $\mathbf{Q}$, $(\mathbf{P} + \mathbf{Q})$ and $\mathbf{R}$. The vectors representing the faces of this closed polyhedral surface are

$$ABED = \mathbf{R} \times \mathbf{P},$$

$$BCFE = \mathbf{R} \times \mathbf{Q},$$

$$ADFC = (\mathbf{P} + \mathbf{Q}) \times \mathbf{R},$$

$$ACB = \tfrac{1}{2}(\mathbf{Q} \times \mathbf{P}),$$

$$DEF = \tfrac{1}{2}(\mathbf{P} \times \mathbf{Q}).$$

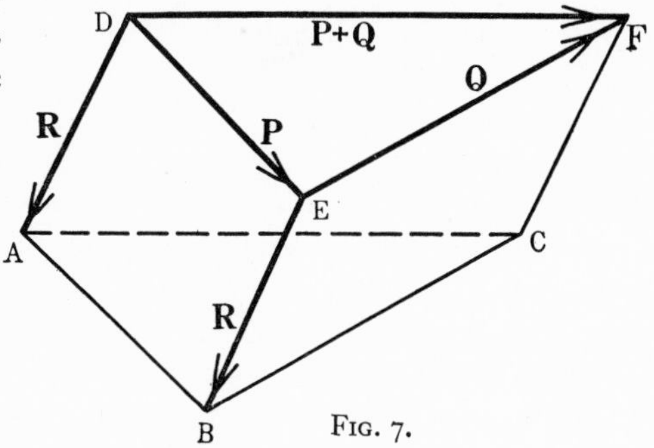

FIG. 7.

Therefore the zero vector representative of the entire polyhedral surface is

$$\mathbf{R}\times\mathbf{P}+\mathbf{R}\times\mathbf{Q}+(\mathbf{P}+\mathbf{Q})\times\mathbf{R}+\tfrac{1}{2}(\mathbf{Q}\times\mathbf{P})+\tfrac{1}{2}(\mathbf{P}\times\mathbf{Q})=0,$$

giving

$$(\mathbf{P}+\mathbf{Q})\times\mathbf{R}=\mathbf{P}\times\mathbf{R}+\mathbf{Q}\times\mathbf{R}, \tag{4-2}$$

which is the distributive law of multiplication.

Consider the unit vectors **i**, **j**, **k**. From the definition of the vector product it follows at once that

$$\left.\begin{aligned} \mathbf{i}\times\mathbf{j}=\mathbf{k},\quad \mathbf{j}\times\mathbf{k}=\mathbf{i},\quad \mathbf{k}\times\mathbf{i}=\mathbf{j},\\ \mathbf{i}\times\mathbf{i}=\mathbf{j}\times\mathbf{j}=\mathbf{k}\times\mathbf{k}=0. \end{aligned}\right\} \tag{4-3}$$

Writing the vectors **P** and **Q** in terms of their rectangular components

$$\mathbf{P}=\mathbf{i}P_x+\mathbf{j}P_y+\mathbf{k}P_z,$$

$$\mathbf{Q}=\mathbf{i}Q_x+\mathbf{j}Q_y+\mathbf{k}Q_z,$$

and, as the distributive law holds for the vector product,

$$\begin{aligned}\mathbf{P}\times\mathbf{Q} &= (\mathbf{i}P_x+\mathbf{j}P_y+\mathbf{k}P_z)\times(\mathbf{i}Q_x+\mathbf{j}Q_y+\mathbf{k}Q_z)\\ &= \mathbf{i}\times\mathbf{i}P_xQ_x+\mathbf{i}\times\mathbf{j}P_xQ_y+\mathbf{i}\times\mathbf{k}P_xQ_z\\ &\quad+\mathbf{j}\times\mathbf{i}P_yQ_x+\mathbf{j}\times\mathbf{j}P_yQ_y+\mathbf{j}\times\mathbf{k}P_yQ_z\\ &\quad+\mathbf{k}\times\mathbf{i}P_zQ_x+\mathbf{k}\times\mathbf{j}P_zQ_y+\mathbf{k}\times\mathbf{k}P_zQ_z\\ &= \mathbf{i}(P_yQ_z-P_zQ_y)+\mathbf{j}(P_zQ_x-P_xQ_z)+\mathbf{k}(P_xQ_y-P_yQ_x).\end{aligned}$$

This expression can be represented compactly by the determinant

$$\mathbf{P}\times\mathbf{Q}=\begin{vmatrix}\mathbf{i} & \mathbf{j} & \mathbf{k}\\ P_x & P_y & P_z\\ Q_x & Q_y & Q_z\end{vmatrix}. \tag{4-4}$$

Problem 4a. The coordinates of the three vertices of a triangle are 1, 2, 5; 6, 3, 8; 5, 7, 9. Compute its area by vector methods. *Ans.* 12.51.

Problem 4b. If l_1, l_2, l_3; m_1, m_2, m_3; n_1, n_2, n_3 are the direction cosines of the rectangular axes $X'Y'Z'$ relative to the rectangular axes XYZ deduce by vector methods the relations $l_1 = m_2n_3 - n_2m_3$, $l_2 = m_3n_1 - m_1n_3$, $l_3 = m_1n_2 - m_2n_1$, etc.

5. Scalar Product of Two Vectors. — The *scalar* or *dot product* of two vectors is defined as a scalar equal in magnitude to the product of the magnitudes of the two vectors by the cosine of the angle between them. The scalar product of **P** and **Q** is denoted by $\mathbf{P}\cdot\mathbf{Q}$. It is clear from the definition that

$$\mathbf{Q}\cdot\mathbf{P} = \mathbf{P}\cdot\mathbf{Q}. \tag{5–1}$$

Therefore the commutative law holds for this product. Geometrically the scalar product of two vectors is equal to the magnitude of either vector multiplied by the projection of the other upon it.

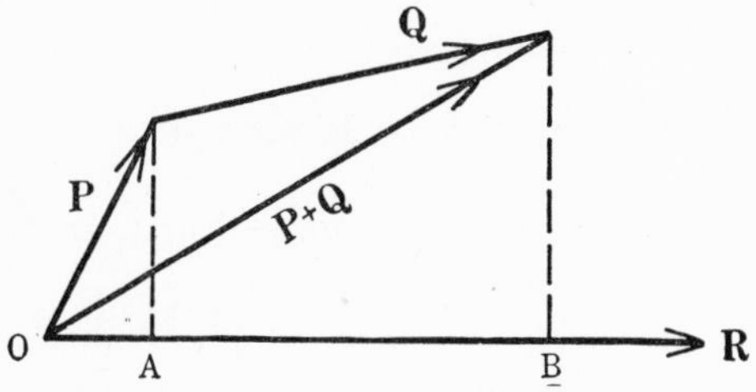

FIG. 8.

To show that the distributive law holds we have from Fig. 8,

$$\mathbf{P}\cdot\mathbf{R} + \mathbf{Q}\cdot\mathbf{R} = \overline{OA}\,R + \overline{AB}\,R$$

$$= \overline{OB}\,R,$$

$$(\mathbf{P} + \mathbf{Q})\cdot\mathbf{R} = \overline{OB}\,R.$$

Therefore

$$(\mathbf{P} + \mathbf{Q})\cdot\mathbf{R} = \mathbf{P}\cdot\mathbf{R} + \mathbf{Q}\cdot\mathbf{R}. \tag{5–2}$$

From the unit vectors **i**, **j**, **k** we can form the scalar products

$$\left.\begin{aligned} \mathbf{i}\cdot\mathbf{i} = \mathbf{j}\cdot\mathbf{j} = \mathbf{k}\cdot\mathbf{k} = 1, \\ \mathbf{i}\cdot\mathbf{j} = \mathbf{j}\cdot\mathbf{k} = \mathbf{k}\cdot\mathbf{i} = 0. \end{aligned}\right\} \tag{5–3}$$

Writing **P** and **Q** in terms of their rectangular components the scalar product $\mathbf{P}\cdot\mathbf{Q}$ may be expanded as follows:

$$\left.\begin{aligned}\mathbf{P}\cdot\mathbf{Q} &= (\mathbf{i}P_x + \mathbf{j}P_y + \mathbf{k}P_z)\cdot(\mathbf{i}Q_x + \mathbf{j}Q_y + \mathbf{k}Q_z) \\ &= \mathbf{i}\cdot\mathbf{i}P_xQ_x + \mathbf{i}\cdot\mathbf{j}P_xQ_y + \mathbf{i}\cdot\mathbf{k}P_xQ_z + \mathbf{j}\cdot\mathbf{i}P_yQ_x + \mathbf{j}\cdot\mathbf{j}P_yQ_y \\ &\qquad + \mathbf{j}\cdot\mathbf{k}P_yQ_z + \mathbf{k}\cdot\mathbf{i}P_zQ_x + \mathbf{k}\cdot\mathbf{j}P_zQ_y + \mathbf{k}\cdot\mathbf{k}P_zQ_z \\ &= P_xQ_x + P_yQ_y + P_zQ_z.\end{aligned}\right\} \quad (5\text{-}4)$$

Also

$$P^2 = \mathbf{P}\cdot\mathbf{P} = P_x^2 + P_y^2 + P_z^2. \quad (5\text{-}5)$$

Problem 5a. Show by use of the expansion of the scalar product that if two vectors have direction cosines l_1, m_1, n_1 and l_2, m_2, n_2, respectively, and θ is the angle between them, then

$$\cos\theta = l_1l_2 + m_1m_2 + n_1n_2.$$

6. Triple Scalar Product. — This product is the scalar

$$(\mathbf{P}\times\mathbf{Q})\cdot\mathbf{R} = \mathbf{R}\cdot(\mathbf{P}\times\mathbf{Q}) = -\,\mathbf{R}\cdot(\mathbf{Q}\times\mathbf{P}) = -\,(\mathbf{Q}\times\mathbf{P})\cdot\mathbf{R},$$

where the vector product $\mathbf{P}\times\mathbf{Q}$ is formed first, and then the scalar product of this vector with $\mathbf{R}$ is taken.

Consider the parallelopiped (Fig. 9) of which **P, Q, R** are the edges. The magnitude of $\mathbf{P}\times\mathbf{Q}$ is equal to the area of the base and $(\mathbf{P}\times\mathbf{Q})\cdot\mathbf{R}$ is the product of the area of the base by the projection of $\mathbf{R}$ along the line $\mathbf{P}\times\mathbf{Q}$ perpendicular to the base, that is, by the altitude. So the scalar $(\mathbf{P}\times\mathbf{Q})\cdot\mathbf{R}$ measures the volume of the parallelopiped. But if we had chosen the face of which $\mathbf{Q}$ and $\mathbf{R}$ are the edges as base, the volume of the parallelopiped would have been $(\mathbf{Q}\times\mathbf{R})\cdot\mathbf{P} = \mathbf{P}\cdot(\mathbf{Q}\times\mathbf{R})$. So

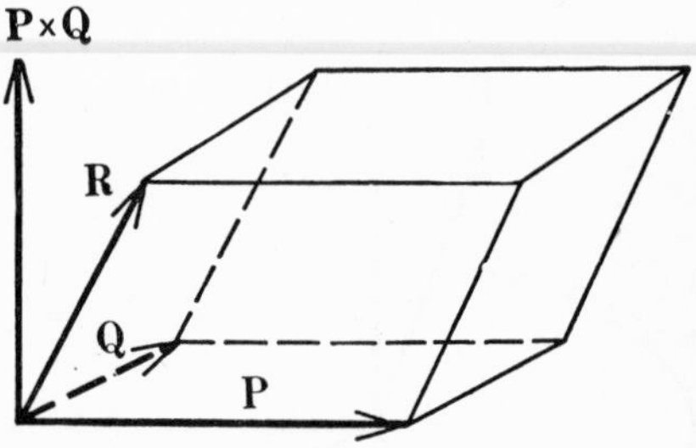

FIG. 9.

$$(\mathbf{P}\times\mathbf{Q})\cdot\mathbf{R} = \mathbf{P}\cdot(\mathbf{Q}\times\mathbf{R}). \quad (6\text{-}1)$$

Therefore the cross and the dot may be interchanged provided the order of the three vectors remains unchanged. Interchange of the positions of two adjacent vectors changes the sign of the product.

It is unnecessary to retain the parentheses in the triple scalar product for $(\mathbf{P}\cdot\mathbf{Q})\times\mathbf{R}$ has no meaning since $\mathbf{P}\cdot\mathbf{Q}$ is a scalar.

As

$$\mathbf{P} \times \mathbf{Q} = \mathbf{i}(P_yQ_z - P_zQ_y) + \mathbf{j}(P_zQ_x - P_xQ_z) + \mathbf{k}(P_xQ_y - P_yQ_x)$$

and

$$\mathbf{R} = \mathbf{i}R_x + \mathbf{j}R_y + \mathbf{k}R_z,$$

it follows that

$$\left.\begin{aligned} \mathbf{P} \times \mathbf{Q} \cdot \mathbf{R} &= P_yQ_zR_x - P_zQ_yR_x + P_zQ_xR_y - P_xQ_zR_y \\ &\quad + P_xQ_yR_z - P_yQ_xR_z \\ &= \begin{vmatrix} P_x & P_y & P_z \\ Q_x & Q_y & Q_z \\ R_x & R_y & R_z \end{vmatrix} \end{aligned}\right\} \qquad (6\text{–}2)$$

Problem 6a. A force **F** acts at a distance **r** from the origin. Show that the torque L about any axis through the origin is $L = \mathbf{r} \times \mathbf{F} \cdot \boldsymbol{\alpha}$ where $\boldsymbol{\alpha}$ is a unit vector in the direction of the axis.

7. Triple Vector Product. — This product is the vector

$$(\mathbf{P} \times \mathbf{Q}) \times \mathbf{R} = -\mathbf{R} \times (\mathbf{P} \times \mathbf{Q}) = \mathbf{R} \times (\mathbf{Q} \times \mathbf{P}),$$

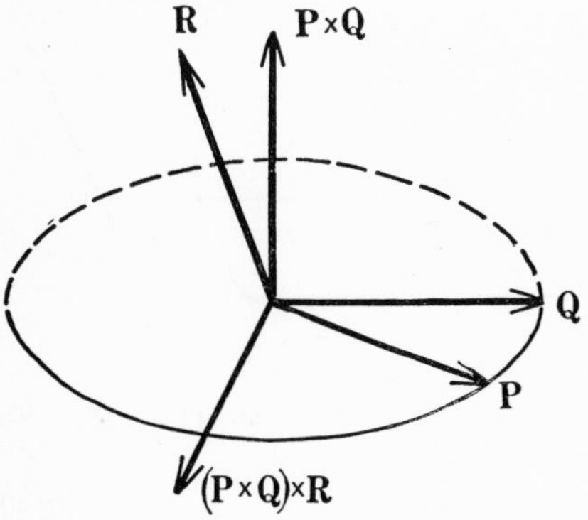

Fig. 10.

where the vector product $\mathbf{P} \times \mathbf{Q}$ is formed first, and then the cross product of this vector with **R** is taken. As $(\mathbf{P} \times \mathbf{Q}) \times \mathbf{R}$ is perpendicular to $\mathbf{P} \times \mathbf{Q}$ (Fig. 10) it must lie in the plane of **P** and **Q**.

Now **R** may be expressed as the sum of three components in the directions of the three non-coplanar vectors **P**, **Q** and $\mathbf{P} \times \mathbf{Q}$, that is,

$$\mathbf{R} = a\mathbf{P} + b\mathbf{Q} + c(\mathbf{P} \times \mathbf{Q}).$$

Therefore

$$(\mathbf{P} \times \mathbf{Q}) \times \mathbf{R} = a(\mathbf{P} \times \mathbf{Q}) \times \mathbf{P} + b(\mathbf{P} \times \mathbf{Q}) \times \mathbf{Q}, \qquad (7\text{–}1)$$

since $(\mathbf{P} \times \mathbf{Q}) \times (\mathbf{P} \times \mathbf{Q}) = 0$.

To evaluate $(\mathbf{P} \times \mathbf{Q}) \times \mathbf{P}$ we note that this vector, like $(\mathbf{P} \times \mathbf{Q}) \times \mathbf{R}$, lies in the plane of $\mathbf{P}$ and $\mathbf{Q}$, and therefore may be expressed in the form

$$(\mathbf{P} \times \mathbf{Q}) \times \mathbf{P} = m\mathbf{Q} + n\mathbf{P}.$$

But, as $(\mathbf{P} \times \mathbf{Q}) \times \mathbf{P}$ is perpendicular to $\mathbf{P}$, it follows that $\mathbf{P}\cdot\{(\mathbf{P} \times \mathbf{Q}) \times \mathbf{P}\} = 0$. Hence

$$m\mathbf{P}\cdot\mathbf{Q} + nP^2 = 0,$$

and $n = -m\mathbf{P}\cdot\mathbf{Q}/P^2$. If we put s for m/P^2,

$$(\mathbf{P} \times \mathbf{Q}) \times \mathbf{P} = s(P^2\mathbf{Q} - \mathbf{P}\cdot\mathbf{Q}\mathbf{P}). \qquad (7\text{–}2)$$

The orientation of the three vectors $\mathbf{P}$, $\mathbf{Q}$ and $(\mathbf{P} \times \mathbf{Q}) \times \mathbf{P}$ is shown in Fig. 11. As the left-hand member of (7–2) is a vector perpendicular to $\mathbf{P}$, the same must be true of the right-hand member. Equating the components perpendicular to $\mathbf{P}$ on both sides of (7–2) we have

$$P^2Q \sin\alpha = sP^2Q \sin\alpha,$$

showing that $s = 1$. Therefore

$$m = P^2,$$

$$n = -\mathbf{P}\cdot\mathbf{Q},$$

and

$$(\mathbf{P} \times \mathbf{Q}) \times \mathbf{P} = P^2\mathbf{Q} - \mathbf{P}\cdot\mathbf{Q}\mathbf{P}.$$

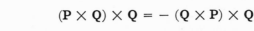

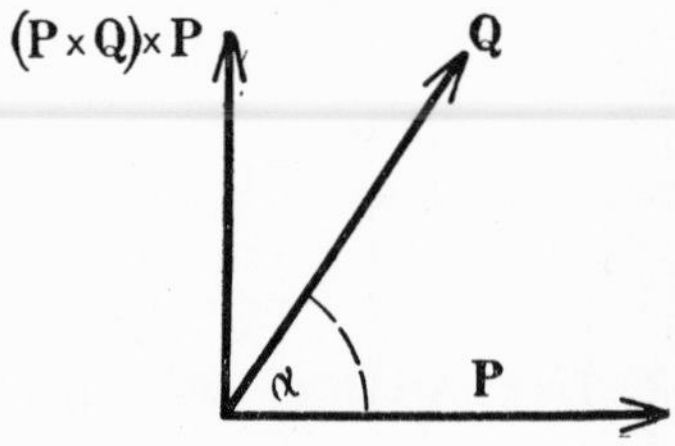

FIG. 11.

Also

$$(\mathbf{P} \times \mathbf{Q}) \times \mathbf{Q} = -(\mathbf{Q} \times \mathbf{P}) \times \mathbf{Q}$$
$$= \mathbf{Q}\cdot\mathbf{P}\mathbf{Q} - Q^2\mathbf{P}.$$

So equation (7–1) for $(\mathbf{P} \times \mathbf{Q}) \times \mathbf{R}$ becomes

$$(\mathbf{P} \times \mathbf{Q}) \times \mathbf{R} = (aP^2 + b\mathbf{P}\cdot\mathbf{Q})\mathbf{Q} - (a\mathbf{P}\cdot\mathbf{Q} + bQ^2)\mathbf{P}.$$

Now

$$\mathbf{R}\cdot\mathbf{P} = aP^2 + b\mathbf{P}\cdot\mathbf{Q},$$

$$\mathbf{R}\cdot\mathbf{Q} = a\mathbf{P}\cdot\mathbf{Q} + bQ^2.$$

So finally

$$(\mathbf{P} \times \mathbf{Q}) \times \mathbf{R} = \mathbf{R} \cdot \mathbf{P} \mathbf{Q} - \mathbf{R} \cdot \mathbf{Q} \mathbf{P}, \tag{7-3}$$

or

$$\mathbf{R} \times (\mathbf{P} \times \mathbf{Q}) = \mathbf{R} \cdot \mathbf{Q} \mathbf{P} - \mathbf{R} \cdot \mathbf{P} \mathbf{Q}. \tag{7-4}$$

The following rule summarizes this expansion: *Dot the exterior vector into the remoter vector inside the parentheses to form the scalar coefficient for the nearer one, then dot the exterior vector into the nearer one to form the scalar coefficient for the remoter one, and subtract the latter expression from the former.*

The parentheses cannot be omitted from the triple vector product, for $\mathbf{P} \times (\mathbf{Q} \times \mathbf{R})$ has a quite different meaning from $(\mathbf{P} \times \mathbf{Q}) \times \mathbf{R}$. In other words the associative law does not hold for cross multiplication.

Problem 7a. Expand $(\mathbf{r} \times \mathbf{a}) \times (\mathbf{b} \times \mathbf{c})$ and show that

$$\mathbf{r} = \mathbf{r} \cdot \mathbf{a}'\mathbf{a} + \mathbf{r} \cdot \mathbf{b}'\mathbf{b} + \mathbf{r} \cdot \mathbf{c}'\mathbf{c}$$

where

$$\mathbf{a}' = \frac{\mathbf{b} \times \mathbf{c}}{\mathbf{a} \cdot \mathbf{b} \times \mathbf{c}}, \quad \mathbf{b}' = \frac{\mathbf{c} \times \mathbf{a}}{\mathbf{a} \cdot \mathbf{b} \times \mathbf{c}}, \quad \mathbf{c}' = \frac{\mathbf{a} \times \mathbf{b}}{\mathbf{a} \cdot \mathbf{b} \times \mathbf{c}}.$$

Show that $\mathbf{a}' \cdot \mathbf{a} = \mathbf{b}' \cdot \mathbf{b} = \mathbf{c}' \cdot \mathbf{c} = 1$; $\mathbf{a}' \cdot \mathbf{b} = \mathbf{a}' \cdot \mathbf{c} = \mathbf{b}' \cdot \mathbf{c} = \mathbf{b}' \cdot \mathbf{a} = \mathbf{c}' \cdot \mathbf{a} = \mathbf{c}' \cdot \mathbf{b} = 0$. On account of these last relations the vectors $\mathbf{a}'$, $\mathbf{b}'$, $\mathbf{c}'$ are said to constitute a set *reciprocal* to the set $\mathbf{a}$, $\mathbf{b}$, $\mathbf{c}$. Show also that

$$\mathbf{r} = \mathbf{r} \cdot \mathbf{a}\mathbf{a}' + \mathbf{r} \cdot \mathbf{b}\mathbf{b}' + \mathbf{r} \cdot \mathbf{c}\mathbf{c}'.$$

8. Transformation of Components of a Vector. — Let P_x, P_y, P_z be the components of a vector $\mathbf{P}$ resolved parallel to the axes XYZ. Evidently the components of $\mathbf{P}$ along any other set of rectangular axes parallel respectively to XYZ are the same quantities P_x, P_y, P_z. Therefore the magnitudes of the components of a vector are independent of the position of the origin and are the same relative to all sets of axes which can be obtained from XYZ by a pure translation. For convenience, then, we may consider the origin of the vector to lie at the origin of the axes XYZ. In such a case the three components of the vector are given by the coordinates x_t, y_t, z_t of its terminus. Now consider a second set of axes $X'Y'Z'$ obtained from XYZ by a rotation about a line through the origin. The components of the vector under consideration relative to $X'Y'Z'$ are given by the coordinates x_t', y_t', z_t' of the terminus of the vector relative to these axes, where in general x_t', y_t', z_t' are not equal to x_t, y_t, z_t respectively. So we see that when we pass from the axes XYZ to the differently oriented axes $X'Y'Z'$ the components must transform in exactly the same way as do the coordinates of a point. This condition is necessary in order that the components P_x', P_y', P_z' relative to $X'Y'Z'$ shall give the same resultant vector as do the components P_x, P_y, P_z relative to XYZ.

If, for instance, the relative orientation of the two sets of axes is given by the scheme in Fig. 12, where l_1, l_2, l_3 are the direction cosines of X' referred to XYZ, etc., the coordinates transform according to the equations

	X	Y	Z
X'	l_1	l_2	l_3
Y'	m_1	m_2	m_3
Z'	n_1	n_2	n_3

FIG. 12.

$$\left.\begin{aligned} x' &= l_1x + l_2y + l_3z, &\quad \text{or}\quad x &= l_1x' + m_1y' + n_1z',\\ y' &= m_1x + m_2y + m_3z, &\quad \text{or}\quad y &= l_2x' + m_2y' + n_2z',\\ z' &= n_1x + n_2y + n_3z, &\quad \text{or}\quad z &= l_3x' + m_3y' + n_3z', \end{aligned}\right\} \quad (8\text{–}1)$$

and, if P_x, P_y, P_z are the components of a vector, it is necessary that

$$\left.\begin{aligned} P_x' &= l_1P_x + l_2P_y + l_3P_z, &\quad \text{or}\quad P_x &= l_1P_x' + m_1P_y' + n_1P_z',\\ P_y' &= m_1P_x + m_2P_y + m_3P_z, &\quad \text{or}\quad P_y &= l_2P_x' + m_2P_y' + n_2P_z',\\ P_z' &= n_1P_x + n_2P_y + n_3P_z, &\quad \text{or}\quad P_z &= l_3P_x' + m_3P_y' + n_3P_z'. \end{aligned}\right\} \quad (8\text{–}2)$$

Expressed as the vector sum of its components,

$$\mathbf{P} = \mathbf{i}P_x + \mathbf{j}P_y + \mathbf{k}P_z = \mathbf{i}'P_x' + \mathbf{j}'P_y' + \mathbf{k}'P_z' \qquad (8\text{–}3)$$

where **i**, **j**, **k** are unit vectors parallel to the axes X, Y, Z and **i′**, **j′**, **k′** unit vectors parallel to the axes X', Y', Z'. In fact we can deduce the relations (8–2) immediately from (8–3) merely by expressing

$\mathbf{i}, \mathbf{j}, \mathbf{k}$ in terms of $\mathbf{i}', \mathbf{j}', \mathbf{k}'$. As the direction cosines of $\mathbf{i}$ relative to $\mathbf{i}', \mathbf{j}', \mathbf{k}'$ are l_1, m_1, n_1, etc.,

$$\mathbf{i} = l_1\mathbf{i}' + m_1\mathbf{j}' + n_1\mathbf{k}',$$

$$\mathbf{j} = l_2\mathbf{i}' + m_2\mathbf{j}' + n_2\mathbf{k}',$$

$$\mathbf{k} = l_3\mathbf{i}' + m_3\mathbf{j}' + n_3\mathbf{k}',$$

and therefore

$$\begin{aligned} \mathbf{i}P_x + \mathbf{j}P_y + \mathbf{k}P_z = \mathbf{i}'(l_1P_x + l_2P_y + l_3P_z) \\ + \mathbf{j}'(m_1P_x + m_2P_y + m_3P_z) \\ +\mathbf{k}'(n_1P_x + n_2P_y + n_3P_z). \end{aligned}$$

Comparison with (8–3) gives P_x', P_y', P_z' in terms of P_x, P_y, P_z.

Problem 8a. A vector has components $x^2A_x + xyA_y + xzA_z$, $xyA_x + y^2A_y + yzA_z$, $xzA_x + yzA_y + z^2A_z$ relative to XYZ, where $\mathbf{A}$ is a constant vector. Show that its components relative to $X'Y'Z'$ are given by the same functions of $x', y', z', A_x', A_y', A_z'$.

9. Scalar and Vector Functions of Position in Space. — Many physical laws involve functions of the coordinates, and often of the components of one or more constant vectors as well. Such functions may themselves be scalars or vectors. We shall discuss scalar functions first.

In order to express a scalar function of the coordinates in analytical form it is necessary to choose a set of axes XYZ. If, for the purpose of illustration, we confine ourselves to the case where only one constant vector $\mathbf{A}$ is involved, we are led to consider a function Φ of x, y, z, A_x, A_y, A_z. At once the question arises whether any *arbitrary* function of these six quantities can enter a physical law. In order to answer this question let us transform to a new set of axes $X'Y'Z'$ oriented relative to XYZ in accord with the scheme of Fig. 12. Then by means of the transformations (8–1) and (8–2) we express Φ as a function of $x', y', z', A_x', A_y', A_z'$. In general the necessary substitution introduces into the function the direction cosines l_1, l_2, l_3, etc. which determine the orientation of $X'Y'Z'$ relative to XYZ. But the presence of these direction cosines makes the function depend not only on the coordinates and the constant vector $\mathbf{A}$, but also on the particular orientation given to the new axes $X'Y'Z'$. Now the use of axes is merely an artifice convenient for the description of physical phenomena and it is certain that the character of a law of nature can depend in no way on the particular orientation given them. We conclude, then, that the only functions of x, y, z, A_x, A_y, A_z which can occur in physical laws are those in which the direction cosines defining the relative orientation of the axes do not appear when we pass from one set of axes to another. Therefore such a function must be the *same* function of x', y', z', A_x', A_y', A_z' whatever may be the orientation of the new axes with respect to the original axes. But when the two sets of axes coincide, $x' = x$, $y' = y$, $z' = z$, $A_x' = A_x$, $A_y' = A_y$, $A_z' = A_z$. So, for any orientation of $X'Y'Z'$ with respect to XYZ, the scalar Φ must be the same function of x', y', z', A_x', A_y', A_z' as it is of x, y, z, A_x, A_y, A_z. A function which satisfies this condition is said to be a *scalar invariant*. Only such functions can enter physical laws. We shall call such a function a *proper scalar function* of the coordinates and of the components of the vector **A**.

Consider a couple of examples. Transforming by means of (8–1) and (8–2) we find that

$$f[x + y + z] = f[(l_1 + l_2 + l_3)x' + (m_1 + m_2 + m_3)y' + (n_1 + n_2 + n_3)z']$$

is not a scalar invariant. On the other hand

$$f[(x^2 + y^2 + z^2), (xA_x + yA_y + zA_z), (A_x^2 + A_y^2 + A_z^2)] = f[(x'^2 + y'^2 + z'^2), (x'A_x' + y'A_y' + z'A_z'), (A_x'^2 + A_y'^2 + A_z'^2)]$$

is a scalar invariant and therefore a proper function.

Next we shall investigate vector functions the components of which are functions of the coordinates and perhaps of the components of one or more constant vectors as well. Such a vector is known as a *vector function of position in space*. It associates a vector with every point in a certain domain of space in such a way that generally the vector associated with one point differs both in magnitude and direction from that associated with another point. The simplest vector function of position in space is the position vector

$\mathbf{r} = \mathbf{i}x + \mathbf{j}y + \mathbf{k}z$ of the point x, y, z relative to the origin of the axes XYZ. This function associates with every point x, y, z a vector having the magnitude and direction of the arrow drawn from the origin to the point in question. As an example of a vector function the components of which are functions of the components of a constant vector as well as of the coordinates, consider the expression

$$\boldsymbol{\omega} \times \mathbf{r} = \mathbf{i}(\omega_y z - \omega_z y) + \mathbf{j}(\omega_z x - \omega_x z) + \mathbf{k}(\omega_x y - \omega_y x)$$

for the linear velocity of the point x, y, z of a rigid body which is rotating with angular velocity $\boldsymbol{\omega}$ about an axis through the origin. Here $\boldsymbol{\omega}$ is the constant vector, the vector function $\boldsymbol{\omega} \times \mathbf{r}$ associating with each point of the rigid body a vector equal in magnitude and direction to its linear velocity. The aggregate of all the vectors which this function associates with the various points of the body constitutes a *vector field*.

For definiteness let us consider a vector function $\mathbf{V}$ of the coordinates x, y, z and of the components A_x, A_y, A_z of a single constant vector $\mathbf{A}$. Then the components V_x, V_y, V_z of $\mathbf{V}$ are three scalar functions of x, y, z, A_x, A_y, A_z. Just as in the case discussed previously, here too there are certain restrictions on the form of the functions V_x, V_y, V_z. For let us transform to a set of axes $X'Y'Z'$ oriented relative to XYZ in accord with the scheme of direction cosines given in Fig. 12. Then we obtain by means of (8–1) and (8–2) the components V_x', V_y', V_z' of $\mathbf{V}$ resolved along the new axes expressed as functions of $x', y', z', A_x', A_y', A_z'$. In general these three new functions involve the direction cosines of $X'Y'Z'$ relative to XYZ. As, however, no physical quantity can depend upon the particular orientation of the axes employed in its description, only those vector functions are admissible whose components relative to $X'Y'Z'$, obtained by transforming from XYZ in accord with (8–1) and (8–2), do not involve l_1, l_2, l_3, etc. Just as in the case of the scalar function already discussed, this condition requires that V_x', V_y', V_z' must be the same three functions of $x', y', z', A_x', A_y', A_z'$ as V_x, V_y, V_z are of x, y, z, A_x, A_y, A_z, respectively. We shall call a vector function which satisfies these conditions a *proper vector function.*

As a simple example consider the two-dimensional vector function whose components are $V_x = y$, $V_y = x$. Let us limit ourselves to a rotation of the axes in the XY plane through the angle θ.

Then $l_1 = \cos\theta$, $l_2 = \sin\theta$, $m_1 = -\sin\theta$, $m_2 = \cos\theta$ in the table of Fig. 12, and we find from (8–1) and (8–2) that

$$V_x' = x'\sin 2\theta + y'\cos 2\theta,$$

$$V_y' = x'\cos 2\theta - y'\sin 2\theta,$$

showing that V_x and V_y are *not* the components of a proper vector function. On the other hand if $V_x = x^2A_x + xyA_y$, $V_y = xyA_x + y^2A_y$, where A_x and A_y are the components of a constant vector, then

$$V_x' = x'^2A_x' + x'y'A_y',$$

$$V_y' = x'y'A_x' + y'^2A_y',$$

which proves that the functions selected in this case are the components of a proper two-dimensional vector function. In fact we recognize that $\mathbf{V} = (\mathbf{A}\cdot\mathbf{r})\mathbf{r}$, where $\mathbf{A}\cdot\mathbf{r}$ is a scalar invariant and $\mathbf{r}$ the position vector.

As a final example consider the vector function whose components are

$$V_x = \frac{\partial\Phi}{\partial x}, \quad V_y = \frac{\partial\Phi}{\partial y}, \quad V_z = \frac{\partial\Phi}{\partial z},$$

where Φ is a proper scalar function of the coordinates and of the components of any number of constant vectors **A**, etc. Then, since it follows from (8–1) that

$$l_1 = \frac{\partial x}{\partial x'}, \quad l_2 = \frac{\partial y}{\partial x'}, \quad l_3 = \frac{\partial z}{\partial x'}, \quad \text{etc.,}$$

we have

$$V_x' = l_1V_x + l_2V_y + l_3V_z = \frac{\partial\Phi}{\partial x}\frac{\partial x}{\partial x'} + \frac{\partial\Phi}{\partial y}\frac{\partial y}{\partial x'} + \frac{\partial\Phi}{\partial z}\frac{\partial z}{\partial x'} = \frac{\partial\Phi}{\partial x'},$$

$$V_y' = m_1V_x + m_2V_y + m_3V_z = \frac{\partial\Phi}{\partial x}\frac{\partial x}{\partial y'} + \frac{\partial\Phi}{\partial y}\frac{\partial y}{\partial y'} + \frac{\partial\Phi}{\partial z}\frac{\partial z}{\partial y'} = \frac{\partial\Phi}{\partial y'},$$

$$V_z' = n_1V_x + n_2V_y + n_3V_z = \frac{\partial\Phi}{\partial x}\frac{\partial x}{\partial z'} + \frac{\partial\Phi}{\partial y}\frac{\partial y}{\partial z'} + \frac{\partial\Phi}{\partial z}\frac{\partial z}{\partial z'} = \frac{\partial\Phi}{\partial z'}.$$

Now, since Φ, when expressed in terms of x', y', z', A_x', A_y', A_z' etc., is the same function of these variables as it is of x, y, z, A_x, A_y, A_z, etc., it follows that the same is true of V_x' and V_x, V_y' and V_y, V_z' and V_z. Therefore the vector **V** is a proper vector function of position in space. This vector function, which will be studied in more detail in a later article, is known as the *gradient* of the scalar function Φ. As in (8–3) we may write

$$\left.\begin{aligned} \mathbf{V} &= \mathbf{i}\frac{\partial\Phi}{\partial x} + \mathbf{j}\frac{\partial\Phi}{\partial y} + \mathbf{k}\frac{\partial\Phi}{\partial z} \\ &= \mathbf{i}'\frac{\partial\Phi}{\partial x'} + \mathbf{j}'\frac{\partial\Phi}{\partial y'} + \mathbf{k}'\frac{\partial\Phi}{\partial z'}. \end{aligned}\right\} \qquad (9\text{–}1)$$

Problem 9a. Show that the scalar product $\mathbf{P}\cdot\mathbf{Q}$ of two proper vectors **P** and **Q** is a proper scalar function.

Problem 9b. Show that the vector product $\mathbf{P}\times\mathbf{Q}$ of two proper vectors **P** and **Q** is a proper vector function.

10. Derivative and Integral of a Vector Function. — Let

$$\mathbf{r} = \mathbf{i}x + \mathbf{j}y + \mathbf{k}z,$$

where

$$x = x(t), \quad y = y(t), \quad z = z(t). \qquad (10\text{–}1)$$

The vector **r** is said to be a *vector function* of the scalar t. If the origin of **r** is kept fixed at the origin of coordinates (Fig. 13) and t is varied, the terminus of **r** describes the curve given in parametric form by equations (10–1). Consider two near-by points A and B on the curve whose position vectors are **r** and $\mathbf{r}_1$, respectively. As

$$\Delta\mathbf{r} = \mathbf{r}_1 - \mathbf{r},$$

$\Delta\mathbf{r}$ is a vector having the direction of the secant AB, which approaches the tangent in direction as B approaches A. Hence the derivative

$$\frac{d\mathbf{r}}{dt}$$

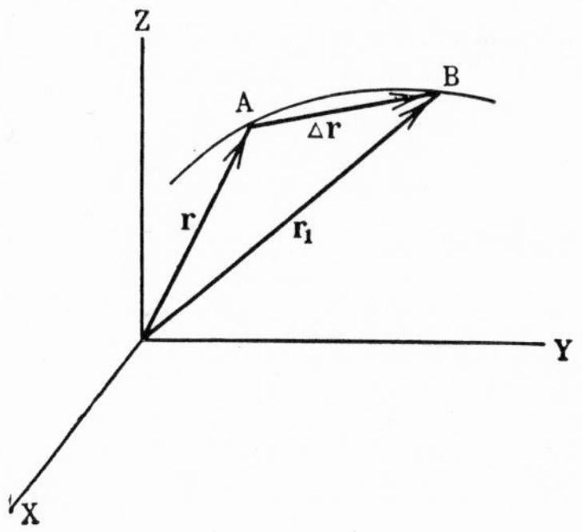

FIG. 13.

is a vector tangent to the curve described by the terminus of **r**. If we put

$$\mathbf{r}_1 = \mathbf{i}x_1 + \mathbf{j}y_1 + \mathbf{k}z_1,$$

then

$$\Delta \mathbf{r} = \mathbf{i}(x_1 - x) + \mathbf{j}(y_1 - y) + \mathbf{k}(z_1 - z)$$

$$= \mathbf{i}\Delta x + \mathbf{j}\Delta y + \mathbf{k}\Delta z,$$

and

$$\frac{d\mathbf{r}}{dt} = \mathbf{i}\frac{dx}{dt} + \mathbf{j}\frac{dy}{dt} + \mathbf{k}\frac{dz}{dt}. \tag{10-2}$$

In like manner

$$\frac{d^2\mathbf{r}}{dt^2} = \mathbf{i}\frac{d^2x}{dt^2} + \mathbf{j}\frac{d^2y}{dt^2} + \mathbf{k}\frac{d^2z}{dt^2}. \tag{10-3}$$

If $\mathbf{r}$ is the position vector of a point in space and t the time (10–2) is the vector velocity and (10–3) the vector acceleration.

It is important to note that the scalar magnitude $\left|\frac{d\mathbf{r}}{dt}\right|$ of the derivative of $\mathbf{r}$ with respect to t is not at all the same thing as the derivative $\frac{dr}{dt}$ of the scalar magnitude of $\mathbf{r}$ with respect to t. Consider, for example, a point moving with constant speed in a circle the center of which coincides with the origin. As r is constant, $\frac{dr}{dt}$ is zero, whereas $\left|\frac{d\mathbf{r}}{dt}\right|$ is equal to the scalar magnitude of the velocity, that is, to the speed of the point. Similarly we must distinguish between $\left|\frac{d^2\mathbf{r}}{dt^2}\right|$ and $\frac{d^2r}{dt^2}$.

Now consider derivatives of the scalar and vector products. As

$$\mathbf{P}\cdot\mathbf{Q} = P_xQ_x + P_yQ_y + P_zQ_z,$$

it follows that

$$\left.\begin{aligned}\frac{d}{dt}(\mathbf{P}\cdot\mathbf{Q}) &= \frac{dP_x}{dt}Q_x + \frac{dP_y}{dt}Q_y + \frac{dP_z}{dt}Q_z + P_x\frac{dQ_x}{dt} + P_y\frac{dQ_y}{dt} + P_z\frac{dQ_z}{dt}\\ &= \frac{d\mathbf{P}}{dt}\cdot\mathbf{Q} + \mathbf{P}\cdot\frac{d\mathbf{Q}}{dt},\end{aligned}\right\} \tag{10-4}$$

that is, we differentiate just as we would an ordinary algebraic product, paying no attention to the dot. Similarly as

$$\mathbf{P} \times \mathbf{Q} = \mathbf{i}(P_yQ_z - P_zQ_y) + \text{etc.},$$

it follows that

$$\left.\begin{aligned} \frac{d}{dt}(\mathbf{P} \times \mathbf{Q}) &= \mathbf{i}\left(\frac{dP_y}{dt}Q_z - \frac{dP_z}{dt}Q_y + P_y\frac{dQ_z}{dt} - P_z\frac{dQ_y}{dt}\right) + \text{etc.} \\ &= \frac{d\mathbf{P}}{dt} \times \mathbf{Q} + \mathbf{P} \times \frac{d\mathbf{Q}}{dt}. \end{aligned}\right\} \quad (10\text{-}5)$$

Again we differentiate the two factors just as in the case of an algebraic product, paying no attention to the cross. However, in the derivative of the cross product the order of the vectors must not be altered unless the sign is changed.

Suppose that $\boldsymbol{\alpha}$ is a vector constant in magnitude but variable in direction. Then $d\boldsymbol{\alpha}$ is a vector perpendicular to $\boldsymbol{\alpha}$, for if it had a component in the direction of $\boldsymbol{\alpha}$, the magnitude of $\boldsymbol{\alpha}$ would not remain constant.

If a vector is a function of several independent variables, such as the coordinates x, y, z, the partial derivative of the vector with respect to one of these variables is defined just as in the case of a vector function of a single variable, the remaining variables being treated as constants.

Vector integration is the inverse of vector differentiation just as in the case of scalar analysis. A definite vector integral may be interpreted as a vector sum in a manner quite analogous to the corresponding scalar case. For instance, suppose it is desired to form the integral of the vector function of the coordinates $\mathbf{V}(x, y, z)$ over the volume τ. If $d\tau = dx\,dy\,dz$ is an element of volume,

$$\int_\tau \mathbf{V}d\tau = \mathbf{i}\int_\tau V_x d\tau + \mathbf{j}\int_\tau V_y d\tau + \mathbf{k}\int_\tau V_z d\tau.$$

Now if $\mathbf{V}_1$ is the value of $\mathbf{V}$ at the volume element $d\tau_1$, $\mathbf{V}_2$ its value at $d\tau_2$, $\mathbf{V}_3$ at $d\tau_3$, etc.,

$$\int_\tau V_x d\tau = V_{x_1}d\tau_1 + V_{x_2}d\tau_2 + V_{x_3}d\tau_3 + \ldots,$$

$$\int_\tau V_y d\tau = V_{y_1}d\tau_1 + V_{y_2}d\tau_2 + V_{y_3}d\tau_3 + \ldots,$$

$$\int_\tau V_z d\tau = V_{z_1}d\tau_1 + V_{z_2}d\tau_2 + V_{z_3}d\tau_3 + \ldots,$$

since these three are scalar integrals. Therefore

$$\int_\tau \mathbf{V}d\tau = \mathbf{i}(V_{x_1}d\tau_1 + V_{x_2}d\tau_2 + V_{x_3}d\tau_3 + \ldots)$$
$$+ \mathbf{j}(V_{y_1}d\tau_1 + V_{y_2}d\tau_2 + V_{y_3}d\tau_3 + \ldots)$$
$$+ \mathbf{k}(V_{z_1}d\tau_1 + V_{z_2}d\tau_2 + V_{z_3}d\tau_3 + \ldots).$$

Combining terms with like numerical subscripts,

$$\int_\tau \mathbf{V}d\tau = \mathbf{V}_1 d\tau_1 + \mathbf{V}_2 d\tau_2 + \mathbf{V}_3 d\tau_3 + \ldots$$
$$= \sum_\tau \mathbf{V}d\tau. \qquad (10\text{–}6)$$

11. **The Gradient.** — We shall investigate now the properties of the proper vector function introduced at the end of article 9. Let $\Phi(x, y, z)$ be a single-valued proper scalar function of the coordinates. Then, if C is a constant,

$$\Phi(x, y, z) = C \qquad (11\text{–}1)$$

represents a surface in space. By giving C a series of constant values we obtain a family of such surfaces. Evidently no two surfaces of the family can intersect, for if $\Phi(x, y, z) = C_1$ and $\Phi(x, y, z) = C_2$ intersected at a point x_0, y_0, z_0 then $\Phi(x_0, y_0, z_0)$ would equal both of the different constants C_1 and C_2.

Now consider the change in $\Phi(x, y, z)$ when we pass from a point A on the surface $\Phi(x, y, z) = C$ to a nearby point B. Let $d\boldsymbol{\lambda}$ be the position vector of B relative to A, that is,

$$d\boldsymbol{\lambda} = \mathbf{i}dx + \mathbf{j}dy + \mathbf{k}dz.$$

Then

$$d\Phi = \frac{\partial\Phi}{\partial x}dx + \frac{\partial\Phi}{\partial y}dy + \frac{\partial\Phi}{\partial z}dz. \qquad (11\text{–}2)$$

First let us examine the case where B as well as A lies on the surface $\Phi(x, y, z) = C$, so that $d\boldsymbol{\lambda}$ is tangent to this surface. Then

$$d\Phi = \frac{\partial\Phi}{\partial x}dx + \frac{\partial\Phi}{\partial y}dy + \frac{\partial\Phi}{\partial z}dz = 0. \qquad (11\text{–}3)$$

Now the direction cosines of $d\boldsymbol{\lambda}$ are proportional to dx, dy, dz. Hence any vector $\mathbf{F}$ with direction cosines proportional to $\frac{\partial\Phi}{\partial x}, \frac{\partial\Phi}{\partial y}, \frac{\partial\Phi}{\partial z}$ is perpendicular to the tangent vector $d\boldsymbol{\lambda}$, for equation (11–3) states that the sum of the products of the direction cosines of the two vectors, which is equal to the cosine of the angle between them, is zero. This statement holds true no matter what the orientation of $d\boldsymbol{\lambda}$ may be, so long as it is tangent to the surface at A. Hence the vector $\mathbf{F}$ is directed along the normal to the surface at A.

The simplest vector $\mathbf{F}$ with direction cosines proportional to $\frac{\partial\Phi}{\partial x}, \frac{\partial\Phi}{\partial y}, \frac{\partial\Phi}{\partial z}$ is

$$\mathbf{F} \equiv \mathbf{i}\frac{\partial\Phi}{\partial x} + \mathbf{j}\frac{\partial\Phi}{\partial y} + \mathbf{k}\frac{\partial\Phi}{\partial z}. \qquad (11\text{–}4)$$

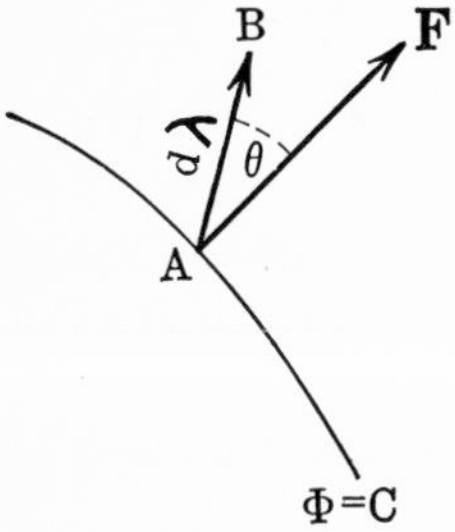

FIG. 14.

This vector is called the *gradient* of Φ. As shown in article 9 it is a proper vector function of the coordinates, since Φ is a proper scalar function.

To investigate the geometrical significance of the gradient $\mathbf{F}$, let us consider the case where B (Fig. 14) does not lie on the surface $\Phi(x, y, z) = C$ through A, but at a point where Φ has a greater value. Then, if $d\Phi$ is the increase in the value of the function in passing from A to B,

$$d\Phi = \frac{\partial\Phi}{\partial x}dx + \frac{\partial\Phi}{\partial y}dy + \frac{\partial\Phi}{\partial z}dz = \mathbf{F}\cdot d\boldsymbol{\lambda}$$

$$= F d\lambda \cos\theta, \qquad (11\text{–}5)$$

where $d\lambda$ is the scalar magnitude of $d\boldsymbol{\lambda}$. Dividing by $d\lambda$ we find that the space rate of increase of Φ in the direction AB is

$$\frac{d\Phi}{d\lambda} = F\cos\theta. \qquad (11\text{–}6)$$

But $F\cos\theta$ is the component of the gradient of Φ in the specified direction. Hence the space rate of increase of Φ in any direction is equal to the component of the gradient **F** in that direction. Since **F** is a vector normal to the surface $\Phi(x, y, z) = C$, the greatest space rate of change of Φ is along the normal and is equal in magnitude to **F** itself.

We conclude, then, that the gradient of Φ is a vector having both the magnitude and the direction of the greatest space rate of increase of Φ. It is normal to the surface $\Phi(x, y, z) = C$ and its component in any direction is equal to the space rate of increase of Φ in that direction.

The vector differential operator ∇ (read del) is defined by

$$\nabla = \mathbf{i}\frac{\partial}{\partial x} + \mathbf{j}\frac{\partial}{\partial y} + \mathbf{k}\frac{\partial}{\partial z}. \tag{11-7}$$

From the results of the analysis employed in article 9 to show that the gradient of Φ is a proper vector, it appears at once that the components of ∇ relative to a set of axes $X'Y'Z'$ differently oriented are $\frac{\partial}{\partial x'}, \frac{\partial}{\partial y'}, \frac{\partial}{\partial z'}$. Hence the components of ∇ have the same form in terms of x', y', z' as in terms of x, y, z and consequently we may call ∇ a *proper vector operator*. It has all the vector properties of a proper vector function, and may be combined vectorially with other proper vector functions according to the usual rules. As in (8–3) we may write

$$\nabla = \mathbf{i}\frac{\partial}{\partial x} + \mathbf{j}\frac{\partial}{\partial y} + \mathbf{k}\frac{\partial}{\partial z} = \mathbf{i}'\frac{\partial}{\partial x'} + \mathbf{j}'\frac{\partial}{\partial y'} + \mathbf{k}'\frac{\partial}{\partial z'}. \tag{11-8}$$

Operating with ∇ on the scalar function of position $\Phi\,(x, y, z)$ we get

$$\nabla\Phi = \mathbf{i}\frac{\partial\Phi}{\partial x} + \mathbf{j}\frac{\partial\Phi}{\partial y} + \mathbf{k}\frac{\partial\Phi}{\partial z}. \tag{11-9}$$

This is just the expression (11–4) defined as the gradient of Φ.

If $\mathbf{p}_1$ is a unit vector, $\mathbf{p}_1\cdot\nabla\Phi$ is the component of the gradient in the direction of $\mathbf{p}_1$ and therefore the space rate of increase of Φ in the direction of $\mathbf{p}_1$. Furthermore, if **P** is any vector, $\mathbf{P}\cdot\nabla\Phi$ is the space rate of increase of Φ in the direction of **P** multiplied by the magnitude of **P**.

If we wish to use spherical coordinates r, θ, ϕ, where r is the radius vector, θ the polar angle and ϕ the azimuth, the components of $\nabla\Phi$ in the directions of increasing r, θ and ϕ, respectively, are

$$\frac{\partial\Phi}{\partial r}, \quad \frac{\partial\Phi}{r\partial\theta}, \quad \frac{\partial\Phi}{r\sin\theta\partial\phi}.$$

Therefore if we denote by $\mathbf{r}_1$, $\boldsymbol{\theta}_1$ and $\boldsymbol{\phi}_1$ unit vectors in the directions of increasing r, θ and ϕ, respectively,

$$\nabla\Phi = \mathbf{r}_1\frac{\partial\Phi}{\partial r} + \boldsymbol{\theta}_1\frac{\partial\Phi}{r\partial\theta} + \boldsymbol{\phi}_1\frac{\partial\Phi}{r\sin\theta\partial\phi}, \tag{11–10}$$

and the operator ∇ itself assumes the form

$$\nabla = \mathbf{r}_1\frac{\partial}{\partial r} + \boldsymbol{\theta}_1\frac{\partial}{r\partial\theta} + \boldsymbol{\phi}_1\frac{\partial}{r\sin\theta\partial\phi}. \tag{11–11}$$

Problem 11a. Express ∇ in cylindrical coordinates r, ϕ, z, denoting unit vectors in the directions in which these variables increase by $\mathbf{r}_1$, $\boldsymbol{\phi}_1$, $\mathbf{k}$ respectively.

Ans. $\nabla = \mathbf{r}_1\frac{\partial}{\partial r} + \boldsymbol{\phi}_1\frac{\partial}{r\partial\phi} + \mathbf{k}\frac{\partial}{\partial z}$.

Problem 11b. Show that $\nabla(\Phi\Psi) = \Psi\nabla\Phi + \Phi\nabla\Psi$.

12. The Divergence. — As

$$\nabla = \mathbf{i}\frac{\partial}{\partial x} + \mathbf{j}\frac{\partial}{\partial y} + \mathbf{k}\frac{\partial}{\partial z}$$

is a proper vector operator, we may form the scalar product of ∇ with a proper vector function of position in space

$$\mathbf{V}(x, y, z) = \mathbf{i}V_x(x, y, z) + \mathbf{j}V_y(x, y, z) + \mathbf{k}V_z(x, y, z)$$

to get a proper scalar function of x, y, z known as the *divergence* of $\mathbf{V}$, namely,

$$\nabla\cdot\mathbf{V} = \frac{\partial V_x}{\partial x} + \frac{\partial V_y}{\partial y} + \frac{\partial V_z}{\partial z}. \tag{12–1}$$

That $\nabla\cdot\mathbf{V}$ is a proper scalar function follows at once from the fact that the components of both ∇ and $\mathbf{V}$ have the same form in x', y', z' when referred to the axes $X'Y'Z'$ as in x, y, z when referred to the axes XYZ.

This quantity has an important application in hydrodynamics. Let $\mathbf{V}$ represent the mass of fluid flowing through a unit cross-section per unit time. Then if ρ is the density of the fluid and $\mathbf{v}$ its velocity,

$$\mathbf{V} = \rho\mathbf{v}$$

since the mass $\mathbf{V}dt$ of fluid flowing through a unit cross-section in a time dt is that contained in a right prism having a base of unit area and an altitude $\mathbf{v}dt$.

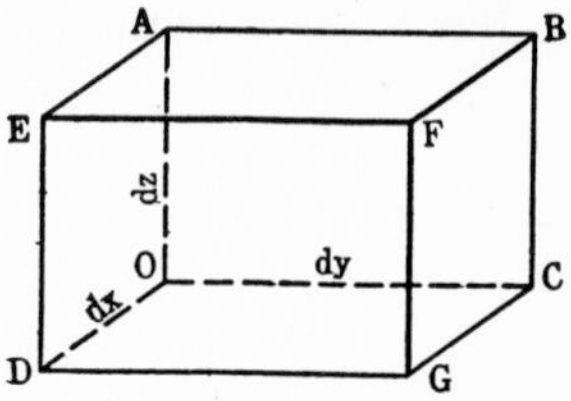

FIG. 15.

Now consider a small fixed rectangular parallelopiped (Fig. 15) of dimensions dx, dy, dz. The mass of fluid flowing in through $OABC$ per unit time is that contained in a prism of base $dy\,dz$ and altitude v_x, that is,

$$\rho v_x\,dy\,dz = V_x\,dy\,dz$$

and that flowing out through $DEFG$ is

$$\left\{\rho v_x + \frac{\partial}{\partial x}(\rho v_x)dx\right\}dy\,dz = \left\{V_x + \frac{\partial V_x}{\partial x}dx\right\}dy\,dz.$$

So the net increase of mass of the fluid inside the parallelopiped per unit time due to the flow through these two faces is

$$V_x\,dy\,dz - \left\{V_x + \frac{\partial V_x}{\partial x}dx\right\}dy\,dz = -\frac{\partial V_x}{\partial x}dx\,dy\,dz.$$

Similarly the net increase in mass per unit time due to the flow through $OAED$ and $CBFG$ is

$$-\frac{\partial V_y}{\partial y}dx\,dy\,dz,$$

and to that through $OCGD$ and $ABFE$

$$-\frac{\partial V_z}{\partial z}dx\,dy\,dz.$$

Adding these three expressions and dividing by the volume $dx\,dy\,dz$ of the parallelopiped, the total increase in mass per unit volume per unit time due to the excess of the flow inward over the flow outward is seen to be

$$-\frac{\partial V_x}{\partial x}-\frac{\partial V_y}{\partial y}-\frac{\partial V_z}{\partial z}=-\nabla\cdot\mathbf{V}.$$

But this is just the time rate of increase of density. Hence

$$\frac{\partial \rho}{\partial t}=-\nabla\cdot\mathbf{V}. \qquad (12\text{-}2)$$

This equation is known as the *equation of continuity*. If the fluid is incompressible

$$\frac{\partial \rho}{\partial t}=0,$$

and hence

$$\nabla\cdot\mathbf{V}=0. \qquad (12\text{-}3)$$

The name divergence originated in this interpretation of $\nabla\cdot\mathbf{V}$. For, since $-\nabla\cdot\mathbf{V}$ represents the excess of the inward over the outward flow, or the *convergence* of the fluid, so $\nabla\cdot\mathbf{V}$ represents the excess of the outward over the inward flow, or the *divergence* of the fluid.

Problem 12a. Show that $\nabla\cdot(u\mathbf{V})=u\nabla\cdot\mathbf{V}+\mathbf{V}\cdot\nabla u$.

13. The Curl or Rotation — If $\mathbf{V}(x, y, z)$ is a proper vector function of position in space, the *curl* or *rotation* of $\mathbf{V}$ is the proper vector function of x, y, z obtained by taking the vector product of the operator ∇ and $\mathbf{V}$. It is

$$\left.\begin{aligned}\nabla\times\mathbf{V}&=\mathbf{i}\left(\frac{\partial V_z}{\partial y}-\frac{\partial V_y}{\partial z}\right)+\mathbf{j}\left(\frac{\partial V_x}{\partial z}-\frac{\partial V_z}{\partial x}\right)+\mathbf{k}\left(\frac{\partial V_y}{\partial x}-\frac{\partial V_x}{\partial y}\right)\\&=\begin{vmatrix}\mathbf{i}&\mathbf{j}&\mathbf{k}\\ \frac{\partial}{\partial x}&\frac{\partial}{\partial y}&\frac{\partial}{\partial z}\\ V_x&V_y&V_z\end{vmatrix}.\end{aligned}\right\} \qquad (13\text{-}1)$$

Since the components of both ∇ and $\mathbf{V}$ have the same form in x', y', z' as in x, y, z it is evident that the components of $\nabla\times\mathbf{V}$ do also, and therefore that the curl of $\mathbf{V}$ is a proper vector function.

This important vector has a simple application in connection with rotation. Consider a rigid body which has an angular velocity $\boldsymbol{\omega}$ about an origin O (Fig. 16) fixed in the body, O itself having the linear velocity $\mathbf{v}_0$. Then if $\mathbf{p}$ is the perpendicular distance of any point P in the body from the axis of rotation, the linear velocity of P relative to O is

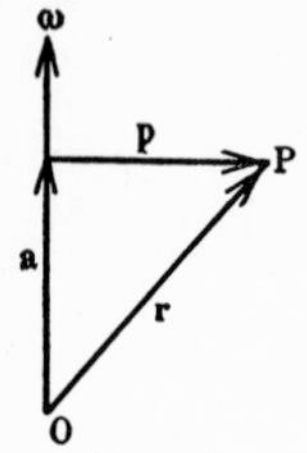

FIG. 16.

$$\boldsymbol{\omega} \times \mathbf{p} = \boldsymbol{\omega} \times (\mathbf{r} - \mathbf{a}) = \boldsymbol{\omega} \times \mathbf{r},$$

and the total linear velocity $\mathbf{v}$ of P is

$$\mathbf{v} = \mathbf{v}_0 + \boldsymbol{\omega} \times \mathbf{r}.$$

Although $\mathbf{v}_0$ and $\boldsymbol{\omega}$ are constants so far as the coordinates x, y, z of P relative to the origin O are concerned,

$$\mathbf{r} = \mathbf{i}x + \mathbf{j}y + \mathbf{k}z.$$

Now

$$\begin{aligned} \nabla \times \mathbf{v} &= \nabla \times \mathbf{v}_0 + \nabla \times (\boldsymbol{\omega} \times \mathbf{r}) \\ &= 0 + \nabla \cdot \overline{\mathbf{r}\boldsymbol{\omega}} - \nabla \cdot \overline{\boldsymbol{\omega}\mathbf{r}} \\ &= (\nabla \cdot \mathbf{r})\boldsymbol{\omega} + \mathbf{r} \cdot \nabla \boldsymbol{\omega} - (\nabla \cdot \boldsymbol{\omega})\mathbf{r} - \boldsymbol{\omega} \cdot \nabla \mathbf{r}, \end{aligned}$$

where $\nabla \times (\boldsymbol{\omega} \times \mathbf{r})$ has been expanded according to the rule for the triple vector product, the bar indicating that ∇, as a differential operator, acts on both the vectors following it. But $\boldsymbol{\omega}$ is a constant in x, y, z. Hence

$$\nabla \times \mathbf{v} = (\nabla \cdot \mathbf{r})\boldsymbol{\omega} - \boldsymbol{\omega} \cdot \nabla \mathbf{r}.$$

Now

$$\nabla \cdot \mathbf{r} = \frac{\partial x}{\partial x} + \frac{\partial y}{\partial y} + \frac{\partial z}{\partial z} = 3,$$

$$\boldsymbol{\omega} \cdot \nabla = \omega_x \frac{\partial}{\partial x} + \omega_y \frac{\partial}{\partial y} + \omega_z \frac{\partial}{\partial z},$$

$$\begin{aligned} \boldsymbol{\omega} \cdot \nabla \mathbf{r} &= \left(\omega_x \frac{\partial}{\partial x} + \omega_y \frac{\partial}{\partial y} + \omega_z \frac{\partial}{\partial z}\right)(\mathbf{i}x + \mathbf{j}y + \mathbf{k}z) \\ &= \mathbf{i}\omega_x + \mathbf{j}\omega_y + \mathbf{k}\omega_z = \boldsymbol{\omega}. \end{aligned}$$

Therefore

$$\nabla \times \mathbf{v} = 3\boldsymbol{\omega} - \boldsymbol{\omega} = 2\boldsymbol{\omega}. \tag{13-2}$$

So the curl of the linear velocity is equal to twice the angular velocity.

Problem 13a. Show that $\nabla \times (u\mathbf{V}) = u\nabla \times \mathbf{V} - \mathbf{V} \times \nabla u$.

Problem 13b. Prove by actual expansion in terms of the components of the vectors involved that

$$\nabla \times (\boldsymbol{\omega} \times \mathbf{r}) = \nabla \cdot \overline{\mathbf{r}\boldsymbol{\omega}} - \nabla \cdot \overline{\boldsymbol{\omega}\mathbf{r}}.$$

14. Successive Applications of ∇. — As $\nabla\Phi$ is a vector, we can take its divergence and get the scalar

$$\left.\begin{aligned}\nabla \cdot \nabla\Phi &= \left(\mathbf{i}\frac{\partial}{\partial x} + \mathbf{j}\frac{\partial}{\partial y} + \mathbf{k}\frac{\partial}{\partial z}\right) \cdot \left(\mathbf{i}\frac{\partial\Phi}{\partial x} + \mathbf{j}\frac{\partial\Phi}{\partial y} + \mathbf{k}\frac{\partial\Phi}{\partial z}\right)\\ &= \frac{\partial^2\Phi}{\partial x^2} + \frac{\partial^2\Phi}{\partial y^2} + \frac{\partial^2\Phi}{\partial z^2}.\end{aligned}\right\} \tag{14-1}$$

The operator

$$\nabla \cdot \nabla = \frac{\partial^2}{\partial x^2} + \frac{\partial^2}{\partial y^2} + \frac{\partial^2}{\partial z^2} \tag{14-2}$$

is called the *Laplacian.* As it is a scalar we may apply it to the vector $\mathbf{V}$ and get the vector

$$\nabla \cdot \nabla\mathbf{V} = \frac{\partial^2\mathbf{V}}{\partial x^2} + \frac{\partial^2\mathbf{V}}{\partial y^2} + \frac{\partial^2\mathbf{V}}{\partial z^2}. \tag{14-3}$$

The vector product $\nabla \times \nabla\Phi$, the curl of the gradient of the scalar function Φ, is identically zero as is evidenced by the fact that we are taking the vector product of ∇ by itself. To prove this by expansion:

$$\left.\begin{aligned}\nabla \times \nabla\Phi &= \begin{vmatrix} \mathbf{i} & \mathbf{j} & \mathbf{k} \\ \dfrac{\partial}{\partial x} & \dfrac{\partial}{\partial y} & \dfrac{\partial}{\partial z} \\ \dfrac{\partial\Phi}{\partial x} & \dfrac{\partial\Phi}{\partial y} & \dfrac{\partial\Phi}{\partial z} \end{vmatrix}\\ &= \mathbf{i}\left(\frac{\partial^2\Phi}{\partial y\partial z} - \frac{\partial^2\Phi}{\partial z\partial y}\right) + \mathbf{j}\left(\frac{\partial^2\Phi}{\partial z\partial x} - \frac{\partial^2\Phi}{\partial x\partial z}\right) + \mathbf{k}\left(\frac{\partial^2\Phi}{\partial x\partial y} - \frac{\partial^2\Phi}{\partial y\partial x}\right) = 0\end{aligned}\right\} \tag{14-4}$$

If the curl of a vector function of position in space **W** vanishes everywhere in the region τ, **W** is said to be *irrotational* in this region. From the above expansion it is seen that if **W** is the gradient of a scalar function Φ, then **W** is irrotational.

Also the scalar product $\nabla\cdot\nabla\times\mathbf{V}$, the divergence of the curl of the vector **V**, is identically zero. For

$$\nabla\times\mathbf{V} = \mathbf{i}\left(\frac{\partial V_z}{\partial y} - \frac{\partial V_y}{\partial z}\right) + \mathbf{j}\left(\frac{\partial V_x}{\partial z} - \frac{\partial V_z}{\partial x}\right) + \mathbf{k}\left(\frac{\partial V_y}{\partial x} - \frac{\partial V_x}{\partial y}\right),$$

$$\left.\begin{aligned}\nabla\cdot\nabla\times\mathbf{V} = {} & \frac{\partial}{\partial x}\left(\frac{\partial V_z}{\partial y} - \frac{\partial V_y}{\partial z}\right) + \frac{\partial}{\partial y}\left(\frac{\partial V_x}{\partial z} - \frac{\partial V_z}{\partial x}\right) \\ & + \frac{\partial}{\partial z}\left(\frac{\partial V_y}{\partial x} - \frac{\partial V_x}{\partial y}\right) = 0.\end{aligned}\right\} \qquad (14\text{-}5)$$

If the divergence of a vector function of position in space **W** vanishes everywhere in the region τ, **W** is said to be *solenoidal* in this region. It follows that if **W** is the curl of a vector function **V**, then **W** is solenoidal.

The vector product $\nabla\times\nabla\times\mathbf{V}$, the curl of the curl of the vector **V**, is very important. Applying the rule for expanding the triple vector product

$$\nabla\times\nabla\times\mathbf{V} = \nabla\times(\nabla\times\mathbf{V}) = \nabla\nabla\cdot\mathbf{V} - \nabla\cdot\nabla\mathbf{V} \qquad (14\text{-}6)$$

To prove this relation by expansion, we have

$$\begin{aligned}\nabla\times\nabla\times\mathbf{V} &= \mathbf{i}\left\{\frac{\partial}{\partial y}\left(\frac{\partial V_y}{\partial x} - \frac{\partial V_x}{\partial y}\right) - \frac{\partial}{\partial z}\left(\frac{\partial V_x}{\partial z} - \frac{\partial V_z}{\partial x}\right)\right\} + \text{etc.}, \\ &= \mathbf{i}\left\{\frac{\partial^2 V_y}{\partial y\partial x} + \frac{\partial^2 V_z}{\partial z\partial x} - \frac{\partial^2 V_x}{\partial y^2} - \frac{\partial^2 V_x}{\partial z^2}\right\} + \text{etc.}, \\ &= \mathbf{i}\left\{\frac{\partial}{\partial x}\left(\frac{\partial V_x}{\partial x} + \frac{\partial V_y}{\partial y} + \frac{\partial V_z}{\partial z}\right) - \left(\frac{\partial^2}{\partial x^2} + \frac{\partial^2}{\partial y^2} + \frac{\partial^2}{\partial z^2}\right)V_x\right\} \\ &\quad + \text{etc.}, \\ &= \nabla\nabla\cdot\mathbf{V} - \nabla\cdot\nabla\mathbf{V}.\end{aligned}$$

Problem 14a. Show that $\nabla\cdot\nabla\left(\frac{1}{r}\right) = 0.$

15. Line and Surface Integrals. — Let $\mathbf{V}(x, y, z)$ be a vector function of position in space and AB (Fig. 17) a curve described in the sense A to B. Divide the curve into vector elements $d\boldsymbol{\lambda}_1$, $d\boldsymbol{\lambda}_2$, $d\boldsymbol{\lambda}_3$, etc., and take the scalar product $\mathbf{V}_1 \cdot d\boldsymbol{\lambda}_1$ of $\mathbf{V}$ at the point A and $d\boldsymbol{\lambda}_1$, $V_2 \cdot d\boldsymbol{\lambda}_2$ of $\mathbf{V}$ at the point C and $d\boldsymbol{\lambda}_2$, $\mathbf{V}_3 \cdot d\boldsymbol{\lambda}_3$ of $\mathbf{V}$ at the point D and $d\boldsymbol{\lambda}_3$, and so on. The sum of these scalar products, that is

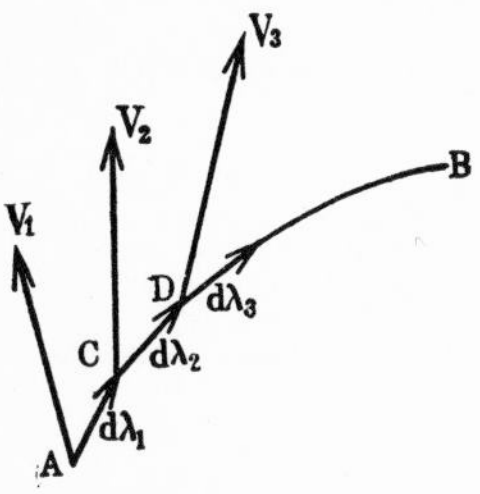

FIG. 17.

$$\Sigma \mathbf{V} \cdot d\boldsymbol{\lambda} = \int_A^B \mathbf{V} \cdot d\boldsymbol{\lambda}$$

summed up along the entire length of the curve, is known as the *line integral* of $\mathbf{V}$ along the curve AB. Obviously the line integral from B to A is the negative of that from A to B.

As

$$\left. \begin{aligned} d\boldsymbol{\lambda} &= \mathbf{i}dx + \mathbf{j}dy + \mathbf{k}dz, \\ \int_A^B \mathbf{V} \cdot d\boldsymbol{\lambda} &= \int_A^B (V_x dx + V_y dy + V_z dz). \end{aligned} \right\} \qquad (15\text{–}1)$$

Suppose $\mathbf{V}$ represents the force on a moving particle. Then the line integral of $\mathbf{V}$ over the path described by the particle is the work done by the force.

If $\mathbf{V}$ is the gradient $\nabla\Phi$ of a scalar function of position

$$V_x = \frac{\partial \Phi}{\partial x}, \quad V_y = \frac{\partial \Phi}{\partial y}, \quad V_z = \frac{\partial \Phi}{\partial z},$$

and

$$\left. \begin{aligned} \int_A^B \mathbf{V} \cdot d\boldsymbol{\lambda} &= \int_A^B (\nabla\Phi) \cdot d\boldsymbol{\lambda} = \int_A^B \left(\frac{\partial \Phi}{\partial x} dx + \frac{\partial \Phi}{\partial y} dy + \frac{\partial \Phi}{\partial z} dz \right) \\ &= \int_A^B d\Phi = \Phi_B - \Phi_A. \end{aligned} \right\} \qquad (15\text{–}2)$$

It follows that the line integral of the gradient of any scalar function of position Φ around a closed curve vanishes. For if the curve is closed the points A and B are coincident and the line integral is equal to $\Phi_A - \Phi_A$ which is zero. The line integral around a closed curve is denoted by an integral sign with a circle through it, thus:

$$\oint \mathbf{V}\cdot d\boldsymbol{\lambda}.$$

Suppose that the line integral of $\mathbf{V}$ vanishes about *every* closed path in space. Denoting the path (Fig. 18) of integration by a subscript under the integral sign,

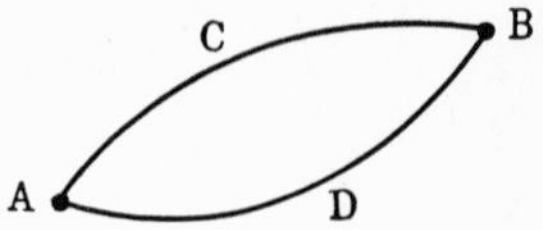

FIG. 18.

$$\int_{ACB} \mathbf{V}\cdot d\boldsymbol{\lambda} - \int_{ADB} \mathbf{V}\cdot d\boldsymbol{\lambda} = \int_{ACB} \mathbf{V}\cdot d\boldsymbol{\lambda} + \int_{BDA} \mathbf{V}\cdot d\boldsymbol{\lambda} = \oint \mathbf{V}\cdot d\boldsymbol{\lambda} = 0,$$

and therefore

$$\int_{ACB} \mathbf{V}\cdot d\boldsymbol{\lambda} = \int_{ADB} \mathbf{V}\cdot d\boldsymbol{\lambda}.$$

This relation shows that the line integral of $\mathbf{V}$ from A to B is independent of the path followed. Therefore, if A is fixed, the value of the integral can depend only upon the coordinates of B. Hence

$$\int_{AB} \mathbf{V}\cdot d\boldsymbol{\lambda} = \Phi_B - C.$$

To determine the value of the constant C, let B coincide with A. Then the integral vanishes and $C = \Phi_A$. Consequently

$$\int_{AB} \mathbf{V}\cdot d\boldsymbol{\lambda} = \Phi_B - \Phi_A.$$

If we take the two points A and B very close together

$$\mathbf{V}\cdot d\boldsymbol{\lambda} = d\Phi = (\nabla\Phi)\cdot d\boldsymbol{\lambda},$$

or

$$(\mathbf{V} - \nabla\Phi)\cdot d\boldsymbol{\lambda} = 0.$$

As this is true for all directions of $d\boldsymbol{\lambda}$, the vector $\mathbf{V} - \nabla\Phi$ can have no component in any direction, and hence it must vanish. Therefore

$$\mathbf{V} = \nabla\Phi. \qquad (15\text{–}3)$$

So if the line integral of **V** vanishes about every closed path, **V** must be the gradient of some scalar function Φ of position in space. Hence, from (14–4), the curl of **V** must vanish, and **V** is an irrotational vector function of position in space.

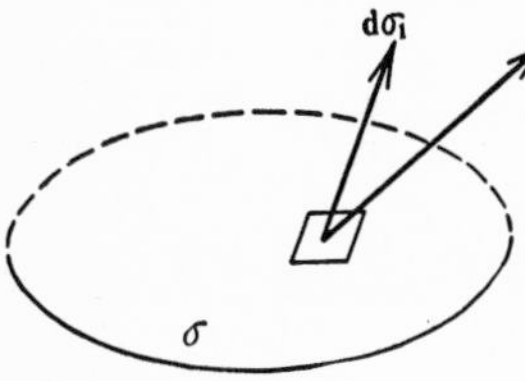

FIG. 19.

Consider a surface σ (Fig. 19). Divide the surface into vector elements $d\boldsymbol{\sigma}_1$, $d\boldsymbol{\sigma}_2$, $d\boldsymbol{\sigma}_3$, etc. Let $\mathbf{V}_1$ be the value of the vector function of position **V** $(x, y\ z)$ at $d\boldsymbol{\sigma}_1$, $\mathbf{V}_2$ its value at $d\boldsymbol{\sigma}_2$, $\mathbf{V}_3$ at $d\boldsymbol{\sigma}_3$, and so on. Then the sum of the scalar products $\mathbf{V}_1 \cdot d\boldsymbol{\sigma}_1$, $\mathbf{V}_2 \cdot d\boldsymbol{\sigma}_2$, $\mathbf{V}_3 \cdot d\boldsymbol{\sigma}_3$, etc., summed up over the whole surface, that is,

$$\Sigma \mathbf{V} \cdot d\boldsymbol{\sigma} = \int_\sigma \mathbf{V} \cdot d\boldsymbol{\sigma}$$

is known as the *surface integral* of **V** over the surface σ. The sign of the integral depends upon which face of the surface is taken as positive. Unless the contrary is explicitly stated, the positive sense of the normal is always taken so as to conform to the conventions of article 3. Reversing the positive sense of the normals to the surface elements changes the sign of the integral. As

$$\left.\begin{aligned} d\boldsymbol{\sigma} &= \mathbf{i}d\sigma_x + \mathbf{j}d\sigma_y + \mathbf{k}d\sigma_z, \\ \int_\sigma \mathbf{V} \cdot d\boldsymbol{\sigma} &= \int_\sigma (V_x d\sigma_x + V_y d\sigma_y + V_z d\sigma_z). \end{aligned}\right\} \tag{15–4}$$

The surface integral of a vector **V** is also called the *flux* of **V** through the surface. If **V** stands for the product of the density by the velocity of a fluid, $\mathbf{V} \cdot d\boldsymbol{\sigma}$ is the product of the density of the fluid by the volume of a prism of cross-section $d\sigma$ and altitude equal to the component of velocity normal to the surface. Therefore $\mathbf{V} \cdot d\boldsymbol{\sigma}$ represents the mass of fluid flowing through the element of surface $d\boldsymbol{\sigma}$ in a unit time, and the integral is equal to the mass of fluid passing through the entire surface in a unit time. The flux of electric intensity, or electric flux, is an important quantity in electrostatics as is the flux of magnetic induction in the theory of alternating currents.

16. Gauss' Theorem. — This theorem states that the volume integral of the divergence of a vector function of position **V** taken over any volume τ is equal to the surface integral of $\mathbf{V}$ taken over the closed surface surrounding the volume τ, that is,

$$\int_\tau \nabla\cdot\mathbf{V}d\tau = \int_\sigma \mathbf{V}\cdot d\boldsymbol{\sigma}, \tag{16–1}$$

where $d\tau = dx\,dy\,dz$ is an element of the volume τ, and the vector element of surface $d\boldsymbol{\sigma}$ has the direction of the outward drawn normal in accord with the convention of article 3. This theorem implies that, if the integrand has the form of the divergence of a vector, the value of a volume integral depends only upon the values of the vector at points on the surface enclosing the volume, and not at all on the values of the vector at points in the interior.

To prove Gauss' theorem, we have

$$\int_\tau \nabla\cdot\mathbf{V}d\tau = \iiint\left\{\frac{\partial V_x}{\partial x} + \frac{\partial V_y}{\partial y} + \frac{\partial V_z}{\partial z}\right\}dx\,dy\,dz$$

$$= \iiint\frac{\partial V_x}{\partial x}dx\,dy\,dz + \iiint\frac{\partial V_y}{\partial y}\,dx\,dy\,dz$$

$$+ \iiint\frac{\partial V_z}{\partial z}\,dx\,dy\,dz.$$

Consider the first integral on the right. Integrating with respect to x, that is along a strip of cross-section $dy\,dz$ extending from P_1 to P_2 (Fig. 20),

$$\iiint\frac{\partial V_x}{\partial x}\,dx\,dy\,dz = \iint\{V_x(x_2, y, z) - V_x(x_1, y, z)\}dy\,dz,$$

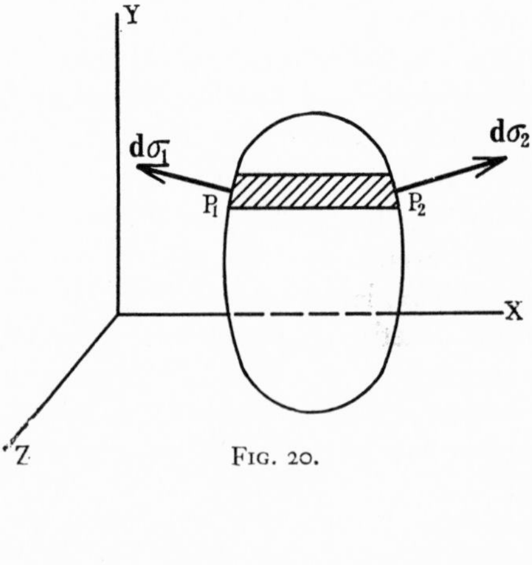

FIG. 20.

where x_1, y, z are the coordinates of P_1 and x_2, y, z, those of P_2. Now at P_1, $dy\, dz = -\, d\sigma_x$, while at P_2, $dy\, dz = d\sigma_x$. So

$$\int\int\int \frac{\partial V_x}{\partial x}\, dx\, dy\, dz = \int V_x(x_2, y, z) d\sigma_x + \int V_x(x_1, y, z) d\sigma_x,$$

where the first surface integral is taken over the right-hand part of the surface σ and the second over the left-hand part. Therefore

$$\int\int\int \frac{\partial V_x}{\partial x} d\, x\, dy\, dz = \int_\sigma V_x d\sigma_x, \tag{16–2}$$

where the surface integral on the right is evaluated over the entire surface. Similarly

$$\int\int\int \frac{\partial V_y}{\partial y}\, dx\, dy\, dz = \int_\sigma V_y d\sigma_y, \tag{16–3}$$

and

$$\int\int\int \frac{\partial V_z}{\partial z}\, dx\, dy\, dz = \int_\sigma V_z d\sigma_z. \tag{16–4}$$

Adding (16–2), (16–3) and (16–4) we get Gauss' theorem

$$\int_\tau \nabla \cdot \mathbf{V} d\tau = \int_\sigma (V_x d\sigma_x + V_y d\sigma_y + V_z d\sigma_z)$$

$$= \int_\sigma \mathbf{V} \cdot d\boldsymbol{\sigma}.$$

While we have proved Gauss' theorem only for a region bounded by a single surface, the theorem can be extended at once to a region bounded by several surfaces. Consider, for instance, the region lying between the two surfaces σ_1 and σ_2 (Fig. 21). By introducing the coincident surfaces *ABCD* and *EFGH* we can divide the region into two regions τ_1 and τ_2 each of which is bounded by a single closed surface. Applying Gauss' theorem to each of these, and adding, we find that the volume integral of $\nabla \cdot \mathbf{V}$ over the entire region $\tau_1 + \tau_2$ is equal to the sum of two surface integrals. Now the surface integral over *ABCD* is annulled by that over *EFGH* since these two surfaces are coincident and have outward drawn normals in opposite senses. Hence we are left the sum of the surface integral over σ_1 and that over

σ_2. In each case the positive normal is outward from the region $\tau_1 + \tau_2$ over which the volume integral is to be evaluated.

The equation of continuity of article 12 can be deduced very simply by the aid of Gauss' theorem. If the vector **V** stands for $\rho\mathbf{v}$,

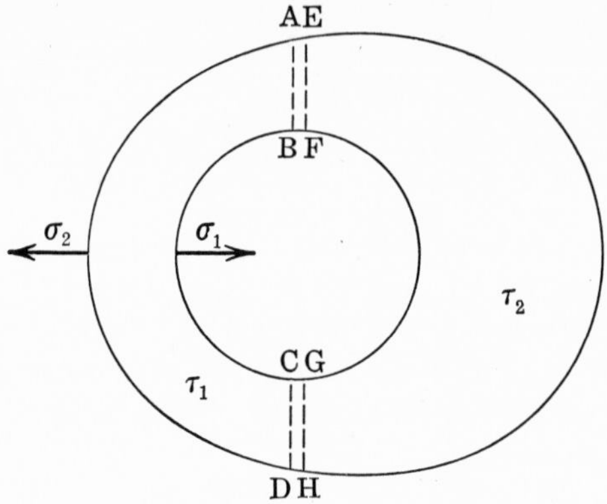

FIG. 21.

the surface integral of **V** over any closed surface σ represents the total mass of fluid passing out through the surface in a unit time. But this is equal to the time rate of decrease of mass inside the surface. Hence

$$-\int_\tau \frac{\partial \rho}{\partial t}\, d\tau = \int_\sigma \mathbf{V}\cdot d\boldsymbol{\sigma}$$

$$= \int_\tau \nabla\cdot\mathbf{V}\, d\tau,$$

by Gauss' theorem. As the volume τ over which the integrals are extended may be made very small the integrands must be equal. Therefore

$$\frac{\partial \rho}{\partial t} = -\nabla\cdot\mathbf{V}.$$

An important corollary of Gauss' theorem states that

$$\int_\tau (u\nabla\cdot\nabla v - v\nabla\cdot\nabla u)\, d\tau = \int_\sigma (u\nabla v - v\nabla u)\cdot d\boldsymbol{\sigma}. \qquad (16\text{–}5)$$

where u and v are two scalar functions of the coordinates. This theorem is known as *Green's theorem*. To prove it, we start with the identities

$$\nabla\cdot(u\nabla v) = u\nabla\cdot\nabla v + (\nabla u)\cdot(\nabla v),$$

$$\nabla\cdot(v\nabla u) = v\nabla\cdot\nabla u + (\nabla v)\cdot(\nabla u).$$

Subtracting and integrating over an arbitrary volume τ,

$$\int_\tau \nabla\cdot\{u\nabla v - v\nabla u\}d\tau = \int_\tau (u\nabla\cdot\nabla v - v\nabla\cdot\nabla u)d\tau.$$

Converting the left-hand side into a surface integral by Gauss' theorem, we have (16–5).

17. Stokes' Theorem. — This theorem states that the surface integral of the curl of a vector function of position **V** taken over any surface σ is equal to the line integral of **V** around the periphery λ of the surface, that is,

$$\int_\sigma \nabla\times\mathbf{V}\cdot d\boldsymbol{\sigma} = \oint \mathbf{V}\cdot d\boldsymbol{\lambda}, \tag{17–1}$$

where $d\boldsymbol{\lambda}$ is a vector element of the periphery taken in the sense of rotation of a right-handed screw advancing from the negative to the positive side of the surface in accord with the convention of article 3. This theorem implies that, if the integrand has the form of the curl of a vector, the value of a surface integral depends only upon the values of the vector at points on the periphery, and therefore that the integral has the same value over all surfaces having the same periphery.

To prove Stokes' theorem, since

$$\nabla\times\mathbf{V} = \mathbf{i}\left(\frac{\partial V_z}{\partial y} - \frac{\partial V_y}{\partial z}\right) + \mathbf{j}\left(\frac{\partial V_x}{\partial z} - \frac{\partial V_z}{\partial x}\right) + \mathbf{k}\left(\frac{\partial V_y}{\partial x} - \frac{\partial V_x}{\partial y}\right),$$

it follows that

$$\left.\begin{aligned}\int_\sigma \nabla\times\mathbf{V}\cdot d\boldsymbol{\sigma} &= \int_\sigma\left(\frac{\partial V_x}{\partial z}d\sigma_y - \frac{\partial V_x}{\partial y}d\sigma_z\right)\\ &+ \int_\sigma\left(\frac{\partial V_y}{\partial x}d\sigma_z - \frac{\partial V_y}{\partial z}d\sigma_x\right)\\ &+ \int_\sigma\left(\frac{\partial V_z}{\partial y}d\sigma_x - \frac{\partial V_z}{\partial x}d\sigma_y\right).\end{aligned}\right\} \tag{17–2}$$

Let P_1P_2 (Fig. 22) be the trace of the surface σ on a plane parallel to the YZ coordinate plane at a distance x from the origin. We will integrate the first integral on the right of (17–2) along a strip of the surface extending from P_1 to P_2. The figure is drawn so that both y and z increase as we proceed from P_1 to P_2. The Y component of $d\boldsymbol{\sigma}$ is positive, and therefore $d\sigma_y = dz\,dx$, but the Z component is negative, and so $d\sigma_z = -dy\,dx$. Therefore

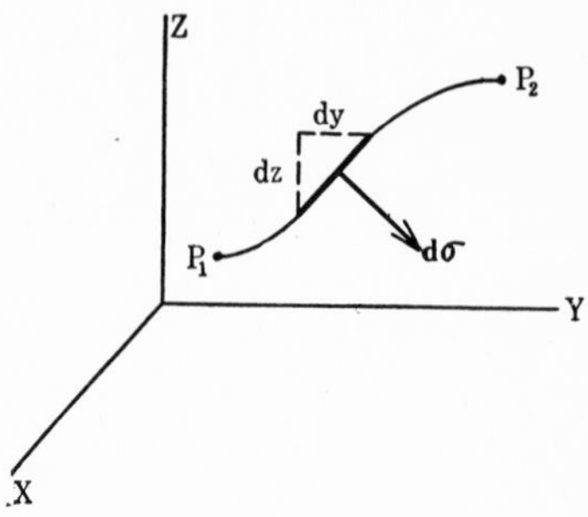

FIG. 22.

$$\int_\sigma \left(\frac{\partial V_x}{\partial z} d\sigma_y - \frac{\partial V_x}{\partial y} d\sigma_z \right) = \int\int \left(\frac{\partial V_x}{\partial z} dz + \frac{\partial V_x}{\partial y} dy \right) dx.$$

But, as x remains constant for integration along the strip P_1P_2,

$$dV_x = \frac{\partial V_x}{\partial y} dy + \frac{\partial V_x}{\partial z} dz.$$

So

$$\int_\sigma \left(\frac{\partial V_x}{\partial z} d\sigma_y - \frac{\partial V_x}{\partial y} d\sigma_z \right) = \int dx \int_{P_1}^{P_2} dV_x$$

$$= \int V_x(x, y_2, z_2)dx - \int V_x(x, y_1, z_1)dx,$$

where x, y_1, z_1 are the coordinates of P_1 and x, y_2, z_2 those of P_2. At P_1 the sense in which the periphery of the surface is described is *into* the paper, whereas at P_2 it is *out from* the paper. So at P_1, $dx = -d\lambda_x$, and at P_2, $dx = d\lambda_x$. Therefore

$$\int_\sigma \left(\frac{\partial V_x}{\partial z} d\sigma_y - \frac{\partial V_x}{\partial y} d\sigma_z \right) = \int V_x(x, y_2, z_2)d\lambda_x + \int V_x(x, y_1, z_1)d\lambda_x,$$

where the first line integral is taken over the right-hand portion of the periphery and the second over the left-hand portion. So

$$\int_\sigma \left(\frac{\partial V_x}{\partial z} d\sigma_y - \frac{\partial V_x}{\partial y} d\sigma_z \right) = \oint V_x d\lambda_x, \qquad (17\text{–}3)$$

the line integral being taken all the way around the periphery. Similarly

$$\int_\sigma \left(\frac{\partial V_y}{\partial x} d\sigma_z - \frac{\partial V_y}{\partial z} d\sigma_x \right) = \oint V_y d\lambda_y, \tag{17-4}$$

and

$$\int_\sigma \left(\frac{\partial V_z}{\partial y} d\sigma_x - \frac{\partial V_z}{\partial x} d\sigma_y \right) = \oint V_z d\lambda_z. \tag{17-5}$$

Adding (17–3), (17–4) and (17–5) we get Stokes' theorem

$$\int_\sigma \nabla \times \mathbf{V} \cdot d\boldsymbol{\sigma} = \oint (V_x d\lambda_x + V_y d\lambda_y + V_z d\lambda_z)$$

$$= \oint \mathbf{V} \cdot d\boldsymbol{\lambda}.$$

If the surface to which Stokes' theorem is applied is a closed surface, the length of the periphery is zero and hence

$$\int_\sigma \nabla \times \mathbf{V} \cdot d\boldsymbol{\sigma} = 0. \tag{17-6}$$

If $\nabla \times \mathbf{V}$ vanishes everywhere, $\mathbf{V}$ is the gradient of a scalar function of position in space. For then the line integral of $\mathbf{V}$ around every closed curve vanishes, and this is just the condition that $\mathbf{V}$ should be the gradient of a scalar function of position in space as was shown in article 15. Now an irrotational vector was defined as one whose curl is everywhere zero. So we have proved that every irrotational vector is the gradient of some scalar function of position in space. This is the converse of the result obtained in article 14 to the effect that the gradient of a scalar function is an irrotational vector.

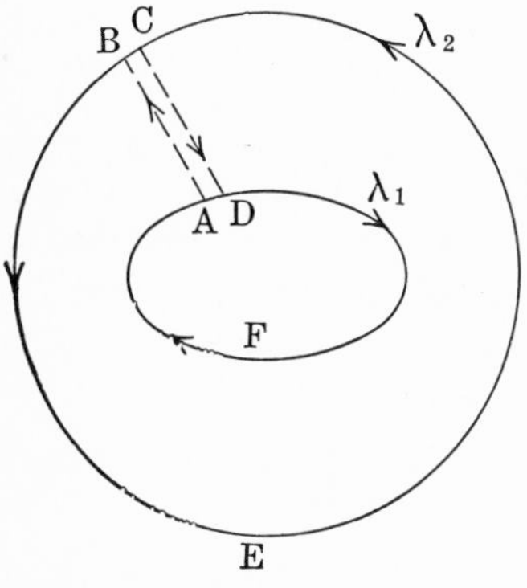

Fig. 23.

Stokes' theorem can be extended easily to the case of a surface bounded by more than one curve. Consider, for instance, the surface (Fig. 23) bounded by two curves λ_1 and λ_2. By introducing the coincident lines AB and CD it becomes a surface bounded by the single closed curve *ABECDFA* and consequently Stokes' theorem can be applied. As, however, *CD* is described in the opposite sense to *AB*, the integrals along these two lines annul each other. Hence there remain only the line integrals along λ_1 and along λ_2. Note that the latter is described in the opposite sense to the former.

Problem 17a. By the use of Gauss' theorem and Stokes' theorem prove that $\nabla\cdot\nabla\times\mathbf{V} = 0$ and $\nabla\times\nabla\Phi = 0$.

Problem 17b. The ends of a strip of paper are glued together so as to form a surface with only one side. Discuss the application of Stokes' theorem to such a surface.

17.1. Orthogonal Curvilinear Coordinates. — In (11–10) we have expressed the gradient in spherical coordinates. In many problems we need to express as well the divergence, curl or Laplacian in spherical or other orthogonal coordinates.

Let us take as coordinate surfaces any three orthogonal families, $\xi(x, y, z) = \text{constant}$, $\eta(x, y, z) = \text{constant}$ and $\zeta(x, y, z) = \text{constant}$, and let λ, μ, ν be the functions of ξ, η, ζ by which we have to multiply $d\xi$, $d\eta$, $d\zeta$, respectively, in order to obtain the distances corresponding to these increments in the coordinates. In spherical coordinates, for example, where ξ, η, ζ become r, θ, ϕ, respectively, $\lambda = 1$, $\mu = r$, $\nu = r\sin\theta$. Furthermore, let $\boldsymbol{\xi}_1, \boldsymbol{\eta}_1, \boldsymbol{\zeta}_1$, be unit vectors in the directions of increasing ξ, η, ζ, respectively, so ordered that they constitute a right-handed set in the sequence given.

Since the component of the gradient of a scalar function Φ in any direction is equal to the space rate of increase of Φ in that direction, it follows that the gradient is given by

$$\nabla\Phi = \boldsymbol{\xi}_1 \frac{\partial\Phi}{\lambda\partial\xi} + \boldsymbol{\eta}_1 \frac{\partial\Phi}{\mu\partial\eta} + \boldsymbol{\zeta}_1 \frac{\partial\Phi}{\nu\partial\zeta}. \qquad (17.1\text{–}1)$$

The divergence and the curl of a vector function

$$\mathbf{V}(\xi, \eta, \zeta) = \boldsymbol{\xi}_1 V_\xi(\xi, \eta, \zeta) + \boldsymbol{\eta}_1 V_\eta(\xi, \eta, \zeta) + \boldsymbol{\zeta}_1 V_\zeta(\xi, \eta, \zeta)$$

can be obtained most easily from Gauss' theorem and from Stokes' theorem, respectively.

To obtain the divergence we apply Gauss' theorem to an elementary rectangular parallelopiped $\Delta\tau = \lambda\mu\nu\Delta\xi\Delta\eta\Delta\zeta$ bounded by coordinate surfaces. Then

$$\nabla\cdot\mathbf{V}\Delta\tau = \int_\sigma \mathbf{V}\cdot d\boldsymbol{\sigma}.$$

Now the net outward flux of **V** through the two faces for which ξ is constant is

$$V_\xi \mu\nu \Delta\eta\Delta\zeta + \frac{\partial}{\partial \xi}(V_\xi \mu\nu)\Delta\xi\Delta\eta\Delta\zeta - V_\xi \mu\nu\Delta\eta\Delta\zeta = \frac{\partial}{\partial\xi}(V_\xi\mu\nu)\Delta\xi\Delta\eta\Delta\zeta,$$

and similar expressions hold for the two remaining pairs of surfaces.

Hence

$$\int_\sigma \mathbf{V}\cdot d\boldsymbol{\sigma} = \left\{\frac{\partial}{\partial\xi}(\mu\nu V_\xi) + \frac{\partial}{\partial\eta}(\nu\lambda V_\eta) + \frac{\partial}{\partial\zeta}(\lambda\mu V_\zeta)\right\}\Delta\xi\Delta\eta\Delta\zeta$$

and

$$\nabla\cdot\mathbf{V} = \frac{1}{\lambda\mu\nu}\left\{\frac{\partial}{\partial\xi}(\mu\nu V_\xi) + \frac{\partial}{\partial\eta}(\nu\lambda V_\eta) + \frac{\partial}{\partial\zeta}(\lambda\mu V_\zeta)\right\}. \qquad (17.1\text{–}2)$$

Since the Laplacian of a scalar function Φ is just the divergence of the gradient, we obtain the Laplacian in the coordinates ξ, η, ζ by replacing the components of **V** in (17.1–2) by the components of the divergence as given by (17.1–1), getting

$$\nabla\cdot\nabla\Phi = \frac{1}{\lambda\mu\nu}\left\{\frac{\partial}{\partial\xi}\left(\frac{\mu\nu}{\lambda}\frac{\partial\Phi}{\partial\xi}\right) + \frac{\partial}{\partial\eta}\left(\frac{\nu\lambda}{\mu}\frac{\partial\Phi}{\partial\eta}\right) + \frac{\partial}{\partial\zeta}\left(\frac{\lambda\mu}{\nu}\frac{\partial\Phi}{\partial\zeta}\right)\right\}. \qquad (17.1\text{–}3)$$

To obtain the curl we apply Stokes' theorem to an elementary rectangle $\Delta\sigma_\xi = \mu\nu\Delta\eta\Delta\zeta$ in the coordinate surface $\xi =$ constant. Then the ξ component of $\nabla \times \mathbf{V}$ is given by

$$|\nabla\times\mathbf{V}|_\xi\Delta\sigma_\xi = \oint \mathbf{V}\cdot d\boldsymbol{\lambda}.$$

Now the line integral of **V** along the two edges for which η is constant is

$$V_\zeta\nu\Delta\zeta + \frac{\partial}{\partial\eta}(V_\zeta\nu)\Delta\eta\Delta\zeta - V_\zeta\nu\Delta\zeta = \frac{\partial}{\partial\eta}(V_\zeta\nu)\Delta\eta\Delta\zeta$$

and along the two edges for which ζ is constant

$$-\left\{V_\eta\mu\Delta\eta + \frac{\partial}{\partial\zeta}(V_\eta\mu)\Delta\zeta\Delta\eta - V_\eta\mu\Delta\eta\right\} = -\frac{\partial}{\partial\zeta}(V_\eta\mu)\Delta\zeta\Delta\eta.$$

Hence

$$\oint \mathbf{V}\cdot d\boldsymbol{\lambda} = \left\{\frac{\partial}{\partial\eta}(\nu V_\zeta) - \frac{\partial}{\partial\zeta}(\mu V_\eta)\right\}\Delta\eta\Delta\zeta$$

and
$$|\nabla \times \mathbf{V}|_\xi = \frac{1}{\mu\nu}\left\{\frac{\partial}{\partial\eta}(\nu V_\zeta) - \frac{\partial}{\partial\zeta}(\mu V_\eta)\right\}. \qquad (17.1\text{–}4)$$

This expression, together with similar expressions for the other components, is given by the determinant

$$\nabla \times \mathbf{V} = \frac{1}{\lambda\mu\nu}\begin{vmatrix} \lambda\boldsymbol{\xi}_1 & \mu\boldsymbol{\eta}_1 & \nu\boldsymbol{\zeta}_1 \\ \frac{\partial}{\partial\xi} & \frac{\partial}{\partial\eta} & \frac{\partial}{\partial\zeta} \\ \lambda V_\xi & \mu V_\eta & \nu V_\zeta \end{vmatrix}. \qquad (17.1\text{–}5)$$

Problem 17.1a. Find the Laplacian of Φ in spherical coordinates.

Ans. $\nabla \cdot \nabla\Phi = \frac{1}{r^2}\left\{\frac{\partial}{\partial r}\left(r^2\frac{\partial\Phi}{\partial r}\right) + \frac{1}{\sin\theta}\frac{\partial}{\partial\theta}\left(\sin\theta\frac{\partial\Phi}{\partial\theta}\right) + \frac{1}{\sin^2\theta}\frac{\partial^2\Phi}{\partial\phi^2}\right\}.$

17.2. The Potential Operator. — Let $u(x_2, y_2, z_2)$ be a finite, continuous and single-valued function of the coordinates x_2, y_2, z_2 of a point P_2 (Fig. 23.1) and let r_{12} be the distance

$$\sqrt{(x_2 - x_1)^2 + (y_2 - y_1)^2 + (z_2 - z_1)^2}$$

of P_2 from another point P_1 with coordinates x_1, y_1, z_1. Describe two spheres about P_1 as center, one a very small sphere of radius r and the other a very large sphere of radius R. The potential of u, designated by Pot u, is defined as the limit of the integral

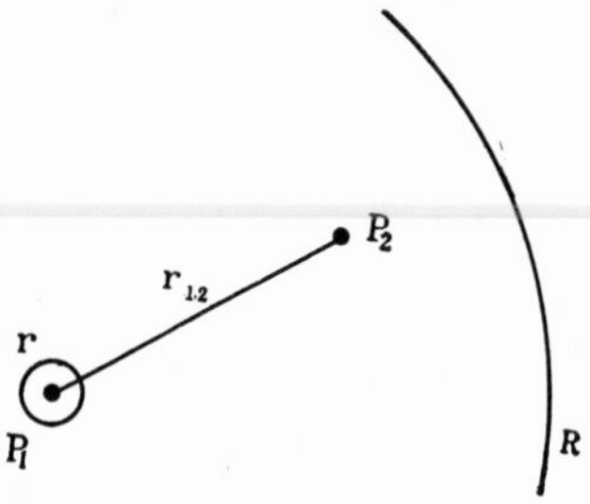

FIG. 23.1.

$$\int_r^R \frac{u(x_2, y_2, z_2)}{r_{12}}\, d\tau_2,$$

where $d\tau_2 \equiv dx_2\, dy_2\, dz_2$, taken over the volume between the two spheres, as $r \to 0$ and $R \to \infty$. Since $d\tau_2 = r_{12}^2 \sin\theta\, dr_{12} d\theta d\phi$ in spherical coordinates, it is evident that Pot u is finite only if the function u falls off more rapidly than $1/r_{12}^2$ at great distances from P_1, or becomes identically zero. Of course the value of Pot u depends on the position of P_1, that is, Pot u is a function of x_1, y_1, z_1, (not of x_2, y_2, z_2). Evidently Pot $(u + v)$ = Pot u + Pot v.

The potential operator has the remarkable property of commuting with the differential operator ∇, that is,

$$\nabla_1 \text{ Pot } u = \text{Pot } \nabla_2\, u \qquad (17.2\text{–}1)$$

where

$$\nabla_1 \equiv \mathbf{i}\frac{\partial}{\partial x_1} + \mathbf{j}\frac{\partial}{\partial y_1} + \mathbf{k}\frac{\partial}{\partial z_1}$$

and

$$\nabla_2 \equiv \mathbf{i}\frac{\partial}{\partial x_2} + \mathbf{j}\frac{\partial}{\partial y_2} + \mathbf{k}\frac{\partial}{\partial z_2}.$$

To prove this, consider a point P_1' with coordinates $x_1 + dx, y_1, z_1$. If Pot u is the potential of u at P_1, then the potential at P_1' is

$$\text{Pot}\, u + \left(\frac{\partial}{\partial x_1}\text{Pot}\, u\right) dx. \qquad (17.2\text{–}2)$$

But the potential of u at P_1' is the same as the potential which would exist at P_1 if the function u at every point x_2, y_2, z_2 were replaced by the value $u + \dfrac{\partial u}{\partial x_2}dx$ of the function at the point $x_2 + dx,\ y_2,\ z_2$. Hence the potential at P_1' is given by

$$\text{Pot}\left(u + \frac{\partial u}{\partial x_2}dx\right) = \text{Pot}\, u + \left(\text{Pot}\frac{\partial u}{\partial x_2}\right)dx. \qquad (17.2\text{–}3)$$

Equating (17.2–2) and (17.2–3) we have

$$\frac{\partial}{\partial x_1}\text{Pot}\, u = \text{Pot}\frac{\partial u}{\partial x_2},$$

and similarly

$$\frac{\partial}{\partial y_1}\text{Pot}\, u = \text{Pot}\frac{\partial u}{\partial y_2},$$

$$\frac{\partial}{\partial z_1}\text{Pot}\, u = \text{Pot}\frac{\partial u}{\partial z_2}.$$

Multiplying the last three equations by **i**, **j** and **k**, respectively, and adding we have (17.2–1).

Evidently the commutation of Pot and ∇ holds if ∇ is repeated. Thus

$$\nabla_1\cdot\nabla_1\,\text{Pot}\, u = \nabla_1\cdot\text{Pot}\,\nabla_2 u = \text{Pot}\,\nabla_2\cdot\nabla_2 u. \qquad (17.2\text{–}4)$$

Henceforth we shall generally omit the subscripts on the differential operator, since ∇ in front of Pot can mean only ∇_1, and ∇ after Pot only ∇_2. While Pot u and $\nabla\cdot\nabla$ Pot u are scalars, ∇Pot u is a vector function.

If **V** is a vector function of x_2, y_2, z_2,

$$\mathbf{V}(x_2, y_2, z_2) = \mathbf{i}V_x(x_2, y_2, z_2) + \mathbf{j}V_y(x_2, y_2, z_2) + \mathbf{k}V_z(x_2, y_2, z_2),$$

and

$$\text{Pot}\,\mathbf{V} = \mathbf{i}\,\text{Pot}\,V_x + \mathbf{j}\,\text{Pot}\,V_y + \mathbf{k}\,\text{Pot}\,V_z.$$

Therefore the scalar function u in the preceding equations can be replaced everywhere by a vector function $\mathbf{V}$. If u or $\mathbf{V}$ is a proper function, Pot u or Pot $\mathbf{V}$ is also.

17.3. Poisson's Theorem. — This theorem states

$$\text{Pot}\,\nabla\cdot\nabla u = -4\pi u. \tag{17.3-1}$$

While the u on the left-hand side is a function of x_2, y_2, z_2, that on the right-hand side is the value of u at P_1, a function of x_1, y_1, z_1. Now we have seen that Pot u is finite only when u falls off more rapidly than $1/r_{12}^2$ at great distances from P_1. Therefore Pot ∇u is finite only when ∇u falls off more rapidly than $1/r_{12}^2$. But, as differentiation reduces the degree of r_{12} by unity, this requires only that u should fall off more rapidly than $1/r_{12}$. Similarly Pot $\nabla\cdot\nabla u$ exists if u goes to zero at infinity with any positive power of $1/r_{12}$ no matter how small.

To prove Poisson's theorem we apply Green's theorem (16–5) to the region between the spheres of radii r and R of article 17.2, replacing v by $1/r_{12}$. Then the first term on the left of (16–5) contains the factor $\nabla\cdot\nabla(1/r_{12})$, which vanishes in accord with the result of problem 14a, and the second term is just the negative of Pot $\nabla\cdot\nabla u$. Hence

$$\text{Pot}\,\nabla\cdot\nabla u = \int_\sigma \frac{1}{r_{12}}\nabla u\cdot d\boldsymbol{\sigma} - \int_\sigma u\nabla\left(\frac{1}{r_{12}}\right)\cdot d\boldsymbol{\sigma}.$$

As u must go to zero at infinity with a positive power of $1/r_{12}$ for Pot $\nabla\cdot\nabla u$ to exist, ∇u must go to zero more rapidly than $1/r_{12}$. Also $\nabla(1/r_{12})$ goes to zero with $1/r_{12}^2$. Hence, since $d\sigma = r_{12}^2 \sin\theta d\theta d\phi$, the surface integrals over the large sphere vanish as $R \rightarrow 0$.

Next we evaluate the surface integrals over the small sphere, assuming that ∇u like u is finite and continuous at P_1. As $d\sigma$ is of the order of r^2 it is clear that the first integral vanishes as $r \rightarrow 0$. Using (11–11) for ∇ and remembering that $d\boldsymbol{\sigma} = -\mathbf{r}_1\, d\sigma$ since the positive normal is directed outward from the volume over which the volume integrals are taken, and therefore toward P_1,

$$\nabla\left(\frac{1}{r_{12}}\right)\cdot d\boldsymbol{\sigma} = d\boldsymbol{\sigma}\cdot\nabla\left(\frac{1}{r_{12}}\right) = -\frac{\partial}{\partial r_2}\left(\frac{1}{r_{12}}\right) r_{12}^2 \sin\theta d\theta d\phi = \sin\theta d\theta d\phi.$$

So, if we understand by u the value of the function at P_1,

$$\int_\sigma u\nabla\left(\frac{1}{r_{12}}\right)\cdot d\sigma = u\int_\sigma \nabla\left(\frac{1}{r_{12}}\right)\cdot d\sigma = 4\pi u,$$

giving (17.3–1).

If u vanishes at infinity rapidly enough so that Pot u exists, we may write (17.3–1) in the form

$$\nabla\cdot\nabla \operatorname{Pot} u = -4\pi u \qquad (17.3\text{–}2)$$

on account of the commutation of ∇ and Pot.

As Poisson's theorem holds for each rectangular component of a vector function $\mathbf{V}$ satisfying the conditions imposed on u, it follows that it is valid for a vector function satisfying those conditions, that is,

$$\operatorname{Pot} \nabla\cdot\nabla\mathbf{V} = -4\pi\mathbf{V}. \qquad (17.3\text{–}3)$$

17.4. Resolution of a Vector Function into Irrotational and Solenoidal Parts. — We are interested here in a vector function $\mathbf{V}$ which, together with its derivatives, is finite, continuous, and single-valued and which vanishes at infinity. Applying the potential operator to the identity (14–6) we have

$$\operatorname{Pot} \nabla\cdot\nabla\mathbf{V} = \operatorname{Pot} \nabla\nabla\cdot\mathbf{V} - \operatorname{Pot} \nabla\times\nabla\times\mathbf{V}.$$

Using Poisson's theorem (17.3–3)

$$\mathbf{V} = -\frac{1}{4\pi}\operatorname{Pot} \nabla\nabla\cdot\mathbf{V} + \frac{1}{4\pi}\operatorname{Pot} \nabla\times\nabla\times\mathbf{V}. \qquad (17.4\text{–}1)$$

Now

$$\nabla\times\operatorname{Pot} \nabla\nabla\cdot\mathbf{V} = \operatorname{Pot} \nabla\times\nabla\nabla\cdot\mathbf{V} = 0$$

by (14–4), and

$$\nabla\cdot\operatorname{Pot} \nabla\times\nabla\times\mathbf{V} = \operatorname{Pot} \nabla\cdot\nabla\times\nabla\times\mathbf{V} = 0$$

by (14–5). Hence the first term on the right of (17.4–1) is irrotational and the second term is solenoidal. We have shown that *any well-behaved vector function which vanishes at infinity can be expressed as the sum of an irrotational part and a solenoidal part.* Furthermore we have proved in (17.4–1) that *the vector function is completely determined if its divergence and its curl are given at all points of space.*

If Pot $\nabla\cdot\mathbf{V}$ and Pot $\nabla\times\mathbf{V}$ exist, (17.4–1) may be written in the form

$$\mathbf{V} = -\nabla\left\{\frac{1}{4\pi}\text{Pot}\,\nabla\cdot\mathbf{V}\right\} + \nabla\times\left\{\frac{1}{4\pi}\text{Pot}\,\nabla\times\mathbf{V}\right\}. \qquad (17.4\text{–}2)$$

If $\mathbf{V}$ is irrotational the second term vanishes and the function is expressed as the gradient of a scalar function as proved otherwise in article 17, whereas if $\mathbf{V}$ is solenoidal the first term vanishes and the function is expressed as the curl of a vector function.

18. Dyadics or Tensors. — Many physical laws are expressed by equating one vector to the product of another vector by a scalar. For instance, if $\mathbf{f}$ is the vector acceleration of a particle acted on by a force $\mathbf{F}$, the second law of motion requires that

$$\mathbf{F} = m\mathbf{f},$$

where the scalar m is the mass of the particle. On the other hand consider a particle P (Fig. 24) fastened to the ends of three long mutually perpendicular springs A, B and C of different degrees of stiffness, the far ends of the springs being attached to a rigid framework. If a force F_x is applied to P in the X direction it will displace the particle in this direction, stretching the spring A but producing no appreciable change in the lengths of the long springs B and C. If a_x is the stiffness of the spring A, that is, the force necessary to stretch the spring a unit distance, the displacement x of P produced by F_x is given by

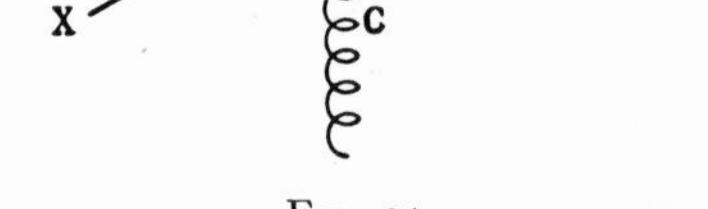

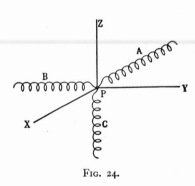

FIG. 24.

$$F_x = a_x x.$$

Similarly a force F_y acting alone in the Y direction will produce a displacement y given by

$$F_y = a_y y,$$

where a_y is the stiffness of spring B, and a force F_z acting alone in the Z direction will give rise to the displacement z where

$$F_z = a_z z.$$

Now if all three forces act simultaneously the resultant force

$$\mathbf{F} = \mathbf{i}F_x + \mathbf{j}F_y + \mathbf{k}F_z$$

is related to the displacement

$$\mathbf{r} = \mathbf{i}x + \mathbf{j}y + \mathbf{k}z$$

by the equation

$$\mathbf{F} = \mathbf{i}a_x x + \mathbf{j}a_y y + \mathbf{k}a_z z$$

$$= a_x\mathbf{ii}\cdot\mathbf{r} + a_y\mathbf{jj}\cdot\mathbf{r} + a_z\mathbf{kk}\cdot\mathbf{r}$$

$$= (a_x\mathbf{ii} + a_y\mathbf{jj} + a_z\mathbf{kk})\cdot\mathbf{r}$$

The operator

$$\Psi = a_x\mathbf{ii} + a_y\mathbf{jj} + a_z\mathbf{kk} \tag{18–1}$$

is known as a *dyadic* or *tensor of the second rank*. By taking the scalar product of the dyadic Ψ by the vector $\mathbf{r}$ a new vector $\mathbf{F}$ is obtained which differs in general from $\mathbf{r}$ in direction as well as in magnitude. For the direction cosines of $\mathbf{r}$ are proportional to x, y, z, respectively, whereas those of $\mathbf{F}$ are proportional to $a_x x$, $a_y y$, $a_z z$. Only when a_x, a_y and a_z are equal is $\mathbf{F}$ parallel to $\mathbf{r}$ for all orientations of the latter vector. The vector $\mathbf{F}$ is said to be a *linear vector function* of the vector $\mathbf{r}$.

In obtaining the expanded form (18–1) of the dyadic Ψ we have chosen axes parallel to the axes of the springs. If we wish to refer the dyadic to axes $X'Y'Z'$ oriented with respect to XYZ according to the scheme of article 8, we must substitute for $\mathbf{i}$, $\mathbf{j}$, $\mathbf{k}$ their values in terms of the unit vectors $\mathbf{i}'$, $\mathbf{j}'$, $\mathbf{k}'$ parallel to the new axes, to wit,

$$\left.\begin{aligned} \mathbf{i} &= l_1\mathbf{i}' + m_1\mathbf{j}' + n_1\mathbf{k}', \\ \mathbf{j} &= l_2\mathbf{i}' + m_2\mathbf{j}' + n_2\mathbf{k}', \\ \mathbf{k} &= l_3\mathbf{i}' + m_3\mathbf{j}' + n_3\mathbf{k}'. \end{aligned}\right\} \tag{18–2}$$

This gives for Ψ

$$\left.\begin{aligned}\Psi = {} & a_{11}\mathbf{i}'\mathbf{i}' + a_{12}\mathbf{i}'\mathbf{j}' + a_{13}\mathbf{i}'\mathbf{k}', \\ & + a_{21}\mathbf{j}'\mathbf{i}' + a_{22}\mathbf{j}'\mathbf{j}' + a_{23}\mathbf{j}'\mathbf{k}', \\ & + a_{31}\mathbf{k}'\mathbf{i}' + a_{32}\mathbf{k}'\mathbf{j}' + a_{33}\mathbf{k}'\mathbf{k}'.\end{aligned}\right\} \tag{18-3}$$

where

$$a_{11} = l_1{}^2a_x + l_2{}^2a_y + l_3{}^2a_z, \text{ etc.,}$$

$$a_{12} = a_{21} = l_1m_1a_x + l_2m_2a_y + l_3m_3a_z, \text{ etc.}$$

Any operator of the form (18–3) is known as a dyadic. If, as in the present case, $a_{ij} = a_{ji}$, the dyadic is said to be *symmetric*. On the other hand, if $a_{ij} = -a_{ji}$, the dyadic is said to be *skew-symmetric*.

It is seen from (18–3) that a term of the dyadic, such as $a_{12}\mathbf{i}'\mathbf{j}'$, is formed by the juxtaposition of two vectors, the two vectors being $a_{12}\mathbf{i}'$ and $\mathbf{j}'$ or $\mathbf{i}'$ and $a_{12}\mathbf{j}'$, in the term cited. If **a** and **l** are two vectors, the operator **al** is known as a *dyad*, the vector **a** being called the *antecedent* and the vector **l** the *consequent*. The vectors comprising a dyad do not obey the commutative law in general, for if **al** operates on the vector **P**,

$$\mathbf{al}\cdot\mathbf{P} \neq \mathbf{la}\cdot\mathbf{P}$$

except when **a** is parallel to **l**. On the other hand, they do obey the distributive law, since

$$(\mathbf{a} + \mathbf{b})\,(\mathbf{l} + \mathbf{m})\cdot\mathbf{P} = (\mathbf{al} + \mathbf{bl} + \mathbf{am} + \mathbf{bm})\cdot\mathbf{P}.$$

A dyadic is simply the sum of a number of dyads.

Consider the dyadic

$$\Phi = \mathbf{al} + \mathbf{bm} + \mathbf{cn} + \mathbf{do}.$$

Provided **l**, **m** and **n** do not lie in a single plane, **o** may be written in the form

$$\mathbf{o} = f\mathbf{l} + g\mathbf{m} + h\mathbf{n}$$

and therefore

$$\Phi = (\mathbf{a} + f\mathbf{d})\mathbf{l} + (\mathbf{b} + g\mathbf{d})\mathbf{m} + (\mathbf{c} + h\mathbf{d})\mathbf{n}.$$

On the other hand, if **n** is parallel to the plane of **l** and **m**, **n** may be put in the form

$$\mathbf{n} = s\mathbf{l} + t\mathbf{m}$$

and

$$\Phi = (\mathbf{a} + s\mathbf{c})\mathbf{l} + (\mathbf{b} + t\mathbf{c})\mathbf{m} + \mathbf{do}.$$

In this way the sum of any number of dyads may be reduced to the sum of three dyads, and hence we may take for the most general form of the dyadic

$$\Phi = \mathbf{al} + \mathbf{bm} + \mathbf{cn}. \tag{18–4}$$

Clearly the sum or difference of two dyadics is a dyadic.

The condition for equality of two dyadics is that each element of the one shall be equal to the corresponding element of the other. For let Ψ be the dyadic (18–3) with elements a_{11}, a_{12}, etc., and Φ a dyadic with elements b_{11}, b_{12}, etc., referred to the same axes. Then, if $\Psi = \Phi$, it follows that $\Psi\cdot\mathbf{i}' = \Phi\cdot\mathbf{i}'$, that is,

$$a_{11}\mathbf{i}' + a_{21}\mathbf{j}' + a_{31}\mathbf{k}' = b_{11}\mathbf{i}' + b_{21}\mathbf{j}' + b_{31}\mathbf{k}',$$

and therefore

$$a_{11} = b_{11}, \quad a_{21} = b_{21}, \quad a_{31} = b_{31}.$$

Similarly the other corresponding elements may be shown to be equal.

If Ψ is a symmetric dyadic, it follows from (18–3) that it makes no difference whether a vector $\mathbf{P}$ by which Ψ may be multiplied appears as a prefactor or a postfactor, that is,

$$\mathbf{P}\cdot\Psi = \Psi\cdot\mathbf{P}. \tag{18–5}$$

Conversely, if (18–5) holds for *any* vector $\mathbf{P}$, Ψ must be symmetric. For let $\mathbf{P}$ be the unit vector $\mathbf{i}'$. Then

$$\mathbf{i}'\cdot\Psi = a_{11}\mathbf{i}' + a_{12}\mathbf{j}' + a_{13}\mathbf{k}',$$

$$\Psi\cdot\mathbf{i}' = a_{11}\mathbf{i}' + a_{21}\mathbf{j}' + a_{31}\mathbf{k}'.$$

As these two vectors are equal

$$a_{21} = a_{12}, \quad a_{13} = a_{31},$$

and similarly

$$a_{32} = a_{23}.$$

For instance, the dyadic

$$\mathbf{aa} + \mathbf{bb} + \mathbf{cc}$$

satisfies the condition just stated. Therefore it is symmetric.

It follows from the above that if a dyadic is symmetric when referred to one set of rectangular axes it is symmetric when referred to any other.

In like manner if Ψ is a skew-symmetric dyadic it follows from (18–3) that

$$\mathbf{P}\cdot\Psi = -\Psi\cdot\mathbf{P}$$

and conversely, if this relation holds for *any* vector **P**, Ψ must be skew-symmetric. Consequently if a dyadic is skew-symmetric when referred to one set of axes it is skew-symmetric when referred to any other.

The *conjugate* of any dyadic

$$\Psi = \mathbf{al} + \mathbf{bm} + \mathbf{cn}$$

is the dyadic

$$\Psi_c = \mathbf{la} + \mathbf{mb} + \mathbf{nc}$$

obtained by interchanging antecedents and consequents. Evidently

$$\mathbf{P}\cdot\Psi = \Psi_c\cdot\mathbf{P} \text{ and } \Psi\cdot\mathbf{P} = \mathbf{P}\cdot\Psi_c.$$

If we write the identity

$$\Psi = \tfrac{1}{2}(\Psi + \Psi_c) + \tfrac{1}{2}(\Psi - \Psi_c)$$

we note that the dyadic $\Psi + \Psi_c$ is symmetric since

$$\mathbf{P}\cdot(\Psi + \Psi_c) = (\Psi + \Psi_c)_c\cdot\mathbf{P} = (\Psi_c + \Psi)\cdot\mathbf{P} = (\Psi + \Psi_c)\cdot\mathbf{P},$$

whereas $\Psi - \Psi_c$ is skew-symmetric since

$$\mathbf{P}\cdot(\Psi - \Psi_c) = (\Psi - \Psi_c)_c\cdot\mathbf{P} = (\Psi_c - \Psi)\cdot\mathbf{P} = -(\Psi - \Psi_c)\cdot\mathbf{P}.$$

Therefore any dyadic may be expressed as the sum of a symmetric dyadic and a skew-symmetric dyadic.

Since $\Psi\cdot\mathbf{P}$ is a vector, $\mathbf{Q}\cdot\Psi\cdot\mathbf{P}$ is a scalar.

The symmetric dyadic

$$\mathbf{I} = \mathbf{ii} + \mathbf{jj} + \mathbf{kk} \tag{18–6}$$

is known as the *idemfactor*. It has the following important property: if a vector **P** is multiplied into **I** by scalar multiplication either as a prefactor or a postfactor the product is the vector **P** itself. For

$$\left.\begin{aligned}\mathbf{P}\cdot\mathbf{I} = \mathbf{I}\cdot\mathbf{P} &= \mathbf{ii}\cdot\mathbf{P} + \mathbf{jj}\cdot\mathbf{P} + \mathbf{kk}\cdot\mathbf{P}\\ &= \mathbf{i}P_x + \mathbf{j}P_y + \mathbf{k}P_z\\ &= \mathbf{P}.\end{aligned}\right\} \tag{18–7}$$

Thus the idemfactor plays the same part in the theory of dyadics that unity does in algebra. For this reason it is also called the *unit dyadic*. If **I** is referred to the axes $X'Y'Z'$ it retains the same form becoming

$$\mathbf{I} = \mathbf{i}'\mathbf{i}' + \mathbf{j}'\mathbf{j}' + \mathbf{k}'\mathbf{k}'$$

as can easily be verified by the use of (18–2), remembering that

$$l_1^2 + l_2^2 + l_3^2 = 1, \quad l_1m_1 + l_2m_2 + l_3m_3 = 0, \text{ etc.}$$

18.1. Reduction of a Symmetric Dyadic to Normal Form. — We have seen that when the directions of the rectangular axes to which it is referred are chosen at random, the dyadic (18–1) takes on the more complicated form (18–3). Now we shall prove conversely that any symmetric dyadic of the form (18–3) may be put in the form (18–1) by a suitable choice of axes XYZ.

Let Ψ be the symmetric dyadic under consideration and let $\boldsymbol{\alpha}$ be a unit vector of variable direction. Then $\boldsymbol{\alpha}\cdot\Psi\cdot\boldsymbol{\alpha}$ is a scalar which we shall designate by u, writing

$$u = \boldsymbol{\alpha}\cdot\Psi\cdot\boldsymbol{\alpha}.$$

If the elements of the dyadic Ψ are finite u will remain finite for all orientations of the unit vector $\boldsymbol{\alpha}$. Therefore there will be some direction of $\boldsymbol{\alpha}$ which will make u a maximum. Let the fixed unit vector **i** be taken in this direction.

Now restrict $\boldsymbol{\alpha}$ to the plane perpendicular to **i** and take the fixed unit vector **j** in the direction assumed by $\boldsymbol{\alpha}$ in order to give u its greatest value subject to this restriction. Finally, take **k** perpendicular to **i** and **j** in such a sense as to make **i, j, k** a right-handed set of unit vectors. We shall prove that the dyadic Ψ, when expressed in terms of unit vectors **i, j, k** so chosen, assumes the simple form (18–1).

In any event Ψ may be written

$$\begin{aligned}\Psi = {} & a_{11}\mathbf{ii} + a_{12}\mathbf{ij} + a_{13}\mathbf{ik} \\ & + a_{21}\mathbf{ji} + a_{22}\mathbf{jj} + a_{23}\mathbf{jk} \\ & + a_{31}\mathbf{ki} + a_{32}\mathbf{kj} + a_{33}\mathbf{kk}\end{aligned} \qquad (18.1\text{–}1)$$

where $a_{ij} = a_{ji}$, since the dyadic is symmetric. Now

$$du = d\mathbf{a}\cdot\Psi\cdot\mathbf{a} + \mathbf{a}\cdot\Psi\cdot d\mathbf{a} = 2\mathbf{a}\cdot\Psi\cdot d\mathbf{a}, \qquad (18.1\text{–}2)$$

and giving $\mathbf{a}$ the value $\mathbf{i}$,

$$du = 2(a_{11}\mathbf{i}\cdot d\mathbf{a} + a_{12}\mathbf{j}\cdot d\mathbf{a} + a_{13}\mathbf{k}\cdot d\mathbf{a}) = 0 \qquad (18.1\text{–}3)$$

since u is a maximum for $\mathbf{a}$ equal to $\mathbf{i}$. As $\mathbf{a}$ is a unit vector $d\mathbf{a}$ must be perpendicular to $\mathbf{a}$. If we take $d\mathbf{a}$ in the direction of $\mathbf{j}$ both $\mathbf{i}\cdot d\mathbf{a}$ and $\mathbf{k}\cdot d\mathbf{a}$ vanish and the equation above reduces to

$$a_{12}\mathbf{j}\cdot d\mathbf{a} = 0.$$

Since $\mathbf{j}\cdot d\mathbf{a}$ is not zero this equation requires a_{12} and its equal a_{21} to vanish. Similarly if we take $d\mathbf{a}$ in (18.1–3) parallel to $\mathbf{k}$ we find that a_{13} and a_{31} are zero.

Next restrict $\mathbf{a}$ to the plane perpendicular to $\mathbf{i}$. Giving it the value $\mathbf{j}$, (18.1–2) becomes

$$du = 2(a_{22}\mathbf{j}\cdot d\mathbf{a} + a_{23}\mathbf{k}\cdot d\mathbf{a}) = 0,$$

since u has its greatest value subject to this restriction for $\mathbf{a}$ equal to $\mathbf{j}$. But $\mathbf{j}\cdot d\mathbf{a}$ vanishes while $\mathbf{k}\cdot d\mathbf{a}$ does not. Hence a_{23} and a_{32} are zero.

We have shown that all the elements off the principal diagonal are zero. Therefore the symmetric dyadic under consideration assumes the *normal form*

$$\Psi = a_{11}\mathbf{ii} + a_{22}\mathbf{jj} + a_{33}\mathbf{kk}, \qquad (18.1\text{–}4)$$

where the unit vectors $\mathbf{i}$, $\mathbf{j}$, $\mathbf{k}$ determine the *principal axes* of the dyadic.

We note that in the general case where a_{11}, a_{22}, a_{33} in (18.1–4) are all different, the equation

$$\Psi\cdot\mathbf{a} = \beta\mathbf{a} \qquad (18.1\text{–}5)$$

is satisfied only when the unit vector $\mathbf{a}$ has the direction of one of the principal axes and β equals the corresponding element of the normal form. This fact provides us with a method of finding the principal axes when the dyadic is expressed in the general form (18–3). Putting

$$\mathbf{a} = l\mathbf{i}' + m\mathbf{j}' + n\mathbf{k}' \qquad (18.1\text{–}6)$$

in terms of its direction cosines l, m, n, and remembering that $a_{ij} = a_{ji}$

since the dyadic is symmetric, the three components of the vector equation (18.1–5) obtained from (18–3) and (18.1–6) are

$$\left.\begin{aligned} (a_{11} - \beta)l + a_{12}m + a_{31}n &= 0, \\ a_{12}l + (a_{22} - \beta)m + a_{23}n &= 0, \\ a_{31}l + a_{23}m + (a_{33} - \beta)n &= 0. \end{aligned}\right\} \qquad (18.1\text{–}7)$$

For these equations to have a solution it is necessary that

$$\begin{vmatrix} a_{11} - \beta & a_{12} & a_{31} \\ a_{12} & a_{22} - \beta & a_{23} \\ a_{31} & a_{23} & a_{33} - \beta \end{vmatrix} = 0. \qquad (18.1\text{–}8)$$

The three roots of this cubic in β are the elements of the normal form of the dyadic, and the values of l, m, n obtained from (18.1–7) for each root specify the direction of one of the three principal axes. If two of the three elements of the normal form are the same, only one principal axis is determined.

Problem 18.1a. Let $\boldsymbol{\alpha}$ be a unit vector of variable direction whose origin coincides with the origin of coordinates. Then as $\boldsymbol{\alpha}$ varies in direction its terminus describes a unit sphere. Let $\mathbf{r}$ be another vector laid off from the origin of coordinates and related to $\boldsymbol{\alpha}$ by the equation

$$\mathbf{r} = \Psi \cdot \boldsymbol{\alpha},$$

where Ψ is a symmetric dyadic.

Prove that as $\boldsymbol{\alpha}$ varies in direction the terminus of $\mathbf{r}$ describes an ellipsoid.

Problem 18.1b. If $\mathbf{r}$ is the vector

$$\mathbf{r} = \mathbf{i}x + \mathbf{j}y + \mathbf{k}z$$

and Ψ is a symmetric dyadic investigate the geometrical interpretation of the scalar equation

$$\mathbf{r} \cdot \Psi \cdot \mathbf{r} = 1.$$

Problem 18.1c. Let Ψ be a skew-symmetric dyadic and $\boldsymbol{\alpha}$ a unit vector of variable direction. Find the value of $\boldsymbol{\alpha} \cdot \Psi \cdot \boldsymbol{\alpha}$.

Problem 18.1d. Reduce the symmetric dyadic

$$\begin{aligned} \Psi = {} & 6\mathbf{i}'\mathbf{i}' + 0\mathbf{i}'\mathbf{j}' + 0\mathbf{i}'\mathbf{k}' \\ & + 0\mathbf{j}'\mathbf{i}' + 34\mathbf{j}'\mathbf{j}' + 12\mathbf{j}'\mathbf{k}' \\ & + 0\mathbf{k}'\mathbf{i}' + 12\mathbf{k}'\mathbf{j}' + 41\mathbf{k}'\mathbf{k}' \end{aligned}$$

to normal form and find the direction cosines of its principal axes.

Ans. $\Psi = 6\mathbf{ii} + 50\mathbf{jj} + 25\mathbf{kk}.$

18.2. Finite Rotations. — The position of any particle of a rigid body may be specified by its position vector $\mathbf{r} = \mathbf{i}x + \mathbf{j}y + \mathbf{k}z$. Suppose that the body is turned through the angle ϵ (Fig. 24.1) about $\mathbf{k}$ as axis. The particle originally at P is displaced to some point P_1 whose position vector is $\mathbf{r}_1$. Let $\mathbf{i}_1$ and $\mathbf{j}_1$ be unit vectors obtained by rotating $\mathbf{i}$ and $\mathbf{j}$, respectively, through the angle ϵ, and let Φ be the dyadic

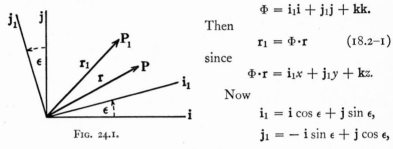

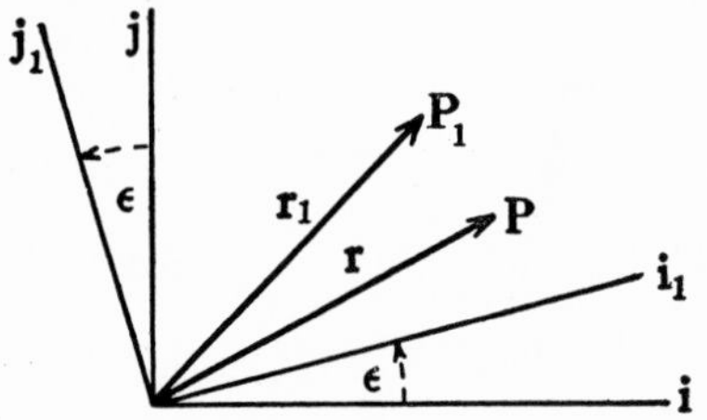

FIG. 24.1.

$$\Phi = \mathbf{i}_1\mathbf{i} + \mathbf{j}_1\mathbf{j} + \mathbf{k}\mathbf{k}.$$

Then

$$\mathbf{r}_1 = \Phi\cdot\mathbf{r} \qquad (18.2\text{–}1)$$

since

$$\Phi\cdot\mathbf{r} = \mathbf{i}_1x + \mathbf{j}_1y + \mathbf{k}z.$$

Now

$$\mathbf{i}_1 = \mathbf{i}\cos\epsilon + \mathbf{j}\sin\epsilon,$$

$$\mathbf{j}_1 = -\mathbf{i}\sin\epsilon + \mathbf{j}\cos\epsilon,$$

and, in terms of the unit vectors $\mathbf{i}$, $\mathbf{j}$, $\mathbf{k}$,

$$\begin{aligned}\Phi = {} & \mathbf{ii}\cos\epsilon - \mathbf{ij}\sin\epsilon \\ & + \mathbf{ji}\sin\epsilon + \mathbf{jj}\cos\epsilon \\ & + \mathbf{kk}.\end{aligned} \qquad (18.2\text{–}2)$$

Making use of the trigonometrical relations $\cos\epsilon = 1 - 2\sin^2\epsilon/2$ and $\sin\epsilon = 2\sin\epsilon/2\cos\epsilon/2$, we find that

$$\Phi = \mathbf{I} + \chi$$

where

$$\chi \equiv -2\sin\frac{\epsilon}{2}\left\{\begin{matrix}\mathbf{ii}\sin\frac{\epsilon}{2} + \mathbf{ij}\cos\frac{\epsilon}{2} \\ -\mathbf{ji}\cos\frac{\epsilon}{2} + \mathbf{jj}\sin\frac{\epsilon}{2}\end{matrix}\right\}. \qquad (18.2\text{–}3)$$

The scalar formed by placing a dot between the antecedent and the consequent of each term of a dyadic χ is designated by χ_s, and the vector formed by putting a cross between the antecedent and the consequent of each term is designated by χ_v. Evidently

$$\chi_s = -4\sin^2\frac{\epsilon}{2} = -4\left(1 - \cos^2\frac{\epsilon}{2}\right), \qquad (18.2\text{–}4)$$

$$\chi_v = -4\mathbf{k}\sin\frac{\epsilon}{2}\cos\frac{\epsilon}{2}. \qquad (18.2\text{–}5)$$

So the scalar χ_s of χ specifies the angle turned through and the vector χ_v of χ specifies in addition the direction of the axis of rotation. In the next article we shall use these expressions to determine the angle turned through and the direction of the axis of the single rotation equivalent to two successive rotations.

Up to this point we have formed only scalar products of dyadics with vectors. We may, however, obtain a new dyadic by taking the vector product of a dyadic with a vector. Thus

$$\begin{aligned} \mathbf{I} \times \mathbf{k} &= (\mathbf{ii} + \mathbf{jj} + \mathbf{kk}) \times \mathbf{k} \\ &= \mathbf{ii} \times \mathbf{k} + \mathbf{jj} \times \mathbf{k} \\ &= -\mathbf{ij} + \mathbf{ji}. \end{aligned} \tag{18.2–6}$$

Therefore (18.2–3) may be written in the convenient form

$$\chi = -2 \sin \frac{\epsilon}{2} \left\{ (\mathbf{I} - \mathbf{kk}) \sin \frac{\epsilon}{2} - \mathbf{I} \times \mathbf{k} \cos \frac{\epsilon}{2} \right\}. \tag{18.2–7}$$

Problem 18.2a. Show that the dyadic $\mathbf{I} \times \mathbf{k}$ gives rise to a rotation through a right angle about $\mathbf{k}$ as axis.

18.3. Successive Finite Rotations. — If a rigid body is subjected to two finite rotations, the result, in general, will depend upon the order in which the rotations occur. For example, hold a card perpendicular to the X axis. If it is given a rotation of 90° about the X axis followed by a rotation of 90° about the Y axis, the final orientation of the card is quite different from that existing if the order of the two angular displacements is reversed. We wish to find the single rotation, including the direction of the axis about which it occurs, which is equivalent to two successive finite rotations.

Let the first rotation be through an angle ϵ about the unit vector $\mathbf{k}$ (Fig. 24.2) as axis. This turns lines in the rigid body having the directions of the unit vectors $\mathbf{i}$ and $\mathbf{j}$ into the directions of certain other unit vectors $\mathbf{i}_1$ and $\mathbf{j}_1$, respectively. It is followed by a second rotation through an angle ϵ' about $\mathbf{k}'$ as axis, which turns lines in the rigid body from $\mathbf{i}'$ and $\mathbf{j}'$ to $\mathbf{i}'_1$ and $\mathbf{j}'_1$, respectively. Without loss of

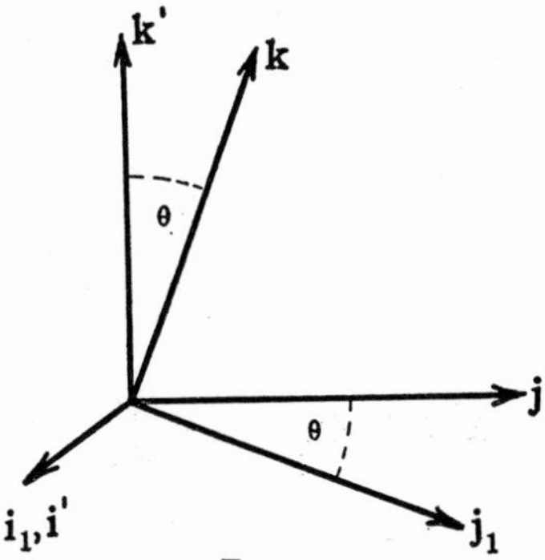

FIG. 24.2.

generality we can choose unit vectors perpendicular to **k** and **k′**, respectively, so that $\mathbf{j}_1$ and $\mathbf{j}'$ are in the plane of **k** and **k′** and the coincident unit vectors $\mathbf{i}_1$ and $\mathbf{i}'$ are perpendicular to this plane. This choice we shall make, as indicated in the figure, in order to simplify the analysis. Let θ be the angle between **k** and **k′**.

For the first rotation we have, in accord with (18.2–1)

$$\mathbf{r}_1 = \Phi\cdot\mathbf{r}$$

and for the second

$$\mathbf{r}'_1 = \Phi'\cdot\mathbf{r}_1 = \Phi'\cdot\Phi\cdot\mathbf{r}.$$

So the dyadic describing the resultant rotation is

$$\Phi_r = \Phi' . \Phi. \qquad (18.3\text{–}1)$$

Here we have the scalar product of two dyadics. As the notation indicates, the dot is between the consequent of every dyad of the first dyadic and the antecedent of every dyad of the second. Evidently $\mathbf{I}\cdot\Phi = \Phi\cdot\mathbf{I} = \Phi$ and $\mathbf{I}\cdot\mathbf{I} = \mathbf{I}$. In general, however,

$$\Phi'\cdot\Phi \neq \Phi\cdot\Phi'.$$

If we replace Φ by $\mathbf{I} + \chi$ and Φ' by $\mathbf{I} + \chi'$,

$$\Phi'\cdot\Phi = \mathbf{I} + \chi + \chi' + \chi'\cdot\chi$$

and the resultant χ is

$$\chi_r = \chi + \chi' + \chi'\cdot\chi. \qquad (18.3\text{–}2)$$

Now

$$\chi = -2\sin\frac{\epsilon}{2}\left\{(\mathbf{I} - \mathbf{kk})\sin\frac{\epsilon}{2} - \mathbf{I}\times\mathbf{k}\cos\frac{\epsilon}{2}\right\},$$

$$\chi' = -2\sin\frac{\epsilon'}{2}\left\{(\mathbf{I} - \mathbf{k'k'})\sin\frac{\epsilon'}{2} - \mathbf{I}\times\mathbf{k}'\cos\frac{\epsilon'}{2}\right\},$$

$$\begin{aligned}\chi'\cdot\chi = 4\sin\frac{\epsilon}{2}\sin\frac{\epsilon'}{2}\Big\{&(\mathbf{I} - \mathbf{kk} - \mathbf{k'k'} + \mathbf{k'k}\cos\theta)\sin\frac{\epsilon}{2}\sin\frac{\epsilon'}{2}\\ &+ (-\mathbf{I}\times\mathbf{k}' + \mathbf{I}\times\mathbf{k}'\cdot\mathbf{kk})\sin\frac{\epsilon}{2}\cos\frac{\epsilon'}{2}\\ &+ (-\mathbf{I}\times\mathbf{k} + \mathbf{k'k'}\cdot\mathbf{I}\times\mathbf{k})\sin\frac{\epsilon'}{2}\cos\frac{\epsilon}{2}\\ &+ (\mathbf{I}\times\mathbf{k}')\cdot(\mathbf{I}\times\mathbf{k})\cos\frac{\epsilon}{2}\cos\frac{\epsilon'}{2}\Big\}.\end{aligned}$$

As $\mathbf{I} \times \mathbf{k}' = -\mathbf{i}'\mathbf{j}' + \mathbf{j}'\mathbf{i}'$ and $\mathbf{I} \times \mathbf{k} = -\mathbf{i}_1\mathbf{j}_1 + \mathbf{j}_1\mathbf{i}_1$, it follows that

$$\mathbf{I} \times \mathbf{k}' \cdot \mathbf{k} = -\mathbf{i}' \sin\theta,$$

$$\mathbf{k}' \cdot \mathbf{I} \times \mathbf{k} = -\mathbf{i}_1 \sin\theta,$$

$$(\mathbf{I} \times \mathbf{k}') \cdot (\mathbf{I} \times \mathbf{k}) = -\mathbf{i}'\mathbf{i}_1 \cos\theta - \mathbf{j}'\mathbf{j}_1.$$

If then we put $\mathbf{i}$ for the coincident unit vectors $\mathbf{i}_1$ and $\mathbf{i}'$,

$$\chi = -2 \sin\frac{\epsilon}{2}\left\{(\mathbf{I} - \mathbf{kk}) \sin\frac{\epsilon}{2} + (\mathbf{ij}_1 - \mathbf{j}_1\mathbf{i}) \cos\frac{\epsilon}{2}\right\}, \tag{18.3-3}$$

$$\chi' = -2 \sin\frac{\epsilon'}{2}\left\{(\mathbf{I} - \mathbf{k}'\mathbf{k}') \sin\frac{\epsilon'}{2} + (\mathbf{ij}' - \mathbf{j}'\mathbf{i}) \cos\frac{\epsilon'}{2}\right\}, \tag{18.3-4}$$

$$\begin{aligned}\chi' \cdot \chi = 4 \sin\frac{\epsilon}{2} \sin\frac{\epsilon'}{2}\Big\{&(\mathbf{I} - \mathbf{kk} - \mathbf{k}'\mathbf{k}' + \mathbf{k}'\mathbf{k} \cos\theta) \sin\frac{\epsilon}{2} \sin\frac{\epsilon'}{2} \\ &+ (\mathbf{ij}' - \mathbf{j}'\mathbf{i} - \mathbf{ik} \sin\theta) \sin\frac{\epsilon}{2} \cos\frac{\epsilon'}{2} \\ &+ (\mathbf{ij}_1 - \mathbf{j}_1\mathbf{i} - \mathbf{k}'\mathbf{i} \sin\theta) \sin\frac{\epsilon'}{2} \cos\frac{\epsilon}{2} \\ &+ (-\mathbf{ii} \cos\theta - \mathbf{j}'\mathbf{j}_1) \cos\frac{\epsilon}{2} \cos\frac{\epsilon'}{2}\Big\}. \end{aligned} \tag{18.3-5}$$

To find the magnitude ϵ_r of the single rotation equivalent to the two rotations ϵ and ϵ' we must evaluate the scalar $(\chi_r)_s$ of χ_r. We have

$$\chi_s = -4 \sin^2\frac{\epsilon}{2},$$

$$\chi_s' = -4 \sin^2\frac{\epsilon'}{2},$$

$$(\chi' \cdot \chi)_s = 4 \sin\frac{\epsilon}{2} \sin\frac{\epsilon'}{2}\left\{(1 + \cos^2\theta) \sin\frac{\epsilon}{2} \sin\frac{\epsilon'}{2} - 2 \cos\theta \cos\frac{\epsilon}{2} \cos\frac{\epsilon'}{2}\right\}.$$

Therefore

$$(\chi_r)_s = -4\left\{1 - \left(\cos\frac{\epsilon}{2} \cos\frac{\epsilon'}{2} - \sin\frac{\epsilon}{2} \sin\frac{\epsilon'}{2} \cos\theta\right)^2\right\} \tag{18.3-6}$$

and, comparing with (18.2–4), we see that

$$\cos\frac{\epsilon_r}{2} = \cos\frac{\epsilon}{2}\cos\frac{\epsilon'}{2} - \sin\frac{\epsilon}{2}\sin\frac{\epsilon'}{2}\cos\theta, \qquad (18.3\text{–}7)$$

which is *independent of the order of the two rotations.*

Finally, to obtain the unit vector $\mathbf{k}_r$ in the direction of the axis of the single equivalent rotation, we must calculate the vector $(\chi_r)_v$ of χ_r. We find

$$\chi_v = -4\mathbf{k}\sin\frac{\epsilon}{2}\cos\frac{\epsilon}{2},$$

$$\chi_v' = -4\mathbf{k}'\sin\frac{\epsilon'}{2}\cos\frac{\epsilon'}{2},$$

$$(\chi'\cdot\chi)_v = 4\sin\frac{\epsilon}{2}\sin\frac{\epsilon'}{2}\Big\{-\mathbf{k}\times\mathbf{k}'\sin\frac{\epsilon}{2}\sin\frac{\epsilon'}{2}\cos\theta$$

$$+ (2\mathbf{k}' + \mathbf{j}_1\sin\theta)\sin\frac{\epsilon}{2}\cos\frac{\epsilon'}{2}$$

$$+ (2\mathbf{k} - \mathbf{j}'\sin\theta)\sin\frac{\epsilon'}{2}\cos\frac{\epsilon}{2} + \mathbf{i}\cos\frac{\epsilon}{2}\cos\frac{\epsilon'}{2}\sin\theta\Big\}.$$

Now

$$\mathbf{j}_1\sin\theta = \mathbf{k}\cos\theta - \mathbf{k}', \quad \mathbf{j}'\sin\theta = \mathbf{k} - \mathbf{k}'\cos\theta, \quad \mathbf{i}\sin\theta = \mathbf{k}\times\mathbf{k}'.$$

Consequently

$$(\chi'\cdot\chi)_v = 4\sin\frac{\epsilon}{2}\sin\frac{\epsilon'}{2}\Big\{\mathbf{k}\left(\sin\frac{\epsilon'}{2}\cos\frac{\epsilon}{2} + \sin\frac{\epsilon}{2}\cos\frac{\epsilon'}{2}\cos\theta\right)$$

$$+ \mathbf{k}'\left(\sin\frac{\epsilon}{2}\cos\frac{\epsilon'}{2} + \sin\frac{\epsilon'}{2}\cos\frac{\epsilon}{2}\cos\theta\right)$$

$$+ \mathbf{k}\times\mathbf{k}'\left(\cos\frac{\epsilon}{2}\cos\frac{\epsilon'}{2} - \sin\frac{\epsilon}{2}\sin\frac{\epsilon'}{2}\cos\theta\right)\Big\},$$

and

$$(\chi_r)_v = -4\mathbf{k}\left\{\sin\frac{\epsilon}{2}\cos\frac{\epsilon}{2}\cos^2\frac{\epsilon'}{2} - \sin^2\frac{\epsilon}{2}\sin\frac{\epsilon'}{2}\cos\frac{\epsilon'}{2}\cos\theta\right\}$$

$$-4\mathbf{k}'\left\{\sin\frac{\epsilon'}{2}\cos\frac{\epsilon'}{2}\cos^2\frac{\epsilon}{2} - \sin^2\frac{\epsilon'}{2}\sin\frac{\epsilon}{2}\cos\frac{\epsilon}{2}\cos\theta\right\}$$

$$+ 4\mathbf{k}\times\mathbf{k}'\sin\frac{\epsilon}{2}\sin\frac{\epsilon'}{2}\left\{\cos\frac{\epsilon}{2}\cos\frac{\epsilon'}{2} - \sin\frac{\epsilon}{2}\sin\frac{\epsilon'}{2}\cos\theta\right\}$$

$$= 4\left(\cos\frac{\epsilon}{2}\cos\frac{\epsilon'}{2} - \sin\frac{\epsilon}{2}\sin\frac{\epsilon'}{2}\cos\theta\right)\left\{-\mathbf{k}\sin\frac{\epsilon}{2}\cos\frac{\epsilon'}{2}\right.$$

$$\left. - \mathbf{k}'\sin\frac{\epsilon'}{2}\cos\frac{\epsilon}{2} + \mathbf{k}\times\mathbf{k}'\sin\frac{\epsilon}{2}\sin\frac{\epsilon'}{2}\right\}$$

$$= -4\cos\frac{\epsilon_r}{2}\left\{\mathbf{k}\sin\frac{\epsilon}{2}\cos\frac{\epsilon'}{2} + \mathbf{k}'\sin\frac{\epsilon'}{2}\cos\frac{\epsilon}{2}\right.$$

$$\left. + \mathbf{k}'\times\mathbf{k}\sin\frac{\epsilon}{2}\sin\frac{\epsilon'}{2}\right\}. \qquad (18.3\text{–}8)$$

Comparing with (18.2–5), we note that

$$\mathbf{k}_r\sin\frac{\epsilon_r}{2} = \mathbf{k}\sin\frac{\epsilon}{2}\cos\frac{\epsilon'}{2} + \mathbf{k}'\sin\frac{\epsilon'}{2}\cos\frac{\epsilon}{2}$$

$$+ \mathbf{k}'\times\mathbf{k}\sin\frac{\epsilon}{2}\sin\frac{\epsilon'}{2}. \qquad (18.3\text{–}9)$$

On account of the last term *the direction of the axis of the single equivalent rotation depends upon the order of the two rotations.* Therefore finite rotations cannot be represented by vectors since they fail to obey the commutative law of addition. If, however, the component rotations are infinitesimal, (18.3–9) reduces to

$$\mathbf{k}_r\epsilon_r = \mathbf{k}\epsilon + \mathbf{k}'\epsilon' \qquad (18.3\text{–}10)$$

since we can neglect all the second and higher order terms in the ϵ's. In this case the single equivalent rotation is independent of the order of the component rotations, and vectorial representation is possible.

Problem 18.3a. Compute $\cos\epsilon_r/2$ from (18.3–9) and show that the result agrees with (18.3–7).

Problem 18.3b. A block is given the following rotations about two mutually perpendicular axes $\mathbf{k}$ and $\mathbf{k}'$:

(1) 90° about $\mathbf{k}$ followed by 90° about $\mathbf{k}'$,

(2) 90° about $\mathbf{k}'$ followed by 90° about $\mathbf{k}$.

Find the resultant rotation and the direction of the axis in each case. Illustrate by figures.

REFERENCES

Gibbs–Wilson: *Vector Analysis*, Charles Scribner's Sons, New York.
Coffin, J. C.: *Vector Analysis*, John Wiley & Sons, New York.
Phillips, H. B.: *Vector Analysis*, John Wiley & Sons, New York.

Part I

DYNAMICS

CHAPTER I

DYNAMICS OF PARTICLES

19. Velocity and Acceleration. — Let

$$\mathbf{r} = \mathbf{i}x + \mathbf{j}y + \mathbf{k}z$$

be the position vector of a moving particle. The *velocity* $\mathbf{v}$ of the particle is defined as the time rate of displacement, that is,

$$\mathbf{v} = \frac{d\mathbf{r}}{dt} = \mathbf{i}\frac{dx}{dt} + \mathbf{j}\frac{dy}{dt} + \mathbf{k}\frac{dz}{dt}. \qquad (19\text{-}1)$$

As noted in article 10, $\mathbf{v}$ is a vector tangent to the path of the moving particle. Its magnitude is given by the square root of the sum of the squares of its components, that is,

$$v = \sqrt{\left(\frac{dx}{dt}\right)^2 + \left(\frac{dy}{dt}\right)^2 + \left(\frac{dz}{dt}\right)^2}. \qquad (19\text{-}2)$$

The *acceleration* $\mathbf{f}$ of a moving particle is defined as the time rate of increase of velocity, that is,

$$\mathbf{f} = \frac{d\mathbf{v}}{dt} = \frac{d^2\mathbf{r}}{dt^2} = \mathbf{i}\frac{d^2x}{dt^2} + \mathbf{j}\frac{d^2y}{dt^2} + \mathbf{k}\frac{d^2z}{dt^2}. \qquad (19\text{-}3)$$

If the velocity vector is laid off from the origin of coordinates the acceleration is tangent to the curve described by its terminus, but not necessarily tangent to the path of the moving particle. The magnitude of the acceleration is

$$f = \sqrt{\left(\frac{d^2x}{dt^2}\right)^2 + \left(\frac{d^2y}{dt^2}\right)^2 + \left(\frac{d^2z}{dt^2}\right)^2}. \qquad (19\text{-}4)$$

When the motion is in a plane it is often convenient to use polar coordinates r and θ (Fig. 25). Let $\mathbf{r}_1$ be a unit vector in the direction of the radius vector and $\boldsymbol{\theta}_1$ a unit vector at right angles thereto in the direction of increasing θ. Then

$$\mathbf{r} = \mathbf{r}_1 r,$$

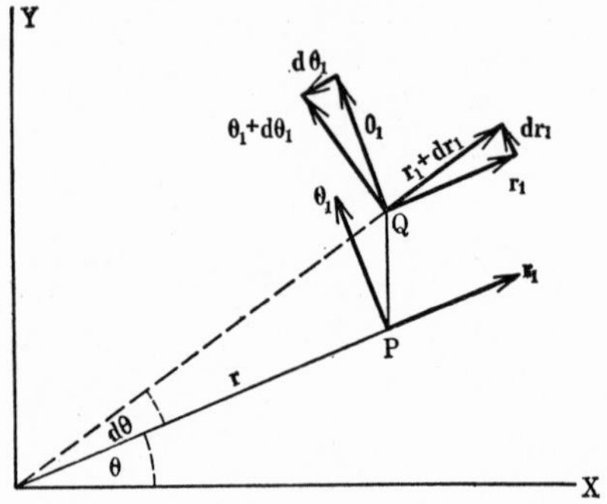

FIG. 25.

is the position vector of the particle P and

$$\mathbf{v} = \frac{d\mathbf{r}}{dt} = \mathbf{r}_1 \frac{dr}{dt} + \frac{d\mathbf{r}_1}{dt} r,$$

where the derivative of the unit vector $\mathbf{r}_1$ does not vanish since $\mathbf{r}_1$ changes direction as the particle P moves to Q. As $\mathbf{r}_1$ is a unit vector, however, $d\mathbf{r}_1$ is perpendicular to $\mathbf{r}_1$ as noted in article 10. It is clear from the figure that $d\mathbf{r}_1$ has the direction of $\boldsymbol{\theta}_1$ and the magnitude $d\theta$. Therefore

$$\mathbf{v} = \mathbf{r}_1 \frac{dr}{dt} + \boldsymbol{\theta}_1 r \frac{d\theta}{dt}. \tag{19-5}$$

The first term on the right is the component of $\mathbf{v}$ along the radius vector and the second that at right angles to the radius vector in the direction of increasing θ.

To get the acceleration we differentiate again and find

$$\mathbf{f} = \frac{d\mathbf{v}}{dt} = \mathbf{r}_1 \frac{d^2 r}{dt^2} + \frac{d\mathbf{r}_1}{dt}\frac{dr}{dt} + \boldsymbol{\theta}_1 r \frac{d^2\theta}{dt^2} + \boldsymbol{\theta}_1 \frac{dr}{dt}\frac{d\theta}{dt} + \frac{d\boldsymbol{\theta}_1}{dt} r \frac{d\theta}{dt}.$$

Now it is clear from the figure that $d\boldsymbol{\theta}_1$ has the opposite direction to $\mathbf{r}_1$ and the magnitude $d\theta$. Hence

$$\frac{d\mathbf{r}_1}{dt} = \boldsymbol{\theta}_1\frac{d\theta}{dt}, \quad \frac{d\boldsymbol{\theta}_1}{dt} = -\,\mathbf{r}_1\frac{d\theta}{dt},$$

and substituting in the expression for $\mathbf{f}$,

$$\mathbf{f} = \mathbf{r}_1\left\{\frac{d^2r}{dt^2} - r\left(\frac{d\theta}{dt}\right)^2\right\} + \boldsymbol{\theta}_1\left\{2\frac{dr}{dt}\frac{d\theta}{dt} + r\frac{d^2\theta}{dt^2}\right\} \tag{19–6}$$

in terms of its components along $\mathbf{r}_1$ and $\boldsymbol{\theta}_1$.

If the motion is in three dimensions it may be convenient to use spherical coordinates r, θ, ϕ where r is the radius vector, θ the polar angle and ϕ the azimuth (Fig. 26). In this case it is necessary to introduce three unit vectors of variable direction, $\mathbf{r}_1$ along the radius vector, $\boldsymbol{\theta}_1$ at right angles to the radius vector in the direction of increasing θ, and $\boldsymbol{\phi}_1$ at right angles to the plane of $\mathbf{r}_1$ and $\boldsymbol{\theta}_1$ in the direction of increasing ϕ. From the figure we have

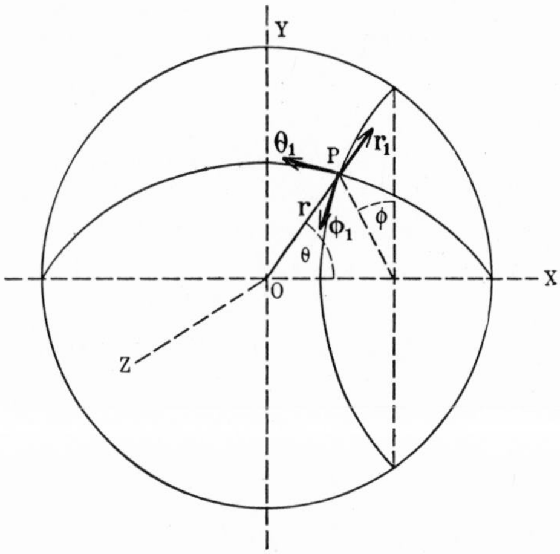

FIG. 26.

$$\mathbf{r}_1 = \mathbf{i}\cos\theta + \mathbf{j}\sin\theta\cos\phi + \mathbf{k}\sin\theta\sin\phi,$$

$$\boldsymbol{\theta}_1 = -\,\mathbf{i}\sin\theta + \mathbf{j}\cos\theta\cos\phi + \mathbf{k}\cos\theta\sin\phi,$$

$$\boldsymbol{\phi}_1 = -\,\mathbf{j}\sin\phi + \mathbf{k}\cos\phi,$$

and

$$\left.\begin{aligned}\frac{d\mathbf{r}_1}{dt} &= (-\,\mathbf{i}\sin\theta + \mathbf{j}\cos\theta\cos\phi + \mathbf{k}\cos\theta\sin\phi)\frac{d\theta}{dt}\\ &\quad + (-\,\mathbf{j}\sin\phi + \mathbf{k}\cos\phi)\sin\theta\frac{d\phi}{dt}\\ &= \boldsymbol{\theta}_1\frac{d\theta}{dt} + \boldsymbol{\phi}_1\sin\theta\frac{d\phi}{dt},\end{aligned}\right\} \tag{19–7}$$

$$\left.\begin{aligned}\frac{d\boldsymbol{\theta}_1}{dt} &= -\ (\mathbf{i}\cos\theta + \mathbf{j}\sin\theta\cos\phi + \mathbf{k}\sin\theta\sin\phi)\frac{d\theta}{dt}\\ &\quad + (-\ \mathbf{j}\sin\phi + \mathbf{k}\cos\phi)\cos\theta\frac{d\phi}{dt}\\ &= -\ \mathbf{r}_1\frac{d\theta}{dt} + \boldsymbol{\phi}_1\cos\theta\frac{d\phi}{dt},\end{aligned}\right\} \tag{19-8}$$

$$\left.\begin{aligned}\frac{d\boldsymbol{\phi}_1}{dt} &= -\ (\mathbf{j}\cos\phi + \mathbf{k}\sin\phi)\frac{d\phi}{dt}\\ &= -\ (\mathbf{i}\cos\theta + \mathbf{j}\sin\theta\cos\phi + \mathbf{k}\sin\theta\sin\phi)\sin\theta\frac{d\phi}{dt}\\ &\quad -(-\ \mathbf{i}\sin\theta + \mathbf{j}\cos\theta\cos\phi + \mathbf{k}\cos\theta\sin\phi)\cos\theta\frac{d\phi}{dt}\\ &= -\ \mathbf{r}_1\sin\theta\frac{d\phi}{dt} - \boldsymbol{\theta}_1\cos\theta\frac{d\phi}{dt}.\end{aligned}\right\} \tag{19-9}$$

Therefore

$$\mathbf{r} = \mathbf{r}_1 r,$$

$$\left.\begin{aligned}\mathbf{v} &= \frac{d\mathbf{r}}{dt} = \mathbf{r}_1\frac{dr}{dt} + \frac{d\mathbf{r}_1}{dt}r\\ &= \mathbf{r}_1\frac{dr}{dt} + \boldsymbol{\theta}_1 r\frac{d\theta}{dt} + \boldsymbol{\phi}_1 r\sin\theta\frac{d\phi}{dt},\end{aligned}\right\} \tag{19-10}$$

$$\left.\begin{aligned}\mathbf{f} = \frac{d\mathbf{v}}{dt} &= \mathbf{r}_1\frac{d^2r}{dt^2} + \frac{d\mathbf{r}_1}{dt}\frac{dr}{dt} + \boldsymbol{\theta}_1 r\frac{d^2\theta}{dt^2} + \boldsymbol{\theta}_1\frac{dr}{dt}\frac{d\theta}{dt} + \frac{d\boldsymbol{\theta}_1}{dt}r\frac{d\theta}{dt}\\ &\quad + \boldsymbol{\phi}_1 r\sin\theta\frac{d^2\phi}{dt^2} + \boldsymbol{\phi}_1 r\cos\theta\frac{d\theta}{dt}\frac{d\phi}{dt} + \boldsymbol{\phi}_1\frac{dr}{dt}\sin\theta\frac{d\phi}{dt}\\ &\quad + \frac{d\boldsymbol{\phi}_1}{dt}r\sin\theta\frac{d\phi}{dt}\\ &= \mathbf{r}_1\left\{\frac{d^2r}{dt^2} - r\left(\frac{d\theta}{dt}\right)^2 - r\sin^2\theta\left(\frac{d\phi}{dt}\right)^2\right\}\\ &\quad + \boldsymbol{\theta}_1\left\{2\frac{dr}{dt}\frac{d\theta}{dt} + r\frac{d^2\theta}{dt^2} - r\sin\theta\cos\theta\left(\frac{d\phi}{dt}\right)^2\right\}\\ &\quad + \boldsymbol{\phi}_1\left\{2\sin\theta\frac{dr}{dt}\frac{d\phi}{dt} + 2r\cos\theta\frac{d\theta}{dt}\frac{d\phi}{dt} + r\sin\theta\frac{d^2\phi}{dt^2}\right\}.\end{aligned}\right\} \tag{19-11}$$

Occasionally it is desirable to resolve the acceleration along the tangent and the normal to the path of the moving particle. Let $\mathbf{t}_1$ (Fig. 27) be a unit vector along the tangent taken in the sense in which the motion is described and $\mathbf{n}_1$ a unit vector directed toward the center of curvature C of the path. Then

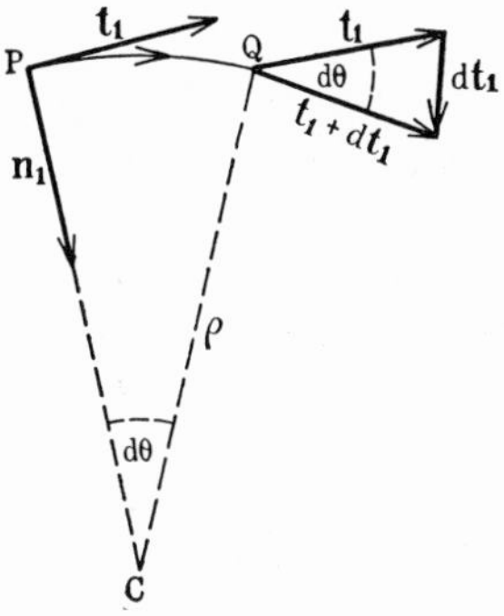

FIG. 27.

$$\mathbf{v} = \mathbf{t}_1 v,$$

and

$$\mathbf{f} = \frac{d\mathbf{v}}{dt} = \mathbf{t}_1 \frac{dv}{dt} + \frac{d\mathbf{t}_1}{dt} v.$$

Now $d\mathbf{t}_1$ has the direction of $\mathbf{n}_1$ and the magnitude $d\theta$. So

$$\mathbf{f} = \mathbf{t}_1 \frac{dv}{dt} + \mathbf{n}_1 v \frac{d\theta}{dt}. \qquad (19\text{–}12)$$

Also, as the distance PQ which the particle has traveled in the time dt is equal to vdt, it follows that $d\theta = PQ/\rho = (v/\rho)dt$, where ρ is the radius of curvature of the path. Therefore

$$\mathbf{f} = \mathbf{t}_1 \frac{dv}{dt} + \mathbf{n}_1 \frac{v^2}{\rho}. \qquad (19\text{–}13)$$

The component of acceleration along the normal $\mathbf{n}_1$ is referred to as the *centripetal acceleration*. It may be written in the three forms

$$\frac{v^2}{\rho} = v \frac{d\theta}{dt} = \rho \left(\frac{d\theta}{dt}\right)^2. \qquad (19\text{–}14)$$

Problem 19a. Show that the ϕ component of the acceleration in spherical coordinates can be put in the form

$$\frac{1}{r \sin \theta} \frac{d}{dt}\left(r^2 \sin^2 \theta \frac{d\phi}{dt}\right).$$

20. Laws of Motion. — Before stating the laws of motion it is necessary to specify the reference frame or axes to which the motion is to be referred. The reference frame relative to which the laws of motion take their customary and simplest form consists of a set of rigid axes fixed relative to the average position of the fixed stars. This frame is designated as the *primary inertial system*. Any set of rigid axes moving with constant velocity and without rotation relative to the primary inertial system constitutes a *secondary inertial system*.

If the motion of a particle is referred to the primary inertial system, Newton's fundamental laws of dynamics take the following form:

(1) *A particle under the action of no forces remains at rest or moves in a straight line with constant speed;*

(2) *The resultant force acting on a particle equals in magnitude and direction the product of its mass* m *by its acceleration* **f**;

(3) *If two particles exert forces on each other, the force exerted by the first on the second (action) is equal and opposite to the force exerted by the second on the first (reaction).*

The first law is really contained in the second, for, if the resultant force on a particle vanishes, its acceleration is zero and therefore it must remain at rest or move with constant velocity.

Now consider a set of axes XYZ fixed in the primary inertial system. Let $X'Y'Z'$ be a set of parallel axes fixed in a secondary inertial system which is moving in the X direction relative to the first inertial system with constant velocity **v**. If x, y, z are the coordinates of a particle relative to XYZ and x', y', z' the coordinates of the same particle relative to $X'Y'Z'$,

$$x' = x - vt - a, \quad y' = y - b, \quad z' = z - c,$$

where t is the time and a, b, c are constants representing the coordinates of the origin of $X'Y'Z'$ relative to XYZ at the time $t = 0$. Differentiating twice with respect to the time

$$\frac{d^2x'}{dt^2} = \frac{d^2x}{dt^2}, \quad \frac{d^2y'}{dt^2} = \frac{d^2y}{dt^2}, \quad \frac{d^2z'}{dt^2} = \frac{d^2z}{dt^2}.$$

Therefore the acceleration of the particle relative to the inertial system $X'Y'Z'$ is identical with that relative to the primary inertial system XYZ.

On the Newtonian dynamics the forces between particles are supposed to be functions only of the distances between them. As these distances are evidently the same in all inertial systems, a force measured relative to $X'Y'Z'$ is identical with that measured relative to the primary inertial system XYZ. Consequently, as the acceleration of a particle and also the force acting on it are the same in $X'Y'Z'$ as in XYZ, it follows that the laws of motion are valid for all inertial systems.

As a simple example of the laws of motion consider a monkey M (Fig. 28) climbing a massless rope which passes over a massless and frictionless pulley P and has fastened on the other end a counterweight W of the same mass as the monkey. Denoting the acceleration due to gravity by g and the tension force in the rope by T, the second law of motion gives for the upward acceleration f_1 of the monkey

$$mf_1 = T_1 - mg$$

and for the upward acceleration f_2 of the counterweight

$$mf_2 = T_2 - mg.$$

But the third law requires that

$$T_1 = T_2.$$

Therefore

$$f_1 = f_2,$$

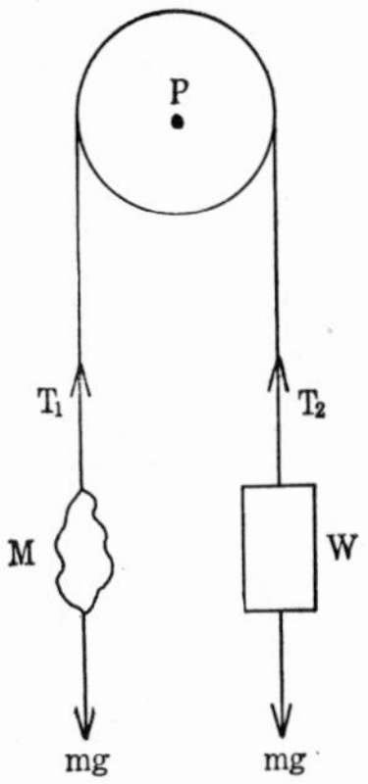

FIG. 28.

and monkey and counterweight have the same upward acceleration. If they start from rest they will ascend at the same rate.

If the forces acting on a particle are denoted by $\mathbf{F}_1$, $\mathbf{F}_2$, $\mathbf{F}_3$, etc., the second law of motion states that

$$\mathbf{F}_1 + \mathbf{F}_2 + \mathbf{F}_3 + \ldots = m\mathbf{f},$$

or

$$\sum \mathbf{F} = m\mathbf{f}. \qquad (20\text{–}1)$$

Writing all the terms on the left-hand side of the equation,

$$\sum \mathbf{F} - m\mathbf{f} = 0. \qquad (20\text{–}2)$$

The vector $-m\mathbf{f}$ is known as the *kinetic reaction*. It follows from equation (20–2) that the second law of motion may be put in the form:

Every particle is in equilibrium under the action of the applied forces and its kinetic reaction, or *the resultant of the applied forces and the kinetic reaction is always zero.*

For instance, consider a particle P (Fig. 29) moving along the path AB. The kinetic reaction has components as follows:

$-m\dfrac{dv}{dt}$ along the tangent $\mathbf{t}_1$, or $m\dfrac{dv}{dt}$ along the negative tangent,

$-m\dfrac{v^2}{\rho}$ along the normal $\mathbf{n}_1$, or $m\dfrac{v^2}{\rho}$ along the negative normal.

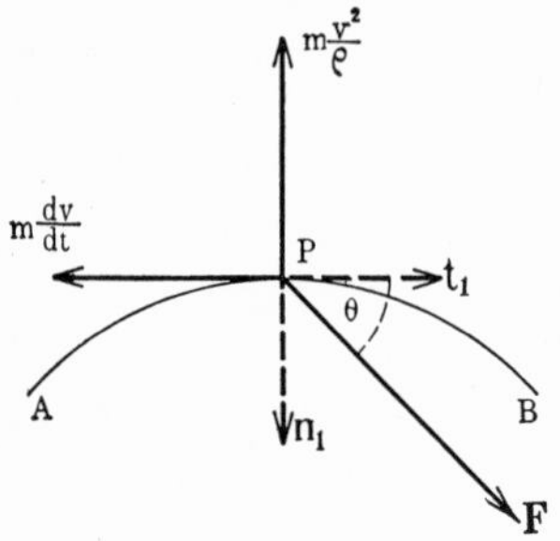

FIG. 29.

If $\mathbf{F}$ is the resultant of the applied forces, the particle must be in equilibrium under the action of $\mathbf{F}$ and the two components of the kinetic reaction represented in the figure. Therefore

$$m\frac{v^2}{\rho} = F\sin\theta,$$

$$m\frac{dv}{dt} = F\cos\theta.$$

The upward component of the kinetic reaction $m\dfrac{v^2}{\rho}$ is often referred to as the *centrifugal force*. It is not, however, an applied force, but merely a component of the kinetic reaction. The component $F\sin\theta$ of the applied force which balances this component of the kinetic reaction is called the *centripetal force*.

21. The Concepts of Mass and Force. — The statement of Newton's laws of motion given in the last article is logically incomplete in that the concepts of mass and force have not been defined. A more searching analysis of the fundamental laws of motion involves four experimental laws and certain deductions from them.

First Experimental Law. Consider two isolated particles, designated by the subscripts 0 and 1 in our analysis, which interact by means of gravitational or electrical attraction, through the agency of a light connecting spring, or in any other manner not involving the introduction of a third body of appreciable inertia. Then, if the motion is referred to an inertial system, we find that the acceleration of the one particle is always opposite to that of the other and that the ratio of the magnitudes of the two accelerations is the same no matter how far apart the particles may be, what their velocities may be (provided that the velocity of neither is comparable with that of light), or what the nature of the interaction between them may be. If we designate the acceleration of 0 due to 1 by $\mathbf{f}_{01}$ and that of 1 due to 0 by $\mathbf{f}_{10}$, we can express this law analytically by the equation

$$\mathbf{f}_{01} = -\, a_{10}\mathbf{f}_{10}, \tag{21-1}$$

where a_{10} is a positive constant independent of the circumstances of the interaction.

Let us take particle 0 as our standard particle. Then we name the constant a_{10} the *mass ratio* of particle 1 relative to the standard particle. Thus we define the ratio of the mass of a particle to that of the standard particle as the negative of the ratio of the acceleration of the standard particle to that of the given particle when the two are isolated. The reason that this ratio is important lies in the fact that it is a constant independent of the conditions under which it is measured. If we arbitrarily call the mass of the standard particle 1 gm, then the mass of 1 is a_{10} gm.

Second Experimental Law. If we allow the isolated particles 0 and 1 to interact we have seen that

$$\mathbf{f}_{01} = -\, a_{10}\mathbf{f}_{10}.$$

Similarly if particle 0 interacts with a third particle 2 after particle 1 has been removed,

$$\mathbf{f}_{02} = -\, a_{20}\mathbf{f}_{20},$$

whereas if particles 1 and 2 interact alone

$$\mathbf{f}_{12} = -\, a_{21}\mathbf{f}_{21}.$$

If we compare the three constants a_{10}, a_{20} and a_{21} we find that

$$a_{21} = \frac{a_{20}}{a_{10}}. \tag{21-2}$$

This is the second experimental law which we need. Obviously it can not be inferred from the first law alone.

Let m_1 be the mass of particle 1 and m_2 that of 2 relative to the standard particle 0. Then (21–2) becomes $a_{21} = m_2/m_1$ and we can rewrite the relation between the accelerations $\mathbf{f}_{12}$ and $\mathbf{f}_{21}$ of *any* two particles in the form

$$m_1\mathbf{f}_{12} = -\, m_2\mathbf{f}_{21}. \tag{21-3}$$

The significance of this law lies in the fact that the constants m_1 and m_2 appearing in the equation relating $\mathbf{f}_{12}$ to $\mathbf{f}_{21}$ are those determined by allowing first particle 1, and then particle 2, to interact alone with the standard particle 0.

These two laws, which are generalizations drawn from a vast number of experimental investigations, provide us with a logical definition of mass and a knowledge of its properties. The second contains implicitly in (21–3) Newton's law of action and reaction. It remains to define force and to examine the significance of Newton's second law of motion. For this purpose we require a third experimental law which represents a generalization of a broader type than that contained in either of the first two.

Third Experimental Law. The acceleration $\mathbf{f}_{12}$ of particle 1 due to particle 2 is the second time derivative of the position vector $\mathbf{r}_1$ of 1 relative to a set of axes fixed in the observer's inertial system. When we investigate the motion of 1 under all the different kinds of interactions between it and 2 which occur in nature, we always find that $\mathbf{f}_{12}$ is the time derivative of $\mathbf{r}_1$ of *lowest order* which can be expressed as a vector function of the distance r_{12} of 1 from 2 (and sometimes of the velocities v_1 and v_2 of the two particles) *containing no arbitrary constants depending on the initial conditions of the motion.* Such a function we may call a *definitive function* of the relative coordinates of the two particles. It may contain constants of nature, such as the gravitational constant or the velocity of light, or constants characteristic of the particles, such as their masses or electrical charges, or constants characteristic of the agency of interaction, such as the stiffness of a connecting spring, but it does not contain any constants depending upon the manner in which the motion originated. Instead of placing the acceleration $\mathbf{f}_{12}$ itself equal to such a function, we will write for a reason to appear later

$$m_1\mathbf{f}_{12} = \mathbf{F}_{12}(r_{12}), \tag{21–4}$$

which is quite permissible since m_1 is a constant. The definitive vector function $\mathbf{F}_{12}(r_{12})$ we name the *force* exerted by particle 2 on particle 1, and (21–4) is called the *differential equation of motion.*

This law, which contains the essential content of Newton's second law of motion, does not specify the form of the function $\mathbf{F}_{12}$. If the interaction of the two particles is gravitational, $F_{12} = -\gamma m_1 m_2/r_{12}^2$, if electrical, $F_{12} = q_1 q_2/r_{12}^2$, if due to a light connecting spring, $F_{12} = -k[r_{12} - (r_{12})_0]$, etc. The law merely tells us that the function $\mathbf{F}_{12}$ contains no arbitrary constants depending on the initial conditions. The mathematical equivalent of the physical generalization which it expresses is that the differential equations of motion are of the second order.

We could, of course, write down an expression for the velocity of particle 1 in terms of its position, but such a function would always involve one or more constants depending on the initial conditions. For instance, if a particle m is free to move along the X axis under the gravitational attraction of a particle M fixed at the origin,

$$v = \sqrt{\frac{2\gamma M}{x} - a},$$

$$f = -\frac{\gamma M}{x^2}.$$

Here γ is a constant of nature but a is a constant which must be determined by the way in which the particle m started on its motion.

The equation for particle 2 corresponding to (21–4) is

$$m_2\mathbf{f}_{21} = \mathbf{F}_{21}(r_{12}).$$

Combining this and (21–4) with (21–3) we *deduce* the law of action and reaction

$$\mathbf{F}_{12} = -\mathbf{F}_{21} \tag{21–5}$$

It was in order to obtain this law in the usual form that we introduced the factor m_1 into (21–4).

The three laws of dynamics which we have stated contain in logical form the content of Newton's three laws of motion. An additional law, which is generally tacitly assumed in developing the theory, also should be explicitly stated.

Fourth Experimental Law. Let $\mathbf{f}_{1,234}$ be the acceleration of particle 1 when particles 2, 3 and 4 are present, $\mathbf{f}_{12}$ being the acceleration of 1 when 3 and 4 are removed, etc. Then we find that

$$\mathbf{f}_{1,234} = \mathbf{f}_{12} + \mathbf{f}_{13} + \mathbf{f}_{14}. \tag{21–6}$$

This law states that the acceleration of a particle subject to the action of a number of other particles is equal to the vector sum of the accelerations which would be produced by these particles acting one at a time. It assures us of the *independence* of the accelerations produced by different interactions and therefore of the forces which give rise to them. For if $\mathbf{F}_{1,234}$ is the force exerted on 1 by 2, 3 and 4, multiplication of (21–6) by m_1 gives us

$$\mathbf{F}_{1,234} = \mathbf{F}_{12} + \mathbf{F}_{13} + \mathbf{F}_{14}, \tag{21–7}$$

which is known as the *law of composition of forces.*

22. Work and Energy. — If a particle on which a force $\mathbf{F}$ is acting suffers a displacement $d\mathbf{r}$ in a direction making an angle θ with the force, the force is said to do an amount of work δW given by

$$\delta W = F dr \cos\theta = \mathbf{F}\cdot d\mathbf{r}. \tag{22–1}$$

The symbol δ is used to indicate that δW is not necessarily an exact differential in the coordinates. The notation dW will be reserved for those small quantities which are exact differentials.

Equation (22–1) shows that the scalar δW is equal to either the product of the displacement by the component of the force in the direction of the displacement, or the product of the force by the component of the displacement in the direction of the force. Denoting the rectangular components of the force $\mathbf{F}$ by F_x, F_y, F_z,

$$\mathbf{F} = \mathbf{i}F_x + \mathbf{j}F_y + \mathbf{k}F_z,$$

and as $\mathbf{r}$ is the position vector of the particle

$$d\mathbf{r} = \mathbf{i}dx + \mathbf{j}dy + \mathbf{k}dz.$$

Hence

$$\delta W = F_x dx + F_y dy + F_z dz. \tag{22–2}$$

If $\mathbf{F}$ represents the resultant of all the forces acting on the particle, the second law of motion requires that

$$m\frac{d^2\mathbf{r}}{dt^2} = \mathbf{F}.$$

Taking the scalar product of this equation with the identity

$$\frac{d\mathbf{r}}{dt}dt = d\mathbf{r},$$

we have

$$m\frac{d\mathbf{r}}{dt}\cdot\frac{d^2\mathbf{r}}{dt^2}dt = \mathbf{F}\cdot d\mathbf{r},$$

and integrating from the time t_0 to the time t,

$$\left| \frac{1}{2} m \frac{d\mathbf{r}}{dt} \cdot \frac{d\mathbf{r}}{dt} \right|_{t_0}^{t} = \int_{t_0}^{t} \mathbf{F} \cdot d\mathbf{r},$$

or, if v_0 is the velocity of the particle at time t_0 and v its velocity at time t,

$$\tfrac{1}{2}mv^2 - \tfrac{1}{2}mv_0^2 = \int_{t_0}^{t} (F_x dx + F_y dy + F_z dz). \qquad (22\text{–}3)$$

The scalar $\frac{1}{2}mv^2$ is known as the *kinetic energy* of the particle and is represented by T. Equation (22–3) states that the increase in kinetic energy in a time $t - t_0$ is equal to the work done on the particle during this time. Now suppose that the force acting on the particle is due to a field of force, such as a gravitational field. If the components of the force are functions of the coordinates only, such that $F_x dx + F_y dy + F_z dz$ is an exact differential $-dV$, the field of force is said to be *conservative*. In this case the right-hand side of (22–3) can be integrated and we have

$$T - T_0 = -(V - V_0), \qquad (22\text{–}4)$$

where V_0 is the value of the function $V(x, y, z)$ obtained by substituting the coordinates of the point occupied by the particle at the time t_0 and V that obtained by substituting the coordinates of the point occupied by the particle at the time t. Therefore

$$T + V = T_0 + V_0 = U \text{ (a constant)}. \qquad (22\text{–}5)$$

The scalar function of position V is known as the *potential energy* of the particle and the constant U as the *total energy*. It is to be noted that the increase in potential energy $V - V_0$ is the *negative* of the work done on the particle by the force due to the field. In other words, the increase in potential energy is the work which would have to be done *against* the field in producing the desired displacement. Thus when a weight near the surface of the earth is raised from a lower to a higher level, work is done against the force of gravity and the potential energy is increased.

Equation (22–5) states that in a conservative field of force a particle moves in such a manner that the sum of its kinetic and potential energies remains constant. This is known as the *law of conservation of dynamical energy*.

It is important to note that the fundamental equation (22–4) is a relation between the change $T - T_0$ in kinetic energy and the change $V - V_0$ in potential energy. While it is customary to take the kinetic energy to be zero when the velocity is zero, there is no necessity to do so. We might just as well suppose the kinetic energy of the particle to have some large finite value when the velocity is zero, as indeed we shall when we develop the relativity dynamics. In either case the quantity $T - T_0$ has the same value. In fact it is quite clear that the usual convention leads to different values of the kinetic energy when this quantity is calculated relative to different inertial systems.

Similar remarks apply to the potential energy, and here it is well recognized that the level of zero potential energy is quite arbitrary. The value of the total energy U is therefore dependent upon the arbitrarily chosen zeros of kinetic and potential energies. While a certain significance is often attached to the value of the total energy, it must be remembered that physical measurements can never determine more than a change in energy.

Since

$$-dV = F_x dx + F_y dy + F_z dz,$$

it follows that

$$F_x = -\frac{\partial V}{\partial x}, \quad F_y = -\frac{\partial V}{\partial y}, \quad F_z = -\frac{\partial V}{\partial z},$$

or, in vector notation,

$$\mathbf{F} = -\nabla V. \tag{22–6}$$

By the potential at a point in a conservative field of force is meant the potential energy per unit quantity of a particle placed at that point. In gravitational theory the potential is the potential energy per unit mass, that is to say, the potential energy of a particle of unit mass placed at the point in question. In electrostatics the potential is the potential energy per unit charge and in magnetostatics it is the potential energy per unit pole. In calculating the potential it is usual to take the potential at infinity as zero. Now just as the negative of the gradient of the potential energy represents the force acting on the particle, so the negative of the gradient of the potential represents the force per unit mass in gravitational theory, the force per unit charge or electric intensity in electrostatics, the force per unit pole or magnetic intensity in magnetostatics.

It was shown in articles 15 and 17 that a vector function of position in space can be represented by the gradient of a scalar function of the coordinates when and only when the curl of the vector function vanishes. So the necessary and sufficient condition for the existence of a potential in a field of force is that the curl of the force per unit quantity should be zero. This is the case whenever the force between particles is an attraction or repulsion depending only on the distance between them, for, assuming the force to be of the form $f(r)\mathbf{r}$,

$$\nabla \times [f(r)\mathbf{r}] = \nabla \times [f(r)(\mathbf{i}x + \mathbf{j}y + \mathbf{k}z)]$$

$$= \mathbf{i}\left[\frac{\partial}{\partial y}\{zf(r)\} - \frac{\partial}{\partial z}\{yf(r)\}\right] + \text{etc.}$$

Now

$$r^2 = x^2 + y^2 + z^2,$$

and therefore

$$\frac{\partial r}{\partial x} = \frac{x}{r}, \quad \frac{\partial r}{\partial y} = \frac{y}{r}, \quad \frac{\partial r}{\partial z} = \frac{z}{r}.$$

So

$$\nabla \times [f(r)\mathbf{r}] = \mathbf{i}\frac{df}{dr}\left[\frac{zy}{r} - \frac{yz}{r}\right] + \text{etc.} = 0. \tag{22-7}$$

Problem 22a. (*a*) Find the gravitational potential at a distance R from a mass M if the force of attraction between two masses M and m a distance r apart is

$$F = -\gamma\frac{Mm}{r^2}.$$

(*b*) Find the electrostatic potential at a distance R from a charge q if

$$F = \frac{qq'}{r^2}.$$

(*c*) Find the magnetic potential at a distance R from a pole m if

$$F = \frac{mm'}{r^2}.$$

Ans. (*a*) $-\gamma\dfrac{M}{R}$, (*b*) $\dfrac{q}{R}$, (*c*) $\dfrac{m}{R}$.

Problem 22b. Find the gravitational potential at a point P (*a*) outside, (*b*) inside a spherical shell of uniform density and radius a having a mass M.

Ans. (*a*) $-\gamma\dfrac{M}{R}$, (*b*) $-\gamma\dfrac{M}{a}$.

Problem 22c. Show that the gravitational potential outside a sphere in which the density is a function of the distance from the center only is the same as if the entire mass of the sphere were concentrated at its center. Prove that two such spheres attract each other as if their masses were concentrated at their centers.

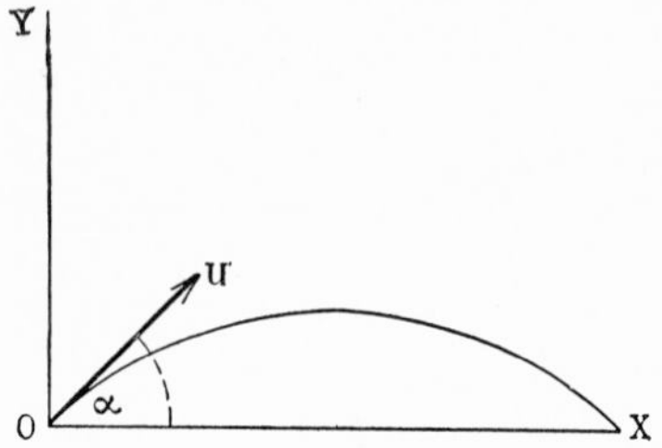

FIG. 30.

23. Motion under a Constant Force. — This is the case of a particle moving under the influence of the force of gravity near the surface of the earth. Let the constant force **F** have the Y direction. If the axes are oriented so that the initial velocity **u** of the particle lies in the XY plane (Fig. 30) the subsequent motion will be entirely in this plane. The second law of motion requires that

$$m\frac{d^2x}{dt^2} = 0,$$

$$m\frac{d^2y}{dt^2} = F.$$

Integrating twice

$$x = a_1t + a_0,$$

$$y = \frac{1}{2}\frac{F}{m}t^2 + b_1t + b_0,$$

where the a's and b's are constants of integration. If these constants are determined by the initial conditions

$$x = 0, \quad y = 0, \quad v_x = u_x, \quad v_y = u_y,$$

when $t = 0$, then

$$v_x = \frac{dx}{dt} = u_x, \tag{23-1}$$

$$v_y = \frac{dy}{dt} = u_y + \frac{F}{m}t, \tag{23-2}$$

$$x = u_xt, \tag{23-3}$$

$$y = u_yt + \frac{1}{2}\frac{F}{m}t^2. \tag{23-4}$$

If the force F is the downward force $-mg$ due to gravity, where g is 980 cm/sec^2 or 32.2 ft/sec^2,

$$v_x = u_x, \tag{23-5}$$

$$v_y = u_y - gt, \tag{23-6}$$

$$x = u_x t, \tag{23-7}$$

$$y = u_y t - \tfrac{1}{2}gt^2, \tag{23-8}$$

and eliminating t from (23–6) and (23–8) and combining with (23–5),

$$v^2 = u^2 - 2gy, \tag{23-9}$$

which is nothing more than the energy equation.

To find the path of the projectile eliminate t from (23–7) and (23–8) obtaining

$$y = x \tan \alpha - \frac{g}{2u^2 \cos^2 \alpha} x^2, \tag{23-10}$$

where α is the angle of projection. This is a parabola with its vertex at the highest point of the path. To get the time of flight t_1 put y equal to zero in (23–8). This gives

$$t_1 = \frac{2u \sin \alpha}{g}. \tag{23-11}$$

Substituting this value of the time in (23–7) we find for the range R

$$R = \frac{2u^2 \sin \alpha \cos \alpha}{g} = \frac{u^2 \sin 2\alpha}{g}. \tag{23-12}$$

Clearly the maximum range u^2/g occurs for an angle of projection of 45°. Any range less than this can be obtained from two angles of projection one of which is the complement of the other.

If we put m for $\tan \alpha$ in the equation of the path (23–10)

$$y = mx - \frac{gx^2}{2u^2}(1 + m^2),$$

or

$$m^2 - \frac{2u^2}{gx} m + \frac{2u^2}{gx^2} y + 1 = 0. \tag{23-13}$$

The two roots of this quadratic in m specify the angles of projection of the two trajectories a and b (Fig. 31) passing through the point

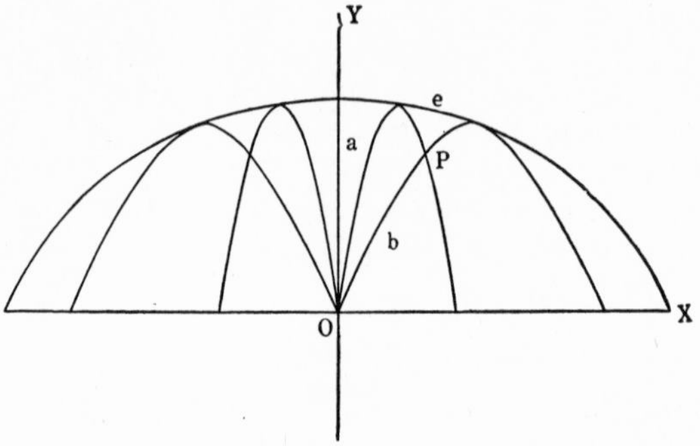

FIG. 31.

$P(x, y)$. As the two trajectories approach each other, P approaches the envelope e of the family of trajectories having the same initial velocity u. Consequently the equation of the envelope is the relation between x and y which makes the roots of (23–13) equal, that is, the relation obtained by equating to zero the discriminant of the quadratic. This equation is

$$x^2 = -\frac{2u^2}{g}\left(y - \frac{u^2}{2g}\right), \tag{23–14}$$

which represents a vertical parabola with vertex on the Y axis at a distance $u^2/2g$ above the origin. No point lying outside the envelope can be reached from O by a projectile having the initial velocity u. A point on the envelope is touched by only a single trajectory, whereas points in the interior may be reached by two trajectories corresponding to two different angles of projection.

Problem 23a. It is desired to fire a projectile so as to hit a target on the same level on the other side of a ridge of height h. The distance of the top of the ridge from the gun is $h \csc \beta$, and that of the top of the ridge from the target is $h \csc \delta$. Show that, if the projectile just grazes the top of the ridge, the angle of projection is given by $\tan \alpha = \tan \beta + \tan \delta$ and the initial velocity by $u^2 = gh(\cot \beta + \cot \delta)/\sin 2\alpha$.

24. Body Falling to the Earth from a Great Distance. — If m is the mass of the body and M that of the earth, Newton's law of gravitation gives for the force of attraction exerted by the earth on the body

$$F = -\gamma \frac{mM}{r^2}. \qquad (24\text{–}1)$$

The constant of gravitation γ is measured by observing the force of attraction of a massive lead sphere on a smaller mass fastened to the arm of a torsion balance. It is found to have the value $6.664\,(10)^{-8}\ \text{gm}^{-1}\ \text{cm}^3\ \text{sec}^{-2}$.

According to the second law of motion

$$m \frac{dv}{dt} = -\gamma \frac{mM}{r^2}.$$

Multiplying by the identity $v\,dt = dr$,

$$v \frac{dv}{dt}\,dt = -\gamma \frac{M}{r^2}\,dr,$$

and integrating we have the energy equation

$$v^2 = 2\gamma \frac{M}{r} + C.$$

If the body starts falling at a distance r_0 from the center of the earth, $v = 0$ when $r = r_0$. Therefore

$$v^2 = 2\gamma M \left(\frac{1}{r} - \frac{1}{r_0}\right). \qquad (24\text{–}2)$$

Let a be the radius of the earth. At the surface $F = -mg$. Substituting this in (24–1),

$$M = \frac{a^2 g}{\gamma}, \qquad (24\text{–}3)$$

from which the mass M of the earth is calculated once γ has been measured in the laboratory. Putting (24–3) in (24–2),

$$v^2 = 2a^2 g \left(\frac{1}{r} - \frac{1}{r_0}\right). \qquad (24\text{–}4)$$

If the body starts falling at a very great distance from the earth

$$v = a\sqrt{\frac{2g}{r}},$$

and by the time it has reached the surface

$$v = a\sqrt{\frac{2g}{a}} = \sqrt{2ag} = 7.0 \text{ mi/sec},$$

provided the resistance of the air is neglected. Conversely it would require a velocity of projection from the surface of the earth of over 7 mi/sec to take a body beyond the influence of the earth's gravitational field even if it were not slowed down by the resistance of the atmosphere.

Problem 24a. Calculate the mass and the mean density of the earth.

Ans. 6.1 $(10)^{27}$ gm, 5.5 gm/cm^3.

25. Body Falling in a Resisting Medium. — In our previous discussion of falling bodies we have neglected the resistance R of the air. Taking this resistance into account the second law of motion takes the form

$$m\frac{dv}{dt} = mg - R, \tag{25–1}$$

if v is taken positive downward. Experiment shows that for low velocities the resistance is proportional to the velocity, whereas for higher velocities it is more nearly proportional to the square of the velocity. Hence we distinguish two cases.

Case I. — If the velocity is small $R = mkv$ where k is a constant, and (25–1) becomes

$$\frac{dv}{dt} = g - kv.$$

So

$$\frac{dv}{v - \frac{g}{k}} = -\,kdt,$$

and integrating

$$v - \frac{g}{k} = Ce^{-kt}.$$

If the velocity at the time $t = 0$ is denoted by u

$$C = u - \frac{g}{k},$$

and

$$v = \frac{g}{k} + \left(u - \frac{g}{k}\right)e^{-kt}. \qquad (25\text{–}2)$$

As the time increases the velocity approaches asymptotically the limiting velocity $w = g/k$. The graph in Fig. 32 shows v plotted against t for (*a*) $u = 0$, (*b*) $0 < u < g/k$, (*c*) $u = g/k$, (*d*) $u > g/k$.

If s is the distance traversed,

$$v = \frac{ds}{dt} = w + (u - w)e^{-kt},$$

and

$$s = wt - \frac{u - w}{k}e^{-kt} + C.$$

Determining the constant of integration by making $s = 0$ when $t = 0$,

$$s = wt + \frac{u - w}{k}(1 - e^{-kt}). \qquad (25\text{–}3)$$

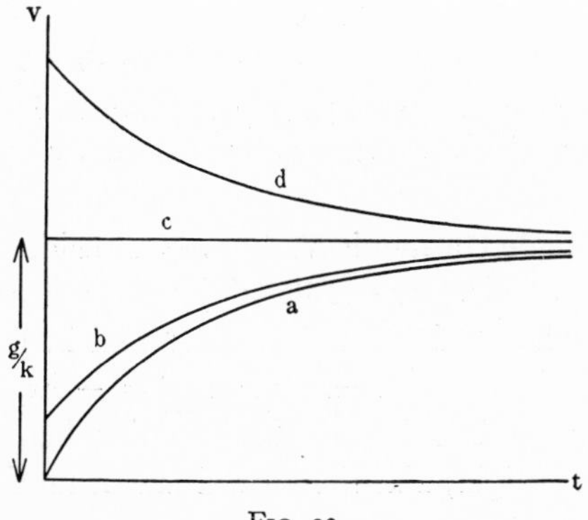

FIG. 32.

Case II.—If the velocity is greater, $R = mlv^2$ where l is a constant, and (25–1) becomes

$$\frac{dv}{dt} = g - lv^2.$$

Therefore

$$\frac{2vdv}{v^2 - \frac{g}{l}} = -\ 2lvdt = -\ 2lds,$$

and if u is the velocity when s is zero

$$v^2 = \frac{g}{l} + \left(u^2 - \frac{g}{l}\right)e^{-2ls}. \tag{25–4}$$

In this case the limiting velocity is $w = \sqrt{g/l}$.

As the velocity is increased beyond that considered in the second case discussed here, the power of v to which the resistance is proportional rises further, becoming as great as 5 when the velocity of sound is reached. Thereafter the power falls, becoming approximately 1.6 at extremely high velocities.

Problem 25a. For Case II of the last article show that

$$v = w\frac{(u + w)e^{lwt} + (u - w)e^{-lwt}}{(u + w)e^{lwt} - (u - w)e^{-lwt}}.$$

Problem 25b. A body falls 360 ft. from rest in 5 sec. Find the limiting velocity (*a*) assuming the resistance to be proportional to the velocity, (*b*) assuming the resistance to be proportional to the square of the velocity.

Ans. (*a*) 468 ft/sec, (*b*) 187 ft/sec.

Problem 25c. In Case II how must the equation of motion be modified if the acceleration is in the opposite direction to the velocity?

26. Linear Simple Harmonic Motion. — Consider a particle free to move along the X axis. Let it be subject to a force of restitution directed toward the origin O and proportional in magnitude to the displacement x of the particle. Then $F = -\ kx$, where k is the magnitude of the force acting on the particle when displaced a unit distance from the origin, and the second law of motion requires that

$$m\frac{d^2x}{dt^2} = -\ kx,$$

or

$$\frac{d^2x}{dt^2} + \frac{k}{m}x = 0. \tag{26–1}$$

Integrating

$$x = A\cos(\omega t - \alpha), \tag{26-2}$$

where

$$\omega \equiv \sqrt{\frac{k}{m}},$$

and A and α are the two constants of integration in the complete solution (26–2) of the differential equation (26–1) of the second order. Their values depend upon the initial conditions under which the motion started. Thus if the particle was pulled out from the origin a distance a and let go at the instant $t = 0$, $x = a$, and $v = 0$ when $t = 0$. Therefore

$$a = A\cos(-\alpha),$$

$$0 = v_0 = \left(\frac{dx}{dt}\right)_0 = [-A\omega\sin(\omega t - \alpha)]_0 = -A\omega\sin(-\alpha).$$

From the second equation we see that $\alpha = 0$, and substituting this value of α in the first, $A = a$. So for this case (26–2) becomes

$$x = a\cos\omega t.$$

It is clear from (26–2) that x is confined to values lying between $-A$ and A. Therefore the particle oscillates between a point A to the left of the origin and one A to the right. The maximum displacement A from the position of equilibrium at the origin is known as the *amplitude* of the motion.

The *period* P of the motion is the time required to execute a complete oscillation. It is therefore the time in which the argument of the cosine increases by 2π. Consequently

$$\omega t - \alpha + 2\pi = \omega(t + P) - \alpha,$$

giving

$$P = \frac{2\pi}{\omega} = 2\pi\sqrt{\frac{m}{k}}. \tag{26-3}$$

The *frequency* ν is the number of oscillations per unit time. Therefore it is equal to the reciprocal of the period, and $\omega = 2\pi\nu$. The argument $\omega t - \alpha$ of the trigonometrical function is known as the *phase* of the oscillation. If we put $\alpha = \beta + \pi/2$, (26–2) becomes

$$x = A\cos\left(\omega t - \beta - \frac{\pi}{2}\right) = A\sin(\omega t - \beta),$$

so the solution of (26–1) may be expressed in the form of either a cosine function of the time or a sine function. The *difference in phase* between two simple harmonic motions is the difference between their phases when both are expressed in cosine form or both in sine form. Finally if we put $\omega\delta$ for α in (26–2) this equation takes the form

$$x = A \cos \omega (t - \delta),$$

where δ has the dimensions of a time.

Consider a particle P revolving with constant angular velocity ω in a circle of radius A described about the origin. The motion of the projection of P on the X axis is then of the form (26–2). This circle is known as the *circle of reference* for the simple harmonic motion (26–2). Since ω is proportional to the frequency of the simple harmonic motion and is equal to the angular velocity of the point P on the circle of reference, it will be referred to as the *angular frequency*.

The kinetic energy of a mass m describing simple harmonic motion along a straight line is

$$T = \frac{1}{2} m \left(\frac{dx}{dt}\right)^2 = \tfrac{1}{2} m A^2 \omega^2 \sin^2 (\omega t - \alpha) = \tfrac{1}{2} k A^2 \sin^2 (\omega t - \alpha), \quad (26\text{–}4)$$

and the potential energy, if we take it to be zero at the equilibrium position O, is

$$V = -\int_0^x F dx = k \int_0^x x dx = \tfrac{1}{2} k x^2 = \tfrac{1}{2} k A^2 \cos^2 (\omega t - \alpha). \quad (26\text{–}5)$$

The total energy

$$U = T + V = \tfrac{1}{2} k A^2 = \tfrac{1}{2} m \omega^2 A^2 \quad (26\text{–}6)$$

is proportional to both the square of the amplitude and the square of the frequency.

Plotting the potential energy V against x gives the parabolic curve shown in Fig. 32.1. A particle having a total energy specified by the ordinate OQ may be regarded as oscillating back and forth along the line MN. At any point P on its path its potential energy is given by the ordinate RS of the parabola and its kinetic energy by SP. At each extremity of its path, its energy is entirely potential, whereas, at the center of its path, its energy is entirely kinetic. The curve MON is called a *potential well.*

Consider the time averages of T and V averaged over a period of the motion. Starting with the time 0, let us divide a period P into a very large number N of equal parts, and denote by T_1 the value of

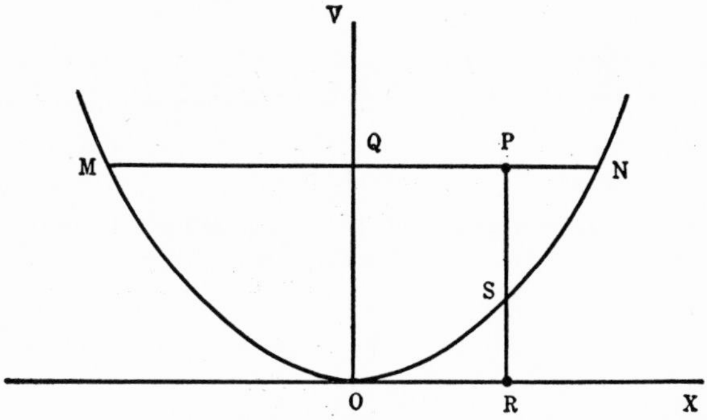

FIG. 32.1.

T at the time P/N, by T_2 the value of T at the time $2P/N$, and so forth. Then the arithmetic mean $\overline{T}$ of all the T's from T_1 to T_N is

$$\overline{T} = \frac{T_1 + T_2 \ldots + T_N}{N}$$

$$= \frac{1}{P}\left\{T_1 \frac{P}{N} + T_2 \frac{P}{N} \ldots + T_N \frac{P}{N}\right\}.$$

Putting Δt for the small interval of time P/N,

$$T_1 \frac{P}{N} + T_2 \frac{P}{N} \ldots + T_N \frac{P}{N} = \sum T\Delta t = \int_0^P T\,dt,$$

and

$$\overline{T} = \frac{1}{P}\int_0^P T\,dt. \tag{26-7}$$

In similar fashion, if Φ is a scalar function of position in space, the average value of Φ averaged over a volume τ is obtained by dividing τ into a very large number N of equal parts. If Φ_1 is the value of Φ at the first of these elementary volumes, Φ_2 the value of Φ at the second, etc., then the average value of Φ is

$$\overline{\Phi} = \frac{\Phi_1 + \Phi_2 \ldots + \Phi_N}{N}$$

$$= \frac{1}{\tau}\left\{\Phi_1 \frac{\tau}{N} + \Phi_2 \frac{\tau}{N} \ldots + \Phi_N \frac{\tau}{N}\right\},$$

and, if we put $\Delta\tau$ for the small volume τ/N,

$$\overline{\Phi} = \frac{1}{\tau}\sum\Phi\Delta\tau = \frac{1}{\tau}\int_\tau \Phi\, d\tau. \tag{26–8}$$

In like manner, if $\mathbf{V}$ is a vector function of position

$$\overline{\mathbf{V}} = \frac{1}{\tau}\int_\tau \mathbf{V}\, d\tau. \tag{26–9}$$

To return to (26–4) and (26–5), the time averages of $\sin^2(\omega t - \alpha)$ and $\cos^2(\omega t - \alpha)$ are

$$\overline{\sin^2(\omega t - \alpha)} = \frac{1}{P}\int_0^P \sin^2(\omega t - \alpha)dt = \tfrac{1}{2},$$

$$\overline{\cos^2(\omega t - \alpha)} = \frac{1}{P}\int_0^P \cos^2(\omega t - \alpha)dt = \tfrac{1}{2}.$$

Therefore

$$\overline{T} = \overline{V} = \tfrac{1}{4}kA^2,$$

from which it is seen that the total energy U is on the average half kinetic and half potential.

If the origin is a position of stable equilibrium, then, whatever function of the coordinates the force may be, it can generally be represented in the neighborhood of the origin by the series

$$F = ax + bx^2 + cx^3 + \ldots$$

where the constant a must be negative. Obviously the motion of a particle subject to such a force is simple harmonic for sufficiently small amplitudes.

Problem 26a. A particle constrained to move along the X axis is subject to a force of restitution $-kx$ and a constant force F. Discuss its motion, finding the frequency and the position of the point of equilibrium.

$$\textit{Ans. } x = F/k + A\cos(\omega t - \delta),\ \omega = \sqrt{\frac{k}{m}}.$$

Problem 26b. A weight of 2 pounds hung from a spring extends the spring $\frac{1}{2}$ inch. Neglecting the mass of the spring, find the period of oscillation (*a*) when a weight of 5 pounds is hung on the end, (*b*) when a weight of 10 pounds is hung on the end. Does it matter whether the spring is vertical or placed horizontally on a perfectly smooth table? Take $g = 32.2$ ft/sec². *Ans.* (*a*) 0.358 sec, (*b*) 0.504 sec.

Problem 26c. A particle constrained to move along the X axis is subject to a force of restitution $-kx$ and a force $\frac{t}{T}F$ which increases uniformly with the time t. Discuss its motion, finding the frequency and the point of equilibrium. $\quad$ *Ans.* $x = \frac{F}{k}\frac{t}{T} + A\cos(\omega t - \delta),\ \omega = \sqrt{\frac{k}{m}}.$

27. Free and Forced Vibrations of a Damped Linear Oscillator. — Consider a particle constrained to move along the X axis. Suppose that in addition to the simple harmonic force of restitution $-kx$ it is subject to a damping resistance $-bv$ proportional to the velocity. Then the equation of motion is

$$m\frac{d^2x}{dt^2} = -kx - b\frac{dx}{dt},$$

or, putting

$$2l \equiv \frac{b}{m},\quad \kappa^2 \equiv \frac{k}{m},$$

$$\frac{d^2x}{dt^2} + 2l\frac{dx}{dt} + \kappa^2 x = 0. \tag{27-1}$$

Try as solution

$$x = Ae^{-\alpha t}\cos(\omega_0 t - \beta).$$

Differentiating with respect to the time and substituting in (27–1)

$$\{2\alpha\omega_0 - 2l\omega_0\}\sin(\omega_0 t - \beta) + \{\kappa^2 + \alpha^2 - 2l\alpha - \omega_0^2\}\cos(\omega_0 t - \beta) = 0,$$

which is satisfied for all values of t if the coefficients of the sine and cosine functions vanish, that is, if

$$\alpha = l,\quad \omega_0^2 = \kappa^2 - l^2.$$

Therefore

$$x = Ae^{-lt} \cos(\omega_0 t - \beta), \quad \omega_0 \equiv \sqrt{\kappa^2 - l^2}, \tag{27–2}$$

is a solution of (27–1) provided $\kappa^2 > l^2$. As it contains two arbitrary constants A and β it is the complete solution. It represents the free vibrations of the oscillator. On account of the exponential factor the amplitude decreases with the time, falling to $1/e$ of its original value in the time $1/l$. The *natural frequency*

$$\omega_0 = \sqrt{\kappa^2 - l^2} = \sqrt{\frac{k}{m} - \frac{b^2}{4m^2}} \tag{27–3}$$

is less than it would have been had no damping been present. Plotting the displacement x against the time t (Fig. 33) it is clear that the curve lies inside the two curves

$$x = Ae^{-lt},$$

and

$$x = -Ae^{-lt},$$

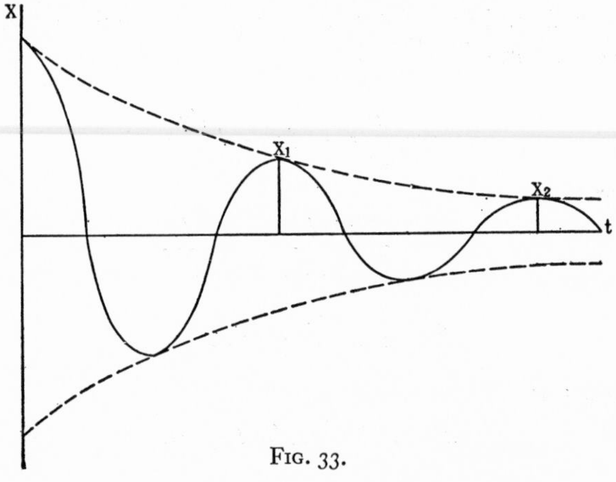

FIG. 33.

which are represented by dotted lines in the diagram. To find the maximum displacements,

$$\frac{dx}{dt} = -Ae^{-lt}\{l \cos(\omega_0 t - \beta) + \omega_0 \sin(\omega_0 t - \beta)\} = 0,$$

giving

$$\tan(\omega_0 t - \beta) = -\frac{l}{\omega_0}.$$

If t_1 is the smallest positive value of t which satisfies this relation, the successive larger values of t which satisfy it are $t_1 + \pi/\omega_0$, $t_1 + 2\pi/\omega_0$, $t_1 + 3\pi/\omega_0$, etc. But it is evident that the stationary values we have determined consist of alternate maxima and minima. Hence the time interval between successive maxima is the period $P = 2\pi/\omega_0$ and the cosine factor in (27–2) has the same value at all maxima. So if X_1 and X_2 are two successive maxima,

$$\frac{X_1}{X_2} = \frac{e^{-lt}}{e^{-l(t+P)}} = e^{lP}.$$

The quantity δ defined by

$$\delta \equiv \log \frac{X_1}{X_2} = lP = \frac{2\pi l}{\sqrt{\kappa^2 - l^2}} \qquad (27\text{–}4)$$

is known as the *logarithmic decrement*. If δ and the period P are measured, the damping constant l may be calculated from (27–4).

If $\kappa^2 < l^2$ the angular frequency ω_0 becomes imaginary and (27–2) is not suitable as a solution of the equation of motion in its present form. For this case try

$$x = Ae^{-\alpha t}.$$

Differentiating and substituting in the differential equation (27–1) we have

$$(\alpha^2 - 2\alpha l + \kappa^2)e^{-\alpha t} = 0,$$

which is satisfied for all values of t if

$$\alpha = l \pm \sqrt{l^2 - \kappa^2}.$$

Therefore the complete solution for $l^2 > \kappa^2$ is

$$x = A_1 e^{-(l+\sqrt{l^2-\kappa^2})t} + A_2 e^{-(l-\sqrt{l^2-\kappa^2})t}, \qquad (27\text{–}5)$$

where A_1 and A_2 are arbitrary constants. As the exponential is always positive, the motion is aperiodic. If the particle is pulled out from the equilibrium position and let go, the damping is so great that it never passes to the other side of the equilibrium point. When $l = \kappa$ the motion is said to be *critically damped.*

The vibrations so far discussed are known as the *free vibrations* of the oscillating particle. If now we subject the particle to a simple harmonic impressed force of the form $c \cos \omega t$ in addition to the force of restitution $-kx$ and the damping force $-bv$ the equation of motion becomes

$$\frac{d^2x}{dt^2} + 2l\frac{dx}{dt} + \kappa^2 x = a \cos \omega t, \quad a \equiv \frac{c}{m}. \tag{27–6}$$

Try as solution

$$x = A \cos (\omega t - \phi).$$

Forming the first two derivatives with respect to the time and substituting in (27–6) we find

$$[a - A\{(\kappa^2 - \omega^2) \cos \phi + 2\omega l \sin \phi\}] \cos \omega t$$
$$- [A\{(\kappa^2 - \omega^2) \sin \phi - 2\omega l \cos \phi\}] \sin \omega t = 0,$$

which is satisfied for all values of t provided the coefficients of $\sin \omega t$ and $\cos \omega t$ vanish. Equating the coefficient of $\sin \omega t$ to zero,

$$\left.\begin{aligned} \tan \phi = \frac{2\omega l}{\kappa^2 - \omega^2}, \quad \sin \phi &= \frac{2\omega l}{\sqrt{(\kappa^2 - \omega^2)^2 + 4\omega^2 l^2}}, \\ \cos \phi &= \frac{\kappa^2 - \omega^2}{\sqrt{(\kappa^2 - \omega^2)^2 + 4\omega^2 l^2}}, \end{aligned}\right\} \tag{27–7}$$

and equating to zero the other coefficient

$$A = \frac{a}{(\kappa^2 - \omega^2) \cos \phi + 2\omega l \sin \phi} = \frac{a}{\sqrt{(\kappa^2 - \omega^2)^2 + 4\omega^2 l^2}}. \tag{27–8}$$

So

$$x = \frac{a}{\sqrt{(\kappa^2 - \omega^2)^2 + 4\omega^2 l^2}} \cos (\omega t - \phi), \quad \tan \phi \equiv \frac{2\omega l}{\kappa^2 - \omega^2}, \tag{27–9}$$

is a solution of the differential equation. As it contains no arbitrary constants it is a particular solution. Now let x_1 be the function of the time represented by the right-hand side of (27–2) or (27–5), and x_2 that represented by the right-hand side of (27–9). Then if we put

$$x = x_1 + x_2$$

and substitute in (27–6)

$$\frac{d^2x_1}{dt^2} + 2l\frac{dx_1}{dt} + \kappa^2 x_1 + \frac{d^2x_2}{dt^2} + 2l\frac{dx_2}{dt} + \kappa^2 x_2 = a \cos \omega t.$$

But as x_1 is a solution of (27–1)

$$\frac{d^2x_1}{dt^2} + 2l\frac{dx_1}{dt} + \kappa^2 x_1 = 0,$$

and as x_2 is a solution of (27–6)

$$\frac{d^2x_2}{dt^2} + 2l\frac{dx_2}{dt} + \kappa^2 x_2 = a \cos \omega t.$$

Therefore $x_1 + x_2$ is a solution of (27–6). As the part x_1 of this solution contains two arbitrary constants, the sum $x_1 + x_2$ is the complete solution of the differential equation. As x_1 contains a damping factor, it becomes smaller and smaller as time goes on. For this reason the oscillations represented by x_1 are termed *transients*. If a time long compared with $1/l$ has elapsed since the beginning of the motion, the transients will have been damped out and the oscillations will consist only of the *forced vibrations* represented by x_2 and given explicitly by (27–9). These vibrations have a frequency equal to that of the impressed force but lag behind it by the phase angle ϕ. If $\omega < \kappa$, ϕ lies between 0 and 90°, whereas, if $\omega > \kappa$, ϕ lies between 90° and 180°.

Consider the amplitude

$$A = \frac{a}{\sqrt{(\kappa^2 - \omega^2)^2 + 4\omega^2 l^2}} \tag{27–10}$$

of the forced vibrations. To find the frequency ω_A of the impressed force for which A is a maximum

$$\frac{d}{d\omega^2}\{(\kappa^2 - \omega^2)^2 + 4\omega^2 l^2\} = -2(\kappa^2 - \omega^2) + 4l^2 = 0,$$

giving

$$\omega_A{}^2 = \kappa^2 - 2l^2. \tag{27–11}$$

This frequency is known as the *frequency of amplitude resonance*. There is no frequency of resonance if $l^2 > \frac{1}{2}\kappa^2$. If we measure the square of the frequency from the point of resonance by putting

$$\Omega \equiv \omega^2 - {\omega_A}^2 = \omega^2 - \kappa^2 + 2l^2$$

we have

$$A = \frac{a}{\sqrt{(\Omega - 2l^2)^2 + 4l^2(\Omega + \kappa^2 - 2l^2)}}$$

$$= \frac{a}{\sqrt{\Omega^2 + 4l^2(\kappa^2 - l^2)}},$$

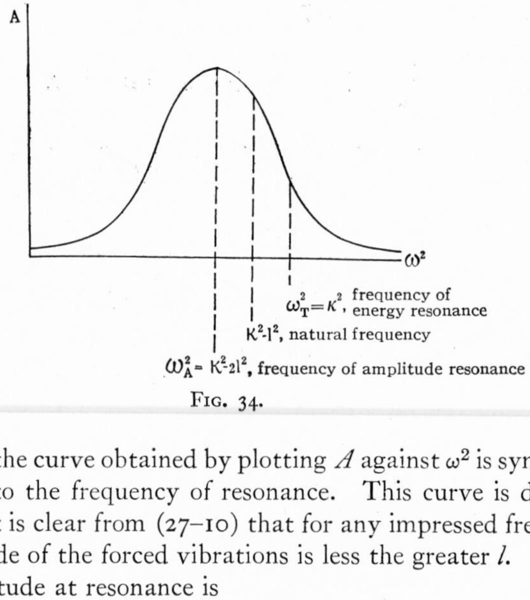

Fig. 34.

showing that the curve obtained by plotting A against ω^2 is symmetric with respect to the frequency of resonance. This curve is depicted in Fig. 34. It is clear from (27–10) that for any impressed frequency ω the amplitude of the forced vibrations is less the greater l.

The amplitude at resonance is

$$A_{\text{max.}} = \frac{a}{2l\sqrt{\kappa^2 - l^2}}. \tag{27–12}$$

For the physical range $0 < l^2 < \kappa^2/2$, this is greater the smaller l, becoming infinite when l equals zero.

The *sharpness of tuning* is measured by the ratio

$$\frac{A_{\text{max.}}}{A} = \sqrt{1 + \left(\frac{\Omega}{2l\sqrt{\kappa^2 - l^2}}\right)^2}, \tag{27–13}$$

where A is the amplitude for a particular Ω. Clearly this ratio is greater the smaller l.

The average kinetic energy of the forced vibrations is

$$\overline{T} = \frac{1}{4} m A^2 \omega^2 = \frac{1}{4} \frac{m a^2 \omega^2}{(\kappa^2 - \omega^2)^2 + 4\omega^2 l^2}. \qquad (27\text{–}14)$$

To find the frequency for maximum average kinetic energy equate to zero the derivative of $\overline{T}$ with respect to ω^2. This gives

$$\omega_T{}^2 = \kappa^2 \qquad (27\text{–}15)$$

for the *frequency of energy resonance.* So the maximum kinetic energy comes at the natural frequency without damping. Now (27–14) may be written

$$\overline{T} = \frac{1}{4} \frac{m a^2}{\kappa^2 \left(\frac{\kappa}{\omega} - \frac{\omega}{\kappa}\right)^2 + 4 l^2},$$

which has the same value for $\omega = n\kappa$ and for $\omega = \kappa/n$. Therefore the kinetic energy is the same an octave above its maximum as an octave below. But the amplitude is less for the higher than for the lower frequency.

The work W necessary to maintain the forced oscillations is that done by the impressed force $c \cos \omega t$. We have

$$W = \int c \cos \omega t dx = am \int \cos \omega t dx.$$

Now

$$dx = -\frac{a\omega}{\sqrt{(\kappa^2 - \omega^2)^2 + 4\omega^2 l^2}} \sin(\omega t - \phi)\, dt$$

$$= -\frac{a\omega}{\sqrt{(\kappa^2 - \omega^2)^2 + 4\omega^2 l^2}} \{\cos \phi \sin \omega t - \sin \phi \cos \omega t\} dt$$

$$= -\frac{a\omega}{(\kappa^2 - \omega^2)^2 + 4\omega^2 l^2} \{(\kappa^2 - \omega^2) \sin \omega t - 2\omega l \cos \omega t\} dt.$$

Therefore

$$W = \frac{a^2 m \omega}{(\kappa^2 - \omega^2)^2 + 4\omega^2 l^2} \int_0^t \{2\omega l \cos^2 \omega t - (\kappa^2 - \omega^2) \sin \omega t \cos \omega t\}\, dt.$$

We will integrate over a whole number of periods so as to eliminate the fluctuations occurring during the course of a single period. Then

$$\int_0^t \sin \omega t \cos \omega t dt = 0,$$

$$\int_0^t \cos^2 \omega t dt = \tfrac{1}{2}t,$$

and

$$W = \frac{ma^2\omega^2 l}{(\kappa^2 - \omega^2)^2 + 4\omega^2 l^2}\, t. \tag{27–16}$$

Therefore the mean power P necessary to maintain the oscillations is

$$P = \frac{dW}{dt} = \frac{ma^2\omega^2 l}{(\kappa^2 - \omega^2)^2 + 4\omega^2 l^2} = mA^2\omega^2 l. \tag{27–17}$$

As the energy supplied is used in overcoming the damping resistance we should obtain the same value of W by calculating the work done against the damping force. Thus

$$W = \int b \frac{dx}{dt} dx = 2ml \int \left(\frac{dx}{dt}\right)^2 dt$$

$$= 4l \int T dt = 4l\overline{T}t$$

$$= \frac{ma^2\omega^2 l}{(\kappa^2 - \omega^2)^2 + 4\omega^2 l^2}\, t.$$

Problem 27a. (*a*) A simple pendulum with a 2-pound bob has a period of 2 seconds and an amplitude of 2 inches. If allowed to execute free vibrations the amplitude falls to 1.5 inches after 10 periods. Find the power necessary to maintain oscillations of 2 inches amplitude. *Ans.* 0.000247 ft-lb/sec.

(*b*) How far would a 20-pound weight have to descend in a day to actuate the pendulum? *Ans.* 12.8 in.

Problem 27b. A damped linear oscillator is subject to two impressed harmonic forces $c_1 \cos \omega_1 t$ and $c_2 \cos (\omega_2 t + \delta)$. Show that the displacement of the forced vibrations is the sum of the displacements due to the impressed forces acting separately, and that the mean rate of absorption of energy is the sum of the rates of absorption of energy due to the impressed forces acting independently.

Problem 27c. Show that for critical damping (27 − 5) becomes $x = (A + Bt)e^{-lt}$.

Problem 27d. Show that (27 − 5) goes over into (27 − 2) when $\kappa^2 > l^2$.

Problem 27e. Show that, when damping is absent and the frequency of the impressed force is that for resonance ($\omega = \kappa$), the solution of (27 − 6) becomes

$$x = \frac{a}{2\kappa} t \sin \kappa t + B \cos (\kappa t + \beta).$$

27.1 Coupled Linear Harmonic Oscillators. — Consider three springs, K_1, K_2 and L (Fig. 34.1), of negligible mass. One end of K_1 is fixed at A and the other end is attached to a particle of mass m_1.

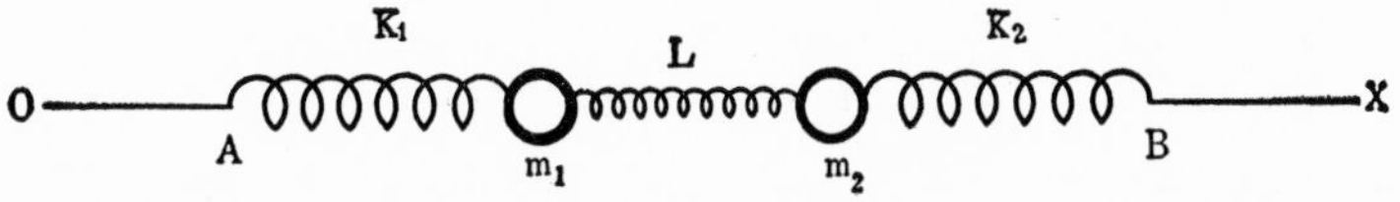

FIG. 34.1.

Similarly one end of K_2 is fixed at B and the other end attached to a particle of mass m_2. The ends of the third spring L are attached to the two particles, which are free to oscillate along the X axis. We shall suppose that none of the springs is extended or compressed when the system is in the equilibrium configuration.

Let x'_{10} and x'_{20} be the distances of m_1 and m_2, respectively, from the origin O when the system is in the equilibrium configuration, and x'_1 and x'_2 these distances when the system is oscillating. Then, if we designate the stiffnesses of the three springs by k_1, k_2 and l and neglect damping, the equations of motion of the two particles are

$$m_1 \frac{d^2x'_1}{dt^2} = - k_1(x'_1 - x'_{10}) + l\{(x'_2 - x'_{20}) - (x'_1 - x'_{10})\}, \quad (27.1\text{–}1)$$

$$m_2 \frac{d^2x'_2}{dt^2} = - k_2(x'_2 - x'_{20}) - l\{(x'_2 - x'_{20}) - (x'_1 - x'_{10})\}. \quad (27.1\text{–}2)$$

These equations are simplified if we put $x_1 \equiv x'_1 - x'_{10}$ and $x_2 \equiv x'_2 - x'_{20}$, that is, if we measure the displacement of each particle from its equilibrium position. Then

$$m_1 \frac{d^2x_1}{dt^2} + (k_1 + l)x_1 - lx_2 = 0,$$

$$m_2 \frac{d^2x_2}{dt^2} + (k_2 + l)x_2 - lx_1 = 0.$$

A further simplification is obtained by making the substitutions

$$\xi_1 \equiv x_1\sqrt{m_1}, \quad \xi_2 \equiv x_2\sqrt{m_2}, \quad \omega_1{}^2 \equiv \frac{k_1+l}{m_1}, \quad \omega_2{}^2 \equiv \frac{k_2+l}{m_2}, \quad c \equiv \frac{l}{\sqrt{m_1 m_2}}.$$

Then

$$\frac{d^2\xi_1}{dt^2} + \omega_1{}^2\xi_1 - c\xi_2 = 0\,, \tag{27.1–3}$$

$$\frac{d^2\xi_2}{dt^2} + \omega_2{}^2\xi_2 - c\xi_1 = 0. \tag{27.1–4}$$

Evidently ω_1 is the angular frequency of m_1 when we keep m_2 fixed in its equilibrium position, ω_2 that of m_2 when m_1 is held fixed, and c is a measure of the strength of the coupling. We shall refer to ξ_1 and ξ_2 as the displacements of the two particles, although strictly these quantities are only proportional to the actual displacements. Without loss of generality we may assume that $\omega_2 > \omega_1$.

We expect solutions of the form

$$\xi_1 = A \cos(\omega t - \alpha), \qquad \xi_2 = B \cos(\omega t - \alpha)$$

Substituting in the differential equations (27.1–3) and (27.1–4) we find

$$(-\,\omega^2 + \omega_1{}^2)\, A = cB, \quad (-\,\omega^2 + \omega_2{}^2)B = cA, \tag{27.1–5}$$

and multiplying these two equations together so as to eliminate A and B, we are left with the quadratic

$$\omega^4 - (\omega_1{}^2 + \omega_2{}^2)\omega^2 + \omega_1{}^2\omega_2{}^2 - c = 0 \tag{27.1–6}$$

in ω^2. Denoting the two frequencies which it defines by ω' and ω'', where $\omega'' > \omega'$, we have

$$\omega'^2 = \frac{\omega_2{}^2 + \omega_1{}^2}{2} - \sqrt{\left(\frac{\omega_2{}^2 - \omega_1{}^2}{2}\right)^2 + c^2}\,, \tag{27.1–7}$$

$$\omega''^2 = \frac{\omega_2{}^2 + \omega_1{}^2}{2} + \sqrt{\left(\frac{\omega_2{}^2 - \omega_1{}^2}{2}\right)^2 + c^2}\,. \tag{27.1–8}$$

Evidently

$$\omega' < \omega_1 < \omega_2 < \omega''.$$

The complete solutions of (27.1–3) and (27.1–4) are therefore

$$\xi_1 = A' \cos(\omega' t - \alpha') + A'' \cos(\omega'' t - \alpha''),$$

$$\xi_2 = B' \cos(\omega' t - \alpha') + B'' \cos(\omega'' t - \alpha''),$$

where

$$\frac{B'}{A'} = \frac{\omega_1^2 - \omega'^2}{c}, \quad \frac{A''}{B''} = -\frac{\omega''^2 - \omega_2^2}{c},$$

in accord with (27.1–5). Putting in the values of ω'^2 and ω''^2 given by (27.1–7) and (27.1–8),

$$\frac{B'}{A'} = \sqrt{1 + \left(\frac{\omega_2^2 - \omega_1^2}{2c}\right)^2} - \frac{\omega_2^2 - \omega_1^2}{2c} = -\frac{A''}{B''}, \qquad (27.1\text{–}9)$$

and if we write

$$g \equiv \sqrt{1 + \left(\frac{\omega_2^2 - \omega_1^2}{2c}\right)^2} - \frac{\omega_2^2 - \omega_1^2}{2c} \qquad (27.1\text{–}10)$$

it is clear that g decreases monotonically from unity at $(\omega_2^2 - \omega_1^2)/2c = 0$ to zero at $(\omega_2^2 - \omega_1^2)/2c = \infty$. Hence for weak coupling (c small), g is small compared with unity.

In terms of g the solutions become

$$\xi_1 = A' \cos(\omega' t - \alpha') - gB'' \cos(\omega'' t - \alpha''), \qquad (27.1\text{–}11)$$

$$\xi_2 = gA' \cos(\omega' t - \alpha') + B'' \cos(\omega'' t - \alpha''). \qquad (27.1\text{–}12)$$

That these constitute complete solutions is evidenced by the fact that they contain four arbitrary constants, A', B'', α' and α''.

Consider the important case of weak coupling. Then the principal vibration of m_1 is with the frequency ω' nearest to its natural frequency ω_1, and it stimulates a weak oscillation of amplitude gA' with frequency ω' in m_2. Similarly the principal vibration of m_2 is with the frequency ω'' nearest to its natural frequency ω_2, and it stimulates a weak oscillation of amplitude gB'' with frequency ω'' in m_1.

Since the frequencies ω'' and ω' are different, there will be times when the two component oscillations to which either particle is subject are in phase, and therefore the energy is a maximum; and other times when the component oscillations are out of phase, and the energy is a minimum. In fact, if A' and B'' are positive constants, the oscillation of m_1 will be least and that of m_2 greatest when

$$(\omega''t - \alpha'') - (\omega't - \alpha') = 0, 2\pi, 4\pi, \ldots$$

and *vice versa* when

$$(\omega''t - \alpha'') - (\omega't - \alpha') = \pi, 3\pi, 5\pi, \ldots.$$

Thus there is a back and forth transfer of energy from the one particle to the other. This can be illustrated by hanging two pendulums from the same not-too-rigid support. If one pendulum is set swinging while the other is at rest, a gradual transfer of energy from the first to the second and then back again will take place.

Problem 27.1a. Find the potential energy of the pair of particles discussed in this article.

Ans. $\frac{1}{2}(k_1 + l)x_1^2 + \frac{1}{2}(k_2 + l)x_2^2 - lx_1x_2$.

Problem 27.1b. Discuss the case where $\omega_2 = \omega_1 \equiv \omega$ and $B'' = A' \equiv A$.

Ans.
$$\xi_1 = \left[2A \sin\left(\frac{\omega'' - \omega'}{2}t - \frac{\alpha'' - \alpha'}{2}\right)\right] \sin\left\{\frac{\omega'' + \omega'}{2}t - \frac{\alpha'' + \alpha'}{2}\right\},$$

$$\xi_2 = \left[2A \cos\left(\frac{\omega'' - \omega'}{2}t - \frac{\alpha'' - \alpha'}{2}\right)\right] \cos\left\{\frac{\omega'' + \omega'}{2}t - \frac{\alpha'' + \alpha'}{2}\right\}.$$

Problem 27.1c. With the substitution $\xi_1 = \eta_1 - g\eta_2$, $\xi_2 = g\eta_1 + \eta_2$, where g is as given in (27.1–10), show that the equations of motion (27.1–3) and (27.1–4) become

$$(1 + g^2)\frac{d^2\eta_1}{dt^2} + (\omega_1^2 + g^2\omega_2^2 - 2gc)\eta_1 = 0,$$

$$(1 + g^2)\frac{d^2\eta_2}{dt^2} + (\omega_2^2 + g^2\omega_1^2 + 2gc)\eta_2 = 0,$$

or, more simply,

$$\frac{d^2\eta_1}{dt^2} + \omega'^2\eta_1 = 0,$$

$$\frac{d^2\eta_2}{dt^2} + \omega''^2\eta_2 = 0.$$

The variables η_1 and η_2 are known as *normal coordinates*.

28. Elliptic Simple Harmonic Motion. — A particle P is attracted toward a fixed point O (Fig. 35) by a force whose magnitude is proportional to the distance r from O. Evidently the particle will describe a path in the plane determined by the initial velocity and the initial radius vector. Choose this plane as the XY plane.

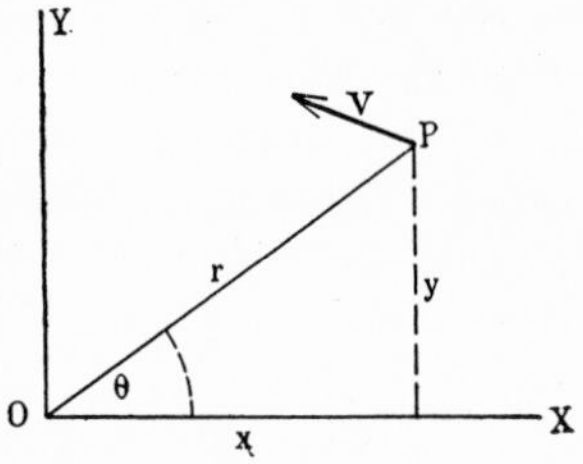

FIG. 35

As the force of restitution is $-kr$ along the radius vector

$$m\frac{d^2x}{dt^2} = -kr\cos\theta = -kx,$$

$$m\frac{d^2y}{dt^2} = -kr\sin\theta = -ky,$$

or

$$\frac{d^2x}{dt^2} + \frac{k}{m}x = 0,$$

$$\frac{d^2y}{dt^2} + \frac{k}{m}y = 0.$$

Integrating

$$\left.\begin{aligned} x &= A\cos(\omega t - \alpha), \\ y &= B\cos(\omega t - \beta). \end{aligned} \quad \omega \equiv \sqrt{\frac{k}{m}},\right\} \qquad (28\text{–}1)$$

The motion consists of two simple harmonic vibrations at right angles having the same period and differing in phase by $\alpha - \beta$. By counting time from the instant α/ω we can put (28–1) in the form

$$\left.\begin{aligned} x &= A\cos\omega t, \\ y &= B\cos(\omega t - \delta), \end{aligned}\right\} \qquad (28\text{–}2)$$

where $\delta = \beta - \alpha$. To find the equation of the path we must eliminate t between these two equations. Expanding the cosine factor in the second

$$y = B \cos \delta \cos \omega t + B \sin \delta \sin \omega t.$$

$$= x \frac{B}{A} \cos \delta + B \sin \delta \sin \omega t.$$

Therefore

$$\frac{x}{A} = \cos \omega t,$$

$$\frac{y}{B \sin \delta} - \frac{x}{A \tan \delta} = \sin \omega t.$$

Squaring and adding

$$\frac{x^2}{A^2 \sin^2 \delta} - 2 \frac{xy}{AB \sin \delta \tan \delta} + \frac{y^2}{B^2 \sin^2 \delta} = 1, \qquad (28\text{–}3)$$

which is the equation of an ellipse. If $A = B$ and the difference in phase δ is 90°, the ellipse degenerates into a circle of radius A. On the other hand if $\delta = 0$ the path becomes the straight line

$$\frac{x}{A} = \frac{y}{B}$$

as appears at once from (28–2).

Consider two simple harmonic motions at right angles having the same amplitudes but different frequencies, such as occur in Lissajous' figures. If ω is the one frequency and $\omega + \epsilon$ the other, we can put

$$x = A \cos \omega t,$$

$$y = A \cos (\omega + \epsilon)t,$$

provided we start counting time when the two vibrations are in phase. Eliminating ωt we have

$$y^2 - 2xy \cos \epsilon t + x^2 = A^2 \sin^2 \epsilon t.$$

To get rid of the product term rotate the axes through the angle θ by means of the substitution

$$x = x' \cos \theta - y' \sin \theta,$$

$$y = x' \sin \theta + y' \cos \theta.$$

Then

$$x'^2(1 - 2 \cos \epsilon t \sin \theta \cos \theta) + y'^2(1 + 2 \cos \epsilon t \sin \theta \cos \theta)$$
$$- 2x'y' \cos \epsilon t (\cos^2 \theta - \sin^2 \theta) = A^2 \sin^2 \epsilon t,$$

from which it appears that the product term vanishes if $\theta = 45°$. Then

$$x'^2(1 - \cos \epsilon t) + y'^2(1 + \cos \epsilon t) = A^2 \sin^2 \epsilon t,$$

or

$$\frac{x'^2}{2A^2 \cos^2 \frac{\epsilon t}{2}} + \frac{y'^2}{2A^2 \sin^2 \frac{\epsilon t}{2}} = 1. \tag{28-4}$$

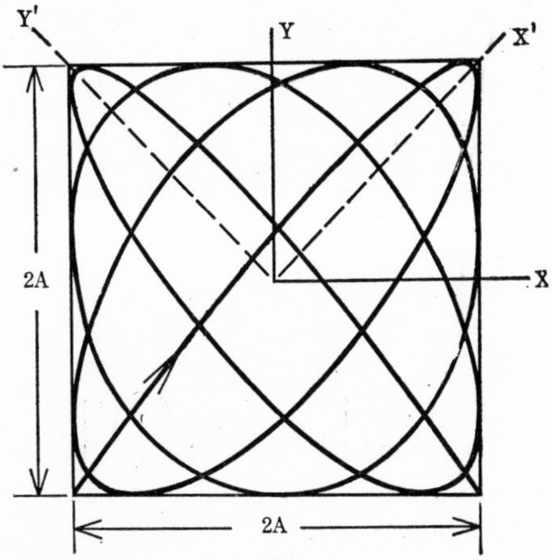

FIG. 36.

The path is an ellipse with axes which change with the time, running from zero to $2\sqrt{2}A$. The time taken by the figure to go through all its phases is $2\pi/\epsilon$. The path is shown in Fig. 36.

Problem 28a. A particle has impressed upon it two simple harmonic motions of the same amplitude and period at right angles to each other,

$$x = A \sin \frac{2\pi}{P} t, \quad y = A \sin \frac{2\pi}{P} (t + \delta).$$

Find the path of the particle if (*a*) $\delta = 0$, (*b*) $\delta = \frac{P}{4}$, (*c*) $\delta = \frac{P}{8}$.

29. The Simple Pendulum. — Consider a particle P (Fig. 37) of mass m suspended from the fixed point O by a massless inextensible flexible cord OP and free to oscillate in the plane of the paper under the influence of gravity. Resolving the forces along r and at right angles thereto in the direction of increasing θ, the equations of motion are

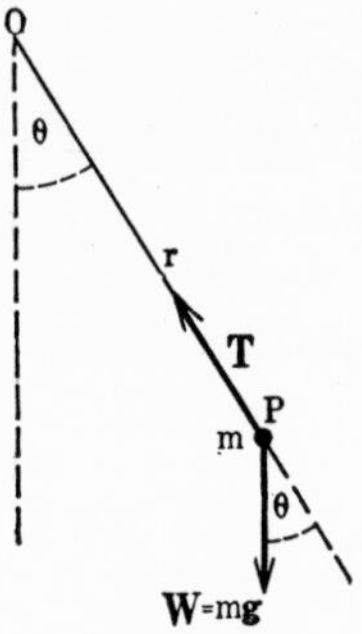

FIG. 37.

$$m\left\{\frac{d^2r}{dt^2} - r\left(\frac{d\theta}{dt}\right)^2\right\} = W\cos\theta - T,$$

$$m\left\{2\frac{dr}{dt}\frac{d\theta}{dt} + r\frac{d^2\theta}{dt^2}\right\} = -W\sin\theta,$$

where T is the tension force in the cord and W the weight of the particle. As r is the constant length l of the cord these become

$$ml\left(\frac{d\theta}{dt}\right)^2 = T - W\cos\theta,$$

$$ml\frac{d^2\theta}{dt^2} = -W\sin\theta,$$

or, as $W = mg$,

$$T = m\left\{g\cos\theta + l\left(\frac{d\theta}{dt}\right)^2\right\}, \tag{29-1}$$

$$\frac{d^2\theta}{dt^2} = -\frac{g}{l}\sin\theta. \tag{29-2}$$

If θ is always small, we may replace $\sin\theta$ by θ in (29–2) and have

$$\frac{d^2\theta}{dt^2} + \frac{g}{l}\theta = 0,$$

of which the solution is

$$\theta = \alpha\cos\sqrt{\frac{g}{l}}(t - \delta). \tag{29-3}$$

So for small amplitudes the motion is angular simple harmonic motion with the period

$$P_0 = 2\pi\sqrt{\frac{l}{g}}. \qquad (29\text{–}4)$$

As in the case of all simple harmonic motions the period is independent of the amplitude. By measuring l and P_0, the acceleration g due to gravity may be determined from this formula to a high degree of accuracy.

To find the period for large amplitudes, form the energy equation by multiplying (29–2) by the identity

$$\frac{d\theta}{dt}\,dt = d\theta.$$

Then

$$\frac{d\theta}{dt}\frac{d^2\theta}{dt^2}\,dt = -\frac{g}{l}\sin\theta d\theta,$$

and integrating

$$\left(\frac{d\theta}{dt}\right)^2 = \frac{2g}{l}\cos\theta + C.$$

If α is the angular amplitude, $\frac{d\theta}{dt} = 0$ when $\theta = \alpha$. Hence

$$\left(\frac{d\theta}{dt}\right)^2 = \frac{2g}{l}(\cos\theta - \cos\alpha), \qquad (29\text{–}5)$$

or

$$dt = \sqrt{\frac{l}{2g}}\frac{d\theta}{\sqrt{\cos\theta - \cos\alpha}}.$$

The period P_α is twice the time taken by the pendulum to swing from $\theta = -\alpha$ to $\theta = \alpha$. Therefore

$$P_\alpha = 2\sqrt{\frac{l}{2g}}\int_{-\alpha}^{\alpha}\frac{d\theta}{\sqrt{\cos\theta - \cos\alpha}}$$

$$= \sqrt{\frac{l}{g}}\int_{-\alpha}^{\alpha}\frac{d\theta}{\sqrt{\sin^2\frac{\alpha}{2} - \sin^2\frac{\theta}{2}}}$$

since

$$\cos\theta = 1 - 2\sin^2\frac{\theta}{2}, \quad \cos\alpha = 1 - 2\sin^2\frac{\alpha}{2}.$$

As θ never becomes greater than α we may put

$$\sin\frac{\theta}{2} = \sin\frac{\alpha}{2}\sin\psi,$$

$$d\theta = \frac{2\sin\frac{\alpha}{2}\cos\psi\, d\psi}{\sqrt{1 - \sin^2\frac{\alpha}{2}\sin^2\psi}}.$$

Then

$$P_\alpha = 2\sqrt{\frac{l}{g}}\int_{-\frac{\pi}{2}}^{\frac{\pi}{2}} \frac{d\psi}{\sqrt{1 - \sin^2\frac{\alpha}{2}\sin^2\psi}}$$

$$= 2\sqrt{\frac{l}{g}}\int_{-\frac{\pi}{2}}^{\frac{\pi}{2}} d\psi\left(1 + \frac{1}{2}\sin^2\frac{\alpha}{2}\sin^2\psi + \frac{3}{8}\sin^4\frac{\alpha}{2}\sin^4\psi\ldots\right),$$

$$= 2\pi\sqrt{\frac{l}{g}}\left(1 + \frac{1}{4}\sin^2\frac{\alpha}{2} + \frac{9}{64}\sin^4\frac{\alpha}{2}\ldots\right),$$

and using (29–4)

$$P_\alpha = P_0\left(1 + \frac{1}{4}\sin^2\frac{\alpha}{2} + \frac{9}{64}\sin^4\frac{\alpha}{2}\ldots\right), \qquad (29\text{–}6)$$

showing that the period increases as the amplitude is made greater. Usually the amplitude is small enough so that we can replace the sine by the angle in the second term and neglect the third term. Then

$$P_\alpha = P_0\left(1 + \frac{\alpha^2}{16}\right), \quad P_0 = P_\alpha\left(1 - \frac{\alpha^2}{16}\right). \qquad (29\text{–}7)$$

For

$$\alpha = 60°, \quad P_\alpha = P_0(1 + .0625 + .0088 + \ldots) = 1.07P_0,$$

$$\alpha = 2°, \quad P_\alpha = P_0(1 + .000076 + \ldots) = 1.000076P_0.$$

To find the tension in the cord substitute (29–5) in (29–1). Then

$$T = mg(3\cos\theta - 2\cos\alpha), \qquad (29\text{–}8)$$

which is maximum for $\theta = 0$.

Since the period of a simple pendulum depends upon the amplitude, it is possible by giving a pendulum two vibrations of different amplitudes at right angles to each other to cause the bob to describe a curve resembling Lissajous' figures.

Problem 29a. (*a*) A pendulum clock keeps correct time when the amplitude is 2°. How many seconds will it gain or lose a day when the amplitude is 10°? (*b*) If the bob weighs 2 pounds, what is the maximum tension for an amplitude of 10°? *Ans.* (*a*) 2 min. 38 sec. (*b*) 2.0612 pounds.

Problem 29b. A particle slides on the concave side of a smooth vertical cycloid generated by a circle of radius a. (*a*) Show that the equation of the cycloid, referred to its lowest point as origin, is

$$x = a(\theta + \sin\theta),$$

$$y = a(1 - \cos\theta).$$

(*b*) Show that the motion of the particle is isochronous and find its period.

$$\textit{Ans.}\ P = 4\pi\sqrt{\frac{a}{g}}.$$

30. Motion under an Inverse Square Force of Attraction. — Consider a particle of mass m subject to the attraction of a second particle of much greater mass M. According to the law of action and reaction M is subject to an equal attraction directed towards m, but as the accelerations produced by equal forces are inversely proportional to the masses of the particles to which they are applied, the more massive particle M will be comparatively undisturbed by the attraction of m. In the present discussion we shall suppose the larger mass to remain stationary at the origin and shall assume the force of attraction to vary inversely with the square of the distance r between the two particles. If, for instance, the larger mass is the sun and the smaller a planet, we have the gravitational force of attraction

$$-\gamma\frac{mM}{r^2},$$

whereas if the larger mass is the nucleus of an atom and the smaller an electron revolving about the nucleus we have the electrical attraction

$$-\frac{e^2Z}{r^2}$$

between the positive charge eZ on the nucleus and the negative charge $-e$ on the electron. The two cases need not be treated separately, for the first reduces to the second if the constant γ is given the value $e^2Z/(mM)$. Therefore the following discussion is confined to the motion of a planet or comet under the influence of the gravitational attraction of the sun.

Clearly the path of the particle m lies in the plane determined by its initial velocity and its initial position vector relative to M. If we use polar coordinates (Fig. 38) the equations of motion are

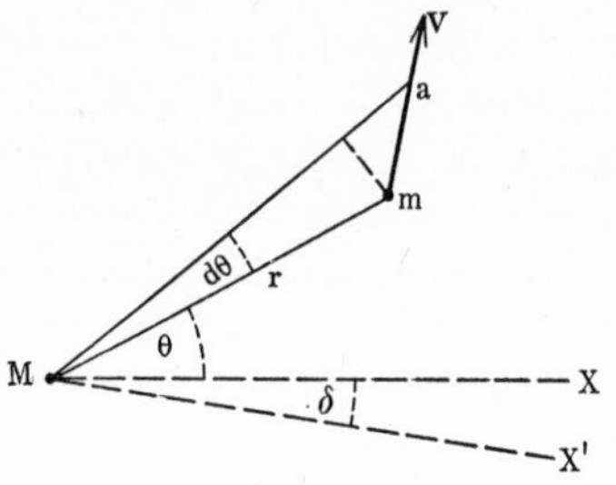

FIG. 38.

$$m\left\{\frac{d^2r}{dt^2} - r\left(\frac{d\theta}{dt}\right)^2\right\} = -\gamma\frac{mM}{r^2}, \qquad (30\text{–}1)$$

$$m\left\{2\frac{dr}{dt}\frac{d\theta}{dt} + r\frac{d^2\theta}{dt^2}\right\} = 0. \qquad (30\text{–}2)$$

Multiplying (30–2) by r/m it becomes

$$\frac{d}{dt}\left(r^2\frac{d\theta}{dt}\right) = 0,$$

of which the integral is

$$r^2\frac{d\theta}{dt} = h \text{ (a constant)}. \qquad (30\text{–}3)$$

As the area of the triangle Mma described by the radius vector in a time dt is $\frac{1}{2}(r)(rd\theta)$, the left-hand side of (30–3) is twice the area described by the radius vector per unit time. Therefore the equation states that the radius vector describes equal areas in equal times. This is known as Kepler's second law of planetary motion. As it comes directly from the equation of motion (30–2), which is valid so long as there is no component of the applied force at right angles to the radius vector, it is true for any central force whether the magnitude of the force varies inversely with the square of the distance or not.

The vector obtained by multiplying the mass by the velocity of a moving particle is known as the *momentum* of the particle, and the vector product of the position vector of the particle relative to any origin O by its momentum is known as the *moment of momentum* or *angular momentum* of the particle about O. Now the left-hand side of (30–3) is the product of the radius vector r by the component of the velocity perpendicular to r. So the product of this by the constant m is equal in magnitude to the angular momentum of the particle. Therefore equation (30–3) states that the angular momentum of m about M remains constant during the motion.

To find the equation of the path it is necessary to eliminate t between (30–1) and (30–3). Putting u for $1/r$ and making use of the latter equation,

$$\frac{dr}{dt} = \frac{dr}{d\theta}\frac{d\theta}{dt} = \frac{h}{r^2}\frac{dr}{d\theta} = -h\frac{du}{d\theta},$$

$$\frac{d^2r}{dt^2} = -h\frac{d^2u}{d\theta^2}\frac{d\theta}{dt} = -h^2u^2\frac{d^2u}{d\theta^2}.$$

So (30–1) becomes

$$-mh^2u^2\frac{d^2u}{d\theta^2} - mh^2u^3 = -\gamma mMu^2,$$

or

$$\frac{d^2u}{d\theta^2} + u = \frac{\gamma M}{h^2},$$

of which the complete solution is

$$u = \frac{\gamma M}{h^2} + A\cos(\theta + \delta). \qquad (30\text{–}4)$$

By measuring the angle θ from the X' axis in Fig. 38 instead of the X axis we can put this equation in the simpler form

$$\frac{1}{r} = \frac{\gamma M}{h^2} + A\cos\theta, \qquad (30\text{–}5)$$

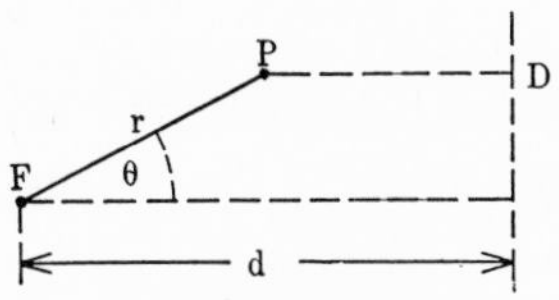

FIG. 39.

where $1/r$ has been restored in place of u.

Now it will be shown that this is the equation in polar coordinates of a conic section referred to one focus as origin. By definition a conic section is the curve traced by a point P (Fig. 39) which moves so that the ratio of its distance from a fixed point F to its distance from a straight line D is constant. The point F is known as a *focus*, D a *directrix*, and the ratio ϵ of the distance of P from the first to its distance from the second is known as the *eccentricity* of the conic. If d is the distance of the focus from the directrix

$$\epsilon = \frac{r}{d - r\cos\theta},$$

or

$$\frac{1}{r} = \frac{1}{\epsilon d} + \frac{1}{d}\cos\theta. \tag{30-6}$$

Comparing with (30–5) it appears that the path of the particle is a conic section of eccentricity

$$\epsilon = \frac{h^2 A}{\gamma M}. \tag{30-7}$$

If $\epsilon < 1$ the point P traces a closed curve known as an *ellipse*. The major axis $2a$ is the sum of the minimum value r_1 of the radius vector corresponding to $\theta = 0$ and the maximum value r_2 corresponding to $\theta = \pi$. As

$$r_1 = \frac{\epsilon d}{1 + \epsilon}, \quad r_2 = \frac{\epsilon d}{1 - \epsilon},$$

it follows that

$$2a = r_1 + r_2 = \frac{2\epsilon d}{1 - \epsilon^2}.$$

Therefore (30–6) may be written in the form

$$\frac{1}{r} = \frac{1 + \epsilon\cos\theta}{a(1 - \epsilon^2)}. \tag{30-8}$$

If the eccentricity (30–7) of the orbit of the particle m is less than unity, the particle describes an ellipse about M as focus. This is the case with planets and constitutes Kepler's first law of planetary motion. Comparing (30–7) and (30–8) with (30–5) it is seen that the semi-major axis of the elliptical orbit is given by

$$\frac{1}{a} = \frac{\gamma M}{h^2}\left\{1 - \left(\frac{h^2 A}{\gamma M}\right)^2\right\}. \tag{30-9}$$

If $\epsilon = 1$ the point P traces a curve of one branch open to the left which is known as a *parabola*. Putting $\epsilon = 1$ in (30–6) and writing $2n$ for d

$$\frac{1}{r} = \frac{1 + \cos\theta}{2n}, \tag{30–10}$$

where n is the distance of the vertex of the curve from both F and D. Comparing with (30–5) and putting ϵ equal to unity in (30–7) it is seen that

$$n = \frac{h^2}{2\gamma M} = \frac{1}{2A}. \tag{30–11}$$

Comets describe orbits about the sun which are very nearly parabolic.

If $\epsilon > 1$ the point P describes a curve of two branches known as a *hyperbola*. The branch B_1 (Fig. 40), nearer to the focus F, for which r is positive, corresponds to values of θ lying in the angular range marked 1 on the figure, which extends from $-\cos^{-1}(-1/\epsilon)$

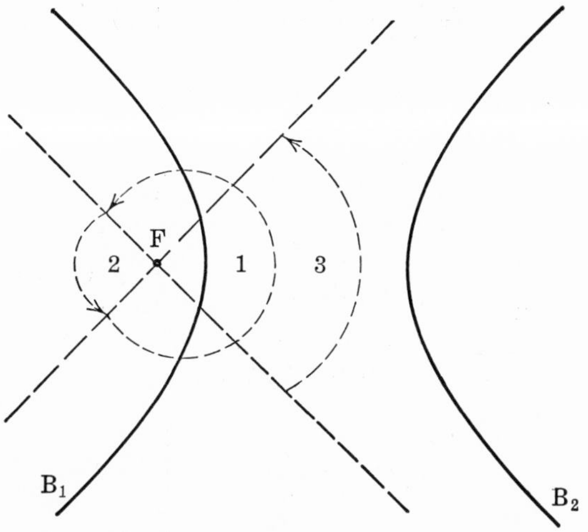

FIG. 40.

to $\cos^{-1}(-1/\epsilon)$. On the other hand, the branch B_2, farther from the focus F, for which r is negative, corresponds to values of θ lying in the range 2 extending from $\cos^{-1}(-1/\epsilon)$ to $2\pi - \cos^{-1}(-1/\epsilon)$. The distance $2a$ between the vertices of the two branches is the difference between the negative of the radius vector r_2 for $\theta = \pi$ and the radius vector r_1 for $\theta = 0$. Therefore

$$2a = -r_2 - r_1 = \frac{2\epsilon d}{\epsilon^2 - 1},$$

and

$$\frac{1}{r} = \frac{1 + \epsilon \cos \theta}{a(\epsilon^2 - 1)}. \qquad (30\text{–}12)$$

Comparing with (30–5) and (30–7) it is seen that

$$\frac{1}{a} = \frac{\gamma M}{h^2} \left\{ \left(\frac{h^2 A}{\gamma M} \right)^2 - 1 \right\} \qquad (30\text{–}13)$$

In discussing dynamical orbits it is more convenient to specify the far branch B_2 of the hyperbola by a separate equation in which the radius vector assumes positive instead of negative values. To do this we write (30–6) in the form

$$-\frac{1}{r} = -\frac{1}{\epsilon d} + \frac{1}{d} \cos (\theta + \pi)$$

and then replace $-r$ by r' and $\theta + \pi$ by θ', getting

$$\frac{1}{r'} = -\frac{1}{\epsilon d} + \frac{1}{d} \cos \theta',$$

where r' is positive and θ' lies in the range 3 (Fig. 40) between $-\cos^{-1}(1/\epsilon)$ and $\cos^{-1}(1/\epsilon)$. Hence, if we restrict ourselves to positive values of the radius vector, we can represent the near and far branches of the hyperbola by the equations

$$\left.\begin{aligned} \frac{1}{r} &= \frac{1}{\epsilon d} + \frac{1}{d} \cos \theta, \\ \frac{1}{r} &= -\frac{1}{\epsilon d} + \frac{1}{d} \cos \theta, \end{aligned}\right\} \qquad (30\text{–}14)$$

respectively. We see from (30–5), then, that a hyperbolic orbit, described under an inverse square force of attraction, always consists of the branch of the hyperbola nearer to the center of attraction.

To obtain the energy equation multiply (30–1) by $\frac{dr}{dt}$, (30–2) by $r\frac{d\theta}{dt}$ and add. Then

$$m\left\{\frac{dr}{dt}\frac{d^2r}{dt^2}+r\frac{dr}{dt}\left(\frac{d\theta}{dt}\right)^2+r^2\frac{d\theta}{dt}\frac{d^2\theta}{dt^2}\right\}=-\frac{\gamma mM}{r^2}\frac{dr}{dt},$$

and integrating

$$\frac{1}{2}m\left\{\left(\frac{dr}{dt}\right)^2+r^2\left(\frac{d\theta}{dt}\right)^2\right\}-\frac{\gamma mM}{r}=U\text{ (a constant)},$$

or, if v is the velocity of the particle m,

$$\frac{1}{2}mv^2-\frac{\gamma mM}{r}=U. \tag{30–15}$$

The first term on the left is the kinetic energy, the second the potential energy, and the constant U the total energy. Now at the point of nearest approach to M the velocity is entirely transverse. If R denotes the radius vector and V the velocity at this point,

$$V=\left(r\frac{d\theta}{dt}\right)_R=\frac{h}{R},$$

by (30–3), and by (30–5)

$$\frac{1}{R}=\frac{\gamma M}{h^2}+A.$$

Therefore

$$V=\frac{\gamma M}{h}+Ah.$$

Substituting these values of R and V in the energy equation (30–15),

$$\frac{2U}{m}=-\left(\frac{\gamma M}{h}\right)^2\left\{1-\left(\frac{h^2A}{\gamma M}\right)^2\right\}$$

$$=-\left(\frac{\gamma M}{h}\right)^2(1-\epsilon^2) \tag{30–16}$$

from (30–7). Therefore

$$\epsilon=\sqrt{1+\frac{2U}{m}\left(\frac{h}{\gamma M}\right)^2}. \tag{30–17}$$

So the orbit is elliptic, parabolic, or hyperbolic according as the total energy is negative, zero, or positive. Suppose, now, that the particle m is removed to rest at infinity. Then both its kinetic and potential energies vanish, and therefore its total energy is zero. Consequently its actual orbit is elliptic, parabolic, or hyperbolic according as its actual velocity is less than, equal to, or greater than the velocity it would acquire in falling from rest at infinity.

In the case of elliptical orbits comparison of (30–9) and (30–16) shows that

$$U = -\frac{\gamma m M}{2a}.$$

Therefore all elliptical orbits of the same major axes have the same energies irrespective of their eccentricities and the energy equation (30–15) may be written

$$\frac{1}{2}mv^2 - \frac{\gamma m M}{r} = -\frac{\gamma m M}{2a}. \tag{30–18}$$

To find the period of revolution P in the case of an elliptical orbit we have for the rate at which the area of the ellipse is described

$$\frac{1}{2}r^2\frac{d\theta}{dt} = \frac{1}{2}h,$$

giving $\frac{1}{2}hP$ for the area of the ellipse. In terms of the semi-major axis a and the eccentricity ϵ the area of an ellipse is $\pi a^2\sqrt{1-\epsilon^2}$. Equating these,

$$hP = 2\pi a^2\sqrt{1-\epsilon^2}.$$

But from (30–7) and (30–9)

$$\sqrt{1-\epsilon^2} = \frac{h}{\sqrt{a\gamma M}}.$$

Therefore

$$P = \frac{2\pi a^{3/2}}{\sqrt{\gamma M}}. \tag{30–19}$$

This equation contains Kepler's third law of planetary motion, which states that the square of the period of revolution of a planet is proportional to the cube of the major axis of its orbit. Knowing

γ and measuring P and a for one of the planets, we can calculate the mass M of the sun. In fact by means of this formula the mass of any heavenly body which has a satellite can be computed, provided the period of the satellite and the major axis of its orbit have been measured.

So far it has been supposed that the larger mass M is so much greater than the smaller mass m that the motion of the former under the attraction of the latter can be neglected. Now we shall consider what modification of the previous theory is necessary in order to take account of the motions of both masses.

Let $\mathbf{r}_1$ be the position vector of the mass m relative to a fixed origin and $\mathbf{r}_2$ that of M. Then $\mathbf{r} = \mathbf{r}_1 - \mathbf{r}_2$ is the position vector of m relative to the moving mass M. If the force exerted by M on m is any function of the distance r between them and is directed along the line joining them, the equations of motion in vector form are

$$m\frac{d^2\mathbf{r}_1}{dt^2} = f(r)\mathbf{r},$$

$$M\frac{d^2\mathbf{r}_2}{dt^2} = -f(r)\mathbf{r},$$

since the law of action and reaction requires that the force on M shall be equal and opposite to that on m. Therefore

$$\frac{d^2}{dt^2}(\mathbf{r}_1 - \mathbf{r}_2) = \left(\frac{1}{m} + \frac{1}{M}\right)f(r)\mathbf{r}.$$

Putting

$$\frac{1}{\mu} \equiv \frac{1}{m} + \frac{1}{M}, \tag{30–20}$$

and replacing $\mathbf{r}_1 - \mathbf{r}_2$ by $\mathbf{r}$,

$$\mu\frac{d^2\mathbf{r}}{dt^2} = f(r)\mathbf{r}. \tag{30–21}$$

This is the equation of motion of m *relative* to M, that is, referred to a set of non-rotating axes whose origin coincides with M and which therefore follow M in its motion. But this equation differs from that which would have described the motion of m if M had been fixed only in the substitution of μ for m in the kinetic reaction. The factor m appearing in the force of gravitation remains unchanged. Therefore all the results previously obtained for the case where M

was supposed to remain fixed apply equally well to the motion of m *relative* to M provided we replace γ by $\gamma m/\mu$. If M is very large compared with m, μ differs very little from m. The quantity μ is known as the *reduced mass*.

We may now correct Kepler's third law so as to take account of the motion of the larger mass M as well as the smaller mass m. Replacing γ in (30–19) by $\gamma m/\mu$ we have

$$P = \frac{2\pi a^{3/2}}{\sqrt{\gamma(M + m)}}. \tag{30–22}$$

Problem 30a. Show that, for a repulsive inverse square force, the orbit is always the far branch of a hyperbola.

Problem 30b. (*a*) Compute the mass of the sun, given $a = 93(10)^6$ miles and $P = 365$ days for the earth. *Ans.* $1.9(10)^{33}$ gm.

(*b*) Compute the mass of the earth, given that the distance of the moon from the earth is 240,000 miles and the period of the moon 27.3 days. *Ans.* $6.1(10)^{27}$ gm.

Problem 30c. An alpha particle of charge $2e$ and mass m approaches an atomic nucleus of charge eZ and much greater mass with a velocity $\mathbf{v}$ so directed as to bring the alpha particle within a distance p of the nucleus if it continued to move undeflected along a straight line. Assuming that the nucleus remains at rest during the encounter, show that the deflection δ experienced by the alpha particle is given by

$$\tan\frac{\delta}{2} = \frac{2e^2Z}{mpv^2}.$$

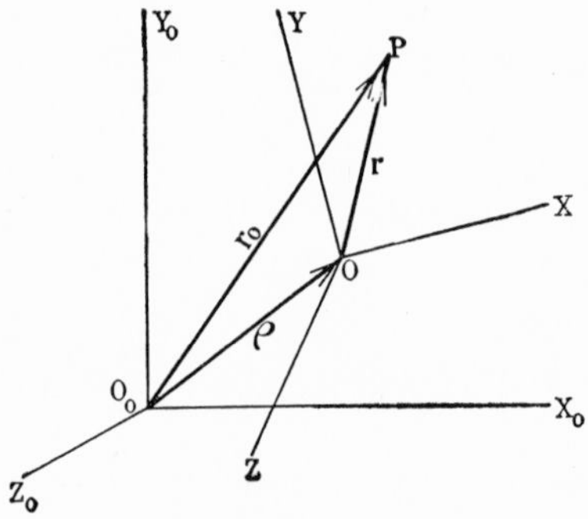

FIG. 41

31. Linear and Angular Velocity Referred to Moving Axes.—Let $X_0Y_0Z_0$ (Fig. 41) represent a set of axes fixed in an inertial system, and XYZ a second set of rigid rectangular axes moving relative to $X_0Y_0Z_0$. We shall assume not only that the origin O of XYZ may be accelerated relative to the fixed axes, but that the moving axes may be rotating as well. As usual we shall designate unit vectors along X_0, Y_0, Z_0 by $\mathbf{i}_0$, $\mathbf{j}_0$, $\mathbf{k}_0$ and along X, Y, Z by $\mathbf{i}$, $\mathbf{j}$, $\mathbf{k}$. The first set of unit vectors are constants in magnitude and direction, but the second set, while constant in magnitude, vary in direction as the moving axes rotate.

Consider a point P moving relative to both sets of axes. Let its position vector relative to the origin O_0 of the fixed axes be $\mathbf{r}_0$ and that relative to the moving origin O be $\mathbf{r}$. Then if $\boldsymbol{\rho}$ is the position vector of O relative to O_0,

$$\mathbf{r}_0 = \boldsymbol{\rho} + \mathbf{r}, \qquad (31\text{–}1)$$

where

$$\mathbf{r}_0 = \mathbf{i}_0 x_0 + \mathbf{j}_0 y_0 + \mathbf{k}_0 z_0,$$

$$\mathbf{r} = \mathbf{i}x + \mathbf{j}y + \mathbf{k}z,$$

and if ξ, η, ζ are the coordinates of O relative to the fixed axes

$$\boldsymbol{\rho} = \mathbf{i}_0\xi + \mathbf{j}_0\eta + \mathbf{k}_0\zeta.$$

To denote differentiation with respect to the time we shall put a dot over the quantity differentiated instead of employing the operator $\frac{d}{dt}$. Then the vector velocity of P relative to $X_0Y_0Z_0$ is

$$\mathbf{v}_0 = \dot{\mathbf{r}}_0 = \dot{\boldsymbol{\rho}} + \dot{\mathbf{r}}, \qquad (31\text{–}2)$$

where

$$\dot{\mathbf{r}} = \mathbf{i}\dot{x} + \mathbf{j}\dot{y} + \mathbf{k}\dot{z} + \dot{\mathbf{i}}x + \dot{\mathbf{j}}y + \dot{\mathbf{k}}z, \qquad (31\text{–}3)$$

since $\mathbf{i}$, $\mathbf{j}$, $\mathbf{k}$ are not constant in direction. The first three terms in this expression represent the apparent velocity $\mathbf{v}$ of the point P relative to the moving axes. If the point P is fixed in the moving set of axes, x, y, z are constant and $\dot{\mathbf{r}}$ reduces to the sum of the last three terms. These terms represent the contribution to the velocity of P due to the rotation of the moving axes. For, if the moving axes do not rotate, $\mathbf{i}$, $\mathbf{j}$, $\mathbf{k}$ remain constant in direction and their derivatives with respect to the time vanish.

Now as $\mathbf{i}$ is a unit vector, $\dot{\mathbf{i}}$ must be perpendicular to $\mathbf{i}$. Hence it has the form

$$\dot{\mathbf{i}} = c\mathbf{j} - b\mathbf{k},$$

and similarly

$$\dot{\mathbf{j}} = a\mathbf{k} - f\mathbf{i},$$

$$\dot{\mathbf{k}} = e\mathbf{i} - d\mathbf{j}.$$

But as

$$\mathbf{i} = \mathbf{j} \times \mathbf{k},$$

it follows that

$$\dot{\mathbf{i}} = \dot{\mathbf{j}} \times \mathbf{k} + \mathbf{j} \times \dot{\mathbf{k}}$$

$$= f\mathbf{j} - e\mathbf{k}.$$

Therefore $f = c$ and $e = b$. Similarly $d = a$. So

$$\left.\begin{aligned} \dot{\mathbf{i}} &= c\mathbf{j} - b\mathbf{k}, \\ \dot{\mathbf{j}} &= a\mathbf{k} - c\mathbf{i}, \\ \dot{\mathbf{k}} &= b\mathbf{i} - a\mathbf{j}. \end{aligned}\right\} \qquad (31\text{–}4)$$

To examine the physical significance of the coefficients a, b, c, consider the coefficient a which appears as the Z component of $\dot{\mathbf{j}}$. It represents the projection of $\dot{\mathbf{j}}$ on the YZ plane, and therefore $a\,dt$ is the projection on this plane of the vector increment $d\mathbf{j}$ in $\mathbf{j}$ which has been produced by the rotation of the axes in the time dt. Let j_1 (Fig. 42) be the projection on the YZ plane of $\mathbf{j}$ at the end of the time dt and OY_1 the projection on this plane of the Y axis at the end of the time dt. Then it is clear from the figure that $a\,dt$ is equal to the angle $d\theta$ between OY_1 and OY. But $d\theta$ is the angle, measured around OX as axis, through which OY and OZ have turned during the time dt. Therefore a is the angular velocity of the axes about OX as axis. Similarly b is the angular velocity of the axes about OY as axis, and c that about OZ as axis.

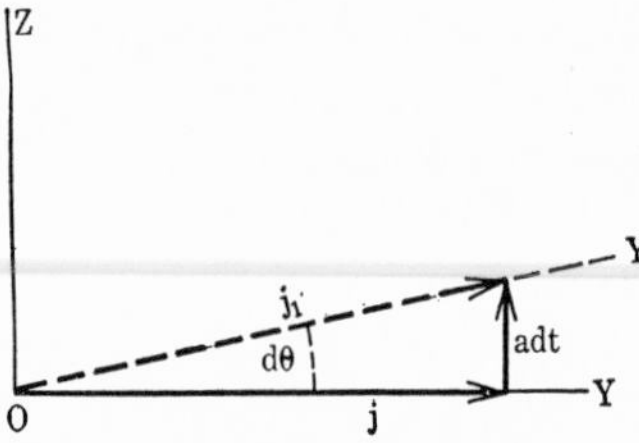

FIG. 42.

Returning to equation (31–3), by substituting (31–4) we see that

$$\left.\begin{aligned} \dot{\mathbf{i}}x + \dot{\mathbf{j}}y + \dot{\mathbf{k}}z &= \mathbf{i}(bz - cy) + \mathbf{j}(cx - az) + \mathbf{k}(ay - bx) \\ &= \begin{vmatrix} \mathbf{i} & \mathbf{j} & \mathbf{k} \\ a & b & c \\ x & y & z \end{vmatrix}. \end{aligned}\right\} \qquad (31\text{–}5)$$

So if we write

$$\boldsymbol{\omega} = \mathbf{i}a + \mathbf{j}b + \mathbf{k}c,$$

where $\boldsymbol{\omega}$, like a, b, c, is not a function of the coordinates although it may be a function of the time, it follows that

$$\dot{\mathbf{i}}x + \dot{\mathbf{j}}y + \dot{\mathbf{k}}z = \boldsymbol{\omega} \times \mathbf{r}, \tag{31–6}$$

and

$$\dot{\mathbf{r}} = \boldsymbol{\omega} \times \mathbf{r} + \mathbf{v}. \tag{31–7}$$

It is important to have a clear understanding of the distinction between $\dot{\mathbf{r}}$ and $\mathbf{v}$ in this formula. The vector $\dot{\mathbf{r}}$ we may call the *true velocity* of P relative to the moving origin O since it is the velocity that would be measured by an observer in a non-rotating set of axes with moving origin O. The vector $\mathbf{v}$, on the other hand, is the *apparent velocity* of P relative to O as determined by an observer in the rotating frame XYZ who ignores the rotation of the axes relative to which he is conducting his measurements. When we speak of the *velocity relative to the moving origin* O we shall always understand the true velocity $\dot{\mathbf{r}}$ relative to a non-rotating set of axes with O as origin, whereas when we speak of the *velocity relative to the moving axes* XYZ we shall mean the apparent velocity $\mathbf{v}$ which would be measured by an observer stationed on these axes who ignores the rotation of his reference frame. Similar remarks apply to all vectors which are laid off from the origin of a set of axes which are not fixed in an inertial system.

That the vector $\boldsymbol{\omega}$ has the direction of the axis through O about which XYZ are rotating is easily shown. For the axis of rotation is defined as the locus of those points which have no linear velocity at the instant considered due to the rotation. Therefore if P lies on the axis through O,

$$\dot{\mathbf{i}}x + \dot{\mathbf{j}}y + \dot{\mathbf{k}}z = 0,$$

and hence $\mathbf{r}$ is parallel to $\boldsymbol{\omega}$ from (31–6). Since $\mathbf{r}$ is drawn from O to *any* other point P on the axis of rotation through O it follows that the axis of rotation is a straight line parallel to the vector $\boldsymbol{\omega}$. As the direction of $\boldsymbol{\omega}$ changes that of the axis does too.

Furthermore the magnitude of $\boldsymbol{\omega}$ is equal to the angular velocity of XYZ about the axis of rotation through the origin. For equation (31–6) states that the linear velocity of any point P due to the rotation is at right angles to the plane of $\boldsymbol{\omega}$ and $\mathbf{r}$, therefore tangent to a circle drawn in a plane perpendicular to $\boldsymbol{\omega}$ with its center on the axis of rotation, and that the magnitude of the linear velocity is equal to the product of ω by the radius of this circle. Therefore ω is equal to the arc of this circle which is described in a unit time divided by the radius, that is, equal to the angle described about the axis of rotation per unit time.

Finally (31–6) shows that the sense of $\boldsymbol{\omega}$ along the axis of rotation is that of advance of a right-handed screw whose sense of rotation agrees with that of the axes XYZ. In consideration of its properties we may name $\boldsymbol{\omega}$ the *vector angular velocity* of the moving axes.

Returning now to (31–2) and substituting (31–7) we have

$$\mathbf{v}_0 = \dot{\boldsymbol{\rho}} + \boldsymbol{\omega} \times \mathbf{r} + \mathbf{v}. \tag{31–8}$$

This equation states that the linear velocity $\mathbf{v}_0$ of the point P is made up of three parts: first, the velocity $\dot{\boldsymbol{\rho}}$ of the moving origin; second, the velocity $\boldsymbol{\omega} \times \mathbf{r}$ due to the rotation of the moving axes; third, the apparent velocity $\mathbf{v}$ relative to the moving axes. If P is rigidly attached to the moving axes the last term vanishes. Therefore the sum of the first two terms is often spoken of as the *velocity of transport* of the moving space XYZ.

32. Linear and Angular Acceleration Referred to Moving Axes. — By the angular acceleration $\boldsymbol{\alpha}$ is meant the vector time rate of increase of angular velocity $\boldsymbol{\omega}$. As

$$\boldsymbol{\omega} = \mathbf{i}a + \mathbf{j}b + \mathbf{k}c, \tag{32–1}$$

it follows that

$$\boldsymbol{\alpha} = \dot{\boldsymbol{\omega}} = \mathbf{i}\dot{a} + \mathbf{j}\dot{b} + \mathbf{k}\dot{c} + \dot{\mathbf{i}}a + \dot{\mathbf{j}}b + \dot{\mathbf{k}}c,$$

and making use of (31–4)

$$\left.\begin{aligned} \boldsymbol{\alpha} &= \mathbf{i}\dot{a} + \mathbf{j}\dot{b} + \mathbf{k}\dot{c} + \mathbf{i}(bc - bc) + \mathbf{j}(ca - ca) + \mathbf{k}(ab - ab) \\ &= \mathbf{i}\dot{a} + \mathbf{j}\dot{b} + \mathbf{k}\dot{c}, \end{aligned}\right\} \tag{32–2}$$

But this is just the time rate of change of angular velocity of the rotating axes relative to the rotating axes XYZ themselves. Therefore the time rate of change of angular velocity of the rotating axes relative to themselves is identical with the angular acceleration of these axes relative to the axes $X_0Y_0Z_0$ fixed in an inertial system.

No such simple relation holds for the linear acceleration. The linear acceleration $\mathbf{f}_0$ of the point P of the last article relative to the fixed axes $X_0Y_0Z_0$ is obtained by differentiating (31–8):

$$\mathbf{f}_0 = \dot{\mathbf{v}}_0 = \ddot{\boldsymbol{\rho}} + \dot{\boldsymbol{\omega}} \times \mathbf{r} + \boldsymbol{\omega} \times \dot{\mathbf{r}} + \dot{\mathbf{v}}. \tag{32–3}$$

Substituting $\dot{\mathbf{r}}$ from (31–7) in the third term on the right

$$\boldsymbol{\omega} \times \dot{\mathbf{r}} = \boldsymbol{\omega} \times \mathbf{v} + \boldsymbol{\omega} \times (\boldsymbol{\omega} \times \mathbf{r}), \tag{32-4}$$

and as the apparent linear velocity $\mathbf{v}$ relative to the moving axes is

$$\mathbf{v} = \mathbf{i}\dot{x} + \mathbf{j}\dot{y} + \mathbf{k}\dot{z},$$

the last term on the right of (32–3) becomes

$$\begin{aligned}\dot{\mathbf{v}} &= \mathbf{i}\ddot{x} + \mathbf{j}\ddot{y} + \mathbf{k}\ddot{z} + \dot{\mathbf{i}}\dot{x} + \dot{\mathbf{j}}\dot{y} + \dot{\mathbf{k}}\dot{z} \\ &= \mathbf{i}\ddot{x} + \mathbf{j}\ddot{y} + \mathbf{k}\ddot{z} + \mathbf{i}(b\dot{z} - c\dot{y}) + \mathbf{j}(c\dot{x} - a\dot{z}) + \mathbf{k}(a\dot{y} - b\dot{x}),\end{aligned}$$

on substituting (31–4). The first three terms represent the apparent linear acceleration $\mathbf{f}$ of P relative to the moving axes, and the last three terms are the expansion of the vector product $\boldsymbol{\omega} \times \mathbf{v}$. Therefore

$$\dot{\mathbf{v}} = \mathbf{f} + \boldsymbol{\omega} \times \mathbf{v}, \tag{32-5}$$

and putting (32–4) and (32–5) in (32–3)

$$\mathbf{f}_0 = \ddot{\mathbf{p}} + \boldsymbol{\omega} \times (\boldsymbol{\omega} \times \mathbf{r}) + \dot{\boldsymbol{\omega}} \times \mathbf{r} + 2\boldsymbol{\omega} \times \mathbf{v} + \mathbf{f}. \tag{32-6}$$

So the acceleration of the point P is made up of five terms. The first represents the acceleration of the origin of the moving axes, the second is the centripetal acceleration due to the rotation of the moving axes, the third the linear acceleration due to the angular acceleration $\dot{\boldsymbol{\omega}}$ of the moving axes, the fourth the so-called acceleration of Coriolis, and the fifth the apparent acceleration of P relative to the moving axes. If P is rigidly attached to the moving axes $\mathbf{v}$ and $\mathbf{f}$ vanish and $\mathbf{f}_0$ reduces to the sum of the first three terms on the right of (32–6). Therefore the sum of these three terms is said to represent the *acceleration of transport* of the moving space XYZ.

Let us consider in more detail certain of the individual terms of which the acceleration $\mathbf{f}_0$ is made up. If p denotes the perpendicular distance of the point P from the axis of rotation, the term $\boldsymbol{\omega} \times (\boldsymbol{\omega} \times \mathbf{r})$ is a vector directed from P toward the axis of rotation having the magnitude $\omega^2 p$. It is therefore the centripetal acceleration (19–14). The term $2\boldsymbol{\omega} \times \mathbf{v}$ exists only when the point P is moving relative to the rotating axes. It is directed perpendicular to the plane of $\boldsymbol{\omega}$ and $\mathbf{v}$ in the sense of advance of a right-handed screw rotated from

$\boldsymbol{\omega}$ to $\mathbf{v}$ and is equal in magnitude to twice the product of $\boldsymbol{\omega}$ by the component of $\mathbf{v}$ perpendicular to $\boldsymbol{\omega}$. Therefore if $\mathbf{v}$ is parallel to $\boldsymbol{\omega}$ the acceleration of Coriolis vanishes.

Now suppose that observations on a moving particle are being conducted from a moving reference frame, such as the earth. The velocity and acceleration measured are $\mathbf{v}$ and $\mathbf{f}$ relative to a set of axes XYZ rigidly attached to the earth. But the earth, on account of its acceleration in its orbit and its diurnal rotation about its axis, does not constitute an inertial system. Therefore the second law of motion does not hold with respect to the apparent acceleration $\mathbf{f}$ relative to the earth. It holds only with respect to the acceleration $\mathbf{f}_0$ relative to a set of axes $X_0Y_0Z_0$ fixed in an inertial system. Therefore if $\mathbf{F}$ is the resultant force acting on the particle we must write

$$m\mathbf{f}_0 = \mathbf{F}.$$

Substituting (32–6) we have for the relative acceleration $\mathbf{f}$,

$$m\mathbf{f} = \mathbf{F} - m\ddot{\boldsymbol{\rho}} - m\boldsymbol{\omega} \times (\boldsymbol{\omega} \times \mathbf{r}) - m\dot{\boldsymbol{\omega}} \times \mathbf{r} - 2m\boldsymbol{\omega} \times \mathbf{v}. \quad (32\text{–}7)$$

The last four terms are terms in the kinetic reaction of the moving particle, although $-m\boldsymbol{\omega} \times (\boldsymbol{\omega} \times \mathbf{r})$ is often referred to as the centrifugal force as already noted, and $-2m\boldsymbol{\omega} \times \mathbf{v}$ is sometimes called the force of Coriolis. If observations are being made from the earth and the center of the earth is chosen as origin, $\ddot{\boldsymbol{\rho}}$ is the acceleration of the center of the earth and $\boldsymbol{\omega}$ the angular velocity of the earth. Since the angular velocity of the earth is effectively constant the term in $\dot{\boldsymbol{\omega}}$ falls out. Moreover the linear acceleration of the center of the earth is so small that the term in $\ddot{\boldsymbol{\rho}}$ is generally negligible. Indeed all the terms to the right of $\mathbf{F}$ are so small in the case of motion relative to the earth that we have not made any substantial error in omitting them from our earlier treatment of motion under the action of gravity.

Problem 32a. Two particles M and m exert forces on each other along the line joining them. Prove the result of article 30 for the motion of m relative to M by the method of article 32. (*Hint.*—Use a set of non-rotating axes with origin at M.)

Problem 32b. Two spheres of equal mass m, connected by a taut inextensible string of length l, have holes drilled through their centers so that they can slide along a straight bar. The bar rotates about a fixed axis at right angles to its length with constant angular velocity ω. Assuming the spheres to be initially at rest relative to the rotating bar at distances d and $d - l$ from the axis, find the speed with which they are sliding along the bar at time t, and determine their positions for no sliding, discussing the stability of the equilibrium configuration. Treat the spheres as particles.

$$Ans.\ v = \tfrac{1}{2}\omega(d - \tfrac{1}{2}l)(e^{\omega t} - e^{-\omega t}).$$

Problem 32c. If we denote by $\frac{d\mathbf{V}}{dt}$ the time derivative of the vector $\mathbf{V}$ relative to a set of axes $X_0Y_0Z_0$ fixed in an inertial system and by $\frac{d\mathbf{V}}{d\tau}$ the time derivative of the vector $\mathbf{V}$ relative to a rotating set of axes XYZ with the same origin, prove that

$$\frac{d\mathbf{V}}{dt} = \frac{d\mathbf{V}}{d\tau} + \boldsymbol{\omega} \times \mathbf{V}.$$

By two successive applications of the operator

$$\frac{d}{dt} = \frac{d}{d\tau} + \boldsymbol{\omega} \times$$

to the position vector $\mathbf{r}$ of a moving point, deduce the formula (32–6) for the case where $\ddot{\boldsymbol{\rho}} = 0$.

32.1. Composition of Angular Velocities and of Angular Accelerations. — Since angular velocities and angular accelerations are vectors, we can combine or resolve them just as we would any vector. Thus, if a rigid body has two angular velocities $\boldsymbol{\omega}_1$ and $\boldsymbol{\omega}_2$ simultaneously, its motion is the same as if it had the single angular velocity $\boldsymbol{\omega}_1 + \boldsymbol{\omega}_2$. This follows at once from the analysis of article 31, or from the fact that infinitesimal angular displacements combine vectorially, as was shown in article 18.3.

Here we shall be interested in a different, but very important, kind of composition. Consider a set of axes XYZ which have angular velocity ω and angular acceleration α relative to the fixed axes $X_0Y_0Z_0$, and a third set of axes $X'Y'Z'$ which have angular velocity ω' and angular acceleration α' relative to XYZ. Without loss of generality we may suppose that the origins of the three sets of axes remain coincident. We wish to find the angular velocity Ω and the angular acceleration A of $X'Y'Z'$ relative to $X_0Y_0Z_0$. The solution of this problem is important, for instance, when we consider the rotation of a rigid body relative to the earth, which is itself in rotation relative to fixed axes.

Let $\mathbf{v}_0$ and $\mathbf{f}_0$ be the linear velocity and the linear acceleration, respectively, of any particle relative to $X_0Y_0Z_0$, $\mathbf{v}$ and $\mathbf{f}$ the linear velocity and the linear acceleration of the same particle relative to XYZ, and $\mathbf{v}'$ and $\mathbf{f}'$ its linear velocity and its linear acceleration relative to $X'Y'Z'$. Then, since $\dot{\boldsymbol{\rho}} = 0$, (31–8) gives

$$\mathbf{v}_0 = \boldsymbol{\omega} \times \mathbf{r} + \mathbf{v}, \qquad \mathbf{v} = \boldsymbol{\omega}' \times \mathbf{r}' + \mathbf{v}', \tag{32.1–1}$$

where $\mathbf{r}' = \mathbf{r}$ evidently. Consequently

$$\mathbf{v}_0 = (\boldsymbol{\omega} + \boldsymbol{\omega}') \times \mathbf{r} + \mathbf{v}'. \tag{32.1–2}$$

But

$$\mathbf{v}_0 = \boldsymbol{\Omega} \times \mathbf{r} + \mathbf{v}'. \tag{32.1–3}$$

Since (32.1–2) and (32.1–3) are valid for *any* $\mathbf{r}$,

$$\boldsymbol{\Omega} = \boldsymbol{\omega} + \boldsymbol{\omega}', \tag{32.1–4}$$

proving that the angular velocity of $X'Y'Z'$ relative to $X_0Y_0Z_0$ is the vector sum of the angular velocity of XYZ relative to $X_0Y_0Z_0$ and that of $X'Y'Z'$ relative to XYZ.

The relation between the angular accelerations is not so simple. From (32–6), since $\ddot{\boldsymbol{\rho}} = 0$,

$$\left.\begin{aligned} \mathbf{f}_0 &= \boldsymbol{\omega} \times (\boldsymbol{\omega} \times \mathbf{r}) + \boldsymbol{\alpha} \times \mathbf{r} + 2\boldsymbol{\omega} \times \mathbf{v} + \mathbf{f}, \\ \mathbf{f} &= \boldsymbol{\omega}' \times (\boldsymbol{\omega}' \times \mathbf{r}') + \boldsymbol{\alpha}' \times \mathbf{r}' + 2\boldsymbol{\omega}' \times \mathbf{v}' + \mathbf{f}', \end{aligned}\right\} \tag{32.1–5}$$

where $\mathbf{r}' = \mathbf{r}$ as before. Eliminating $\mathbf{f}$ and expressing $\mathbf{v}$ in terms of $\mathbf{v}'$ by (32.1–1), we get, after a little reduction,

$$\begin{aligned} \mathbf{f}_0 = (\boldsymbol{\omega} + \boldsymbol{\omega}') \times \{(\boldsymbol{\omega} + \boldsymbol{\omega}') \times \mathbf{r}\} &+ (\boldsymbol{\alpha} + \boldsymbol{\alpha}' + \boldsymbol{\omega} \times \boldsymbol{\omega}') \times \mathbf{r} \\ &+ 2(\boldsymbol{\omega} + \boldsymbol{\omega}') \times \mathbf{v}' + \mathbf{f}'. \end{aligned} \tag{32.1–6}$$

But

$$\mathbf{f}_0 = \boldsymbol{\Omega} \times (\boldsymbol{\Omega} \times \mathbf{r}) + \mathbf{A} \times \mathbf{r} + 2\boldsymbol{\Omega} \times \mathbf{v}' + \mathbf{f}'. \tag{32.1–7}$$

Comparing (32.1–6) and (32.1–7) after using (32.1–4), we find that

$$\mathbf{A} = \boldsymbol{\alpha} + \boldsymbol{\alpha}' + \boldsymbol{\omega} \times \boldsymbol{\omega}'. \qquad (32.1\text{–}8)$$

Problem 32.1a. Supply the missing steps in obtaining (32.1–6) from (32.1–5).

33. Motion Relative to the Earth. — The earth rotates with a constant angular velocity

$$\omega = \frac{2\pi}{86{,}164.1 \text{ sec}} = 0.0000729211/\text{sec}.$$

As the acceleration of the center of the earth is negligible, the equation of motion (32–7) of a particle relative to the earth becomes

$$m\mathbf{f} = \mathbf{F} - m\boldsymbol{\omega} \times (\boldsymbol{\omega} \times \mathbf{r}) - 2m\boldsymbol{\omega} \times \mathbf{v} \qquad (33\text{–}1)$$

referred to an origin at the center of the earth. If the only impressed force acting on the particle is the force $\mathbf{F}_g$ due to the gravitational attraction of the earth, $\mathbf{F} = \mathbf{F}_g$ and

$$m\mathbf{f} = \mathbf{F}_g - m\boldsymbol{\omega} \times (\boldsymbol{\omega} \times \mathbf{r}) - 2m\boldsymbol{\omega} \times \mathbf{v}. \qquad (33\text{–}2)$$

The acceleration $\mathbf{g}$ of gravity as measured by a pendulum which has no appreciable velocity relative to the earth is not, however, the acceleration due to $\mathbf{F}_g$ alone, but rather the acceleration due to the resultant of $\mathbf{F}_g$ and the centrifugal reaction $-m\boldsymbol{\omega} \times (\boldsymbol{\omega} \times \mathbf{r})$. Hence

$$m\mathbf{g} = \mathbf{F}_g - m\boldsymbol{\omega} \times (\boldsymbol{\omega} \times \mathbf{r}),$$

and substituting in (33–2) we find for the apparent acceleration relative to the earth of a freely falling body

$$\mathbf{f} = \mathbf{g} - 2\boldsymbol{\omega} \times \mathbf{v}. \qquad (33\text{–}3)$$

As this equation does not involve the position vector $\mathbf{r}$ of the particle, we can take the origin of coordinates at any convenient point instead of at the center of the earth.

Consider a body falling from rest. The velocity $\mathbf{v}$ is at all times nearly downward, and, as $\boldsymbol{\omega}$ is directed from South to North, the vector $-2\boldsymbol{\omega} \times \mathbf{v}$ is directed Eastward. Take origin at the point from which the body is dropped with the X axis pointing Eastward. Then in addition to the vertically downward acceleration $\mathbf{g}$ the body is subject to an Eastward acceleration

$$\frac{d^2x}{dt^2} = 2\omega v \cos \gamma,$$

where γ is the latitude. To a sufficient degree of approximation v is equal to the product of g by the time t during which the body has been falling, so

$$\frac{d^2x}{dt^2} = 2\omega gt \cos \gamma.$$

Integrating

$$x = \tfrac{1}{3}\omega gt^3 \cos \gamma.$$

But the height h through which the body has fallen is very closely

$$h = \tfrac{1}{2}gt^2.$$

Therefore the Eastward deflection from the vertical as determined by a plumb bob is

$$x = \tfrac{1}{3}\omega \cos \gamma \sqrt{\frac{8h^3}{g}}, \tag{33-4}$$

which is proportional to the cosine of the latitude and the three-halves power of the height.

Wind	Velocity	Horizontal Component of Deflecting Acceleration $-2\boldsymbol{\omega} \times \mathbf{v}$	Direction of Deflection in Northern Hemisphere
West	$\frac{dx}{dt} = v$	$\frac{d^2y}{dt^2} = -2\omega v \sin \gamma$	South
South	$\frac{dy}{dt} = v$	$\frac{d^2x}{dt^2} = 2\omega v \sin \gamma$	East
East	$\frac{dx}{dt} = -v$	$\frac{d^2y}{dt^2} = 2\omega v \sin \gamma$	North
North	$\frac{dy}{dt} = -v$	$\frac{d^2x}{dt^2} = -2\omega v \sin \gamma$	West

The acceleration of Coriolis $2\boldsymbol{\omega} \times \mathbf{v}$ gives rise to cyclones. Consider winds blowing from the West, South, East and North with speed v. If the X axis points East and the Y axis North, and γ denotes the latitude, the deflections due to the second term on the right of (33–3) are given in the table on the opposite page.

The deflection is always to the right in the Northern Hemisphere. Therefore the winds blowing in toward a low-pressure area give rise to a cyclonic motion in the counterclockwise sense as viewed from above the surface of the earth, as is indicated in Fig. 43. As the deflection depends upon the sine of the latitude, it has the opposite sense in the Southern Hemisphere.

As a final example of motion relative to the earth consider the simple pendulum of article 29. As the measured force of gravity includes the centrifugal reaction $-m\boldsymbol{\omega} \times (\boldsymbol{\omega} \times \mathbf{r})$ we may write (33–1) in the form

$$m\mathbf{f} = m\mathbf{g} + \mathbf{T} - 2m\boldsymbol{\omega} \times \mathbf{v}, \tag{33–5}$$

where $\mathbf{T}$ represents the tension force exerted by the cord supporting the pendulum bob. As this equation does not contain the position vector $\mathbf{r}$ we may take the origin of the coordinates XYZ attached to the earth at the point of suspension of the pendulum with the Z axis vertically up. Now take another set of axes $X'Y'Z'$ with the same origin as XYZ and with the Z' axis parallel to the Z axis, but with the $X'Y'$ axes in rotation relative to the XY axes with constant angular velocity ω'. Then the relation between the acceleration $\mathbf{f}'$ relative to the axes $X'Y'Z'$ and the acceleration $\mathbf{f}$ relative to XYZ is given by an equation of the same form as the equation (32–6) between the acceleration $\mathbf{f}$ and the acceleration $\mathbf{f}_0$ relative to the axes $X_0Y_0Z_0$, except that the term in $\ddot{\mathbf{p}}$ falls out because the origins of the two sets of axes are coincident and the term in $\dot{\boldsymbol{\omega}}'$ disappears since $\boldsymbol{\omega}'$ is constant. Hence

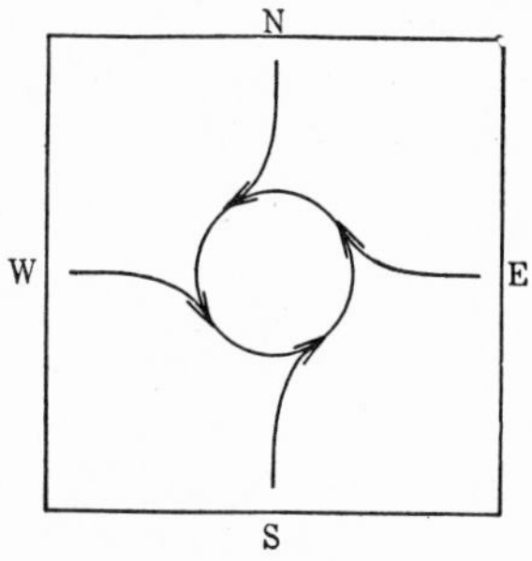

FIG. 43.

$$\mathbf{f} = \boldsymbol{\omega}' \times (\boldsymbol{\omega}' \times \mathbf{r}') + 2\boldsymbol{\omega}' \times \mathbf{v}' + \mathbf{f}', \tag{33–6}$$

and as $\mathbf{v}$ now takes the place of $\mathbf{v}_0$ equation (31–8) gives

$$\boldsymbol{\omega}' \times \mathbf{v} = \boldsymbol{\omega}' \times \mathbf{v}' + \boldsymbol{\omega}' \times (\boldsymbol{\omega}' \times \mathbf{r}'), \tag{33–7}$$

whence (33–6) may be written

$$\mathbf{f} = 2\boldsymbol{\omega}' \times \mathbf{v} - \boldsymbol{\omega}' \times (\boldsymbol{\omega}' \times \mathbf{r}') + \mathbf{f}'.$$

Substituting this for **f** in (33–5)

$$m\mathbf{f}' = m\mathbf{g} + \mathbf{T} - 2m(\boldsymbol{\omega} + \boldsymbol{\omega}') \times \mathbf{v} + m\boldsymbol{\omega}' \times (\boldsymbol{\omega}' \times \mathbf{r}'). \quad (33\text{–}8)$$

For small oscillations the motion is constrained to a horizontal plane. So if $\boldsymbol{\omega}'$ is made equal to $-\mathbf{k}\omega_z$ the horizontal components of the third term on the right vanish. Furthermore the last term is negligible because the small quantity ω' appears in it twice as a factor and r' is small. Therefore the motion in the horizontal plane is given very closely by the equation

$$m\mathbf{f}' = m\mathbf{g} + \mathbf{T} \quad (33\text{–}9)$$

But this equation is of the same form as the equation of motion relative to fixed axes. Therefore the motion relative to the axes $X'Y'Z'$, rotating with respect to the earth with angular velocity $\omega' = -\,\omega_z$ about the vertical, is the same as if these axes were fixed in an inertial system. As ω_z is equal to $\omega \sin \gamma$, where ω represents the angular velocity of the earth and γ the latitude, the plane of oscillation of a pendulum located in the Northern Hemisphere rotates about the vertical in the clockwise sense as viewed from above the point of suspension with angular velocity $\omega \sin \gamma$. This change in orientation relative to the earth of the plane of oscillation of a pendulum, first observed by Foucault in 1851, provides a striking demonstration of the rotation of the earth.

Problem 33a. A body is dropped from an elevation of 200 feet at latitude 41° N. How far East of the point directly beneath it will it strike the ground?

Ans. 0.31 inch.

Problem 33b. A body is thrown vertically upward. Where will it strike the ground?

Ans. $\frac{4}{3}\,\omega \cos \gamma \sqrt{\frac{8h^3}{g}}$ to the West.

REFERENCES

Mach, Ernst: *The Science of Mechanics*, Open Court Pub. Co., Chicago.
Lindsay, R. B.: *Physical Mechanics*, D. Van Nostrand Co., New York.
Webster, A. G.: *The Dynamics of Particles and of Rigid, Elastic and Fluid Bodies*, B. G. Teubner, Leipzig.

CHAPTER II

DYNAMICS OF RIGID BODIES

34. Motion of Center of Mass of a Group of Particles. — Consider a group of particles of masses m_1, m_2, m_3, etc., and position vectors $\mathbf{r}_1$, $\mathbf{r}_2$, $\mathbf{r}_3$, etc., relative to an origin O fixed in an inertial system. We shall separate the force acting on each particle into two parts: the force $\mathbf{F}$ due to external causes and the force $\mathbf{F}'$ due to the attractions and repulsions of other particles in the group. Therefore the equation of motion for the ith particle is

$$m_i \frac{d^2\mathbf{r}_i}{dt^2} = \mathbf{F}_i + \mathbf{F}_i'.$$

Summing up over all the particles in the group

$$\sum_i m_i \frac{d^2\mathbf{r}_i}{dt^2} = \sum_i \mathbf{F}_i + \sum_i \mathbf{F}_i'. \tag{34-1}$$

According to the third law of motion the internal forces consist of equal and opposite actions and reactions between pairs of particles. Therefore

$$\sum_i \mathbf{F}_i' = 0.$$

If m denotes the sum $\sum_i m_i$ of the masses of all the particles, the *center of mass* is defined as the point whose position vector $\bar{\mathbf{r}}$ is given by

$$\bar{\mathbf{r}} = \frac{1}{m} \sum_i m_i \mathbf{r}_i.$$

Therefore its coordinates are

$$\bar{x} = \frac{1}{m} \sum_i m_i x_i, \quad \bar{y} = \frac{1}{m} \sum_i m_i y_i, \quad \bar{z} = \frac{1}{m} \sum_i m_i z_i.$$

So

$$\sum_i m_i \frac{d^2\mathbf{r}_i}{dt^2} = \frac{d^2}{dt^2} \left(\sum_i m_i \mathbf{r}_i\right) = \frac{d^2}{dt^2} (m\bar{\mathbf{r}}) = m \frac{d^2\bar{\mathbf{r}}}{dt^2},$$

and (34–1) becomes

$$m \frac{d^2\bar{\mathbf{r}}}{dt^2} = \sum_i \mathbf{F}_i. \tag{34–2}$$

This equation states that the motion of the center of mass is the same as would be the case if all the mass were concentrated at that point and all the external forces applied there. This statement is true no matter whether the particles are rigidly connected as in a rigid body, or are moving relative to one another as is the case with the molecules of a mass of gas. However, it is important to note that the external forces applied at the center of mass are those actually operating on the various particles of the group and not necessarily those that would exist if these particles were transferred to the center of mass.

Problem 34a. Find the center of mass of a uniform lamina in the shape of a crescent bounded by arcs of two circles of radius a whose centers lie a distance d apart.

Ans. $\bar{x} = \dfrac{\pi d}{2\pi - 4\alpha + 2\dfrac{d}{a}\sin\alpha}$ measured from a point midway between the two centers, where $\cos\alpha = d/2a$.

35. Linear Momentum and Impulse. — The equation of motion of the ith particle of a group may be written

$$m_i \frac{d^2\mathbf{r}_i}{dt^2} = \mathbf{F}_i + \mathbf{F}_i', \tag{35–1}$$

where $\mathbf{F}_i$ is the resultant of the external forces and $\mathbf{F}_i'$ that of the internal forces. Multiplying both sides of this equation by dt and summing up over all the particles

$$\sum_i m_i \frac{d^2\mathbf{r}_i}{dt^2}\, dt = \sum_i \mathbf{F}_i dt,$$

since the sum of the internal forces vanishes. Integrating

$$\sum_i m_i\mathbf{v}_i - \sum_i m_i\mathbf{v}_{i0} = \sum_i \int_{t_0}^{t} \mathbf{F}_i dt, \tag{35–2}$$

where $\mathbf{v}_{i0}$ is the velocity of the ith particle at the time t_0 and $\mathbf{v}_i$ its velocity at the time t. The vector

$$\mathbf{G} \equiv \sum_i m_i \mathbf{v}_i$$

is known as the *linear momentum* of the group of particles, and the vector

$$\mathbf{I} \equiv \sum_i \int_{t_0}^{t} \mathbf{F}_i dt$$

as the *linear impulse*. Equation (35–2) states that the increase in momentum which occurs in the time $t-t_0$ is equal to the impulse due to the external forces. This statement holds no matter whether the particles are rigidly connected or in motion relative to one another.

If we denote by $\mathbf{F}$ the resultant $\sum_i \mathbf{F}_i$ of the external forces and make the time $t-t_0$ very small, (35–2) becomes

$$(\mathbf{G} + d\mathbf{G}) - \mathbf{G} = \mathbf{F}dt,$$

or

$$\mathbf{F} = \frac{d\mathbf{G}}{dt}. \tag{35–3}$$

Therefore the resultant external force acting on the group of particles is equal to the time rate of increase of linear momentum.

If no external forces are acting on the group of particles, either (35–2) or (35–3) requires that the total linear momentum of the group shall remain constant. This is the *law of conservation of linear momentum*. If one particle gains momentum, others in the group lose an equal amount.

An interesting application of the relation (35–2) between increase in linear momentum and linear impulse is the case of a particle, such as a raindrop, which is gaining mass by condensation or losing mass by evaporation. Let m be the mass of the particle and $\mathbf{v}$ its velocity at the time t, and let Δm be the mass added to m during the time Δt. We shall suppose that the added mass Δm had the velocity $\mathbf{v}_0$ before attachment to m; after attachment its velocity is of course the same as the velocity $\mathbf{v} + \Delta\mathbf{v}$ of m. By $\mathbf{F}$ we shall understand the force on m and by $\Delta\mathbf{F}$ the force on Δm at the time t. Then (35–2) gives

$$m\Delta\mathbf{v} + \Delta m(\mathbf{v} + \Delta\mathbf{v} - \mathbf{v}_0) = (\mathbf{F} + \Delta\mathbf{F})\Delta t.$$

Dividing by Δt and passing to the limit,

$$\mathbf{F} = m\frac{d\mathbf{v}}{dt} + \frac{dm}{dt}(\mathbf{v} - \mathbf{v}_0). \tag{35-4}$$

Two special cases are of interest. First let us suppose that Δm is at rest relative to the observer's inertial system before attachment to m. Then $\mathbf{v}_0 = 0$ and

$$\mathbf{F} = \frac{d}{dt}(m\mathbf{v}). \tag{35-5}$$

As this is a case of inelastic impact, dynamical energy is not conserved. In fact the time rate of increase of kinetic energy is

$$\frac{d}{dt}(\tfrac{1}{2}mv^2) = m\mathbf{v}\cdot\frac{d\mathbf{v}}{dt} + \frac{1}{2}\frac{dm}{dt}v^2,$$

whereas the rate at which work is done by the impressed force is

$$\mathbf{F}\cdot\mathbf{v} = m\mathbf{v}\cdot\frac{d\mathbf{v}}{dt} + \frac{dm}{dt}v^2.$$

Comparing we see that the energy dissipated per unit time is

$$\frac{1}{2}\frac{dm}{dt}v^2,$$

If, on the other hand, the added mass Δm has the same velocity as m before attachment, $\mathbf{v}_0 = \mathbf{v}$ in (35–4) and

$$\mathbf{F} = m\frac{d\mathbf{v}}{dt}. \tag{35-6}$$

In this case the attachment of the added mass does not alter the equation of motion of m, and dynamical energy is conserved.

Problem 35a. Two particles M and m collide elastically, that is, without dissipation of dynamical energy. Show that the magnitude of the relative velocity is the same after collision as before.

Problem 35b. A mass M to which a chain of mass λ per unit length is attached is projected upward from the surface of the earth with velocity u. Find (*a*) the greatest height h attained, (*b*) the velocity v with which M strikes the earth on its return.

$$\textit{Ans.}\ h = \frac{M}{\lambda}\left\{\sqrt[3]{1 + \frac{3}{2}\frac{\lambda u^2}{Mg}} - 1\right\},\quad v = \sqrt{2gh}.$$

Problem 35c. Moisture condenses at the rate λ units of mass per unit time on a falling raindrop. If the raindrop falls from rest and has an initial mass M, find the distance fallen in time t. Neglect air resistance.

$$Ans.\ \frac{1}{2}g\left\{\frac{1}{2}t^2 + \frac{M}{\lambda}t - \frac{M^2}{\lambda^2}\log\left(1 + \frac{\lambda}{M}t\right)\right\}.$$

Problem 35d. A large mass M (the earth) and a small mass m in contact with it are moving as a unit with velocity $\mathbf{V}$ relative to an inertial system S. The two masses together, then, are at rest in an inertial system S' which has a velocity $\mathbf{V}$ relative to S. Suddenly the smaller mass is projected away from the larger with a velocity $\mathbf{v}$ relative to S'. Compute the change in kinetic energy, first relative to S and then to S', and show that both calculations lead to the same result.

$$Ans.\ \Delta T = \frac{1}{2}mv^2\left(1 + \frac{m}{M}\right).$$

36. Angular Momentum and Impulse. — If we take the vector product of the position vector $\mathbf{r}_i$ of the ith particle by both sides of (35–1) we get

$$m_i\mathbf{r}_i \times \frac{d^2\mathbf{r}_i}{dt^2} = \mathbf{r}_i \times \mathbf{F}_i + \mathbf{r}_i \times \mathbf{F}'_i,$$

where $\mathbf{r}_i \times \mathbf{F}_i$ is known as the *torque* about the origin exerted by the force $\mathbf{F}_i$. Now

$$\frac{d}{dt}\left(\mathbf{r}_i \times \frac{d\mathbf{r}_i}{dt}\right) = \mathbf{r}_i \times \frac{d^2\mathbf{r}_i}{dt^2} + \frac{d\mathbf{r}_i}{dt} \times \frac{d\mathbf{r}_i}{dt}$$

$$= \mathbf{r}_i \times \frac{d^2\mathbf{r}_i}{dt^2},$$

since the vector product of a vector by itself vanishes. Therefore

$$m_i\frac{d}{dt}\left(\mathbf{r}_i \times \frac{d\mathbf{r}_i}{dt}\right) = \mathbf{r}_i \times \mathbf{F}_i + \mathbf{r}_i \times \mathbf{F}'_i. \qquad (36\text{–}1)$$

In order to eliminate the internal forces when we multiply this equation by dt and sum up over all the particles, we need another law in addition to Newton's three laws of motion. This fourth law states that *the forces between two particles are along the line joining them.* Although we shall see later that it is not always valid for the instantaneous forces between moving charged particles, yet it holds for the time average forces between neutral particles, such as we are generally concerned with in dynamics.

Consider now the forces between two particles m_1 and m_2 whose position vectors are $\mathbf{r}_1$ and $\mathbf{r}_2$, respectively. Assuming that these forces are directed along the line joining the two particles, the force on m_1 due to m_2 may be written $\mathbf{F}'_1 = a(\mathbf{r}_1 - \mathbf{r}_2)$, where a is a function of the coordinates of m_1 and m_2. Then the law of action and reaction requires that the force on m_2 due to m_1 should be $\mathbf{F}'_2 = a(\mathbf{r}_2 - \mathbf{r}_1)$. Consequently

$$\mathbf{r}_1 \times \mathbf{F}'_1 + \mathbf{r}_2 \times \mathbf{F}'_2 = a\mathbf{r}_1 \times (\mathbf{r}_1 - \mathbf{r}_2) + a\mathbf{r}_2 \times (\mathbf{r}_2 - \mathbf{r}_1)$$

$$= -a\mathbf{r}_1 \times \mathbf{r}_2 - a\mathbf{r}_2 \times \mathbf{r}_1 = 0.$$

So if we multiply (36–1) by dt and sum up over all the particles in the group the torques due to the internal forces disappear. Hence, if $\mathbf{L}_i$ is put for the torque $\mathbf{r}_i \times \mathbf{F}_i$ about the origin of the external force $\mathbf{F}_i$,

$$\sum_i m_i \frac{d}{dt}\left(\mathbf{r}_i \times \frac{d\mathbf{r}_i}{dt}\right) dt = \sum_i \mathbf{L}_i dt.$$

Integrating from the time t_0 to t

$$\sum_i m_i(\mathbf{r}_i \times \mathbf{v}_i) - \sum_i m_i(\mathbf{r}_i \times \mathbf{v}_i)_0 = \sum_i \int_{t_0}^{t} \mathbf{L}_i dt, \qquad (36\text{–}2)$$

where the subscript $_0$ refers to the time t_0. The vector

$$\mathbf{H} \equiv \sum_i m_i(\mathbf{r}_i \times \mathbf{v}_i)$$

is known as the *angular momentum* of the group of particles about the origin O, and the vector

$$\mathbf{J} \equiv \sum_i \int_{t_0}^{t} \mathbf{L}_i \, dt$$

as the *angular impulse* about the origin. Equation (36–2) states that the increase in angular momentum which occurs in the time t–t_0 is equal to the angular impulse due to the external torques. This equation is valid no matter whether the particles are rigidly connected or in motion relative to one another.

Denoting by $\mathbf{L}$ the resultant $\sum_i \mathbf{L}_i$ of the external torques and making the time t–t_0 very small, (36–2) becomes

$$(\mathbf{H} + d\mathbf{H}) - \mathbf{H} = \mathbf{L}dt,$$

or

$$\mathbf{L} = \frac{d\mathbf{H}}{dt}. \quad (36\text{–}3)$$

So the resultant external torque about any fixed point as origin is equal to the time rate of increase of angular momentum about that point.

If no external torques are acting on the group of particles, either (36–2) or (36–3) requires that the total angular momentum of the group, taken about any fixed point as origin, shall remain constant. This is the *law of conservation of angular momentum.* Conversely, if a rigid body is at rest in an inertial system, the sum of the torques acting on it, taken about any point, must vanish. If a group of particles is free from external forces the center of mass of the group remains fixed in an inertial system and the angular momentum of the group is constant in magnitude and direction. The plane through the center of mass perpendicular to the angular momentum is known as the *invariable plane* of such an isolated system.

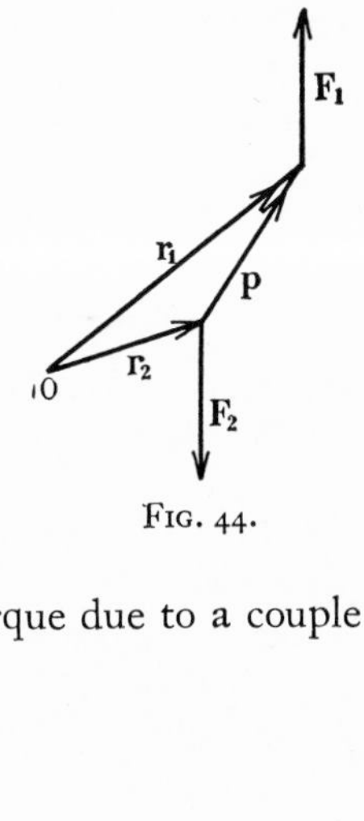

FIG. 44.

A particular type of torque of considerable importance is that due to two equal and opposite forces not in the same line. Such a combination of forces is known as a *couple.* The torque due to a couple (Fig. 44) is

$$\mathbf{L} = \mathbf{r}_1 \times \mathbf{F}_1 + \mathbf{r}_2 \times \mathbf{F}_2$$

$$= (\mathbf{r}_1 - \mathbf{r}_2) \times \mathbf{F}_1,$$

as $\mathbf{F}_2 = -\mathbf{F}_1$. If $\mathbf{p}$ is the vector drawn from the point of application of $\mathbf{F}_2$ to that of $\mathbf{F}_1$,

$$\mathbf{r}_1 - \mathbf{r}_2 = \mathbf{p},$$

and

$$\mathbf{L} = \mathbf{p} \times \mathbf{F}_1.$$

So the torque due to a couple is the vector product of the vector drawn from the point of application of the one force to that of the other force by the latter force. The magnitude of the torque is equal to the product of either force by the perpendicular distance between the two forces. Note that the torque due to a couple is independent of the position of the origin O.

The fundamental relation (36–3) connecting the resultant external torque with the time rate of increase of angular momentum of a group of particles holds when the torques and the angular momenta of the individual particles are taken about any point fixed in an inertial system. We shall now prove that the same equation holds when the torques and angular momenta are taken about the center of mass, even though this point does not remain at rest in an inertial system. To do this we shall employ a moving origin O coincident with the center of mass of the group of particles, as well as the origin O_0 of a set of axes $X_0Y_0Z_0$ fixed in an inertial system. Then from (31–2) the velocity $\mathbf{v}_{0i}$ of the ith particle in the group relative to the fixed axes is

$$\mathbf{v}_{0i} = \dot{\boldsymbol{\rho}} + \dot{\mathbf{r}}_i,$$

where $\boldsymbol{\rho}$ is the position vector and $\dot{\boldsymbol{\rho}}$ the velocity of the center of mass and $\mathbf{r}_i$ is the position vector of ith particle relative to the center of mass O. So the angular momentum $\mathbf{H}_0$ of the group of particles about the fixed origin O_0 of the axes $X_0Y_0Z_0$ is

$$\begin{aligned}\mathbf{H}_0 &= \sum_i m_i(\boldsymbol{\rho} + \mathbf{r}_i) \times (\dot{\boldsymbol{\rho}} + \dot{\mathbf{r}}_i)\\ &= m\boldsymbol{\rho} \times \dot{\boldsymbol{\rho}} + \boldsymbol{\rho} \times (\sum_i m_i\dot{\mathbf{r}}_i) + (\sum_i m_i\mathbf{r}_i) \times \dot{\boldsymbol{\rho}} + \sum_i m_i\mathbf{r}_i \times \dot{\mathbf{r}}_i,\end{aligned}$$

where $m = \sum_i m_i$ is the total mass of the particles. Now as $\mathbf{r}_i$ is measured from the center of mass,

$$\sum_i m_i\mathbf{r}_i = 0, \quad \sum_i m_i\dot{\mathbf{r}}_i = \frac{d}{dt}(\sum_i m_i\mathbf{r}_i) = 0.$$

Moreover if the angular momentum of the particles about the moving origin O is denoted by $\mathbf{H}$,

$$\mathbf{H} = \sum_i m_i\mathbf{r}_i \times \dot{\mathbf{r}}_i.$$

Therefore

$$\mathbf{H}_0 = m\boldsymbol{\rho} \times \dot{\boldsymbol{\rho}} + \mathbf{H}. \tag{36–4}$$

The torque $\mathbf{L}_0$ about the fixed origin O_0 is

$$\mathbf{L}_0 = \sum_i \mathbf{L}_{0i} = \sum_i (\boldsymbol{\rho} + \mathbf{r}_i) \times \mathbf{F}_i = \boldsymbol{\rho} \times \sum_i \mathbf{F}_i + \sum_i \mathbf{r}_i \times \mathbf{F}_i.$$

But $\sum_i \mathbf{r}_i \times \mathbf{F}_i$ is the torque $\mathbf{L}$ of the external forces about the center of mass O of the particles. Therefore

$$\mathbf{L}_0 = \boldsymbol{\rho} \times \sum_i \mathbf{F}_i + \mathbf{L}. \tag{36–5}$$

Now, as

$$\mathbf{L}_0 = \frac{d\mathbf{H}_0}{dt}$$

in accord with (36–3), it follows from (36–4) and (36–5) that

$$\boldsymbol{\rho} \times \sum_i \mathbf{F}_i + \mathbf{L} = \frac{d}{dt}(m\boldsymbol{\rho} \times \dot{\boldsymbol{\rho}}) + \frac{d\mathbf{H}}{dt}. \tag{36–6}$$

But

$$\sum_i \mathbf{F}_i = m\ddot{\boldsymbol{\rho}}$$

since the acceleration $\ddot{\boldsymbol{\rho}}$ of the center of mass is that of a particle of mass m subject to the same external forces as are applied to the group. Therefore

$$\boldsymbol{\rho} \times \sum_i \mathbf{F}_i = m\boldsymbol{\rho} \times \ddot{\boldsymbol{\rho}} = m\boldsymbol{\rho} \times \ddot{\boldsymbol{\rho}} + m\dot{\boldsymbol{\rho}} \times \dot{\boldsymbol{\rho}} = \frac{d}{dt}(m\,\boldsymbol{\rho} \times \dot{\boldsymbol{\rho}})$$

as $\dot{\boldsymbol{\rho}} \times \dot{\boldsymbol{\rho}}$ is zero. Subtracting this equation from (36–6) we obtain again the relation

$$\mathbf{L} = \frac{d\mathbf{H}}{dt}. \tag{36–7}$$

Consequently the impressed torque equals the time rate of increase of angular momentum, no matter whether these quantities are computed about a fixed point or about a moving center of mass.

37. Motion of a Rigid Body. — A *rigid body* is an assemblage of particles so constituted that the distance between any two particles does not change with the time. As shown in article 34 the motion of the center of mass of a rigid body is identical with that of a particle whose mass is equal to that of the body and which is subject to the same external forces as are applied to the body. Therefore the motion of translation of the center of mass is determined by the same methods as were employed in discussing the motion of a particle.

To investigate the rotation of a rigid body we use equation (36–7), computing the resultant torque and the angular momentum either about a point fixed in an inertial system or about the center of mass of the body. In order that the equations obtained shall be manageable, however, it is usually essential that the point about which the torque and the angular momentum are calculated should be fixed in the body itself. Hence we have two general cases to consider: (*a*) one point of the rigid body is fixed in an inertial system, (*b*) no point is fixed. Although the same equation (36–7) holds in case (*a*) if we take either the fixed point or the center of mass as the origin about which to calculate the torque and the angular momentum, it is usually more convenient to take the fixed point as origin since then the forces applied at this point exert no torques. In case (*b*) we must take the center of mass as origin in order that equation (36–7) may hold. Then we can determine the rotation of the rigid body about its center of mass, the translation of this point being obtained by the methods of particle dynamics.

Since the same equation (36–7) describes the rotation of the body in either of the two cases under discussion, we may treat the two together, taking a set of axes XYZ attached to the rigid body with either a fixed point or the center of mass as origin. As the particles of the rigid body are at rest with respect to these moving axes, equation (31–7) for the true velocity relative to their origin O becomes

$$\dot{\mathbf{r}}_i = \boldsymbol{\omega} \times \mathbf{r}_i,$$

where the angular velocity $\boldsymbol{\omega}$ of the axes attached to the rigid body is, of course, identical with that of the body itself. Therefore

$$\left.\begin{aligned} \mathbf{H} &= \sum_i m_i \mathbf{r}_i \times (\boldsymbol{\omega} \times \mathbf{r}_i) \\ &= \sum_i m_i (\mathbf{r}_i \cdot \mathbf{r}_i \boldsymbol{\omega} - \mathbf{r}_i \cdot \boldsymbol{\omega} \mathbf{r}_i) \\ &= \Big\{ \sum_i m_i (r_i^2 \mathbf{I} - \mathbf{r}_i \mathbf{r}_i) \Big\} \cdot \boldsymbol{\omega} \\ &= \Phi \cdot \boldsymbol{\omega}, \end{aligned}\right\} \qquad (37\text{–}1)$$

indicating that $\mathbf{H}$ and $\boldsymbol{\omega}$ do not in general have the same direction.

Here Φ is the symmetric dyadic

$$\Phi = \sum m_i \{ r_i^2 \mathbf{I} - \mathbf{r}_i \mathbf{r}_i \},$$

where **I** represents the idemfactor. Changing from a sum to the corresponding integral for a continuous body of density ρ and volume τ,

$$\Phi = \int_\tau \{r^2\mathbf{I} - \mathbf{rr}\}\rho d\tau,$$

since $\rho d\tau$ is the mass contained in the volume element $d\tau$. This dyadic is known as the *momental dyadic*. Written out in terms of its nine elements referred to the axes XYZ,

$$\begin{aligned}\Phi = \mathbf{ii}\int_\tau (y^2 + z^2)\rho d\tau - \mathbf{ij}\int_\tau xy\rho d\tau - \mathbf{ik}\int_\tau xz\rho d\tau \\ - \mathbf{ji}\int_\tau yx\rho d\tau + \mathbf{jj}\int_\tau (z^2 + x^2)\rho d\tau - \mathbf{jk}\int_\tau yz\rho d\tau \\ - \mathbf{ki}\int_\tau zx\rho d\tau - \mathbf{kj}\int_\tau zy\rho d\tau + \mathbf{kk}\int_\tau (x^2 + y^2)\rho d\tau.\end{aligned}$$

The elements

$$A \equiv \int_\tau (y^2 + z^2)\rho d\tau, \quad B \equiv \int_\tau (z^2 + x^2)\rho d\tau, \quad C \equiv \int_\tau (x^2 + y^2)\rho d\tau,$$

are known as the *moments of inertia* of the body about the axes X, Y, Z, respectively, and the elements

$$D \equiv \int_\tau yz\rho d\tau, \qquad E \equiv \int_\tau zx\rho d\tau, \qquad F \equiv \int_\tau xy\rho d\tau,$$

as the *products of inertia*. In terms of these symbols

$$\left.\begin{aligned}\Phi = \mathbf{ii}A - \mathbf{ij}F - \mathbf{ik}E \\ - \mathbf{ji}F + \mathbf{jj}B - \mathbf{jk}D \\ - \mathbf{ki}E - \mathbf{kj}D + \mathbf{kk}C.\end{aligned}\right\} \qquad (37\text{–}2)$$

As the dyadic is symmetric it is always possible to orient the axes XYZ attached to the rigid body so that the products of inertia vanish and the momental dyadic reduces to

$$\Phi = \mathbf{ii}A + \mathbf{jj}B + \mathbf{kk}C, \qquad (37\text{–}3)$$

where A, B, C are the *principal moments of inertia*. If, for instance, the body is symmetrical this simplification is attained by taking

X, Y, Z parallel to the axes of symmetry. Since the axes XYZ are attached to the rigid body the elements of the momental dyadic do not change with the time. Therefore they may be treated as constants when we differentiate (37–1) in order to get the time rate of change of angular momentum appearing in the equation of motion. It is for this reason that moving axes attached to the rigid body are employed.

Written out in terms of its components along the axes XYZ the expression (37–1) for the angular momentum about the origin O becomes

$$\left.\begin{aligned}\mathbf{H} = \mathbf{i}(A\omega_x - F\omega_y - E\omega_z) + \mathbf{j}(-F\omega_x + B\omega_y - D\omega_z)\\ +\mathbf{k}(-E\omega_x - D\omega_y + C\omega_z).\end{aligned}\right\} \quad (37\text{–}4)$$

Now writing

$$\mathbf{H} = \mathbf{i}H_x + \mathbf{j}H_y + \mathbf{k}H_z,$$

we have

$$\frac{d\mathbf{H}}{dt} = \mathbf{i}\dot{H}_x + \mathbf{j}\dot{H}_y + \mathbf{k}\dot{H}_z + \dot{\mathbf{i}}H_x + \dot{\mathbf{j}}H_y + \dot{\mathbf{k}}H_z,$$

as $\mathbf{i}$, $\mathbf{j}$, $\mathbf{k}$ are parallel to the axes X, Y, Z which rotate with the body. Referring to (31–4) and remembering that the a, b, c used there are our present ω_x, ω_y, ω_z, we have

$$\dot{\mathbf{i}}H_x + \dot{\mathbf{j}}H_y + \dot{\mathbf{k}}H_z = \mathbf{i}(\omega_y H_z - \omega_z H_y) + \mathbf{j}(\omega_z H_x - \omega_x H_z)$$
$$+ \mathbf{k}(\omega_x H_y - \omega_y H_x).$$

Therefore (36–7) becomes

$$\left.\begin{aligned}\mathbf{L} = \mathbf{i}\{\dot{H}_x + \omega_y H_z - \omega_z H_y\} + \mathbf{j}\{\dot{H}_y + \omega_z H_x - \omega_x H_z\}\\ + \mathbf{k}\{\dot{H}_z + \omega_x H_y - \omega_y H_x\}.\end{aligned}\right\} \quad (37\text{–}5)$$

Since this equation depends only on (36–7) it holds either for the rotation of a rigid body about a fixed point not necessarily its center of mass, or for the rotation about the center of mass of a rigid body none of whose points are fixed in an inertial system. It suffices to determine the rotation about the fixed point in the first case or about the center of mass in the second.

We shall now consider the application of (37–5) to three important special cases.

Case I. — Rotation about a fixed axis. In this case it is convenient to take the Z axis as axis of rotation, the X and Y axes rotating about it with the body. Then $\omega_x = \omega_y = 0$, $\omega_z = \omega$, and (37–4) gives

$$\mathbf{H} = -\,\mathbf{i}E\omega - \mathbf{j}D\omega + \mathbf{k}C\omega.$$

Therefore the equation of motion (37–5) becomes

$$\mathbf{L} = \mathbf{i}\left(-E\frac{d\omega}{dt} + D\omega^2\right) + \mathbf{j}\left(-D\frac{d\omega}{dt} - E\omega^2\right) + \mathbf{k}C\frac{d\omega}{dt}. \tag{37–6}$$

As an example consider two massive particles A and B (Fig. 45) rotating about the Z axis. They may be supposed to be attached to the ends of a light rod firmly fastened to a collar K which turns on a vertical axle. Take the rotating Y axis in the plane of Z and AB. Then the X axis will be out from the paper.

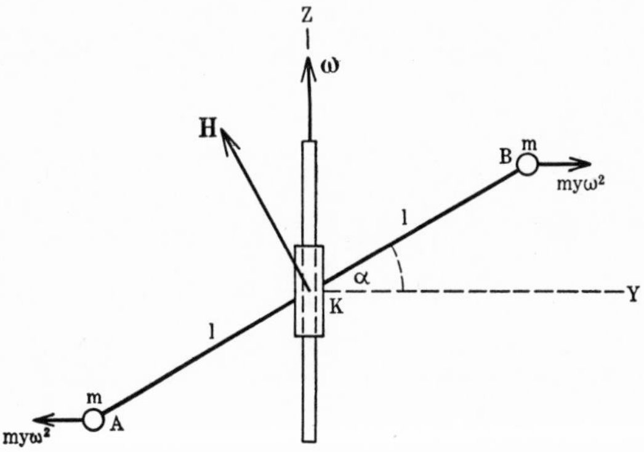

FIG. 45.

Now

$$C = 2ml^2\cos^2\alpha, \qquad D = 2ml^2\sin\alpha\cos\alpha, \qquad E = 0,$$

$$H_x = 0, \qquad H_y = -\,(2ml^2\sin\alpha\cos\alpha)\omega, \qquad H_z = (2ml^2\cos^2\alpha)\omega$$

showing that the vector $\mathbf{H}$ is perpendicular to AB and therefore not parallel to the angular velocity $\boldsymbol{\omega}$. The equation of motion (37–6) becomes

$$\mathbf{L} = \mathbf{i}(2ml^2\sin\alpha\cos\alpha)\omega^2 - \mathbf{j}(2ml^2\sin\alpha\cos\alpha)\frac{d\omega}{dt} + \mathbf{k}(2ml^2\cos^2\alpha)\frac{d\omega}{dt}.$$

The X component of the impressed torque is required to balance the centrifugal couple due to the components $my\omega^2$ of the kinetic reaction. If the angular velocity remains constant this is the only impressed couple necessary to maintain the motion. In the mechanism under consideration this couple is exerted by the axle on the collar. The remaining part of the torque, required to increase the angular velocity, has the direction of the angular momentum **H**.

(*a*) If the body is symmetrical with respect to a plane perpendicular to the axis of rotation, the description of the motion becomes very simple. Taking the Z axis as the axis of rotation with the origin in the plane of symmetry, D and E vanish on account of the factor z in the integrand of each and the equation of motion (37–6) reduces to

$$L_z = C\frac{d\omega}{dt}, \qquad (37\text{–}7)$$

and, as C involves only x and y, the body may be treated as a lamina. The moment of inertia C for this simple case is usually designated by the letter I. Occasionally it is convenient to introduce a quantity k known as the *radius of gyration*. This is defined as the square root of the quotient of the moment of inertia I of the body by its mass m. It is the distance from the axis of rotation at which the entire mass of the body would have to be concentrated to produce a moment of inertia equal to that actually existing. Therefore

$$I = mk^2. \qquad (37\text{–}8)$$

(*b*) If the body is symmetrical about the axis of rotation, the description of the motion is equally simple. Taking the Z axis along the axis of rotation as before, D and E vanish on account of the factors y and x in the integrands and the equation of motion becomes the same as in (*a*).

Case II. — Only one point fixed. Generally it is convenient to take axes XYZ attached to the body with origin at the fixed point, orienting the axes so as to make the products of inertia vanish. Then from (37–4)

$$\mathbf{H} = \mathbf{i}A\omega_x + \mathbf{j}B\omega_y + \mathbf{k}C\omega_z,$$

and the equation of motion (37–5) becomes

$$\left.\begin{aligned} \mathbf{L} = \mathbf{i}\{A\dot{\omega}_x + (C - B)\omega_y\omega_z\} + \mathbf{j}\{B\dot{\omega}_y + (A - C)\omega_z\omega_x\} \\ + \mathbf{k}\{C\dot{\omega}_z + (B - A)\omega_x\omega_y\}. \end{aligned}\right\} \qquad (37\text{–}9)$$

This is known as *Euler's equation*. Application to problems in rotation will be given in succeeding articles.

(*a*) If a rotating body possesses symmetry of revolution about the axis of spin (like a top) we may use in place of axes attached to the body a set of axes with origin at the fixed point and Z axis parallel to the axis of spin, but with X and Y axes which rotate with an angular velocity different from that of the spinning body. If $\boldsymbol{\omega}$ is the angular velocity of the axes XYZ and s the angular velocity of spin of the body relative to these axes, the total angular velocity of the body is $\boldsymbol{\omega} + \mathbf{k}s$, as shown in article 32.1, and

$$\dot{\mathbf{r}}_i = (\boldsymbol{\omega} + \mathbf{k}s) \times \mathbf{r}_i.$$

Thus we get in place of (37–1),

$$\mathbf{H} = \Phi\cdot(\boldsymbol{\omega} + \mathbf{k}s) = \mathbf{i}A\omega_x + \mathbf{j}A\omega_y + \mathbf{k}C(\omega_z + s),$$

since the products of inertia vanish on account of symmetry, and the two moments of inertia A and B are equal. Now, since the moments of inertia about all axes perpendicular to the axis of symmetry are the same, A does not change with the time even though it is not referred to an axis attached to the body. Hence the equation of motion (37–5) becomes

$$\left.\begin{aligned}\mathbf{L} = \mathbf{i}\{A\dot{\omega}_x &+ (C - A)\omega_y\omega_z + Cs\omega_y\}\\ &+ \mathbf{j}\{A\dot{\omega}_y + (A - C)\omega_z\omega_x - Cs\omega_x\} + \mathbf{k}C(\dot{\omega}_z + \dot{s}).\end{aligned}\right\} \quad (37\text{–}10)$$

Case III. — No point fixed in an inertial system. As the equation (36–7) for the motion about the center of mass is identical with that for the motion about a fixed point, the methods of Case II may be applied to this case provided the origin of the axes XYZ is taken at the center of mass.

(*a*) In the case of a rigid body rolling on a stationary surface without slipping, the point of contact lies on the instantaneous axis of rotation. If we take the instantaneous position of this point as the fixed origin of a set of axes XYZ rotating with the same angular velocity as the body and so oriented as to eliminate the products of inertia,

$$\mathbf{H} = \mathbf{i}A\omega_x + \mathbf{j}B\omega_y + \mathbf{k}C\omega_z.$$

As the origin is fixed, equation (36–7) is valid. But, as the point in the body which is in contact with the surface is momentarily at rest, the time derivatives of the coordinates x, y, z of every particle in the rigid body are zero at the instant considered even though the axes relative to which these coordinates are measured are not permanently attached to the body. Therefore the time derivatives of A, B, C vanish, and Euler's equation (37–9) is applicable. Of course, the equation so determined describes only the momentary motion of the body. At a later time a set of axes with origin at the point of contact at that time must be employed, and generally a new set of moments of inertia.

This method is useful in problems such as the rolling of a uniform hoop or disk which remains in a single plane. Then, if we take the Z axis in the direction of the instantaneous axis of rotation, Euler's equation reduces to (37–7) and the moment of inertia C appearing in this equation remains unchanged as the motion progresses, on account of the symmetry of the body.

Problem 37a. Using the notation of problem 32c show that (37–5) may be written in the form

$$\mathbf{L} = \frac{d\mathbf{H}}{d\tau} + \boldsymbol{\omega} \times \mathbf{H},$$

where the first term on the right is the rate of change of momentum relative to the rotating axes, or in the forms

$$\mathbf{L} = \Phi \cdot \frac{d\boldsymbol{\omega}}{dt} + \boldsymbol{\omega} \times \Phi \cdot \boldsymbol{\omega}$$

$$= \Phi \cdot \frac{d\boldsymbol{\omega}}{d\tau} + \boldsymbol{\omega} \times \Phi \cdot \boldsymbol{\omega}.$$

38. Calculation of Moments of Inertia.—The few simple theorems contained in this article often facilitate the calculation of moments of inertia.

Theorem I.—The moment of inertia C' about any axis is equal to the sum of the moment of inertia C about a parallel axis through the center of mass and the product of the mass m of the body by the square of the perpendicular distance d between the two axes.

Take the origin at the center of mass with the Z axis parallel to the axis about which the moment of inertia is to be computed. Then if x', y' are the coordinates of the point of intersection of the latter axis with the XY plane,

$$C' = \sum_i m_i\{(x_i - x')^2 + (y_i - y')^2\}$$

$$= \sum_i m_i(x_i^2 + y_i^2) + m(x'^2 + y'^2) - 2x'\sum_i m_i x_i - 2y'\sum_i m_i y_i.$$

But, as the origin is at the center of mass,

$$\sum_i m_i x_i = \sum_i m_i y_i = 0, \quad C = \sum_i m_i(x_i^2 + y_i^2).$$

Therefore

$$C' = C + md^2. \tag{38-1}$$

Theorem II.—The moment of inertia C of a lamina about an axis Z which is perpendicular to its plane equals the sum of the moments of inertia A and B about two rectangular axes X and Y which lie in the plane of the lamina with their origin on the first axis.

$$C = \sum_i m_i(x_i^2 + y_i^2) = \sum_i m_i x_i^2 + \sum_i m_i y_i^2 = A + B. \tag{38-2}$$

Theorem III.—The sum of the moments of inertia A, B, C of a body about three rectangular axes equals twice the sum of the products of the masses of the particles of the body by the squares of their distances r from the origin.

$$\left.\begin{aligned} A+B+C &= \sum_i m_i(y_i^2+z_i^2)+\sum_i m_i(z_i^2+x_i^2)+\sum_i m_i(x_i^2+y_i^2) \\ &= 2\sum_i m_i(x_i^2+y_i^2+z_i^2) = 2\sum_i m_i r_i^2. \end{aligned}\right\} \tag{38-3}$$

Problem 38a. (*a*) Find the moment of inertia of a uniform cylinder of radius a and length l (1) about its axis of figure, (2) about a generatrix.

Ans. (1) $\frac{1}{2}ma^2$, (2) $\frac{3}{2}ma^2$.

(*b*) Find the moment of inertia of a cylinder of radius a and length l (1) about an axis perpendicular to the axis of figure through the center of mass, (2) about a parallel axis through one end.

Ans. (1) $m\left(\frac{a^2}{4} + \frac{l^2}{12}\right)$, (2) $m\left(\frac{a^2}{4} + \frac{l^2}{3}\right)$.

(*c*) Find the moment of inertia of a uniform sphere of radius a (1) about a diameter, (2) about a tangent. *Ans.* (1) $\frac{2}{5}ma^2$, (2) $\frac{7}{5}ma^2$.

(*d*) Find the moment of inertia of a uniform rectangular parallelopiped of edges a, b, c about an axis through its center parallel to the edge c.

Ans. $\frac{m}{12}(a^2 + b^2)$.

Problem 38b. A uniform cylinder of radius a rolls in a cylindrical trough of greater radius b under the influence of gravity. Find the period P_0 for small amplitudes, show that the period P_α for finite amplitude α is given in terms of P_0 by the same expression (29–6) as in the case of the simple pendulum, and explain how the radius of the trough can be determined from the measurement of P_0 and a.

$$Ans.\ P_0 = 2\pi\sqrt{\frac{3(b-a)}{2g}}.$$

Problem 38c. An inextensible string, one end of which is attached to the ceiling, is wound around the periphery of a uniform disk. The disk is allowed to roll down the taut vertical string under the influence of gravity. Find the distance traversed by its center of mass in a time t, starting from rest.

Ans. $\frac{1}{3}gt^2$.

Problem 38d. (*a*) If $\boldsymbol{\alpha}$ is a unit vector show that the moment of inertia I about an axis through the origin in the direction of $\boldsymbol{\alpha}$ is given by

$$I = \boldsymbol{\alpha}\cdot\Phi\cdot\boldsymbol{\alpha}.$$

(*b*) Putting

$$\boldsymbol{\eta} \equiv \frac{\boldsymbol{\alpha}}{\sqrt{I}}$$

show that if η is laid off from the origin the equation

$$\boldsymbol{\eta}\cdot\Phi\cdot\boldsymbol{\eta} = 1$$

represents an ellipsoid and that the moment of inertia of the body about any axis is equal to the square of the reciprocal of the radius vector in the direction of the axis. This ellipsoid is known as the *ellipsoid of inertia.*

39. Work and Energy of a Rigid Body. — Separating the force on the ith particle of a rigid body into the external force $\mathbf{F}_i$ and the internal force $\mathbf{F}_i'$ the work done on the particle when it suffers a displacement $d\mathbf{r}_{0i}$ relative to the fixed axes $X_0Y_0Z_0$ is

$$\delta W_i = \mathbf{F}_i\cdot d\mathbf{r}_{0i} + \mathbf{F}_i'\cdot d\mathbf{r}_{0i},$$

and the total work done on all the particles constituting the body is

$$\delta W = \sum_i \mathbf{F}_i\cdot d\mathbf{r}_{0i} + \sum_i \mathbf{F}_i'\cdot d\mathbf{r}_{0i}. \quad (39\text{–}1)$$

Consider two particles m_1 and m_2. If we assume that the forces between them are directed along the line joining them we can write for the force on m_1 due to m_2

$$\mathbf{F}_1' = a(\mathbf{r}_1 - \mathbf{r}_2),$$

and for that on m_2 due to m_1

$$\mathbf{F}_2' = -a(\mathbf{r}_1 - \mathbf{r}_2),$$

as in article 36. Now if m_1 suffers a displacement $d\mathbf{r}_1$ and m_2 a displacement $d\mathbf{r}_2$ the work done by the two forces together is

$$\delta W = \mathbf{F}_1'\cdot d\mathbf{r}_1 + \mathbf{F}_2'\cdot d\mathbf{r}_2$$

$$= a(\mathbf{r}_1 - \mathbf{r}_2)\cdot d(\mathbf{r}_1 - \mathbf{r}_2).$$

But since the distance between the two particles is invariable,

$$(\mathbf{r}_1 - \mathbf{r}_2)\cdot(\mathbf{r}_1 - \mathbf{r}_2) = \text{Constant}$$

and

$$(\mathbf{r}_1 - \mathbf{r}_2)\cdot d(\mathbf{r}_1 - \mathbf{r}_2) = 0.$$

Therefore the work done by the two forces taken together vanishes. As all the internal forces consist of equal and opposite actions and reactions between pairs of particles, the net work done by the internal forces during any displacement of a rigid body is zero. So (39–1) becomes

$$\delta W = \sum_i \mathbf{F}_i\cdot d\mathbf{r}_{0i} = \sum_i \mathbf{F}_i\cdot \mathbf{v}_{0i}dt.$$

Furthermore all external forces which do no work, such as the reactions of fixed smooth surfaces, may be omitted from this expression.

Now we shall introduce a set of axes XYZ attached to the body. As the velocity $\mathbf{v}_{0i}$ relative to $X_0Y_0Z_0$ is

$$\mathbf{v}_{0i} = \dot{\boldsymbol{\rho}} + \dot{\mathbf{r}}_i = \dot{\boldsymbol{\rho}} + \boldsymbol{\omega}\times\mathbf{r}_i$$

we have

$$\delta W = \sum_i \mathbf{F}_i\cdot\dot{\boldsymbol{\rho}}dt + \sum_i \mathbf{F}_i\cdot\boldsymbol{\omega}\times\mathbf{r}_i dt$$

$$= (\sum_i \mathbf{F}_i)\cdot\dot{\boldsymbol{\rho}}dt + (\sum_i \mathbf{r}_i\times\mathbf{F}_i)\cdot\boldsymbol{\omega}dt,$$

since the dot and the cross are interchangeable in the triple scalar product and the order of any two adjacent vectors may be altered provided the sign of the product is changed. Now $\sum_i \mathbf{F}_i$ is the resultant external force $\mathbf{F}$, and $\sum_i \mathbf{r}_i\times\mathbf{F}_i$ the resultant external torque $\mathbf{L}$ about the origin O of the axes XYZ. Therefore

$$\delta W = \mathbf{F}\cdot\dot{\boldsymbol{\rho}}dt + \mathbf{L}\cdot\boldsymbol{\omega}dt. \qquad (39\text{–}2)$$

The first term represents the work done by the external forces considered as acting at the origin O of the axes XYZ attached to the body, and the second term the work done by the torques about this origin. In case a point of the body is fixed in an inertial system it is convenient to take the origin O at the fixed point. Then the first term of (39–2) drops out and

$$\delta W = \mathbf{L}\cdot\boldsymbol{\omega}dt. \tag{39–3}$$

In case no point of the body remains at rest in an inertial system it is convenient to take the center of mass as the origin of the axes attached to the rigid body. Then the first term of (39–2) represents the work done by the external forces considered as acting at the center of mass and the second term the work done by the external torques about the center of mass.

Next we shall consider the kinetic energy T of a rigid body relative to a set of fixed axes $X_0Y_0Z_0$. We have

$$\begin{aligned} T &= \tfrac{1}{2}\sum_i m_i v_{0i}^2 = \tfrac{1}{2}\sum_i m_i(\dot{\boldsymbol{\rho}} + \boldsymbol{\omega}\times\mathbf{r}_i)\cdot(\dot{\boldsymbol{\rho}} + \boldsymbol{\omega}\times\mathbf{r}_i) \\ &= \tfrac{1}{2}m\dot{\rho}^2 + \tfrac{1}{2}\sum_i m_i(\boldsymbol{\omega}\times\mathbf{r}_i)\cdot(\boldsymbol{\omega}\times\mathbf{r}_i) + \dot{\boldsymbol{\rho}}\cdot\boldsymbol{\omega}\times\left(\sum_i m_i\mathbf{r}_i\right) \end{aligned}$$

where $m = \sum_i m_i$ is the total mass of the body. Now

$$\left.\begin{aligned} \tfrac{1}{2}\sum_i m_i(\boldsymbol{\omega}\times\mathbf{r}_i)\cdot(\boldsymbol{\omega}\times\mathbf{r}_i) &= \tfrac{1}{2}\sum_i m_i\boldsymbol{\omega}\cdot\{\mathbf{r}_i\times(\boldsymbol{\omega}\times\mathbf{r}_i)\} \\ &= \tfrac{1}{2}\boldsymbol{\omega}\cdot\left\{\sum_i m_i\mathbf{r}_i\times(\boldsymbol{\omega}\times\mathbf{r}_i)\right\} \\ &= \tfrac{1}{2}\boldsymbol{\omega}\cdot\Phi\cdot\boldsymbol{\omega} \\ &= \tfrac{1}{2}A\omega_x^2 + \tfrac{1}{2}B\omega_y^2 + \tfrac{1}{2}C\omega_z^2 - D\omega_y\omega_z \\ &\quad - E\omega_z\omega_x - F\omega_x\omega_y, \end{aligned}\right\} \tag{39–4}$$

from (37–1) and (37–2), where Φ is the momental dyadic. Therefore

$$T = \tfrac{1}{2}m\dot{\rho}^2 + \tfrac{1}{2}\boldsymbol{\omega}\cdot\Phi\cdot\boldsymbol{\omega} + \dot{\boldsymbol{\rho}}\cdot\boldsymbol{\omega}\times\left(\sum_i m_i\mathbf{r}_i\right). \tag{39–5}$$

In case a point of the body is fixed, it is convenient to take the origin of the axes XYZ attached to the body at the fixed point. Then $\dot{\boldsymbol{\rho}}$ is zero and T reduces to

$$T = \tfrac{1}{2}\boldsymbol{\omega}\cdot\Phi\cdot\boldsymbol{\omega}, \tag{39–6}$$

and, if the axes XYZ are so oriented as to make the products of inertia vanish,

$$T = \tfrac{1}{2}A\omega_x^2 + \tfrac{1}{2}B\omega_y^2 + \tfrac{1}{2}C\omega_z^2. \tag{39–7}$$

In case no point of the body is at rest in an inertial system it is convenient to take the origin O of the axes attached to the moving body at the center of mass. Then the last term in (39–5) vanishes and

$$T = \tfrac{1}{2}m\dot{\rho}^2 + \tfrac{1}{2}\boldsymbol{\omega}\cdot\Phi\cdot\boldsymbol{\omega}. \qquad (39\text{–}8)$$

The first term represents the kinetic energy of a particle coincident with the center of mass having a mass equal to that of the entire body. It is spoken of as the *kinetic energy of translation* of the body. The second term represents the *kinetic energy of rotation* about the center of mass. If the axes attached to the body are so oriented as to make the products of inertia vanish we may write (39–8) in the form

$$T = \tfrac{1}{2}m\dot{\rho}^2 + \tfrac{1}{2}A\omega_x^2 + \tfrac{1}{2}B\omega_y^2 + \tfrac{1}{2}C\omega_z^2. \qquad (39\text{–}9)$$

It was shown in article 22 that the increase in kinetic energy of a particle is equal to the work done on the particle by the forces applied to it. So for the aggregate of particles constituting a rigid body

$$T - T_0 = \int_{t_0}^{t}\mathbf{F}\cdot\dot{\boldsymbol{\rho}}dt + \int_{t_0}^{t}\mathbf{L}\cdot\boldsymbol{\omega}dt \qquad (39\text{–}10)$$

from (39–2), where T_0 is the kinetic energy of the body at the time t_0 and T its kinetic energy at the time t. If $\mathbf{F}\cdot\dot{\boldsymbol{\rho}}dt + \mathbf{L}\cdot\boldsymbol{\omega}dt$ is expressible as an exact differential $-\,dV$ in the coordinates relative to the fixed axes $X_0Y_0Z_0$, then

$$T - T_0 = -\,(V - V_0),$$

or

$$T + V = T_0 + V_0 = U \text{ (a constant)}, \qquad (39\text{–}11)$$

and the field of force is said to be conservative, V being the potential energy and U the total energy.

If the origin of the axes XYZ is taken at the center of mass (39–10) may be split into two equations. For the motion of the center of mass is identical with that of a particle having a mass equal to the mass of the entire body and subject to the same external forces as are applied to the body. Therefore the increase in kinetic energy of translation of the body is equal to the work done by the applied forces considered as acting at the center of mass, that is,

$$\tfrac{1}{2}m\dot{\rho}^2 - \tfrac{1}{2}m\dot{\rho}_0^{\,2} = \int_{t_0}^{t} \mathbf{F}\cdot\dot{\boldsymbol{\rho}}dt. \tag{39–12}$$

In the right-hand member of this equation all the external forces must be included, for they all do work if applied at the moving center of mass.

Subtracting this equation from (39–10), remembering that T is given by (39–8) for the case under discussion,

$$\tfrac{1}{2}\boldsymbol{\omega}\cdot\Phi\cdot\boldsymbol{\omega} - \tfrac{1}{2}\boldsymbol{\omega}_0\cdot\Phi\cdot\boldsymbol{\omega}_0 = \int_{t_0}^{t} \mathbf{L}\cdot\boldsymbol{\omega}\, dt. \tag{39–13}$$

Hence the increase in kinetic energy of rotation about the center of mass is equal to the work done by the external torque about this point.

Problem 39a. A uniform disk (*a*) slides down a smooth inclined plane of height h without rolling, (*b*) rolls down the inclined plane without slipping. Find the velocity of translation of the center of mass at the bottom of the plane in each case. *Ans.* (*a*) $\sqrt{2gh}$, (*b*) $\sqrt{\tfrac{4}{3}gh}$.

Problem 39b. Two spheres of equal radius a and equal mass m are free to slide on a bar of negligible inertia as in Problem 32*b*. The spheres are equidistant from the axis of rotation on opposite sides, the distance of each from the axis being controlled by strings. This common distance is increased from d to d', the rotating system being subject to no external torque. Find the ratio of the angular velocity ω' in the second configuration to the angular velocity ω in the first, and the ratio of the kinetic energies.

Ans. $\dfrac{\omega'}{\omega} = \dfrac{T'}{T} = \dfrac{2a^2 + 5d^2}{2a^2 + 5d'^2}$.

40. Kater's Reversible Pendulum. — This pendulum is used for the accurate determination of the acceleration g due to gravity. It consists of a rigid body (Fig. 46) symmetrical with respect to the plane in which it oscillates. It is provided with knife edges so that it may be set in oscillation about a fixed axis through K_1 at a distance h_1 from the center of mass C, or about an axis through K_2 at a distance h_2 from C.

The torque about K_1 as origin due to the weight $\mathbf{W}_i$ of each particle m_i is

$$\mathbf{L} = \sum_i \mathbf{r}_i \times \mathbf{W}_i = (\sum_i m_i\mathbf{r}_i) \times \mathbf{g} = \bar{\mathbf{r}} \times m\mathbf{g}, \tag{40–1}$$

where $\bar{\mathbf{r}}$ is the position vector of the center of mass. Therefore the torque due to weight is the same as if the entire weight of the body were applied at the center of mass. For this reason the center of mass is also called the *center of gravity.*

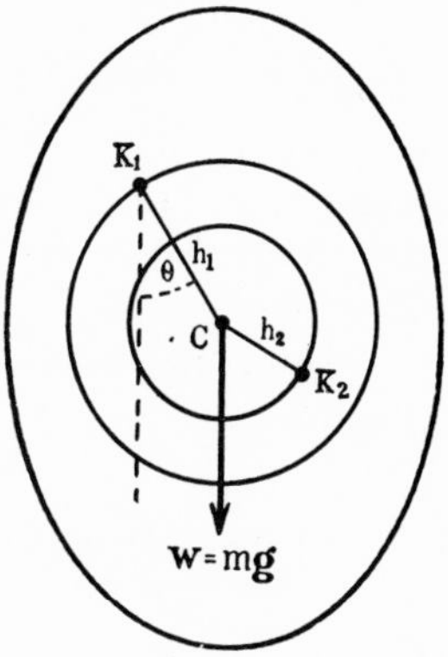

FIG. 46.

If I_c is the moment of inertia about an axis parallel to K_1 through the center of mass and k_c is the corresponding radius of gyration

$$I_c = mk_c^2.$$

Therefore the moment of inertia about the axis through K_1 is

$$I_1 = I_c + mh_1^2 = m(k_c^2 + h_1^2),$$

and that about K_2

$$I_2 = I_c + mh_2^2 = m(k_c^2 + h_2^2).$$

The equation of motion for suspension at K_1 is

$$I_1 \frac{d^2\theta}{dt^2} = - mgh_1 \sin \theta,$$

or

$$\frac{d^2\theta}{dt^2} + \frac{mgh_1}{I_1} \sin \theta = 0. \tag{40-2}$$

This is just the equation (29–2) which was encountered in the theory of the simple pendulum. Therefore the period P_1 for small oscillations is

$$P_1 = 2\pi\sqrt{\frac{I_1}{mgh_1}} = 2\pi\sqrt{\frac{k_c^2 + h_1^2}{gh_1}}. \tag{40-3}$$

Similarly, for suspension at K_2,

$$P_2 = 2\pi\sqrt{\frac{I_2}{mgh_2}} = 2\pi\sqrt{\frac{k_c^2 + h_2^2}{gh_2}}. \tag{40-4}$$

These periods are the same if

$$(k_c^2 + h_1^2)h_2 = (k_c^2 + h_2^2)h_1,$$

or

$$k_c^2(h_2 - h_1) = h_1h_2(h_2 - h_1),$$

giving either $h_2 = h_1$ or $h_1h_2 = k_c^2$. The second case is the one in which we are interested. Then

$$P_1 = P_2 = 2\pi\sqrt{\frac{h_1 + h_2}{g}}, \tag{40-5}$$

which is the same as the period of a simple pendulum of length $h_1 + h_2$. Evidently K_1 may be taken anywhere on a circle of radius h_1 about C as center, and K_2 anywhere on a circle of radius h_2. Clearly it is most convenient to place K_1 and K_2 at opposite ends of a straight line passing through C. Then $h_1 + h_2$ is just the distance of one set of knife edges from the other.

In practice it is difficult to adjust the knife edges so as to make the periods the same within the experimental error. If they are not the same

$$k_c^2 = \frac{P_1^2gh_1}{4\pi^2} - h_1^2 = \frac{P_2^2gh_2}{4\pi^2} - h_2^2,$$

and

$$\frac{4\pi^2}{g} = \frac{h_1P_1^2 - h_2P_2^2}{h_1^2 - h_2^2} = \frac{P_1^2 + P_2^2}{2(h_1 + h_2)} + \frac{P_1^2 - P_2^2}{2(h_1 - h_2)}. \tag{40-6}$$

Now, if the periods are nearly the same, the second term on the right is a small correction to the larger first term, all the quantities in which can be measured accurately.

Problem 40a. Borda's pendulum consists of a spherical bob of radius a suspended by a rod of negligible mass. If l is the distance from the point of suspension to the center of mass of the bob, find the period of Borda's pendulum for small oscillations. What is the error in considering Borda's pendulum as a simple pendulum with all the mass concentrated at the center of the bob if the ratio of a to l is (1) 1 per cent, (2) 5 per cent?

Ans. $P = 2\pi\sqrt{\frac{l}{g}\left(1 + \frac{2}{5}\frac{a^2}{l^2}\right)}$, 0.002 per cent, 0.05 per cent.

Problem 40b. Find the period for small oscillations of a uniform ring of rectangular cross-section suspended on a knife edge. Take a and b for the inner and outer radii of the ring.

Ans. $P = 2\pi\sqrt{\frac{b^2 + 3a^2}{2ga}}$.

Problem 40c. Show that the period of Kater's pendulum is a minimum when $h_1 = k_c$.

41. Center of Percussion. — A rigid lamina subject to no constraints is given a blow at the point A (Fig. 47) in the direction of the arrow. It is desired to find the point O about which the body starts to turn. This point is known as the *center of percussion.* Representing the impulse due to the blow by $\mathbf{F}\Delta t$, the velocity $\mathbf{v}$ acquired by the center of mass is given by

$$\mathbf{F}\Delta t = m\mathbf{v}. \tag{41-1}$$

Therefore the point O about which the body starts to rotate must lie on a line through the center of mass C perpendicular to the force $\mathbf{F}$. Denoting the angular velocity acquired by ω,

$$v = \omega x,$$

and

$$F\Delta t = m\omega x.$$

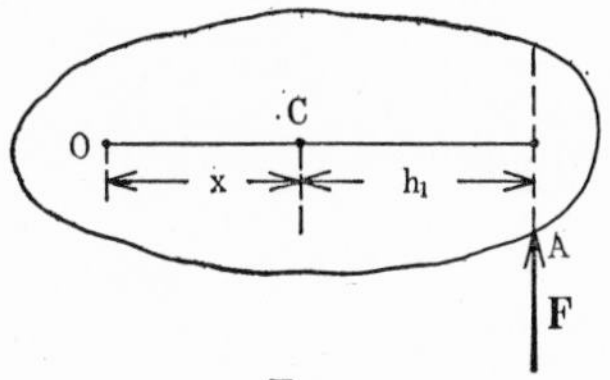

FIG. 47.

But the angular impulse about O is

$$L\Delta t = (x + h_1)F\Delta t = m\omega(x^2 + xh_1). \tag{41-2}$$

The angular impulse is equal to the product of the moment of inertia I about O by the angular velocity acquired. Therefore

$$L\Delta t = I\omega = (I_c + mx^2)\omega = m\omega(k_c^2 + x^2), \tag{41-3}$$

where I_c is the moment of inertia and k_c the radius of gyration about the center of mass C. Comparing (41–2) with (41–3) it is seen that

$$x = \frac{k_c^2}{h_1}. \tag{41-4}$$

Therefore the relation between x and h_1 is the same as that between h_2 and h_1 in Kater's pendulum.

Problem 41a. A horizontal uniform rod of length $2d$ is suspended by two vertical cords of length l attached to its ends (bifilar suspension). Find the period for small oscillations about a vertical axis through the center of the rod.

Ans. $P = 2\pi\sqrt{\frac{lk^2}{gd^2}}$ where k is the radius of gyration.

42. Motion of a Rigid Body Under No Torque. — If one point of the body is fixed, we shall take the fixed point as origin. Otherwise we shall take the center of mass as origin. In either case the angular momentum $\mathbf{H}$ about the origin is constant in magnitude and direction and the kinetic energy T of rotation about the origin is constant. So we have the two equations

$$\Phi\cdot\boldsymbol{\omega} = \mathbf{H} \text{ (a constant in magnitude and direction)}, \tag{42-1}$$

$$\boldsymbol{\omega}\cdot\Phi\cdot\boldsymbol{\omega} = 2T \text{ (a scalar constant)}. \tag{42-2}$$

Combining them,

$$\boldsymbol{\omega}\cdot\mathbf{H} = 2T. \tag{42-3}$$

These equations contain a complete description of the motion.

If we refer the momental dyadic Φ to a set of axes XYZ attached to the rigid body and oriented so as to make the products of inertia vanish it assumes the form given in (37–3). Laying off the vector $\boldsymbol{\omega}$ from the origin and denoting the coordinates of its terminus referred to the same axes by x, y, z,

$$\boldsymbol{\omega} = \mathbf{i}x + \mathbf{j}y + \mathbf{k}z,$$

and equation (42–2) may be written

$$Ax^2 + By^2 + Cz^2 = 2T. \tag{42–4}$$

Thus (42–2) is the equation of an ellipsoid fixed in the rigid body with its center at the origin. The angular velocity is represented by the radius vector of the ellipsoid, all *radii vectores* corresponding to the same kinetic energy T. So equation (42–2) does not limit the magnitude of the angular velocity to a single value, but merely specifies the magnitude it must have once its direction relative to the axes XYZ attached to the body is assigned. The situation here should be contrasted with that existing in the corresponding case of linear motion of a particle, where the magnitude of the linear velocity is completely determined by that of the kinetic energy.

To pass from one point on this ellipsoid to a neighboring point we differentiate (42–2) obtaining

$$d\boldsymbol{\omega}\cdot\Phi\cdot\boldsymbol{\omega} + \boldsymbol{\omega}\cdot\Phi\cdot d\boldsymbol{\omega} = 0,$$

or

$$d\boldsymbol{\omega}\cdot\Phi\cdot\boldsymbol{\omega} = 0$$

since Φ is symmetric. Now $d\boldsymbol{\omega}$, since it connects two neighboring points on the surface, lies in the tangent plane. Therefore the tangent plane is perpendicular to $\Phi\cdot\boldsymbol{\omega}$, and in view of (42–1), perpendicular to the fixed vector $\mathbf{H}$. Hence the orientation of the tangent plane relative to stationary axes $X_0Y_0Z_0$ remains fixed during the motion. Furthermore, as

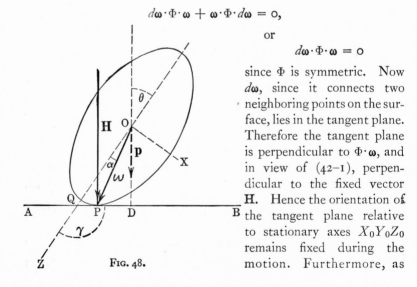

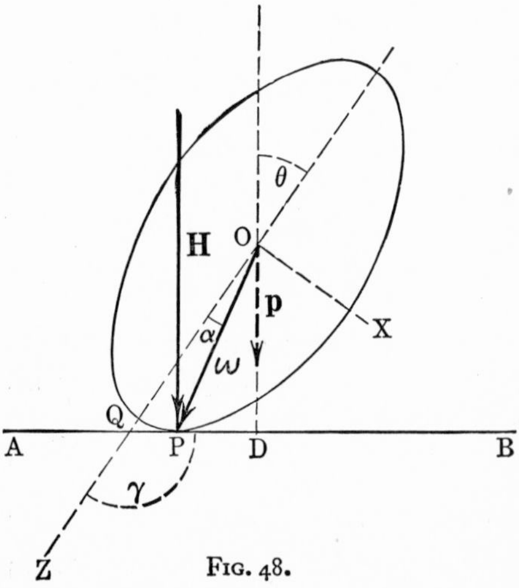

FIG. 48.

$\boldsymbol{\omega}\cdot\mathbf{H}$ in (42–3) represents the product of the component of $\boldsymbol{\omega}$ in the direction of $\mathbf{H}$ by the constant magnitude of this vector, this equation requires that the distance d of the tangent plane from the origin should remain unchanged during the motion. If the origin is fixed, the tangent plane remains fixed both in orientation and position as the motion proceeds. Consequently the motion consists in the rolling on the fixed tangent plane of the ellipsoid attached to the rigid body which is represented by equation (42–2) or (42–4). There can be no sliding on the tangent plane since the point of tangency lies on the axis of rotation. The fixed tangent plane AB and the various vectors involved are shown in Fig. 48.

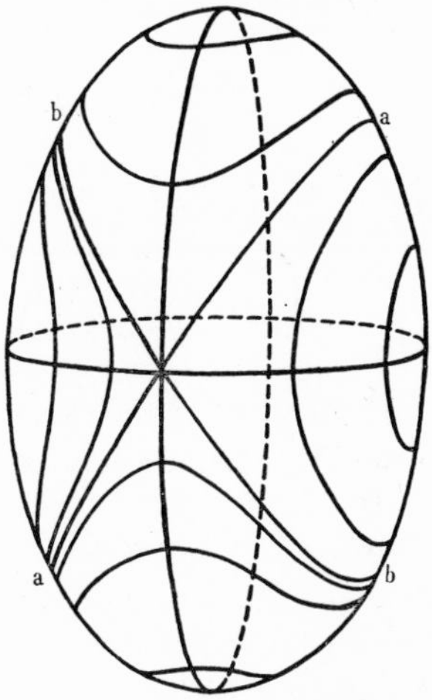

FIG. 49.

The point P in which the axis of rotation intersects the ellipsoid is called the *pole* of the axis. The locus of the pole on the ellipsoid is called by Poinsot the *polhode*, and its locus on the tangent plane the *herpolhode* (pol = axis, hode = path Gk). As the polhode lies on the ellipsoid its coordinates must satisfy equation (42–4).

Now (42–3) may be written

$$Hd = 2T, \qquad (42\text{–}5)$$

and, as $\mathbf{H} = \mathbf{i}Ax + \mathbf{j}By + \mathbf{k}Cz$ in terms of its components along XYZ, the square of (42–5) is

$$A^2d^2x^2 + B^2d^2y^2 + C^2d^2z^2 = 4T^2. \qquad (42\text{–}6)$$

As the pole of the axis is nothing more than the terminus of the vector $\boldsymbol{\omega}$ laid off from the origin, this equation also must be satisfied by the polhode. Eliminating the constant terms between (42–4) and (42–6),

$$\frac{A}{2T}\left(\frac{1}{d^2} - \frac{A}{2T}\right)x^2 + \frac{B}{2T}\left(\frac{1}{d^2} - \frac{B}{2T}\right)y^2 + \frac{C}{2T}\left(\frac{1}{d^2} - \frac{C}{2T}\right)z^2 = 0 \qquad (42\text{–}7)$$

is found to be the equation of the cone with vertex at the origin which is described by the axis of rotation relative to the axes XYZ attached to the rigid body. Now the semi-axes of the ellipsoid (42–4) are

$$a = \sqrt{\frac{2T}{A}}, \quad b = \sqrt{\frac{2T}{B}}, \quad c = \sqrt{\frac{2T}{C}}.$$

Therefore (42–7) becomes

$$\left(\frac{1}{d^2} - \frac{1}{a^2}\right)\frac{x^2}{a^2} + \left(\frac{1}{d^2} - \frac{1}{b^2}\right)\frac{y^2}{b^2} + \left(\frac{1}{d^2} - \frac{1}{c^2}\right)\frac{z^2}{c^2} = 0. \quad (42\text{–}8)$$

If $a < b < c$, the cone is real only if $a \leq d \leq c$. If d is equal to the intermediate semi-axis b, then

$$\left(\frac{1}{a^2} - \frac{1}{d^2}\right)\frac{x^2}{a^2} = \left(\frac{1}{d^2} - \frac{1}{c^2}\right)\frac{z^2}{c^2},$$

representing two intersecting planes through the Y axis. Their traces on the ellipsoid are shown by aa and bb in Fig. 49. They separate the polhodes around the major axis from those around the minor axis.

The case where the two moments of inertia A and B are equal is of especial interest. Then the energy ellipsoid (42–4) becomes a spheroid. To be definite we shall suppose that $C < A$ so that $c > a$ and the spheroid is prolate. Evidently the herpolhode described on the fixed tangent plane AB (Fig. 48) is a circle of radius DP with center at D. The angular velocity Ω of spin is defined as the component of the total angular velocity $\boldsymbol{\omega}$ along the axis of symmetry OZ. The motion of the axis of spin OZ about the fixed line OD is known as *precession*, the rate $\dfrac{d\psi}{dt}$ of precession being the angle described about D per unit time by the point Q where OZ intersects the tangent plane. Since the perpendicular distance of Q from the instantaneous axis OP is $OQ \sin \alpha$, the linear velocity of Q along the periphery of the circle which it describes around D in the tangent plane is $\omega\, OQ \sin \alpha$. Dividing this by the radius $DQ = OQ \sin \theta$ of the circle, we have

$$\frac{d\psi}{dt} = \omega \frac{\sin \alpha}{\sin \theta} = \Omega \frac{\tan \alpha}{\sin \theta}$$

since the angular velocity Ω of spin is equal to $\omega \cos \alpha$. The equation of the elliptical section of the prolate spheroid shown in the figure is

$$\frac{z^2}{c^2} + \frac{x^2}{a^2} = 1,$$

and

$$\tan \alpha = \frac{x}{z},$$

$$\tan \theta = -\cot \gamma = -\frac{dz}{dx} = \frac{c^2 x}{a^2 z} = \frac{Ax}{Cz}.$$

Hence

$$\tan \alpha = \frac{C}{A} \tan \theta$$

and the rate of precession is

$$\frac{d\psi}{dt} = \frac{C\Omega}{A \cos \theta}. \tag{42-9}$$

Problem 42a. Show that the ellipsoid of article 42 is similar to the ellipsoid of inertia of problem 38*d* and may be obtained from the latter by increasing the axes in the ratio $\sqrt{2T}$. Show therefore that the motion represented in Fig. 48 may be specified equally well as the rolling on a fixed tangent plane of the ellipsoid of inertia of the rigid body.

43. Heavy Symmetrical Top or Gyroscope. — In the previous article we considered the motion of a rigid body subject to no external torque. Now we shall consider the motion of a rotating body with one point fixed which is subject to a torque exerted by gravity. As shown in (40–1) the torque due to gravity is the same as if the entire weight of the body acted at the center of mass. We shall limit ourselves to a body, such as a top or gyroscope, which has symmetry of revolution about the axis of spin. Therefore the moments of inertia about any two axes perpendicular to the axis of spin are the same.

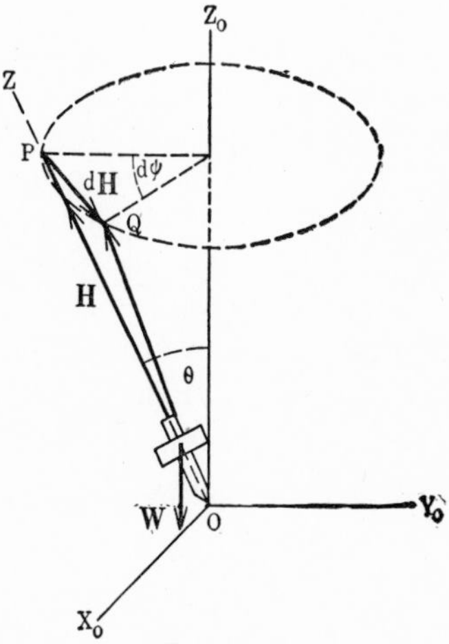

FIG. 50.

Before going into the exact theory of the motion we shall consider an approximate solution of the problem of the top which holds when the velocity of spin Ω is large. Let O (Fig. 50) be the fixed point, and $X_0Y_0Z_0$ a set of fixed axes, Z_0 being vertical. Take the Z axis attached to the top along the axis of spin. If the motion of the axis of the top is small, the total angular momentum $\mathbf{H}$ is very nearly along the axis of spin and equal to $C\Omega$, where C is the moment of inertia about the Z axis. Now the torque due to gravity is at right angles to the plane of the Z and Z_0 axes, and therefore in the time dt it produces an increment $d\mathbf{H}$ in the angular momentum in a direction perpendicular to $\mathbf{H}$. Therefore the equation of motion is satisfied if the axis of the top swings around the Z_0 axis from OP to OQ during the time dt, the velocity of spin and the inclination of the axis to the vertical remaining unchanged. The rate of precession is the angle about the Z_0 axis described by the point P in a unit time.

If l is the distance of the center of gravity from the fixed point O the torque due to gravity is $Wl \sin \theta$ and the equation of motion is

$$\left|\frac{d\mathbf{H}}{dt}\right| = Wl \sin \theta.$$

But

$$|d\mathbf{H}| = H \sin \theta d\psi = C\Omega \sin \theta d\psi$$

from the figure. Therefore the rate of precession is

$$\frac{d\psi}{dt} = \frac{Wl}{C\Omega}. \tag{43-1}$$

Our approximation consists in the assumption that the total angular momentum is that due to spin about the Z axis. On account of precession, however, there are components of angular momentum about axes perpendicular to OZ. But if the velocity of spin Ω is large, (43–1) shows that the rate of precession is small and therefore proves *a posteriori* that the error made in neglecting the components of angular momentum perpendicular to OZ is negligible.

Let us now investigate the motion in more detail. As the top is symmetrical we may utilize a set of axes XYZ (Fig. 51) with origin at the fixed point and Z axis along the axis of spin which rotate with an angular velocity $\boldsymbol{\omega}$ different from that of the top itself. Let us take for X axis the line of intersection OX of the plane through O perpendicular to the Z axis with the fixed X_0Y_0

plane. This line is known as the *line of nodes.* We shall denote by θ the angle between the axis OZ of the top and the vertical OZ_0 and by ψ the precessional angle which the rotating line of nodes makes with the fixed axis OX_0. These two angles, together with the angle ϕ which a line OS rotating with the top in the XY plane makes with the line of nodes, are known as the *Eulerian angles.*

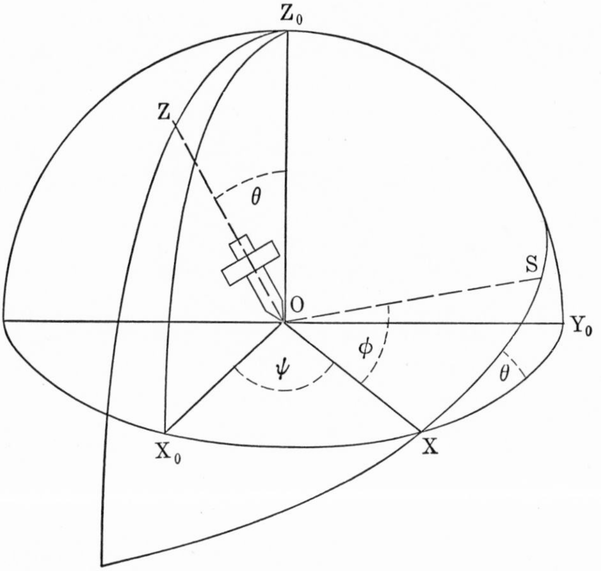

FIG. 51.

The rotating axes have angular velocities $\frac{d\psi}{dt}$ about OZ_0 and $\frac{d\theta}{dt}$ about the line of nodes. Resolving these along XYZ,

$$\left.\begin{aligned} \omega_x &= \frac{d\theta}{dt}, \\ \omega_y &= \frac{d\psi}{dt}\sin\theta, \\ \omega_z &= \frac{d\psi}{dt}\cos\theta. \end{aligned}\right\} \qquad (43\text{–}2)$$

The torque due to gravity is $Wl \sin\theta$ along the line of nodes OX.

Therefore the three components of the equation of motion (37–10) are

$$\left.\begin{aligned} A\dot{\omega}_x + (C - A)\omega_y\omega_z + Cs\omega_y &= Wl\sin\theta, \\ A\dot{\omega}_y + (A - C)\omega_z\omega_x - Cs\omega_x &= 0, \\ C(\dot{\omega}_z + \dot{s}) &= 0. \end{aligned}\right\} \qquad (43\text{–}3)$$

The last shows that the total angular velocity $\omega_z + s$ of spin about the Z axis remains constant during the motion. Putting Ω for this constant angular velocity and eliminating s from the first two equations we get

$$\left.\begin{aligned} A\dot{\omega}_x - A\omega_y\omega_z + C\Omega\omega_y &= Wl\sin\theta, \\ A\dot{\omega}_y + A\omega_z\omega_x - C\Omega\omega_x &= 0. \end{aligned}\right\} \qquad (43\text{–}4)$$

Multiplying the first by ω_x and the second by ω_y and adding

$$A(\omega_x\dot{\omega}_x + \omega_y\dot{\omega}_y) = Wl\sin\theta\frac{d\theta}{dt} \qquad (43\text{–}5)$$

provided we substitute from (43–2) for ω_x on the right-hand side. Integrating with respect to the time

$$\tfrac{1}{2}A(\omega_x^2 + \omega_y^2) = U - Wl\cos\theta. \qquad (43\text{–}6)$$

This is the energy equation, U being the total energy of the top less the constant kinetic energy of rotation about the Z axis and $Wl\cos\theta$ being the potential energy relative to the horizontal X_0Y_0 plane.

Another integral can be obtained from the second equation in (43–4). Expressing ω_x, ω_y, ω_z in terms of ψ and θ, and multiplying the equation by $\sin\theta$,

$$A\left(\sin^2\theta\frac{d^2\psi}{dt^2} + 2\sin\theta\cos\theta\frac{d\psi}{dt}\frac{d\theta}{dt}\right) - C\Omega\sin\theta\frac{d\theta}{dt} = 0,$$

which can be integrated at once, giving

$$A\sin^2\theta\frac{d\psi}{dt} + C\Omega\cos\theta = H \text{ (a constant)}. \qquad (43\text{–}7)$$

Physically, as is evident at once from the figure, the constant of integration H represents the constant component of angular momentum along the vertical Z_0 axis.

Writing the angular velocities ω_x and ω_y in terms of θ, ψ and their derivatives the energy equation (43–6) becomes

$$\left(\frac{d\theta}{dt}\right)^2 + \sin^2\theta\left(\frac{d\psi}{dt}\right)^2 = u - w\cos\theta, \tag{43-8}$$

where the constants u and w stand for

$$u \equiv \frac{2U}{A}, \quad w \equiv \frac{2Wl}{A}.$$

Similarly (43–7) may be written

$$\sin^2\theta\frac{d\psi}{dt} = h - p\cos\theta, \tag{43-9}$$

where

$$h \equiv \frac{H}{A}, \quad p \equiv \frac{C}{A}\Omega.$$

Eliminating $\frac{d\psi}{dt}$ between (43–8) and (43–9),

$$\sin^2\theta\left(\frac{d\theta}{dt}\right)^2 + (h - p\cos\theta)^2 = \sin^2\theta(u - w\cos\theta). \tag{43-10}$$

Putting z for $\cos\theta$ this becomes

$$\left(\frac{dz}{dt}\right)^2 = (1 - z^2)(u - wz) - (h - pz)^2 \equiv f(z), \tag{43-11}$$

where $f(z)$ stands for the function of z appearing on the right-hand side of the equation. In terms of z equation (43–9) takes the form

$$\frac{d\psi}{dt} = \frac{h - pz}{1 - z^2}. \tag{43-12}$$

The variable z is evidently the elevation above the fixed point O of a point P on the axis of the top a unit distance from O. The point P is called the *apex* of the top.

Since equation (43–11) is the only one containing a single dependent variable it is necessary to solve this equation first. Then substituting the solution in (43–12) ψ may be found as a function of the time.

As $\frac{dz}{dt}$ must always be real, the function of z represented by the right-hand side of (43–11) must be positive. As it is a cubic it can vanish for no more than three values of z. We find

$$f(-\infty)=-\infty,\ f(-1)=-(h+p)^2,\ f(+1)=-(h-p)^2,\ f(\infty)=\infty,$$

since w is essentially positive. As z stands for $\cos\theta$ it is limited to values between -1 and $+1$. So if the constants are such that the motion is physically possible, the graph of $f(z)$ plotted against z must be as represented in Fig. 52, z being confined to values between

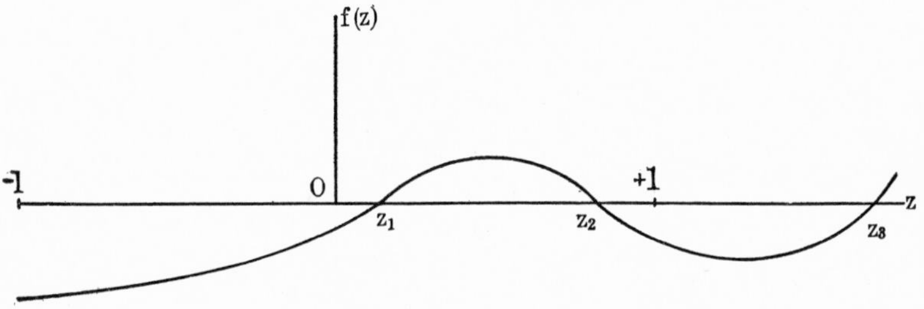

FIG. 52.

the *libration limits* z_1 and z_2 since $f(z)$ must be positive. Therefore the cone described by the axis of the top lies between two right circular cones of angle θ_1 and θ_2, where $\cos\theta_1 = z_1$ and $\cos\theta_2 = z_2$. The cone generated by the axis of the top generally meets the limiting cones tangentially, as in Fig. 53 (*a*) and (*c*), although in special cases it may have cuspidal edges, as in Fig. 53 (*b*).

Evidently the nature of the contact depends upon whether the rate of precession (43–12) is negative, zero, or positive at the roots z_1 and z_2 of $f(z) = 0$, cuspidal contact occurring when the rate of precession is zero. Let z_i be one of these two roots. Then

$$u - wz_i = \frac{(h - pz_i)^2}{1 - z_i^2} \qquad (43\text{–}13)$$

from (43–11), and, on differentiating $f(z)$,

$$f'(z_i) = -w(1 - z_i^2) - 2z_i\ (u - wz_i) + 2p(h - pz_i)$$

$$= -w(1 - z_i^2) - 2z_i\ \frac{(h - pz_i)^2}{1 - z_i^2} + 2p(h - pz_i). \qquad (43\text{–}14)$$

The constants u and w are essentially positive, and it is evident from their definitions that h and p have the same sign. Changing the sign of these two constants merely changes the sign of the precession as specified by (43–12), leaving the equation (43–11) for z unaltered. Therefore it is clear that we lose no generality by taking the constants h and p, as well as u and w, to be positive.

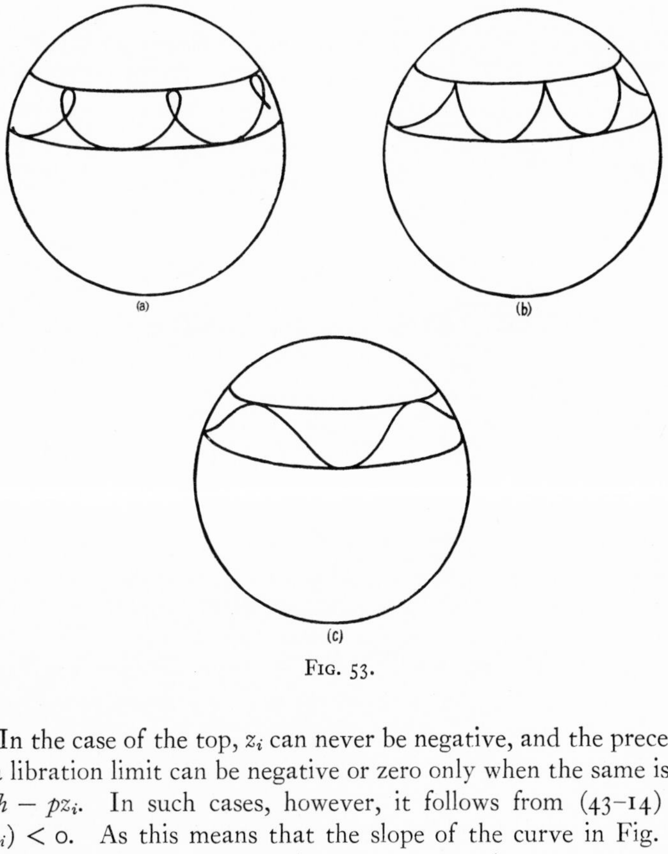

FIG. 53.

In the case of the top, z_i can never be negative, and the precession at a libration limit can be negative or zero only when the same is true of $h - pz_i$. In such cases, however, it follows from (43–14) that $f'(z_i) < 0$. As this means that the slope of the curve in Fig. 52 is negative at the root z_i, a negative or zero precession can occur only at the larger root z_2. If the precession vanishes and therefore the contact is cuspidal,

$$z_2 = \frac{h}{p} = \frac{u}{w}$$

from (43–12) and (43–13).

Since the axis of the gyroscope may make an angle of more than 90° with the vertical, we have to consider here a possible negative value of the libration limit z_i. But (43–12) shows that, with positive h and p, the precession can never be negative or zero for a negative value of z.

The path of the apex of the top on a unit sphere is shown in Fig. 53 for the three cases under consideration. In (*a*) is depicted the case where the axis is given an initial velocity opposed to the precession; in (*b*) the case where the axis starts from rest, the top falling until it acquires sufficient velocity to bring the gyroscopic action into play; in (*c*) the case where the axis is given an initial velocity in the direction of the precession. The rise and fall of the axis from the one to the other limiting cone is known as *nutation*.

Even though $\frac{dz}{dt}$ vanishes at the libration limits, the axis of the top can no more remain at one of the libration limits than a pendulum can remain at rest at the end of its swing. To see this more clearly we note that, as

$$\frac{dz}{dt} = \sqrt{f(z)},$$

it follows that

$$\frac{d^2z}{dt^2} = \frac{1}{2}\frac{\frac{df}{dz}}{\sqrt{f(z)}}\frac{dz}{dt}$$

$$= \frac{1}{2}\frac{df}{dz}.$$

Consequently the second derivative, representing the acceleration of the axis, is positive at z_1 (Fig. 52) and negative at z_2. This causes the axis, on reaching one of the libration limits, to reverse its motion and start toward the other.

Finally we shall consider the conditions for precession without nutation. In order that there may be no nutation the two limiting cones must coincide, that is, z_2 must be equal to z_1. Therefore z_1

must be a double root of the equation

$$f(z) \equiv (1 - z^2)(u - wz) - (h - pz)^2 = 0$$

and hence a root of

$$f'(z) \equiv -w(1 - z^2) - 2z(u - wz) + 2p(h - pz) = 0.$$

Eliminating $u - wz$ between these two equations and solving for $h - pz$ we get

$$h - pz = \frac{p(1 - z^2)}{2z}\left\{1 \pm \sqrt{1 - \frac{2wz}{p^2}}\right\},$$

and substituting in (43–12) the rate of precession without nutation is found to be

$$\frac{d\psi}{dt} = \frac{p}{2\cos\theta}\left\{1 \pm \sqrt{1 - \frac{2w\cos\theta}{p^2}}\right\} \tag{43–15}$$

for a given inclination θ of the axis of the top with the vertical.

If the velocity of spin is large the second term in the radical is small compared with unity and the two rates of precession without nutation are approximately

$$\left.\begin{aligned}\left(\frac{d\psi}{dt}\right)_1 &= \frac{w}{2p} = \frac{Wl}{C\Omega},\\ \left(\frac{d\psi}{dt}\right)_2 &= \frac{p}{\cos\theta} = \frac{C\Omega}{A\cos\theta}.\end{aligned}\right\} \tag{43–16}$$

The first is the approximate solution (43–1) given at the beginning of this article and the second is a very rapid precession difficult to obtain. As the latter is independent of W it must be a Poinsot motion such as was discussed in article 42; in fact comparison with (42–9) shows that it is identical with the precession found for a rigid body with axial symmetry under the action of no torque. It should be noted that the first of these steady rates of precession is greater the less the velocity of spin. This does not imply that the precession becomes infinitely great as Ω approaches zero, for our approximation is not valid for small values of Ω. In fact precession without nutation is impossible for values of Ω less than that for which the radical in (43–15) vanishes.

If the axis of the top remains vertical, the top is said to *sleep*. As $z = 1$ must be a double root of $f(z) = 0$ in this case, inspection of the expressions for $f(z)$ and $f'(z)$ on page 165 shows that $h = p$ and $u = w$. Hence

$$f(z) = (1 - z)^2\{(1 + z)w - p^2\},$$

and the root z_3 is equal to $p^2/w - 1$. Now p, since it is proportional to the angular velocity Ω of spin, is gradually diminished by friction at the peg of an actual top, decreasing the value of the root z_3. When z_3 becomes less than unity, $f(z)$ is positive for $z_3 < z < 1$, and nutation between these libration limits sets in, the wobble of the top becoming greater and greater as its spin decreases, until it finally falls over.

Problem 43a. A gyroscope consists of a disk of radius 4 cm and mass 1 kg at a distance of 5 cm from the pivot, and a weight of 800 gm 10 cm on the other side of the pivot. The disk is rotated at the rate of 15 r.p.s. Find the steady slow precession for the axis horizontal. *Ans.* -0.62 r.p.s.

Problem 43b. A top has moments of inertia $C = 2000$ gm-cm^2, $A = 6000$ gm-cm^2 and it is spun so that $w = 8/\text{sec}^2$, $p = 12.65/\text{sec}$, $u = 6.00/\text{sec}^2$, $h = 5.10/\text{sec}$. Find (*a*) the velocity of spin Ω, (*b*) maximum torque Wl, (*c*) limiting cones θ_1 and θ_2, (*d*) limiting rates of precession. *Ans.* (*a*) 6.04 r.p.s., (*b*) 24.5 gm-wt cm, (*c*) 60° and 75.5°, (*d*) 2.07 radian/sec and -1.63 radian/sec.

Problem 43c. The top of problem 43*b* is spinning with its axis vertical. At what velocity of spin will it start to wobble? *Ans.* 1.91 r.p.s.

Problem 43d. A top is spinning on a perfectly smooth horizontal plane. How does its motion differ from that discussed in this article?

Problem 43e. Using a set of axes completely attached to the rotating top, derive (43–8) and (43–9) by the method described in Case II of article 37.

44. Gyroscope Subject to Arbitrary Torque. — In the preceding article we have treated the motion of a rigid body which is symmetrical about the axis of spin, when subjected to the torque of gravity. Let us now consider the motion of rotation of such a body when subject to an arbitrary torque **L**, limiting the discussion, however, to the case where the angular velocity Ω of spin is large. We can adapt the fundamental relations deduced in the last article to the present problem provided the torque and the angular momentum are referred either to a fixed point or to the center of mass of the body. Putting Ω for $\omega_z + s$ in equations (43–3) and replacing the right-hand members by the three components L_x, L_y, L_z of the impressed torque, we have

$$\left.\begin{aligned} A\dot{\omega}_x - A\omega_y\omega_z + C\Omega\omega_y &= L_x, \\ A\dot{\omega}_y + A\omega_z\omega_x - C\Omega\omega_x &= L_y, \\ C\dot{\Omega} &= L_z. \end{aligned}\right\} \tag{44–1}$$

Evidently the only effect of the component torque L_z along the axis of spin is to increase the angular velocity Ω of spin. The torques L_x and L_y, however, tend to turn the axis of the gyrostat. If Ω is sufficiently large we can neglect the first two terms on the left of the first two equations as compared with the third, and write to a sufficient degree of approximation

$$\omega_y = \frac{\Omega L_x}{C\Omega^2}, \quad \omega_x = -\frac{\Omega L_y}{C\Omega^2}.$$

These two scalar equations can be combined in the single vector equation

$$\boldsymbol{\omega} = \frac{1}{C\Omega^2}(\boldsymbol{\Omega} \times \mathbf{L}) \tag{44–2}$$

where $\boldsymbol{\Omega}$ has the direction of the axis of spin.

The angular velocity $\boldsymbol{\omega}$, at right angles to $\boldsymbol{\Omega}$ and $\mathbf{L}$, specifies the rate of turning of the axis of spin. As $C\Omega^2$ is always positive, the axis turns toward the resultant torque, as illustrated in Fig. 54, the angular velocity of rotation of the axis being proportional to the component of the torque at right angles to the axis.

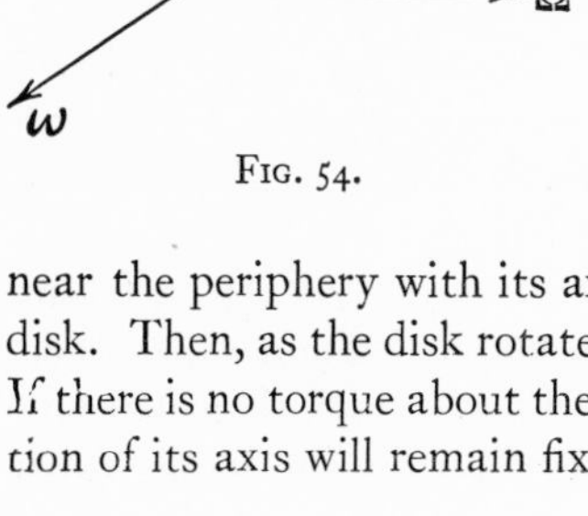

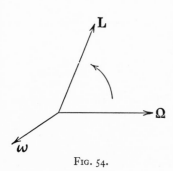

FIG. 54.

As an application of (44–2) consider a disk rotating about its axis of symmetry, which we will take as the Z_0 axis of a fixed set $X_0Y_0Z_0$ with origin at the center of the disk. Now suppose that a gyrostat is attached at its center of mass to a point on the disk near the periphery with its axis making an angle with the axis of the disk. Then, as the disk rotates, the gyrostat is carried around with it. If there is no torque about the center of mass of the gyrostat, the direction of its axis will remain fixed in space, or will precess about a fixed direction, as shown in the latter part of article 42. This means that the axis of the gyrostat, or the fixed direction about which it precesses, will rotate *relative* to the disk in the opposite sense to that in which the disk is rotating. Now, if the disk exerts a force on the axis of the gyrostat opposing the motion of the axis relative to the disk, this force will produce a torque about the center of mass of the gyrostat in the direction of the Z_0 axis. Under its influence the axis of the gyrostat will turn toward the axis about which the disk is rotating, and, if this motion is unopposed, the gyrostat will ultimately orient itself with its axis parallel to the axis of rotation of the disk.

Thus a gyrostat attached to the earth, and subject to a force opposing any rotation of its axis relative to the earth, tends to orient itself parallel to the axis of rotation of the earth. This is the principle of the gyroscopic compass, to be discussed in more detail in a later article. Again, since the elementary molecular magnets in iron are microscopic gyrostats, an unmagnetized cylindrical iron bar will become magnetized by rotation about its axis of symmetry.

The rising of a top is an interesting phenomenon which can be explained qualitatively by (44–2). An actual top does not rotate about a fixed point as was supposed in the case of the ideal top discussed in article 43, for the peg of the top is never perfectly sharp. If the peg is slightly rounded, the force of friction exerted on the top by the plane on which it is spinning lies a little to one side of the axis of a top which is not vertical. Referring to Fig. 51, where the angular velocity of spin of the top is directed along the Z axis, a component of the force of friction acts a little to the left of this axis and in the direction opposite to OX. This force gives rise to a torque about the center of mass which lies in the ZOZ_0 plane nearly at right angles to OZ and directed toward the vertical. In accord with (44–2), then, the axis of the top tends to rise. If the spin of the top is large, the axis will ultimately reach the vertical, and the top will sleep.

45. Precession of the Equinoxes. — On account of the equatorial bulge the attraction of the sun or moon on the earth gives rise to a torque about the center of mass of the latter which causes the axis of the earth to precess about the normal to the plane of the ecliptic.

Let S (Fig. 55) be the center of the sun and E the center of the earth. Take origin at the center of the earth and orient the axes so that the Z axis is parallel to the axis of rotation of the earth and $\mathbf{R}$ lies in the YZ plane. Let P be a point in the interior of the earth with coordinates x, y, z relative to E. The position vector of P is

$$\boldsymbol{\rho} = \mathbf{i}x + \mathbf{j}y + \mathbf{k}z, \qquad (45\text{–}1)$$

and the force with which the sun attracts a mass dm situated at P is

$$d\mathbf{F} = -\gamma \frac{Mdm}{r^3} \{\mathbf{i}x + \mathbf{j}(R \sin \alpha + y) + \mathbf{k}(-R \cos \alpha + z)\}. \qquad (45\text{–}2)$$

The torque $\mathbf{L}$ about E due to this force is $\boldsymbol{\rho} \times d\mathbf{F}$. However it is clear from symmetry that the resultant torque on the entire earth

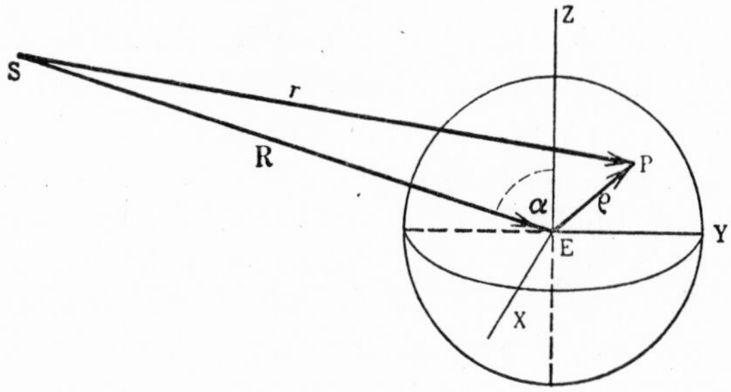

FIG. 55.

is about the X axis. Therefore we need calculate only the X component of $\mathbf{L}$, that is,

$$\left.\begin{aligned} dL_x = |\boldsymbol{\rho} \times d\mathbf{F}|_x &= -\gamma \frac{Mdm}{r^3} \{y(-R \cos \alpha + z) - z(R \sin \alpha + y)\} \\ &= \gamma \frac{MR}{r^3} \{y \cos \alpha + z \sin \alpha\}\, dm. \end{aligned}\right\} \qquad (45\text{–}3)$$

Now

$$\begin{aligned} r^2 &= R^2 + 2\mathbf{R}\cdot\boldsymbol{\rho} + \rho^2 \\ &= R^2 + 2R(y \sin \alpha - z \cos \alpha) + \rho^2, \end{aligned}$$

and

$$\frac{1}{r^3} = \frac{1}{R^3}\left\{1 - \frac{3}{R}(y \sin \alpha - z \cos \alpha) \ldots\right\},$$

to a sufficient degree of approximation. Substituting this in (45–3)

$$L_x = \gamma \frac{M}{R^2} \int \left\{1 - \frac{3}{R}(y \sin \alpha - z \cos \alpha)\right\} \{y \cos \alpha + z \sin \alpha\}\, dm.$$

On account of symmetry integrals containing the first power of y or z or the product yz vanish. Therefore

$$L_x = -3\frac{\gamma M}{R^3}\sin\alpha\cos\alpha\left\{\int y^2 dm - \int z^2 dm\right\}$$

$$= -3\frac{\gamma M}{R^3}\sin\alpha\cos\alpha\left\{\int (x^2+y^2)dm - \int (z^2+x^2)dm\right\}.$$

The first of these integrals is the moment of inertia C about the Z axis and the second the moment of inertia B about the Y axis. So

$$\mathbf{L} = 3\frac{\gamma M}{R^5}(C-B)\mathbf{R}\cdot\mathbf{k}\mathbf{R}\times\mathbf{k}. \qquad (45\text{–}4)$$

Now return to Fig. 51, the X_0Y_0 plane representing the plane of the ecliptic and the spinning earth taking the place of the top. If p is the angular velocity of the earth's revolution about the sun,

$$\mathbf{R} = R(\mathbf{i}_0\cos pt + \mathbf{j}_0\sin pt),$$

$\mathbf{i}_0$ and $\mathbf{j}_0$ being unit vectors along the fixed X_0 and Y_0 axes. In terms of the unit vectors $\mathbf{i}$, $\mathbf{j}$, $\mathbf{k}$ along the moving axes X, Y, Z,

$$\mathbf{i}_0 = \mathbf{i}\cos\psi - \mathbf{j}\cos\theta\sin\psi + \mathbf{k}\sin\theta\sin\psi,$$

$$\mathbf{j}_0 = \mathbf{i}\sin\psi + \mathbf{j}\cos\theta\cos\psi - \mathbf{k}\sin\theta\cos\psi,$$

$$\mathbf{R}\cdot\mathbf{k} = -R\sin\theta\sin(pt-\psi),$$

$$\mathbf{R}\times\mathbf{k} = R\{\mathbf{i}\cos\theta\sin(pt-\psi) - \mathbf{j}\cos(pt-\psi)\},$$

and the torque (45–4) becomes

$$\mathbf{L} = 3\frac{\gamma M}{R^3}(C-B)\{-\mathbf{i}\sin\theta\cos\theta\sin^2(pt-\psi)$$
$$+\,\mathbf{j}\sin\theta\sin(pt-\psi)\cos(pt-\psi)\}. \qquad (45\text{–}5)$$

The components of torque on the right-hand side of (43–4) must be replaced by those of (45–5). In writing down the equations of motion, however, we may omit products of the small quantities ω_x, ω_y, ω_z. Therefore, remembering that the moment of inertia A in (43–4) is the same as our present B, we have

$$B\dot{\omega}_x + C\Omega\omega_y = -\frac{3}{2}\frac{\gamma M}{R^3}(C-B)\sin\theta\cos\theta\{1-\cos 2(pt-\psi)\},$$

$$B\dot{\omega}_y - C\Omega\omega_x = \frac{3}{2}\frac{\gamma M}{R^3}(C - B) \sin\theta \sin 2(pt - \psi),$$

where Ω is the angular velocity of the earth's diurnal rotation.

These equations show that ω_x and ω_y have the angular frequency $2p$. Therefore $\dot{\omega}_x$ and $\dot{\omega}_y$ are of the order of magnitude of $2p\omega_x$ and $2p\omega_y$, which are negligible as compared with $\Omega\omega_x$ and $\Omega\omega_y$. So if we neglect the terms involving $\dot{\omega}_x$ and $\dot{\omega}_y$ in the equations above we have

$$\left.\begin{aligned} \frac{d\theta}{dt} &= \omega_x = -\frac{3}{2}\frac{\gamma M}{R^3\Omega}\frac{C - B}{C}\sin\theta \sin 2(pt - \psi), \\ \frac{d\psi}{dt} &= \frac{\omega_y}{\sin\theta} = -\frac{3}{2}\frac{\gamma M}{R^3\Omega}\frac{C - B}{C}\cos\theta\{1 - \cos 2(pt - \psi)\}. \end{aligned}\right\} \quad (45\text{–}6)$$

The first equation represents the nutation and the second the precession of the earth's axis, the mean precession being given by the first term on the right-hand side of the second equation. The negative sign indicates that the precession has the opposite sense to the velocity Ω of the earth's rotation, that is, the equinoxes precess from East to West. The nutation has an amplitude of about 9″ and the precession has a period of about 25,800 years. The greater part of the precession is due to the moon whose proximity more than compensates for its smaller mass. From the observed value of the precession the ratio of the moments of inertia B and C can be calculated.

46. Foucault's Gyroscope or Gyroscopic Compass. — A simple form of gyroscopic compass consists of a rapidly rotating disk D (Fig. 56) suspended at its center of mass. The axis of the disk is constrained to move in a horizontal plane by means of a pendulum bob B attached to the axle ab on which the disk is turning. Take the Z axis along the axis of rotation of the disk and denote the velocity of spin by s. As the disk is symmetrical about the Z axis it is not necessary for the X and Y axes to rotate with the disk in order that the equal moments of inertia A and B about these axes may remain constant. Therefore we shall take the Y axis vertical and the X axis in the horizontal plane perpendicular to Z and use

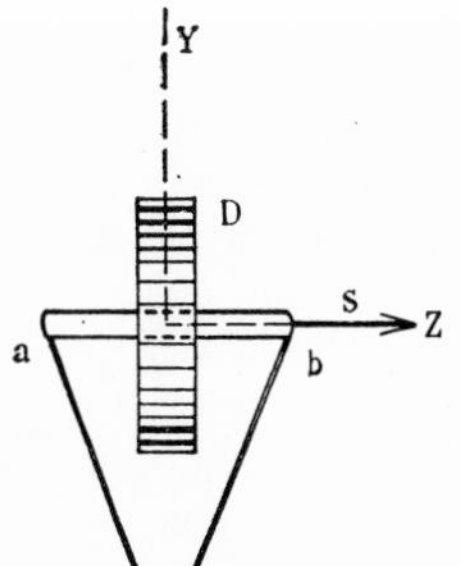

FIG. 56.

equation (37–10) in our investigation of the motion. Denote by Ω the angular velocity of the earth, by γ the latitude, and by ϕ the angle measured positive to the West which the Z axis makes with the meridian. The vertical component of the angular velocity of the earth is $\Omega \sin \gamma$ and the Northward horizontal component $\Omega \cos \gamma$. Therefore the components of angular velocity of the axes XYZ resolved along these axes are:

$$\omega_x = -\Omega \cos \gamma \sin \phi,$$

$$\omega_y = \Omega \sin \gamma + \dot{\phi},$$

$$\omega_z = \Omega \cos \gamma \cos \phi.$$

We are concerned only with rotation about the Y axis. As there is no applied torque about this axis (37–10) gives

$$A\ddot{\phi} - (A - C)\Omega^2 \cos^2 \gamma \sin \phi \cos \phi + Cs\Omega \cos \gamma \sin \phi = 0.$$

As Ω is very small compared with s we may neglect the term in Ω^2. Then

$$\ddot{\phi} + \left(\frac{C}{A} s\Omega \cos \gamma\right) \sin \phi = 0. \qquad (46\text{–}1)$$

This equation has the same form as that of the pendulum. Therefore the axis of spin oscillates about the meridian, the effective torque of restitution being maximum at the equator and falling off with the cosine of the latitude to zero at the poles. The period for small amplitudes is

$$P = 2\pi \sqrt{\frac{A}{Cs\Omega \cos \gamma}}, \qquad (46\text{–}2)$$

which is greater the higher the latitude and less the more rapid the spin. If there is some damping the axis of the gyroscope ultimately comes to rest pointing toward the true geographical North. The instrument is particularly useful as a compass in submarines since the enclosing steel hull of such vessels prohibits the use of a magnetic compass.

Problem 46a. Calculate the period of Foucault's gyroscope at latitude 40° if $s = 100$/sec. Take $C = 2A$. *Ans.* 3 min 8 sec.

REFERENCES

Routh, E. J.: *Dynamics of a System of Rigid Bodies*, Macmillan & Co., London.

Gray, Andrew: *Gyrostatics and Rotational Motion*, Macmillan & Co., London.

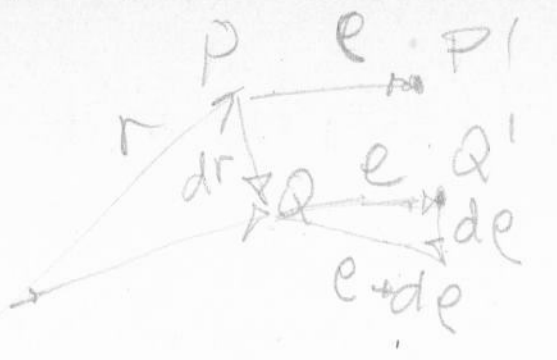

CHAPTER III

DYNAMICS OF DEFORMABLE BODIES

47. Strain and Stress. — Consider a homogeneous elastic medium which, when it is in an unstrained state, is at rest relative to axes *XYZ* fixed in an inertial system. By

$$\mathbf{r} = \mathbf{i}x + \mathbf{j}y + \mathbf{k}z$$

we shall designate the position vector of a point *P* of the medium when no strains are present. When the medium is strained the point *P* becomes displaced from its original position. This displacement we shall denote by the vector

$$\boldsymbol{\rho} = \mathbf{i}\xi + \mathbf{j}\eta + \mathbf{k}\zeta.$$

As the displacement of different points of the medium may be different at the same instant of time, $\boldsymbol{\rho}$ is a function of x, y, z as well as of the time t.

Now consider a point *Q* near to *P*. Its position vector when the medium is in the unstrained state is $\mathbf{r} + d\mathbf{r}$, and its displacement when the medium is strained is $\boldsymbol{\rho} + d\boldsymbol{\rho}$, where

$$d\boldsymbol{\rho} = dx\frac{\partial\boldsymbol{\rho}}{\partial x} + dy\frac{\partial\boldsymbol{\rho}}{\partial y} + dz\frac{\partial\boldsymbol{\rho}}{\partial z} = d\mathbf{r}\cdot\nabla\boldsymbol{\rho}. \qquad (47\text{–}1)$$

The dyadic

$$\left.\begin{aligned} \nabla\boldsymbol{\rho} = {} & \mathbf{ii}\frac{\partial\xi}{\partial x} + \mathbf{ij}\frac{\partial\eta}{\partial x} + \mathbf{ik}\frac{\partial\zeta}{\partial x} \\ & + \mathbf{ji}\frac{\partial\xi}{\partial y} + \mathbf{jj}\frac{\partial\eta}{\partial y} + \mathbf{jk}\frac{\partial\zeta}{\partial y} \\ & + \mathbf{ki}\frac{\partial\xi}{\partial z} + \mathbf{kj}\frac{\partial\eta}{\partial z} + \mathbf{kk}\frac{\partial\zeta}{\partial z} \end{aligned}\right\} \qquad (47\text{–}2)$$

is known as the *strain dyadic.* The vector $d\boldsymbol{\rho} = d\mathbf{r}\cdot\nabla\boldsymbol{\rho}$ represents the displacement of Q relative to P, which we shall suppose to be always small compared with $d\mathbf{r}$. If, for instance, $d\mathbf{r}$ is parallel to the X axis

$$d\boldsymbol{\rho}_Q = dx\mathbf{i}\cdot\nabla\boldsymbol{\rho} = \mathbf{i}\frac{\partial\xi}{\partial x}dx + \mathbf{j}\frac{\partial\eta}{\partial x}dx + \mathbf{k}\frac{\partial\zeta}{\partial x}dx.$$

The first component represents an elongation of the line PQ. The elongation $\dfrac{\partial\xi}{\partial x}$ per unit original length is known as the *tension strain*. The second and third components on the other hand represent sidewise distortions. Suppose, for instance, that the second component alone exists. Then a rectangular parallelopiped of the medium of dimensions dx, dy, dz becomes strained from the shape $PQRS$ (Fig. 57*a*) to $PQ'R'S$, where

$$QQ' = \frac{\partial\eta}{\partial x}dx.$$

This distortion is known as a *shear*. The displacement QQ' per unit distance between P and Q is defined as the *shearing strain*.

Now if we consider the displacement of S relative to P we have

$$d\boldsymbol{\rho}_S = dy\mathbf{j}\cdot\nabla\boldsymbol{\rho} = \mathbf{i}\frac{\partial\xi}{\partial y}dy + \mathbf{j}\frac{\partial\eta}{\partial y}dy + \mathbf{k}\frac{\partial\zeta}{\partial y}dy.$$

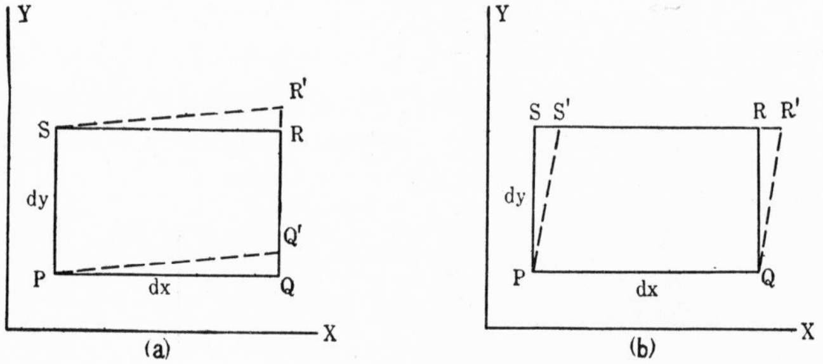

FIG. 57.

As before the second component represents an elongation of the line PS. If the first component alone is operative the rectangular parallelopiped $PQRS$ suffers the shear illustrated by the broken line parallelogram in Fig. 57*b*. The shear produced here is of the same kind as that represented in Fig. 57*a*, for the broken line parallelogram in 57*b* can be brought into the same orientation as that of 57*a* by a simple rotation about an axis through P parallel to the Z coordinate axis. Therefore the total shearing strain about the Z axis is

$$\frac{\partial \eta}{\partial x} + \frac{\partial \xi}{\partial y}.$$

If then we designate by a, b, c the tension strains parallel to the X, Y, Z axes respectively and by f, g, h the shearing strains about these axes,

$$\left.\begin{aligned} a &= \frac{\partial \xi}{\partial x}, & b &= \frac{\partial \eta}{\partial y}, & c &= \frac{\partial \zeta}{\partial z}, \\ f &= \frac{\partial \zeta}{\partial y} + \frac{\partial \eta}{\partial z}, & g &= \frac{\partial \xi}{\partial z} + \frac{\partial \zeta}{\partial x}, & h &= \frac{\partial \eta}{\partial x} + \frac{\partial \xi}{\partial y}. \end{aligned}\right\} \qquad (47\text{–}3)$$

Now the dyadic $\nabla \boldsymbol{\rho}$ may be written as the sum of a symmetric dyadic $\Phi = \frac{1}{2}\{\nabla \boldsymbol{\rho} + (\nabla \boldsymbol{\rho})_c\}$ and a skew-symmetric dyadic $\Theta = \frac{1}{2}\{\nabla \boldsymbol{\rho} - (\nabla \boldsymbol{\rho})_c\}$, where the conjugate $(\nabla \boldsymbol{\rho})_c$ of $\nabla \boldsymbol{\rho}$ is formed from (47–2) by interchanging the coefficients of **ij** and **ji**, **jk** and **kj**, **ki** and **ik**. The displacement $d\boldsymbol{\rho}$ of a nearby point Q relative to P given by (47–1) is then

$$d\boldsymbol{\rho} = d\mathbf{r}\cdot\Phi + d\mathbf{r}\cdot\Theta. \qquad (47\text{–}4)$$

Consider first the relative displacement specified by the second term in this expression. We shall show that $d\mathbf{r}\cdot\Theta$ represents displacements of neighboring points due to a rotation about an axis through P unaccompanied by distortion. For

$$\begin{aligned} d\mathbf{r}\cdot\Theta &= \tfrac{1}{2}d\mathbf{r}\cdot\{\nabla \boldsymbol{\rho} - (\nabla \boldsymbol{\rho})_c\} \\ &= \tfrac{1}{2}\{d\mathbf{r}\cdot\nabla \boldsymbol{\rho} - \nabla \boldsymbol{\rho}\cdot d\mathbf{r}\} \\ &= \tfrac{1}{2}(\nabla \times \boldsymbol{\rho}) \times d\mathbf{r} \end{aligned} \qquad (47\text{–}5)$$

since $d\mathbf{r}$ used as a prefactor with the conjugate of a dyadic is equivalent to $d\mathbf{r}$ as a postfactor with the dyadic itself. But, if $\boldsymbol{\theta}$ is a vector having the direction of the axis of a pure rotation about P, and a magnitude equal to the angle turned through, the linear displacement of a point Q initially at a distance $d\mathbf{r}$ from P is $\boldsymbol{\theta} \times d\mathbf{r}$, provided the angle θ is small. Comparing with (47–5) we see that $d\mathbf{r}\cdot\Theta$ represents a displacement of neighboring points relative to P such as would be caused by a rotation $\boldsymbol{\theta} = \frac{1}{2}(\nabla \times \boldsymbol{\rho})$ about an axis through P.

When the medium is strained P suffers a displacement $\boldsymbol{\rho}$ and a neighboring point Q a displacement $\boldsymbol{\rho} + d\boldsymbol{\rho}$. Hence the position vector of Q relative to P in the strained state is

$$d\mathbf{r} + d\boldsymbol{\rho} = d\mathbf{r}\cdot(\mathbf{I} + \Phi + \Theta).$$

Let us fix the magnitude of $d\mathbf{r}$ but allow it to assume all directions. Then its terminus describes a sphere which represents the locus of particles equidistant from P in the unstrained state of the medium. In the strained state of the medium the position vector relative to P of a particle originally at a distance $d\mathbf{r}$ becomes $d\mathbf{r}\cdot(\mathbf{I} + \Phi + \Theta)$. Now, since $\mathbf{I} + \Phi$ is a symmetric dyadic, the terminus of the vector $d\mathbf{r}\cdot(\mathbf{I} + \Phi)$ laid off from P describes the surface of an ellipsoid as $d\mathbf{r}$ varies in direction (problem 18*a*). Altogether, then, the most

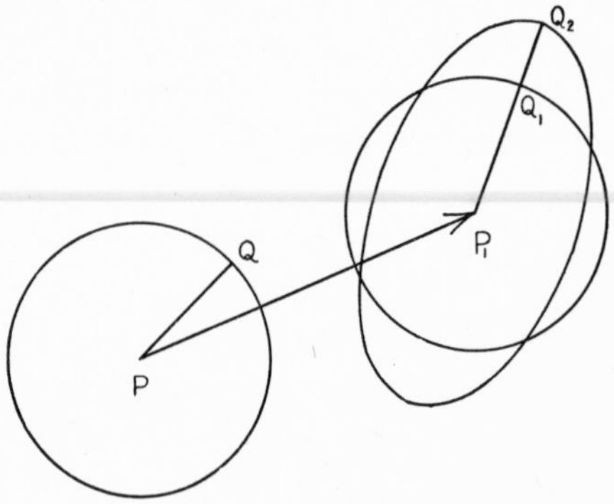

Fig. 58.

general type of small strain consists of a rotation $\frac{1}{2}\nabla \times \boldsymbol{\rho}$ of neighboring points about P plus a distortion such as would convert a small sphere with P as center into an ellipsoid. The displacements are illustrated in Fig. 58 where P goes to P_1, Q is first displaced to Q_1 on account of the rotation and then to Q_2 on account of the distortion.

Since $d\mathbf{r}\cdot\Theta$ represents the rotation of the medium about P and $d\mathbf{r}\cdot\Phi$ the distortion of the medium relative to P, the dyadic Θ may be named the *rotation dyadic* and Φ the *pure-strain dyadic.*

From (47–2) we see that

$$\left.\begin{aligned}\Phi = \mathbf{ii}\frac{\partial\xi}{\partial x} &+ \mathbf{ij}\tfrac{1}{2}\left(\frac{\partial\eta}{\partial x}+\frac{\partial\xi}{\partial y}\right) + \mathbf{ik}\tfrac{1}{2}\left(\frac{\partial\xi}{\partial z}+\frac{\partial\zeta}{\partial x}\right)\\ &+ \mathbf{ji}\tfrac{1}{2}\left(\frac{\partial\eta}{\partial x}+\frac{\partial\xi}{\partial y}\right) + \mathbf{jj}\frac{\partial\eta}{\partial y} + \mathbf{jk}\tfrac{1}{2}\left(\frac{\partial\zeta}{\partial y}+\frac{\partial\eta}{\partial z}\right)\\ &+ \mathbf{ki}\tfrac{1}{2}\left(\frac{\partial\xi}{\partial z}+\frac{\partial\zeta}{\partial x}\right) + \mathbf{kj}\tfrac{1}{2}\left(\frac{\partial\zeta}{\partial y}+\frac{\partial\eta}{\partial z}\right) + \mathbf{kk}\frac{\partial\zeta}{\partial z}\end{aligned}\right\} \quad (47\text{–}6)$$

or, when expressed in terms of the tension strains a, b, c and the shearing strains f, g, h,

$$\left.\begin{aligned}\Phi &= a\mathbf{ii} + \tfrac{1}{2}h\mathbf{ij} + \tfrac{1}{2}g\mathbf{ik}\\ &+ \tfrac{1}{2}h\mathbf{ji} + b\mathbf{jj} + \tfrac{1}{2}f\mathbf{jk}\\ &+ \tfrac{1}{2}g\mathbf{ki} + \tfrac{1}{2}f\mathbf{kj} + c\mathbf{kk}.\end{aligned}\right\} \quad (47\text{–}7)$$

As this dyadic is symmetric it may be put in the form

$$\Phi = a\mathbf{ii} + b\mathbf{jj} + c\mathbf{kk} \quad (47\text{–}8)$$

by a suitable orientation of the axes XYZ.

Consider a rectangular parallelopiped of the unstrained medium of dimensions dx, dy, dz. Using (47–7) we find that when the medium suffers a pure strain this rectangular block is distorted into a parallelopiped whose edges are

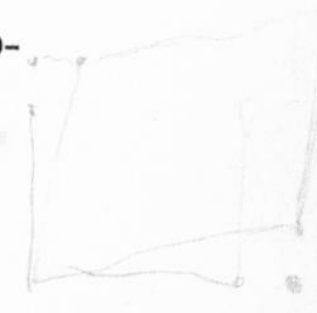

$$\begin{aligned}\mathbf{i}dx + dx\,\mathbf{i}\cdot\Phi &= \{(1+a)\mathbf{i} + \tfrac{1}{2}h\mathbf{j} + \tfrac{1}{2}g\mathbf{k}\}\,dx,\\ \mathbf{j}dy + dy\,\mathbf{j}\cdot\Phi &= \{\tfrac{1}{2}h\mathbf{i} + (1+b)\mathbf{j} + \tfrac{1}{2}f\mathbf{k}\}\,dy,\\ \mathbf{k}dz + dz\,\mathbf{k}\cdot\Phi &= \{\tfrac{1}{2}g\mathbf{i} + \tfrac{1}{2}f\mathbf{j} + (1+c)\mathbf{k}\}\,dz.\end{aligned}$$

The volume of this parallelopiped is given by the triple scalar product of the three edges. As the strains are small we can neglect terms involving the products of two strains, getting

$$\begin{vmatrix} 1+a, & \tfrac{1}{2}h, & \tfrac{1}{2}g\\ \tfrac{1}{2}h, & 1+b, & \tfrac{1}{2}f\\ \tfrac{1}{2}g, & \tfrac{1}{2}f, & 1+c\end{vmatrix}\,dx\,dy\,dz = (1+a+b+c)\,dx\,dy\,dz$$

for the volume. Denoting by V the original volume $dx\,dy\,dz$, the increase in volume is

$$dV = (a+b+c)V.$$

The *dilatation* is defined as the increase in volume per unit original volume. It is

$$\frac{dV}{V} = a + b + c = \frac{\partial \xi}{\partial x} + \frac{\partial \eta}{\partial y} + \frac{\partial \zeta}{\partial z} = \nabla \cdot \boldsymbol{\rho}. \tag{47-9}$$

Next we shall consider the stresses in a homogeneous elastic medium. Suppose the medium to be divided into two parts by a plane through P perpendicular to the unit vector $\mathbf{n}_1$. The stress $\mathbf{S}_n$ across the plane is defined as the force exerted by the portion of the medium on the positive side of the plane on the portion of the medium on the negative side per unit area of the surface of separation. Usually the stress $\mathbf{S}_n$ is resolved into components normal and tangential to the plane separating the two portions of the medium. The former is designated as a *tension* if positive or a *pressure* if negative; the latter is known as a *shearing stress*. Reversal of the direction of the unit vector $\mathbf{n}_1$ perpendicular to the plane through P changes the former positive side of the plane into the negative side and *vice versa*. Therefore the law of action and reaction requires that reversal of the direction of $\mathbf{n}_1$ should reverse the direction of the stress. Consequently a tension remains a tension, or a pressure a pressure, irrespective of the arbitrary sense of the positive normal to the plane across which it is acting.

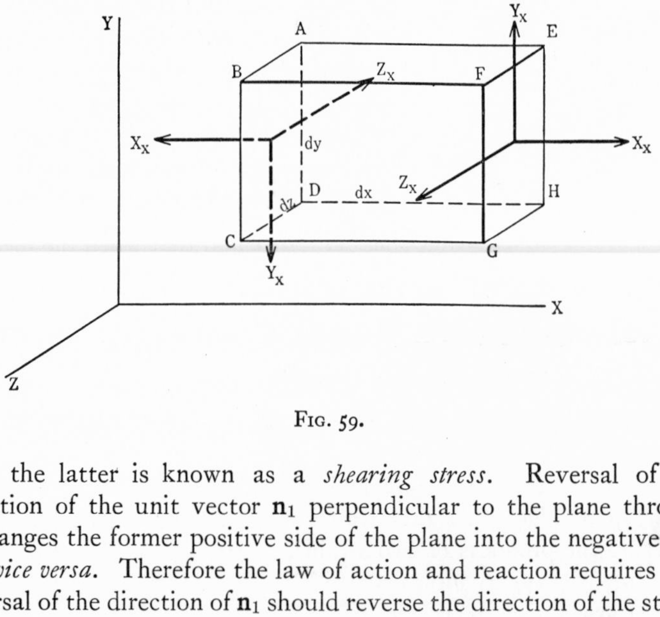

FIG. 59.

In order to devise a convenient notation, let us consider the stresses acting on a small rectangular parallelopiped of the medium of dimensions dx, dy, dz (Fig. 59). We shall designate the components of stress on the surface *EFGH* perpendicular to the X axis by X_x, Y_x, Z_x. In each case the capital letter indicates the direction of the stress and the subscript the direction of the positive normal to the surface on which it acts. Similarly X_y, Y_y, Z_y are the components of stress on *ABFE* and X_z, Y_z, Z_z those on *BCGF*. As the positive normal to *ABCD* has the opposite sense to that to *EFGH* the components of stress are reversed as indicated in the figure. For our present purposes we need not take into account infinitesimal differences in the magnitudes of corresponding stresses on opposite faces.

Suppose we wish to find the stress $\mathbf{S}_n$ on a surface whose normal $\mathbf{n}_1$ makes an angle with the coordinate axes, such as the surface *ABC* in Fig. 60. Consider the small tetrahedron *OABC*, the outward drawn normal to each face being taken as positive. If σ denotes the area of the face *ABC* and l_1, l_2, l_3 the direction cosines of the normal, the areas of the faces *OBC*, *OCA* and *OAB* are respectively σl_1, σl_2 and σl_3. Since the amount of matter inside the tetrahedron can be made as small as desired by making the tetrahedron itself sufficiently small, the forces on the surface *ABC* must be in equilibrium with those on the faces *OAB*, *OBC* and *OCA*. Therefore

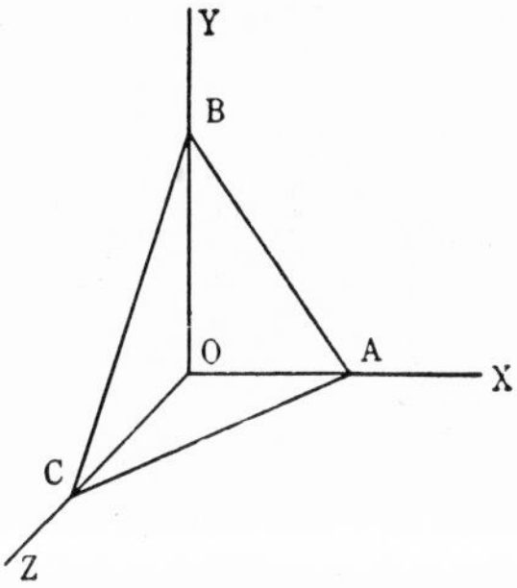

FIG. 60.

$$\sigma \mathbf{S}_n = \mathbf{i}(\sigma l_1 X_x + \sigma l_2 X_y + \sigma l_3 X_z) + \mathbf{j}(\sigma l_1 Y_x + \sigma l_2 Y_y + \sigma l_3 Y_z) + \mathbf{k}(\sigma l_1 Z_x + \sigma l_2 Z_y + \sigma l_3 Z_z).$$

Dividing by σ and remembering that the unit normal $\mathbf{n}_1$ to *ABC* is given by

$$\mathbf{n}_1 = \mathbf{i}l_1 + \mathbf{j}l_2 + \mathbf{k}l_3,$$

we have

$$\left.\begin{aligned} \mathbf{S}_n = {} & \mathbf{i}(l_1 X_x + l_2 X_y + l_3 X_z) + \mathbf{j}(l_1 Y_x + l_2 Y_y + l_3 Y_z) \\ & + \mathbf{k}(l_1 Z_x + l_2 Z_y + l_3 Z_z) \\ = {} & \mathbf{n}_1 \cdot \mathbf{ii} X_x + \mathbf{n}_1 \cdot \mathbf{ij} Y_x + \mathbf{n}_1 \cdot \mathbf{ik} Z_x \\ & + \mathbf{n}_1 \cdot \mathbf{ji} X_y + \mathbf{n}_1 \cdot \mathbf{jj} Y_y + \mathbf{n}_1 \cdot \mathbf{jk} Z_y \\ & + \mathbf{n}_1 \cdot \mathbf{ki} X_z + \mathbf{n}_1 \cdot \mathbf{kj} Y_z + \mathbf{n}_1 \cdot \mathbf{kk} Z_z \\ = {} & \mathbf{n}_1 \cdot \Psi, \end{aligned}\right\} \quad (47\text{–}10)$$

where Ψ is the *stress dyadic*

$$\begin{aligned}\Psi = \quad & \mathbf{ii}X_x + \mathbf{ij}Y_x + \mathbf{ik}Z_x \\ & + \mathbf{ji}X_y + \mathbf{jj}Y_y + \mathbf{jk}Z_y \\ & + \mathbf{ki}X_z + \mathbf{kj}Y_z + \mathbf{kk}Z_z.\end{aligned}$$

That this dyadic is symmetric can be shown very simply. For consider the torque about the Z axis due to the stresses on the faces of the rectangular parallelopiped of Fig. 59. The torque is due to two couples of moments $(Y_x dy\, dz)dx$ and $-(X_y dz\, dx)dy$ respectively. Equating the torque to the product of the moment of inertia C of the block about an axis through its center of mass parallel to the Z coordinate axis by its angular acceleration about this axis,

$$(Y_x dy\, dz)dx - (X_y dz\, dx)dy = C\frac{d\omega_z}{dt} = D\, dx\, dy\, dz\, \frac{dx^2 + dy^2}{12}\frac{d\omega_z}{dt},$$

where D is the density of the medium. Therefore

$$Y_x - X_y = D\frac{dx^2 + dy^2}{12}\frac{d\omega_z}{dt}.$$

Hence, as dx and dy are infinitesimals, in the limit Y_x must equal X_y. Similarly Z_y is equal to Y_z and X_z to Z_x. So instead of nine independent components of stress we have but six. Putting

$$\begin{aligned} P &\equiv X_x, & S &\equiv Z_y = Y_z, \\ Q &\equiv Y_y, & T &\equiv X_z = Z_x, \\ R &\equiv Z_z, & U &\equiv Y_x = X_y, \end{aligned}$$

the stress dyadic may be written

$$\left.\begin{aligned}\Psi = \quad & P\mathbf{ii} + U\mathbf{ij} + T\mathbf{ik} \\ & + U\mathbf{ji} + Q\mathbf{jj} + S\mathbf{jk} \\ & + T\mathbf{ki} + S\mathbf{kj} + R\mathbf{kk}.\end{aligned}\right\} \qquad (47\text{–}11)$$

By a suitable orientation of the axes this dyadic may be put in the form

$$\Psi = P\mathbf{ii} + Q\mathbf{jj} + R\mathbf{kk}. \qquad (47\text{–}12)$$

Hooke's law states that the stresses are homogeneous linear functions of the pure strains, provided the elastic limit of the material is not exceeded. In an anisotropic medium directions of the coordinate axes are fixed by the geometry of the substance; therefore the stress and strain dyadics must be taken in the forms (47–11) and (47–7), respectively. Consequently we have to consider six stresses and six strains. As each stress is a function of all the strains, there are thirty-six coefficients of elasticity. These, however, are not all independent, and may be reduced in number to twenty-one.

We shall confine our subsequent discussion to isotropic media. First we shall orient the coordinate axes so as to bring the stress dyadic into the form (47–12), in which only tension stresses appear. As the medium has the same properties in all directions, it is clear that a tension stress can produce only a tension strain. Hence the pure-strain dyadic will assume the form (47–8) when referred to the same axes. By this orientation of axes the shears have been eliminated and all the strains reduced to tensions. In fact it is quite clear that the shear of the unit cube $OABC$ represented by the broken line quadrilateral section in Fig. 61 may be viewed as a tension along the diagonal OB. We have then the three tensions P, Q, R and the three tension strains a, b, c to consider. If the tension P is applied alone it produces a compression at right angles as well as an elongation parallel to itself. Therefore P is a function of b and c as well as of a, though symmetry requires that it should depend in the same way on both b and c. Consequently we may write

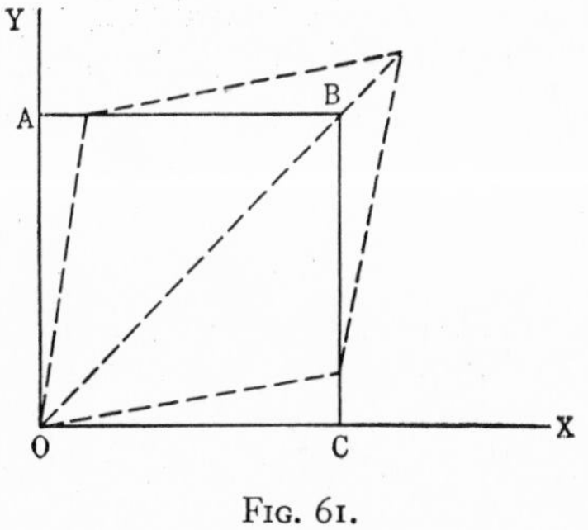

FIG. 61.

$$P = Aa + Bb + Bc$$

and similar relations for Q and R. We shall find it more convenient, however, to write these relations in the form

$$\left.\begin{aligned} P &= \lambda(a+b+c) + 2\mu a = \lambda\nabla\cdot\boldsymbol{\rho} + 2\mu\frac{\partial\xi}{\partial x}, \\ Q &= \lambda(a+b+c) + 2\mu b = \lambda\nabla\cdot\boldsymbol{\rho} + 2\mu\frac{\partial\eta}{\partial y}, \\ R &= \lambda(a+b+c) + 2\mu c = \lambda\nabla\cdot\boldsymbol{\rho} + 2\mu\frac{\partial\zeta}{\partial z}. \end{aligned}\right\} \quad (47\text{–}13)$$

Therefore, as Ψ has the form (47–12) and Φ the form (47–8) when referred to the coordinate axes which we have selected,

$$\Psi = \lambda\nabla\cdot\boldsymbol{\rho}\,\mathbf{I} + 2\mu\Phi. \quad (47\text{–}14)$$

As this is an equation between dyadics it holds no matter whether the axes are oriented so that Ψ and Φ have the simple forms (47–12) and (47–8) or oriented so that Ψ and Φ are expressed by the more general forms (47–11) and (47–7). In the first case the equation is equivalent to the three scalar equations obtained by equating each element of the dyadic on the left to the sum of the corresponding elements of the two dyadics on the right; in the second case it is equivalent to nine scalar equations obtained in the same way, of which, however, three are redundant.

To investigate the physical significance of the two elastic constants λ and μ we shall consider two special cases.

Case I. — With the axes oriented so that Ψ and Φ have the simple forms (47–12) and (47–8), suppose that we have a hydrostatic tension such that $P = Q = R$. Then $a = b = c$ from (56–13) and

$$\begin{aligned} P &= (\lambda + \tfrac{2}{3}\mu)(a+b+c) = (\lambda + \tfrac{2}{3}\mu)\nabla\cdot\boldsymbol{\rho} \\ &= (\lambda + \tfrac{2}{3}\mu)\frac{dV}{V}, \end{aligned}$$

from (47–9). The *modulus of volume elasticity* k is defined as the ratio of the hydrostatic tension P to the dilatation dV/V. Therefore

$$k = \lambda + \tfrac{2}{3}\mu. \quad (47\text{–}15)$$

Case II. — With the axes oriented so that Ψ and Φ have the more general forms (47–11) and (47–7) let us pick out the **ij** elements in the equation (47–14). We get

$$U = \mu h.$$

Now U is the shearing stress about the Z axis and h the shearing strain about this axis. The ratio μ of the shearing stress to the shearing strain is known as the *modulus of shearing elasticity* or the *rigidity*.

In terms of the modulus of volume elasticity k and the rigidity μ equation (47–14) relating stress to strain becomes

$$\Psi = (k - \tfrac{2}{3}\mu)\nabla\cdot\boldsymbol{\rho}\mathbf{I} + 2\mu\Phi. \quad * \qquad (47\text{–}16)$$

It is of interest to express in terms of these elastic constants the familiar *Young's modulus Y* which represents the ratio of the tension stress on a stretched wire or rod to the tension strain. Returning to (47–13) let us take the X axis along the length of the wire. Then $Q = R = 0$ and $b = c = -[\lambda/2(\lambda + \mu)]a$. Consequently

$$P = (\lambda - \frac{\lambda^2}{\lambda + \mu} + 2\mu)a = \frac{\mu(3\lambda + 2\mu)}{\lambda + \mu}\, a,$$

and Young's modulus is

$$Y = \frac{P}{a} = \frac{\mu(3\lambda + 2\mu)}{\lambda + \mu} = \frac{3k\mu}{k + \frac{1}{3}\mu}. \qquad (47\text{–}17)$$

The ratio

$$\sigma_p = -\frac{b}{a} = \frac{\lambda}{2(\lambda + \mu)} = \frac{1}{2}\frac{3k - 2\mu}{3k + \mu} \qquad (47\text{–}18)$$

of the compression strain at right angles to P to the tension strain parallel to P is known as *Poisson's ratio*. Poisson supposed that $\lambda = \mu$ and hence $\sigma_p = \frac{1}{4}$. Actually isotropic media have a Poisson's ratio nearly equal to this value. In any event, this ratio cannot exceed one-half, for if it did (47–18) would require that either k or μ should be negative.

Problem 47a. Write out the nine scalar equations equivalent to equation (47–16) when Ψ and Φ are expressed in the general forms (47–11) and (47–7).

Problem 47b. Show that the potential energy per unit volume of a strained isotropic body is

$$\tfrac{1}{2}\lambda(a + b + c)^2 + \mu(a^2 + b^2 + c^2 + \tfrac{1}{2}f^2 + \tfrac{1}{2}g^2 + \tfrac{1}{2}h^2).$$

* M&F write this: $\Psi = \lambda \mathbf{I}\,\nabla\cdot\rho + \mu(\nabla\rho + \rho\nabla)$ (p. 1787), where $\rho\nabla \equiv (\nabla\rho)_c$ (p. 175)

(*Hint.* — Find the work done by the tension P in producing the strain a, b and c being kept zero; then the work done by Q in producing the strain b, a being kept constant and c being kept zero; etc.)

48. Torsion Pendulum. — Consider a vertical wire (Fig. 62) of radius a and length l fixed at the upper end. Let a couple be applied at the lower end sufficient to twist the wire through an angle θ about the Z axis. Then the shearing strain on a hollow cylindrical shell of inner radius r and outer radius $r + dr$ is

$$s = \frac{r\theta}{l},$$

and the shearing stress

$$S = \mu s = \mu \frac{r\theta}{l},$$

where μ is the rigidity of the material of which the wire is composed. The torque about the Z axis per unit area of the base of the shell is

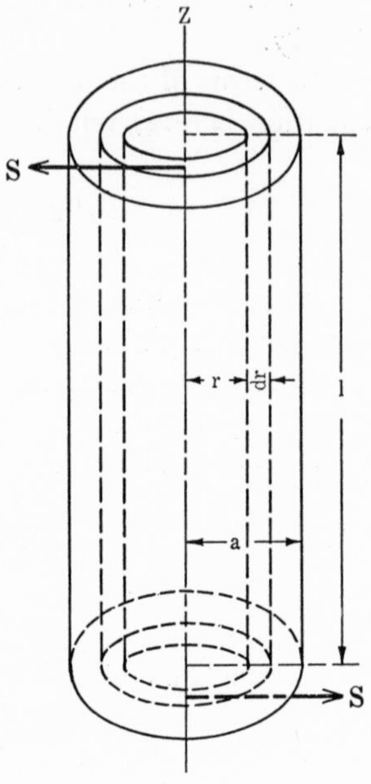

FIG. 62.

$$rS = \mu \frac{\theta}{l} r^2$$

and the torque on the whole base of the shell

$$dL = 2\pi\mu \frac{\theta}{l} r^3 dr.$$

Integrating from 0 to a

$$L = \frac{\pi}{2} \mu \frac{a^4}{l} \theta. \qquad (48\text{–}1)$$

If a uniform horizontal bar or disk is rigidly attached at its center to the lower end of the wire and twisted through an angle θ the wire will exert on it a restoring torque equal to L. So if the moment of inertia of the bar or disk about a vertical axis through its center of mass is denoted by I the equation of motion of the free oscillations is

$$I\frac{d^2\theta}{dt^2} = -\frac{\pi}{2}\mu\frac{a^4}{l}\theta,$$

provided the moment of inertia of the wire itself is negligible, or

$$\frac{d^2\theta}{dt^2} + \frac{\pi\mu a^4}{2lI}\theta = 0. \tag{48-2}$$

This is the equation of simple harmonic angular motion with period

$$P = 2\pi\sqrt{\frac{2lI}{\pi\mu a^4}}. \tag{48-3}$$

If P, I, l and a are measured the coefficient of rigidity can be calculated from this formula.

If a second disk having a moment of inertia I' is fastened below the first, the period P' is

$$P' = 2\pi\sqrt{\frac{2l(I+I')}{\pi\mu a^4}}.$$

Dividing this equation by (44–3) and solving for I',

$$I' = I\frac{P'^2 - P^2}{P^2}. \tag{48-4}$$

Therefore if I is known I' can be determined by measuring the period with and without the second disk.

Problem 48a. To calibrate a torsion fibre a cylindrical rod of mass 200 gm, length 10 cm and diameter 1 cm is suspended from the fibre, and, when set in oscillation, is found to have a period of 3 sec. Find the torque necessary to twist the fibre through 1°. *Ans.* 129 dyne cm per 1°.

49. Transverse Waves along Wires. — Consider a horizontal wire stretched by a force S. We shall confine ourselves to a consideration of small vertical oscillations of the particles of the wire. Denoting the vertical displacement of a point P of the wire (Fig. 63) by η, the curve assumed by the wire when distorted is

$$y = \eta(x, t).$$

Now consider a small section of the wire of length dx. Denote the coordinates of its mid-point P by x and η. On the right end B we have the force S acting at the angle α_2 where

$$\tan \alpha_2 = \left(\frac{\partial \eta}{\partial x}\right)_B = \left(\frac{\partial \eta}{\partial x}\right)_P + \frac{\partial}{\partial x}\left(\frac{\partial \eta}{\partial x}\right)\frac{dx}{2},$$

and on the left end A the same force S acting at the angle α_1 where

$$\tan \alpha_1 = \left(\frac{\partial \eta}{\partial x}\right)_A = \left(\frac{\partial \eta}{\partial x}\right)_P - \frac{\partial}{\partial x}\left(\frac{\partial \eta}{\partial x}\right)\frac{dx}{2}.$$

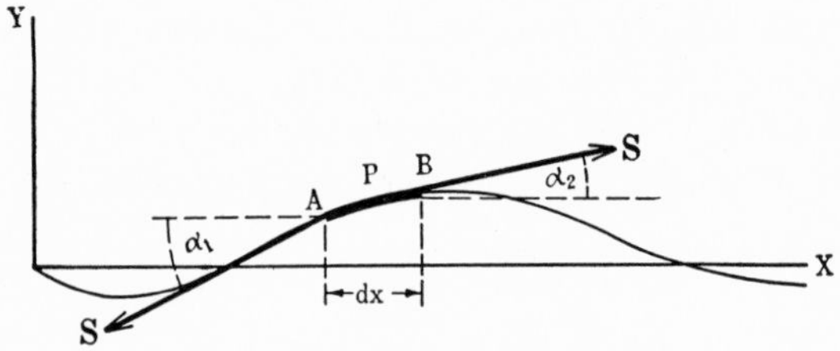

FIG. 63.

The total upward force on this section of the wire is

$$dK_y = S \sin \alpha_2 - S \sin \alpha_1 \doteq S(\tan \alpha_2 - \tan \alpha_1)$$

since the tangents are approximately equal to the sines as the angles are small. Therefore

$$dK_y = S \frac{\partial^2 \eta}{\partial x^2} dx. \tag{49–1}$$

If D is the mass of the wire per unit length the mass of the section under consideration is Ddx, and its vertical acceleration is $\frac{\partial^2 \eta}{\partial t^2}$. Therefore the equation of motion is

$$Ddx \frac{\partial^2 \eta}{\partial t^2} = S \frac{\partial^2 \eta}{\partial x^2} dx,$$

or

$$\frac{\partial^2 \eta}{\partial t^2} = \frac{S}{D} \frac{\partial^2 \eta}{\partial x^2}. \tag{49–2}$$

This equation is known as the *wave equation*. Its general solution is

$$\eta = f_1(x - vt) + f_2(x + vt), \qquad v \equiv \sqrt{\frac{S}{D}}, \tag{49–3}$$

where f_1 and f_2 are arbitrary functions, as may easily be verified by substitution.

Consider the solution

$$\eta_1 = f_1(x - vt). \tag{49–4}$$

As

$$x + v\tau - v(t + \tau) = x - vt$$

the value of the displacement η_1 at the distance $x + v\tau$ from the origin at the time $t + \tau$ is the same as that at x at the time t. Hence (49–4) represents a wave progressing in the positive X direction with velocity v. Similarly in the case of the solution

$$\eta_2 = f_2(x + vt) \tag{49–5}$$

we note that

$$x - v\tau + v(t + \tau) = x + vt,$$

which shows that the displacement η_2 at the distance $x - v\tau$ from the origin at the time $t + \tau$ is the same as that at x at the time t. Therefore (49–5) represents a wave progressing in the negative X direction with velocity v.

If the wave is a simple harmonic wave moving to the right we may write

$$\eta = A \sin a(x - vt),$$

where A is the amplitude, or

$$\eta = A \cos a(x - vt).$$

As the wave length λ is the distance from one crest to the next,

$$a(x - vt) + 2\pi = a(x + \lambda - vt),$$

and

$$a = \frac{2\pi}{\lambda}.$$

Therefore

$$\eta = A \sin \frac{2\pi}{\lambda}(x - vt). \tag{49–6}$$

Also, if P is the period, $v = \lambda/P$. Hence

$$\eta = A \sin 2\pi \left(\frac{x}{\lambda} - \frac{t}{P}\right). \tag{49–7}$$

Finally, if we put $\omega \equiv 2\pi/P$ and $\sigma \equiv 2\pi/\lambda$, then $v = \lambda/P = \omega/\sigma$ and

$$\eta = A \sin (\sigma x - \omega t). \tag{49–8}$$

As convenience suggests we may use one or another of these three expressions for the displacement. In any case we may add an arbitrary phase angle or change from the sine to the cosine function.

Let us compute the energy per unit length of a wire along which the progressive wave (49–8) is traveling. The vertical velocity of a point P is

$$\frac{\partial \eta}{\partial t} = -\omega A \cos (\sigma x - \omega t),$$

and therefore the kinetic energy per unit length is

$$T = \tfrac{1}{2} D\omega^2 A^2 \cos^2 (\sigma x - \omega t). \tag{49–9}$$

The force of restitution (49–1) per unit length is

$$F_y = S \frac{\partial^2 \eta}{\partial x^2} = -S\sigma^2 A \sin (\sigma x - \omega t) = -D\omega^2 \eta,$$

and the potential energy of a unit length is

$$\left.\begin{aligned} V &= -\int_0^\eta F_y d\eta = D\omega^2 \int \eta d\eta = \tfrac{1}{2} D\omega^2 \eta^2 \\ &= \tfrac{1}{2} D\omega^2 A^2 \sin^2 (\sigma x - \omega t). \end{aligned}\right\} \tag{49–10}$$

Evidently the mean potential and kinetic energies are the same. The constant total energy per unit length is

$$U = T + V = \tfrac{1}{2} D\omega^2 A^2. \tag{49–11}$$

Problem 49a. Show that two progressive waves of the same amplitude and frequency traveling in opposite directions along a stretched wire give rise to standing waves. Find the positions of nodes and loops, calculate the kinetic and potential energies per unit length, and show that the mean total energy is the sum of the energies of the two progressive waves taken separately.

50. Reflection of Waves Along Wires. — Consider two wires 1 and 2 (Fig. 64) of linear densities D_1 and D_2, respectively, connected at the point O and under a uniform stretching force S. A progressive simple harmonic wave

$$\eta_1 = A_1 \cos(\sigma_1 x - \omega t), \qquad \sigma_1 = \frac{\omega}{v_1} = \omega\sqrt{\frac{D_1}{S}},$$

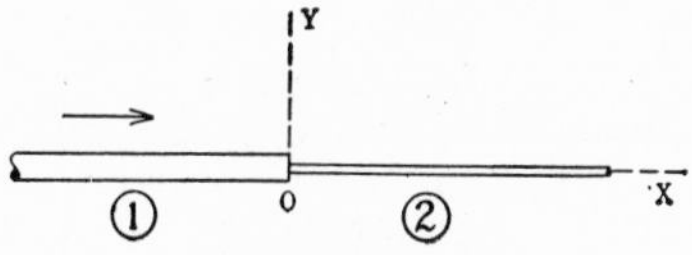

FIG. 64.

is traveling along wire 1 toward the right. At O it is partially reflected and partially transmitted. Evidently the reflected and transmitted waves must have the same frequency as the incident wave. So we have for the reflected wave

$$\eta'_1 = A'_1 \cos(\sigma_1 x + \omega t + \epsilon'_1),$$

and for the transmitted wave

$$\eta_2 = A_2 \cos(\sigma_2 x - \omega t + \epsilon_2), \qquad \sigma_2 = \frac{\omega}{v_2} = \omega\sqrt{\frac{D_2}{S}},$$

where ϵ'_1 and ϵ_2 are included to take account of any possible change of phase.

As the vertical displacements of the two wires at the point O must be the same,

$$(\eta_1 + \eta'_1)_{x=0} = (\eta_2)_{x=0}. \qquad (50\text{–}1)$$

Furthermore, the vertical forces exerted by the two wires on the point of junction O must be equal and opposite. As this force, in the notation of the last article, is

$$K_y = S \sin\alpha$$

$$\doteq S \tan\alpha = S\frac{\partial \eta}{\partial x},$$

it follows that

$$\left(\frac{\partial \eta_1}{\partial x} + \frac{\partial \eta'_1}{\partial x}\right)_{x=0} = \left(\frac{\partial \eta_2}{\partial x}\right)_{x=0} \qquad (50\text{–}2)$$

since the stretching force S is the same in each wire.

Equations (50–1) and (50–2) are known as *boundary conditions.* Putting in the values of η_1, η'_1, η_2 and of their derivatives at $x = 0$, we find

$$A_1 \cos \omega t + A'_1 \cos (\omega t + \epsilon'_1) = A_2 \cos (\omega t - \epsilon_2), \qquad (50\text{–}3)$$

$$\sigma_1\{A_1 \sin \omega t - A'_1 \sin (\omega t + \epsilon'_1)\} = \sigma_2 A_2 \sin (\omega t - \epsilon_2). \qquad (50\text{–}4)$$

Expanding the trigonometrical functions these relations become

$$(A_1 + A'_1 \cos \epsilon'_1) \cos \omega t - A'_1 \sin \epsilon'_1 \sin \omega t$$
$$= A_2 \cos \epsilon_2 \cos \omega t + A_2 \sin \epsilon_2 \sin \omega t,$$

$$\sigma_1\{(A_1 - A'_1 \cos \epsilon'_1) \sin \omega t - A'_1 \sin \epsilon'_1 \cos \omega t\}$$
$$= \sigma_2 A_2 \cos \epsilon_2 \sin \omega t - \sigma_2 A_2 \sin \epsilon_2 \cos \omega t.$$

These equations must hold for all values of the time. If we make $\omega t = 0$ we find

$$A_1 + A'_1 \cos \epsilon'_1 = A_2 \cos \epsilon_2, \qquad \sigma_1 A'_1 \sin \epsilon'_1 = \sigma_2 A_2 \sin \epsilon_2,$$

whereas if $\omega t = \pi/2$

$$-A'_1 \sin \epsilon'_1 = A_2 \sin \epsilon_2, \qquad \sigma_1(A_1 - A'_1 \cos \epsilon'_1) = \sigma_2 A_2 \cos \epsilon_2.$$

Evidently these conditions are sufficient to satisfy (50–3) and (50–4) for all values of the time.

Eliminating $\sin \epsilon'_1$ from the equations involving the sines, we have

$$(\sigma_1 + \sigma_2) A_2 \sin \epsilon_2 = 0.$$

Therefore $\epsilon_2 = 0$ and in consequence $\epsilon'_1 = 0$. The remaining equations then become

$$A_1 + A'_1 = A_2, \qquad (50\text{–}5)$$

$$\sigma_1(A_1 - A'_1) = \sigma_2 A_2. \qquad (50\text{–}6)$$

The *coefficient of reflection R* is defined as the ratio of the amplitude of the reflected wave to that of the incident wave. Dividing (50–6) by (50–5) to eliminate A_2,

$$\frac{A_1 - A'_1}{A_1 + A'_1} = \frac{\sigma_2}{\sigma_1}$$

and

$$R = \frac{A'_1}{A_1} = \frac{\sigma_1 - \sigma_2}{\sigma_1 + \sigma_2} = \frac{\sqrt{D_1} - \sqrt{D_2}}{\sqrt{D_1} + \sqrt{D_2}}. \qquad (50\text{–}7)$$

If $D_1 > D_2$ the coefficient of reflection is positive and A'_1 has the same sign as A_1. In this case reflection takes place without change in phase. If, on the other hand, $D_1 < D_2$, A'_1 has the opposite sign to A_1 and the reflected wave is 180° out of phase with the incident wave at O.

The *reflecting power* is the ratio of energy reflected to the energy incident. As the energy of a simple harmonic wave is proportional to the square of its amplitude by (49–11) the reflecting power is equal to the square of the coefficient of reflection.

Problem 50a. Wires of mass per unit length $D_1 =$ 16 gm/cm and $D_2 = 9$ gm/cm are connected and under tension. Find the coefficient of reflection and the reflecting power (*a*) when the reflection takes place in the denser wire, (*b*) when the reflection takes place in the less dense wire. *Ans.* (*a*) 1/7, 1/49; (*b*) – 1/7, 1/49.

Problem 50b. Obtain the coefficient of reflection using sine instead of cosine functions.

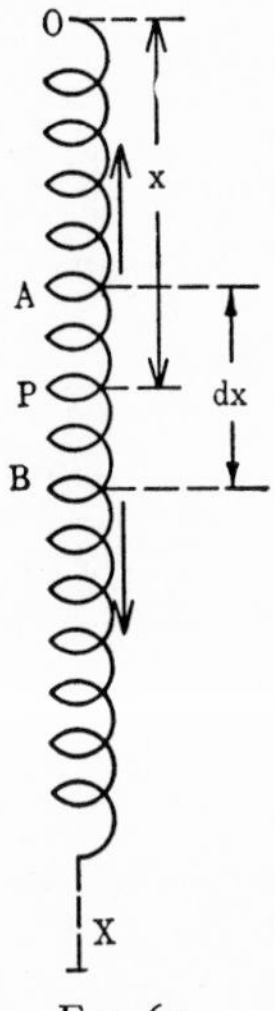

FIG. 65.

51. Longitudinal Waves in Springs. — Consider a section dx (Fig. 65) of a long helical spring fixed at the upper end. If F is the force stretching the spring at the mid-point P of dx, the upward force exerted on this section at the end A by the portion of the spring above is

$$F - \frac{\partial F}{\partial x}\frac{dx}{2}$$

and the downward force at the end B due to the portion of the spring below is

$$F + \frac{\partial F}{\partial x}\frac{dx}{2}.$$

Therefore the net force downward on the section dx is $\frac{\partial F}{\partial x}\,dx$. If ξ denotes the downward displacement of P, the strain at this point is $\frac{\partial \xi}{\partial x}$. Therefore

$$F = k\frac{\partial \xi}{\partial x}, \tag{51-1}$$

where k is the elastic constant of the spring, and the net downward force on the section dx is

$$\frac{\partial F}{\partial x}\,dx = k\frac{\partial^2 \xi}{\partial x^2}\,dx.$$

Equating this to the product of the mass of the section dx by the acceleration of P we obtain the equation of motion

$$D dx\frac{\partial^2 \xi}{\partial t^2} = k\frac{\partial^2 \xi}{\partial x^2}\,dx,$$

where D is the mass per unit length, or

$$\frac{\partial^2 \xi}{\partial t^2} = \frac{k}{D}\frac{\partial^2 \xi}{\partial x^2}. \tag{51-2}$$

This equation has the same form as (49–2). Therefore it represents a longitudinal wave traveling with velocity

$$v = \sqrt{k/D}. \tag{51-3}$$

Now suppose the spring is stretched slowly and uniformly so as to avoid the production of waves. Let ξ' be the displacement of the bottom of the spring due to a stretching force F' applied there. Then

$$F' = a\xi',$$

where a is the force necessary to stretch the spring a unit length. If we neglect the weight of the spring the displacement of P is

$$\xi = \frac{x}{l}\,\xi',$$

where l is the length of the unstretched spring. Therefore

$$\frac{\partial \xi}{\partial x} = \frac{\xi'}{l},$$

and

$$k = \frac{F}{\dfrac{\partial \xi}{\partial x}} = \frac{Fl}{\xi'} = \frac{F'l}{\xi'} = al,$$

since the stretching force F at P is the same as F' at the end when all parts of the spring are in equilibrium. Consequently the velocity of propagation of longitudinal waves along the spring may be written

$$v = \sqrt{\frac{k}{D}} = \sqrt{\frac{al}{D}} = l\sqrt{\frac{a}{Dl}} = l\sqrt{\frac{a}{m}}, \qquad (51\text{–}4)$$

where m is the mass Dl of the entire spring.

Suppose that a mass M is hung on the lower end of the spring, the upper end being attached to a rigid support. Let us investigate those vertical oscillations in which all points move in the same phase. Writing v for $\sqrt{k/D}$, the equation of motion (51–2) becomes

$$\frac{\partial^2 \xi}{\partial t^2} = v^2 \frac{\partial^2 \xi}{\partial x^2},$$

and we look for a solution of the form

$$\xi = f(x) \cos \omega t.$$

Substituting in the equation of motion

$$-\omega^2 f(x) \cos \omega t = v^2 \frac{d^2 f}{dx^2} \cos \omega t,$$

which is satisfied for all values of t if

$$\frac{d^2 f}{dx^2} + \frac{\omega^2}{v^2} f = 0.$$

The solution of this equation is

$$f(x) = A \sin\left(\frac{\omega}{v} x + \delta\right).$$

Therefore

$$\xi = A \sin\left(\frac{\omega}{v}x + \delta\right)\cos \omega t. \tag{51-5}$$

We have two boundary conditions to satisfy. At the point of suspension O the displacement ξ must vanish at all times. Therefore $\delta = 0$. At the bottom of the spring the stretching force (51–1) must equal the product of the mass M of the attached body by its acceleration. Therefore

$$-k\left(\frac{\partial \xi}{\partial x}\right)_{x=l} = M\left(\frac{\partial^2 \xi}{\partial t^2}\right)_{x=l},$$

or

$$-kA\frac{\omega}{v}\cos\frac{\omega}{v}l\cos \omega t = -M\omega^2 A \sin\frac{\omega}{v}l\cos \omega t,$$

which is satisfied for all values of t if

$$\frac{kl}{v^2 M} = \left(\frac{\omega}{v}l\right)\tan\left(\frac{\omega}{v}l\right).$$

Making use of (51–4) this equation may be written

$$\frac{m}{M} = \theta \tan \theta, \tag{51-6}$$

where

$$\theta \equiv \frac{\omega}{v}l = \omega\sqrt{\frac{m}{a}}.$$

If the mass m of the spring is small compared with the mass M of the attached body, θ is small and we may approximate by replacing $\tan \theta$ by the first two terms in its series expansion, getting

$$\frac{m}{M} = \theta\left(\theta + \frac{\theta^3}{3}\ldots\right) = \theta^2\left(1 + \frac{\theta^2}{3}\ldots\right),$$

and

$$\theta = \sqrt{\frac{m}{M}\Big/\left(1 + \frac{1}{3}\frac{m}{M}\right)} = \sqrt{\frac{m}{M + \frac{1}{3}m}}. \tag{51-7}$$

Therefore the period of oscillation is very closely

$$P = \frac{2\pi}{\omega} = \frac{2\pi}{\theta}\sqrt{\frac{m}{a}} = 2\pi\sqrt{\frac{M + \frac{1}{3}m}{a}}, \tag{51-8}$$

showing that the effect of the mass of the spring is equivalent to that of a mass one-third as great attached to the bottom of the spring.

Problem 51a. Two springs having constants k_1, D_1, and k_2, D_2 respectively are fastened together. Find the coefficients of reflection for longitudinal waves and discuss the change of phase on reflection.

$$\textit{Ans. } R = \frac{\sqrt{D_1k_1} - \sqrt{D_2k_2}}{\sqrt{D_1k_1} + \sqrt{D_2k_2}}.$$

Problem 51b. Investigate the physical significance of the roots of (51–6) in the neighborhood of $\theta = \pi, 2\pi$, etc.

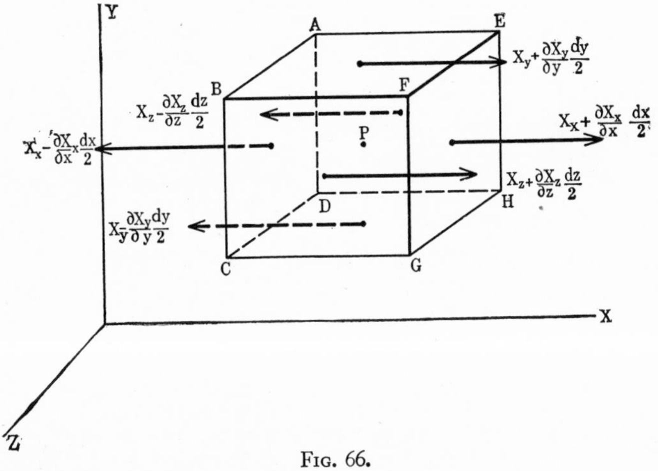

FIG. 66.

52. Waves in a Homogeneous Isotropic Medium. — Consider a rectangular parallelopiped (Fig. 66) of the medium of dimensions dx, dy, dz, the point $P(x, y, z)$ lying at its center. The component of the force on the face $EFGH$ in the X direction is

$$\left(X_x + \frac{\partial X_x}{\partial x}\frac{dx}{2}\right) dy\, dz,$$

and that on the face $ABCD$ in the opposite direction is

$$\left(X_x - \frac{\partial X_x}{\partial x}\frac{dx}{2}\right) dy\, dz.$$

Subtracting the latter from the former the net force to the right on these two faces is seen to be

$$\frac{\partial X_x}{\partial x}\, dx\, dy\, dz.$$

Similarly the net force to the right on the two faces *ABFE* and *DCGH* is

$$\frac{\partial X_y}{\partial y}\, dx\, dy\, dz,$$

and that on *BCGF* and *ADHE* is

$$\frac{\partial X_z}{\partial z}\, dx\, dy\, dz.$$

Therefore the component in the X direction of the total force $d\mathbf{K}$ on the entire block is

$$dK_x = \left(\frac{\partial X_x}{\partial x} + \frac{\partial X_y}{\partial y} + \frac{\partial X_z}{\partial z}\right) dx\, dy\, dz = \left(\frac{\partial P}{\partial x} + \frac{\partial U}{\partial y} + \frac{\partial T}{\partial z}\right) dx\, dy\, dz,$$

and similar expressions hold for the Y and Z components. Dividing by the volume $dx\, dy\, dz$ of the block the force per unit volume is found to be

$$\left.\begin{aligned} \mathbf{F} &= \mathbf{i}\left(\frac{\partial P}{\partial x} + \frac{\partial U}{\partial y} + \frac{\partial T}{\partial z}\right) + \mathbf{j}\left(\frac{\partial U}{\partial x} + \frac{\partial Q}{\partial y} + \frac{\partial S}{\partial z}\right) \\ &\quad + \mathbf{k}\left(\frac{\partial T}{\partial x} + \frac{\partial S}{\partial y} + \frac{\partial R}{\partial z}\right) \\ &= \nabla\cdot\Psi, \end{aligned}\right\} \qquad (52\text{–}1)$$

where Ψ is the stress dyadic (47–11). The stresses are given in terms of the strains by (47–16). Since $\nabla\cdot\mathbf{I} = \nabla$, substitution of the right-hand side of (47–16) for Ψ gives

$$\mathbf{F} = (k - \tfrac{2}{3}\mu)\nabla\nabla\cdot\boldsymbol{\rho} + 2\mu\nabla\cdot\Phi. \qquad (52\text{–}2)$$

We want to express $\mathbf{F}$ as a function of $\boldsymbol{\rho}$. Since

$$\Phi = \tfrac{1}{2}\{\nabla\boldsymbol{\rho} + (\nabla\boldsymbol{\rho})_c\},$$

we have

$$\nabla\cdot\Phi = \tfrac{1}{2}\{\nabla\cdot\nabla\boldsymbol{\rho} + \nabla\nabla\cdot\boldsymbol{\rho}\}$$

by following the method used in establishing (47–5), the ∇ dotted into $\boldsymbol{\rho}$ in the second term being the ∇ operating on Φ. Putting this in (52–2) we have

$$\begin{aligned}\mathbf{F} &= (k - \tfrac{2}{3}\mu)\nabla\nabla\cdot\boldsymbol{\rho} + \mu\nabla\cdot\nabla\boldsymbol{\rho} + \mu\nabla\nabla\cdot\boldsymbol{\rho}\\ &= (k + \tfrac{4}{3}\mu)\nabla\nabla\cdot\boldsymbol{\rho} - \mu(\nabla\nabla\cdot\boldsymbol{\rho} - \nabla\cdot\nabla\boldsymbol{\rho}).\end{aligned}$$

The factor in parentheses in the second term is just the expansion of $\nabla\times(\nabla\times\boldsymbol{\rho})$. So finally

$$\mathbf{F} = (k + \tfrac{4}{3}\mu)\nabla\nabla\cdot\boldsymbol{\rho} - \mu\nabla\times\nabla\times\boldsymbol{\rho}. \tag{52–3}$$

Since **F** is the force per unit volume the equation of motion is obtained by equating the right-hand side of (52–3) to the product of the mass D of a unit cube of the medium by its acceleration, giving

$$D\frac{\partial^2\boldsymbol{\rho}}{\partial t^2} = (k + \tfrac{4}{3}\mu)\nabla\nabla\cdot\boldsymbol{\rho} - \mu\nabla\times\nabla\times\boldsymbol{\rho}. \tag{52–4}$$

Since we know from article 17.4 that any well-behaved vector function of the coordinates can be expressed as the sum of an irrotational part and a solenoidal part, we shall treat separately the case where the displacement is irrotational and the case where it is solenoidal, secure in the knowledge that the most general case is merely a combination of these two special cases.

Case I. — The displacement $\boldsymbol{\rho}$ is irrotational. Then $\nabla\times\boldsymbol{\rho}$ vanishes and

$$\nabla\times\nabla\times\boldsymbol{\rho} = \nabla\nabla\cdot\boldsymbol{\rho} - \nabla\cdot\nabla\boldsymbol{\rho} = 0, \qquad \nabla\nabla\cdot\boldsymbol{\rho} = \nabla\cdot\nabla\boldsymbol{\rho}.$$

Hence (52–4) reduces to

$$\frac{\partial^2\boldsymbol{\rho}}{\partial t^2} = \frac{k + \tfrac{4}{3}\mu}{D}\nabla\cdot\nabla\boldsymbol{\rho}, \tag{52–5}$$

or, writing out the operator $\nabla\cdot\nabla$ in full,

$$\frac{\partial^2\boldsymbol{\rho}}{\partial t^2} = \frac{k + \tfrac{4}{3}\mu}{D}\left(\frac{\partial^2\boldsymbol{\rho}}{\partial x^2} + \frac{\partial^2\boldsymbol{\rho}}{\partial y^2} + \frac{\partial^2\boldsymbol{\rho}}{\partial z^2}\right). \tag{52–6}$$

This equation, as is suggested by its similarity in form to equation (49–2) for the propagation of a wave in one dimension, is known as the *wave equation in three dimensions*. We shall apply it to the case of a plane wave advancing in the X direction. As all points in the wave front have the same displacement at a given instant, we must look for a solution in which $\boldsymbol{\rho}$ is not a function of y or z. Therefore (52–6) reduces to

$$\frac{\partial^2 \boldsymbol{\rho}}{\partial t^2} = \frac{k + \frac{4}{3}\mu}{D} \frac{\partial^2 \boldsymbol{\rho}}{\partial x^2}, \tag{52–7}$$

which is equivalent to the three scalar equations

$$\left.\begin{aligned} \frac{\partial^2 \xi}{\partial t^2} &= \frac{k + \frac{4}{3}\mu}{D} \frac{\partial^2 \xi}{\partial x^2}, \\ \frac{\partial^2 \eta}{\partial t^2} &= \frac{k + \frac{4}{3}\mu}{D} \frac{\partial^2 \eta}{\partial x^2}, \\ \frac{\partial^2 \zeta}{\partial t^2} &= \frac{k + \frac{4}{3}\mu}{D} \frac{\partial^2 \zeta}{\partial x^2}. \end{aligned}\right\} \tag{52–8}$$

These are the equations of a wave advancing along the X axis with velocity

$$v = \sqrt{\frac{k + \frac{4}{3}\mu}{D}}. \tag{52–9}$$

The general solutions of (52–8) for a wave progressing in the positive X direction are

$$\left.\begin{aligned} \xi &= f(x - vt), \\ \eta &= g(x - vt), \\ \zeta &= h(x - vt). \end{aligned}\right\} \tag{52–10}$$

But as the displacement $\boldsymbol{\rho}$ is irrotational,

$$\nabla \times \boldsymbol{\rho} = \mathbf{i}\left(\frac{\partial \zeta}{\partial y} - \frac{\partial \eta}{\partial z}\right) + \mathbf{j}\left(\frac{\partial \xi}{\partial z} - \frac{\partial \zeta}{\partial x}\right) + \mathbf{k}\left(\frac{\partial \eta}{\partial x} - \frac{\partial \xi}{\partial y}\right) = 0,$$

and as ξ is a function of neither y nor z the last two components give

$$\frac{\partial \eta}{\partial x} = 0, \quad \frac{\partial \zeta}{\partial x} = 0.$$

Therefore, in view of (52–10), η and ζ can be functions of neither x nor t. Consequently the wave motion is limited to the component ξ of the displacement, and as we are not interested in constant displacements which may be superposed on the displacement due to the wave we shall take the constant values of η and ζ to be zero. As the variable component ξ of the displacement is parallel to the direction of propagation the wave is *longitudinal*. However, if we had applied equation (52–5) to a wave which is not plane we would have found that the transverse components of the displacement are not necessarily constants. Therefore the type of wave specified by this differential equation is more properly called *irrotational*.

Case II. — The displacement $\boldsymbol{\rho}$ is solenoidal. Then $\nabla \cdot \boldsymbol{\rho}$ vanishes and

$$\nabla \times \nabla \times \boldsymbol{\rho} = \nabla\nabla \cdot \boldsymbol{\rho} - \nabla \cdot \nabla \boldsymbol{\rho} = - \nabla \cdot \nabla \boldsymbol{\rho}.$$

Therefore equation (52–4) reduces to

$$\frac{\partial^2 \boldsymbol{\rho}}{\partial t^2} = \frac{\mu}{D} \nabla \cdot \nabla \boldsymbol{\rho}. \tag{52–11}$$

As in Case I we shall apply this equation to the case of a plane wave advancing in the X direction. As we must obtain a solution in which $\boldsymbol{\rho}$ is not a function of y or z (52–11) reduces to

$$\frac{\partial^2 \boldsymbol{\rho}}{\partial t^2} = \frac{\mu}{D} \frac{\partial^2 \boldsymbol{\rho}}{\partial x^2}, \tag{52–12}$$

which represents a plane wave advancing along the X axis with velocity

$$v = \sqrt{\frac{\mu}{D}}, \tag{52–13}$$

the components of the displacement being

$$\left.\begin{aligned} \xi &= f(x - vt), \\ \eta &= g(x - vt), \\ \zeta &= h(x - vt). \end{aligned}\right\} \tag{52–14}$$

In this case the displacement is solenoidal. Therefore

$$\nabla \cdot \boldsymbol{\rho} = \frac{\partial \xi}{\partial x} + \frac{\partial \eta}{\partial y} + \frac{\partial \zeta}{\partial z} = 0,$$

and as η and ζ are not functions of y or z it follows that

$$\frac{\partial \xi}{\partial x} = 0.$$

Therefore ξ must be a constant, which we shall take to be zero, the wave motion being confined to the components η and ζ of the displacement. As these components are perpendicular to the direction of propagation the wave is *transverse*. However, in the case of a wave which is not plane (52–11) does not always lead to a constant displacement in the direction of propagation. Therefore the type of wave under discussion is more properly called *solenoidal.*

In a longitudinal plane wave a particle of the medium can vibrate only along a line parallel to the direction of propagation, whereas in a transverse wave a particle can vibrate in two independent directions at right angles to the direction of propagation. In the first case the wave is said to have one degree of freedom; in the second case two degrees of freedom.

Consider a simple harmonic transverse wave advancing in the X direction. We may write

$$\left.\begin{aligned} \eta &= A \cos\left\{\frac{2\pi}{\lambda}(x - vt) + \alpha\right\}, \\ \zeta &= B \cos\left\{\frac{2\pi}{\lambda}(x - vt) + \beta\right\}. \end{aligned}\right\} \qquad (52\text{–}15)$$

For a given x these are the equations of elliptic harmonic motion (Art. 28) in a plane at right angles to the direction of propagation. Each particle of the medium describes an ellipse and the wave is said to be *elliptically polarized.*

If $B = A$ and $\beta = \alpha \pm \pi/2$ equations (52–15) become

$$\left.\begin{aligned} \eta &= A \cos\left\{\frac{2\pi}{\lambda}(x - vt) + \alpha\right\}, \\ \zeta &= A \cos\left\{\frac{2\pi}{\lambda}(x - vt) + \alpha \pm \frac{\pi}{2}\right\} = \mp A \sin\left\{\frac{2\pi}{\lambda}(x - vt) + \alpha\right\}. \end{aligned}\right\} \qquad (52\text{–}16)$$

These represent circular vibrations in planes perpendicular to the direction of propagation. In this case the wave is said to be *circularly polarized.* There are two senses in which a wave may be circularly polarized, the upper sign in (52–16) corresponding to counterclockwise or right-handed rotation about the direction of propagation and the lower sign corresponding to clockwise or left-handed rotation of the particles of the medium.

Finally if $\beta = \alpha$ in (52–15) the vibration is along a straight line perpendicular to the direction of propagation. In this case the wave is said to be *plane polarized.*

It follows from the preceding discussion that the most general kind of disturbance in a homogeneous isotropic solid is propagated as two waves, the irrotational wave outstripping the solenoidal wave on account of its greater velocity. These two types of waves are well exemplified in the earthquake waves which travel out from a center of disturbance through the solid portion of the earth's body. If we suppose that Poisson's ratio for the earth is $\frac{1}{4}$, $k = \frac{5}{3}\mu$ and the ratio of the velocity of the irrotational to that of the solenoidal wave is $\sqrt{3} = 1.73$. Actually the velocities of the two waves are found to be about 7 km/sec and 4 km/sec, so that their ratio is in good agreement with this assumption. A study of earthquake waves indicates that the rigidity of the solid shell which surrounds the central liquid core of the earth is greater than that of steel.

As a fluid has no rigidity it is incapable of transmitting a solenoidal wave, and the expression for the velocity of an irrotational wave traveling through it reduces to

$$v = \sqrt{\frac{k}{D}}. \tag{52–17}$$

In the case of a wave passing through a gas the rarefactions and condensations take place so rapidly that there is no time for equalization of temperature between different layers. Therefore the expansions and contractions must be treated as adiabatic rather than as isothermal. If we denote by dV the change in volume due to an increase dp in pressure, the modulus of volume elasticity k is

$$k = -\frac{dp}{\frac{dV}{V}} = -V\frac{dp}{dV}.$$

Now the equation of an adiabatic for an ideal gas is $pV^{\gamma} =$ constant, where γ is the ratio of the specific heat at constant pressure to that at constant volume. Hence

$$V^\gamma \frac{dp}{dV} + \gamma p V^{\gamma - 1} = 0,$$

and

$$\frac{dp}{dV} = - \gamma \frac{p}{V}.$$

Consequently the velocity of propagation (52–17) of a compressional wave in an ideal gas is

$$v = \sqrt{\gamma \frac{p}{D}}, \tag{52–18}$$

an expression first obtained by Laplace. It is this type of wave which gives rise to the sensation of sound.

Since light waves travel through space devoid of matter, the physicists of the last century felt the necessity of postulating an all-pervading medium to carry these waves. This medium they named the *ether*. As light exhibits the phenomenon of polarization light waves must be transverse. Therefore it was necessary to give the properties of an elastic solid to the ether. At once there arose the difficulty of getting rid of the longitudinal wave which such a medium transmits in addition to the transverse wave. As the velocity of the longitudinal wave (52–9) depends upon the rigidity as well as the volume elasticity of the medium this wave cannot be eliminated by making k equal to zero. Green, who was the first to develop the elastic solid theory of the ether, assumed k to be infinite. By this device he succeeded in reducing the energy carried away from a source of disturbance by the longitudinal wave to an infinitesimal as compared with that carried off by the transverse wave, but his theory did not lead to results agreeing with experiment when used to compute the coefficients of reflection of light from the interface between two media. Finally Kelvin proposed a medium in which $k = - \frac{4}{3}\mu$. This eliminates the longitudinal wave entirely and leads to results in agreement with observation. But Kelvin's ether is unstable: it would have to be attached to a rigid framework at the confines of the universe to prevent it from exploding or collapsing. Ultimately the great success of the electromagnetic theory of light and the advent of the relativity theory led physicists to discard the hypothesis of an elastic solid ether as an encumbrance rather than an aid to the progress of science.

Problem 52a. (*a*) Calculate the velocity of sound waves in water. $D = 1$ gm/cm^3, $k = 2.04(10)^{10}$ dyne/cm^2. *Ans.* 1430 meter/sec.

(*b*) Calculate the velocity of sound in air at standard pressure and temperature. $D = 0.001293$ gm/cm^3, $\gamma = 1.402$. *Ans.* 336 meter/sec.

(*c*) Show how the velocity of sound in air varies with the temperature.

Problem 52b. If Φ is a scalar function of the radius vector r satisfying the wave equation

$$\frac{\partial^2\Phi}{\partial t^2} = v^2\nabla\cdot\nabla\Phi$$

prove that

$$\Phi = \frac{1}{r}f(r \pm vt).$$

REFERENCE

Love, A. E. H.: *Mathematical Theory of Elasticity*, Cambridge University Press, Cambridge.

CHAPTER IV

ADVANCED DYNAMICS

53. Brachistochrone. — As the most powerful methods of attacking dynamical problems depend so largely upon the principles of the calculus of variations, we shall introduce the subject of advanced dynamics by a consideration of the simplest and earliest application of this calculus. The problem of the brachistochrone (Gk. shortest time), which led to the invention of the calculus of variations, is the following. A particle is to be allowed to slide under the force of gravity along a frictionless pathway extending from A to B (Fig. 67). It is desired to find the shape of this pathway such that the time of descent from A to B shall be a minimum. We are to pick out from all possible curves connecting A to B the one which represents the path of least time of descent.

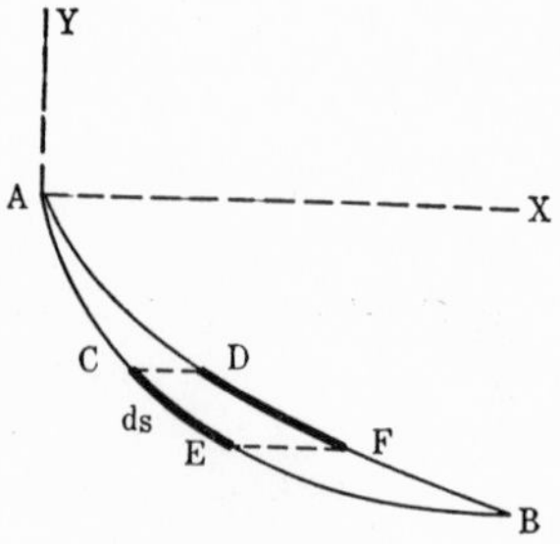

FIG. 67.

Let ds be an element of the path ACB of quickest descent from A to B, and dt the time required for the particle sliding along the curve to describe this portion of its path. Then if v denotes the velocity of the particle

$$dt = \frac{ds}{v},$$

and the time of descent is

$$t = \int_A^B \frac{ds}{v}. \tag{53–1}$$

If we denote by u the initial velocity of the particle, and take A as the origin of coordinates, the energy equation gives

$$v^2 = u^2 - 2gy.$$

Moreover

$$ds = \sqrt{dx^2 + dy^2} = \sqrt{1 + q^2}dy,$$

where q stands for the derivative of x with respect to y, that is, the reciprocal of the slope of the curved path. Then (53–1) becomes

$$t = \int_A^B \frac{\sqrt{1 + q^2}}{\sqrt{u^2 - 2gy}}\, dy. \tag{53–2}$$

Now consider a neighboring path ADB connecting the same end points A and B. This curve is known as a *varied* path. A point D, having the same ordinate as C, will have a slightly different slope. Therefore the time of descent along ADB is

$$t + \delta t = \int_A^B \frac{\sqrt{1 + (q + \delta q)^2}}{\sqrt{u^2 - 2gy}}\, dy. \tag{53–3}$$

We are using d here to denote a differential taken along a path and δ to denote a differential off the path. Thus dy is the difference of the ordinates of two nearby points such as E and C on the same path whereas δq is the difference of the reciprocals of the slopes of two neighboring curves at points C and D which have the same ordinate.

Subtracting (53–2) from (53–3),

$$\left.\begin{aligned} \delta t &= \int_A^B \left\{ \sqrt{\frac{1 + (q + \delta q)^2}{u^2 - 2gy}} - \sqrt{\frac{1 + q^2}{u^2 - 2gy}} \right\} dy \\ &= \int_A^B \frac{q\delta q\, dy}{\sqrt{(1 + q^2)(u^2 - 2gy)}}. \end{aligned}\right\} \tag{53–4}$$

If the time along the path ACB is to be a minimum it is necessary that δt should vanish.

Consider two small segments PQ and RS (Fig. 68) of any two adjacent paths lying in the XY plane. If we take x, y for the coordinates of P, the coordinates of Q are $x + dx$, $y + dy$, and those of R are $x + \delta x$, $y + \delta y$ provided we agree to take R as the point on the second path

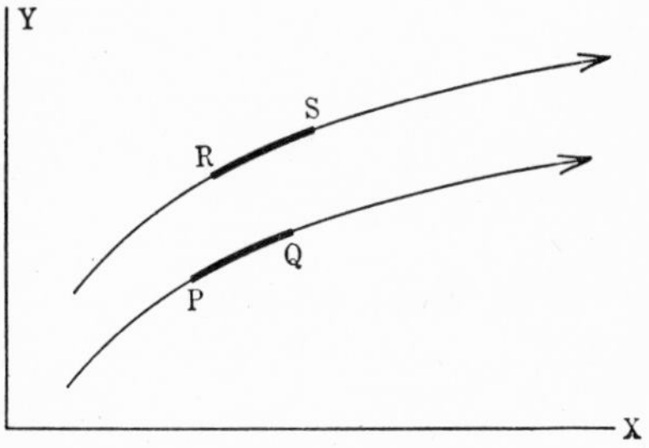

FIG. 68.

corresponding to the point P on the first. Now if we pass from R to the point S corresponding to Q, the coordinates of S are

$$(x + \delta x) + d(x + \delta x) = x + \delta x + dx + d\delta x,$$

$$(y + \delta y) + d(y + \delta y) = y + \delta y + dy + d\delta y,$$

whereas if we pass from Q to S the coordinates of S take the form

$$(x + dx) + \delta(x + dx) = x + dx + \delta x + \delta dx,$$

$$(y + dy) + \delta(y + dy) = y + dy + \delta y + \delta dy.$$

Comparing we see that

$$\delta dx = d\delta x, \quad \delta dy = d\delta y. \tag{53-5}$$

Consequently

$$\left.\begin{aligned} \delta q &= \delta\left(\frac{dx}{dy}\right) = \frac{\delta dx}{dy} - \frac{dx\delta dy}{dy^2} \\ &= \frac{d\delta x}{dy} - \frac{dx}{dy}\frac{d\delta y}{dy} \\ &= \frac{d}{dy}(\delta x) - \frac{dx}{dy}\frac{d}{dy}(\delta y). \end{aligned}\right\} \tag{53-6}$$

In the problem of the brachistochrone we took as corresponding points on the two paths of Fig. 67 the points C and D which have the same ordinate. Therefore, $\delta y = 0$ and

$$\delta q = \frac{d}{dy}(\delta x).$$

Putting this in (53-4) and integrating by parts

$$\delta t = \int_A^B \frac{q\dfrac{d}{dy}(\delta x)dy}{\sqrt{(1 + q^2)(u^2 - 2gy)}}$$

$$= \left|\frac{q\delta x}{\sqrt{(1+q^2)(u^2-2gy)}}\right|_A^B - \int_A^B \delta x \frac{d}{dy}\left(\frac{q}{\sqrt{(1+q^2)(u^2-2gy)}}\right) dy = 0.$$

Since the two paths coincide at the termini A and B, δx vanishes at these two points. Therefore

$$\int_A^B \delta x \frac{d}{dy}\left(\frac{q}{\sqrt{(1 + q^2)(u^2 - 2gy)}}\right) dy = 0. \qquad (53\text{–}7)$$

Now any path lying close to the path of quickest descent may be taken as the varied path. Suppose, for instance, we take as varied path a path which coincides exactly with the original path everywhere along its length except in the immediate neighborhood of the point C. Then δx vanishes everywhere except at C. Consequently the integrand of (53–7) is zero at all points of the path except C and the equation reduces to

$$\left[\delta x \frac{d}{dy}\left(\frac{q}{\sqrt{(1 + q^2)(u^2 - 2gy)}}\right)\right]_C = 0.$$

As δx is not zero at C the remaining factor must vanish. Moreover we might have taken the region where the varied path diverged from the path of quickest descent anywhere along this path. Therefore it is necessary that

$$\frac{d}{dy}\left(\frac{q}{\sqrt{(1 + q^2)(u^2 - 2gy)}}\right) = 0$$

at every point on the path of quickest descent. This is the differential equation of the desired curve. It is a necessary consequence of (53–7) in view of the fact that δx is arbitrary. Integrating once

$$\frac{q}{\sqrt{(1 + q^2)(u^2 - 2gy)}} = c \text{ (a constant).}$$

Solving for q

$$q^2 = \left(\frac{dx}{dy}\right)^2 = \frac{c^2(u^2 - 2gy)}{1 - c^2(u^2 - 2gy)} = \frac{\dfrac{u^2}{2g} - y}{\dfrac{1}{2gc^2} - \dfrac{u^2}{2g} + y} = \frac{a - y}{b + y},$$

where we have put

$$a \equiv \frac{u^2}{2g}, \quad b \equiv \frac{1}{2gc^2} - \frac{u^2}{2g}, \quad a + b = \frac{1}{2gc^2}.$$

Therefore

$$\frac{dx}{dy} = \sqrt{\frac{a-y}{b+y}}. \tag{53-8}$$

Now change to a new independent variable θ by means of the relations

$$y = \frac{a-b}{2} - \frac{a+b}{2}\cos\theta, \qquad dy = \frac{a+b}{2}\sin\theta d\theta,$$

$$a - y = \frac{a+b}{2}(1+\cos\theta), \qquad b + y = \frac{a+b}{2}(1-\cos\theta).$$

Then equation (53–8) becomes

$$dx = \frac{a+b}{2}\sqrt{\frac{1+\cos\theta}{1-\cos\theta}}\sin\theta d\theta = \frac{a+b}{2}(1+\cos\theta)d\theta.$$

Integrating we have the equation of the curve of quickest descent given in parametric form by

$$\left.\begin{aligned} x + d &= \frac{a+b}{2}(\theta + \sin\theta), \\ y + b &= \frac{a+b}{2}(1-\cos\theta), \end{aligned}\right\} \tag{53-9}$$

the first equation being the integral of the differential equation above and the second the equation relating the ordinate y to the parameter θ.

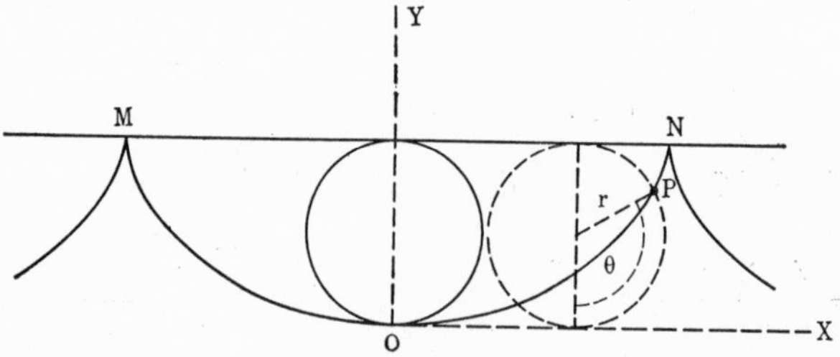

FIG. 69.

Consider the curve MON (Fig. 69) traced by a point P on the circumference of a circle of radius r which rolls along the straight line MN. This curve is called a *cycloid*. If the origin is taken at the lowest point of the curve, the coordinates of the generating point P in terms of the angle θ through which the circle has turned are

$$x = r\theta + r\sin\theta = r(\theta + \sin\theta),$$

$$y = r - r\cos\theta = r(1 - \cos\theta).$$

Therefore the brachistochrone (53–9) is a cycloid traced by a point on the periphery of a circle of radius $\frac{1}{2}(a + b)$. The constant a is determined by the initial velocity alone, b and d depending upon the coordinates of the points A and B which the curve is to connect.

Strictly speaking, we have not proved that the time of descent along the arc of a cycloid is less than that along any other path. We have merely shown that the time of descent has a stationary value along the cycloidal path. It is, however, obvious physically without formal mathematical proof that this stationary value is a minimum.

Problem 53a. Show that the time of descent along the brachistochrone is

$$t = \sqrt{\frac{a + b}{2g}}\,\Delta\theta.$$

54. Hamilton's Principle. — Consider a system of particles which may or may not be subject to certain constraints. For instance they may be rigidly connected so as to constitute a rigid body, or they may be sliding on a curved surface, or connected by taut inextensible strings. The equation of motion of the ith particle may be written

$$\frac{d}{dt}\left(m_i \frac{d\mathbf{r}_i}{dt}\right) = \mathbf{F}_i, \qquad (54\text{–}1)$$

where $\mathbf{r}_i$ is the position vector of this particle and $\mathbf{F}_i$ the force acting on it. Let $\delta\mathbf{r}_i$ be any arbitrary displacement of the particle consistent with the constraints of the problem under consideration. This displacement takes us from a point on the original dynamical path of the particle to a corresponding point on a neighboring varied path. While the original path is one consistent with the equations of motion the varied path need not be. Taking the scalar product of $\delta\mathbf{r}_i$ with (54–1) and summing up over all the particles,

$$\sum_i \frac{d}{dt}\left(m_i \frac{d\mathbf{r}_i}{dt}\right)\cdot\delta\mathbf{r}_i = \sum_i \mathbf{F}_i\cdot\delta\mathbf{r}_i, \qquad (54\text{–}2)$$

where we may omit from the second term all forces which do no work, such as the internal forces of a rigid body, the reactions of smooth fixed surfaces and the forces due to taut inextensible connecting strings. Now

$$\frac{d}{dt}\left(m_i \frac{d\mathbf{r}_i}{dt}\right) \cdot \delta\mathbf{r}_i = \frac{d}{dt}\left(m_i \frac{d\mathbf{r}_i}{dt} \cdot \delta\mathbf{r}_i\right) - m_i \frac{d\mathbf{r}_i}{dt} \cdot \frac{d}{dt}(\delta\mathbf{r}_i). \quad (54\text{-}3)$$

Let us agree to take as corresponding points on the dynamical path and the varied path those points which are reached at the same time. Then $\delta t = 0$. So if we replace x by $\mathbf{r}$ and y by t in (53–6)

$$\delta\left(\frac{d\mathbf{r}}{dt}\right) = \frac{d}{dt}(\delta\mathbf{r}) - \frac{d\mathbf{r}}{dt}\frac{d}{dt}(\delta t) = \frac{d}{dt}(\delta\mathbf{r}), \quad (54\text{-}4)$$

and

$$\frac{d\mathbf{r}_i}{dt} \cdot \frac{d}{dt}(\delta\mathbf{r}_i) = \frac{d\mathbf{r}_i}{dt} \cdot \delta\left(\frac{d\mathbf{r}_i}{dt}\right) = \frac{1}{2}\,\delta v_i^2,$$

where $\mathbf{v}_i$ is the velocity of the ith particle. Therefore (54–3) becomes

$$\frac{d}{dt}\left(m_i \frac{d\mathbf{r}_i}{dt}\right) \cdot \delta\mathbf{r}_i = \frac{d}{dt}\left(m_i \frac{d\mathbf{r}_i}{dt} \cdot \delta\mathbf{r}_i\right) - \delta(\tfrac{1}{2}m_i v_i^2),$$

and substituting in (54–2)

$$\frac{d}{dt}\left\{\sum_i \left(m_i \frac{d\mathbf{r}_i}{dt}\right) \cdot \delta\mathbf{r}_i\right\} = \delta\sum_i \tfrac{1}{2}m_i v_i^2 + \sum_i \mathbf{F}_i \cdot \delta\mathbf{r}_i. \quad (54\text{-}5)$$

Now $\sum_i \frac{1}{2}m_i v_i^2$ is the kinetic energy T of the system of particles, and if the forces are conservative $\sum_i \mathbf{F}_i \cdot \delta\mathbf{r}_i = -\delta V$ where V is the potential energy. We shall limit our subsequent discussion to conservative systems. Then we can write

$$\frac{d}{dt}\left\{\sum_i \left(m_i \frac{d\mathbf{r}_i}{dt}\right) \cdot \delta\mathbf{r}_i\right\} = \delta(T - V).$$

If we integrate this equation with respect to the time from the initial instant t_0 to the final instant t of the motion

$$\left|\sum_i m_i \frac{d\mathbf{r}_i}{dt} \cdot \delta\mathbf{r}_i\right|_{t_0}^{t} = \delta\int_{t_0}^{t} (T - V)\,dt,$$

since $\delta dt = d\delta t = 0$.

Now let us restrict the varied path in much the same way as in the problem of the brachistochrone; that is, we shall confine ourselves to varied paths which have the same termini as the dynamical path. Then $\delta\mathbf{r}_i$ is zero for every particle at the limits t and t_0, and

$$\delta\int_{t_0}^{t}(T - V)dt = 0. \qquad (54\text{–}6)$$

This is *Hamilton's principle.* The quantity $T - V$ is usually designated by L and is called the *Lagrangian function* or *kinetic potential.* Hamilton's principle states that if we compare a dynamical path with varied paths which have the same termini and which are described in the same time, then the time integral of the kinetic potential has a stationary value for the dynamical path. The specification that the varied path shall be described in the same time as the dynamical path is equivalent to stating that corresponding points on the two paths are reached at the same time, for if the total time of flight is the same for the varied path as for the dynamical path we can find for every point on the dynamical path a point on the varied path which is reached at the same time and *vice versa.* Hamilton's principle does not state that the time integral of the kinetic potential is a minimum for the dynamical path. Only in certain cases is it a minimum, but it always has a stationary value. This principle forms a basis from which all the theorems of dynamics may be deduced.

Problem 54a. A mass m has a simple harmonic motion under a force of restitution $F_x = -m\omega^2 x$. Then the integrated equation of motion is $x = a \sin \omega t$. (*a*) Find the time integral of the kinetic potential over the dynamical path extending from $t = 0$ to $t = \pi/4\omega$. (*b*) The varied path $x = a(\sin \omega t + \lambda \sin 4\omega t)$ has the same termini as the dynamical path at the times $t = 0$ and $t = \pi/4\omega$. Find the time integral of the kinetic potential over this path and show that it is greater than that over the dynamical path no matter whether λ is positive or negative.

Ans. (*a*) $\frac{1}{4}ma^2\omega$, (*b*) $\frac{1}{4}ma^2\omega + \frac{15}{16}\pi ma^2\omega\lambda^2$.

55. Principle of Least Action. — This principle is like Hamilton's principle in that it compares a dynamical path with a varied path which has the same termini, but differs in that corresponding points on the two paths are not chosen as points reached at the same time and therefore the varied path is not necessarily described in the same time as the dynamical path. Instead the varied path is taken so that the energy $T + V$ is the same as on the dynamical path, and hence when we pass from a point on the latter to the corresponding point on the former $\delta V = -\,\delta T$.

In this case δt does not vanish in (54–4) and consequently

$$\frac{d\mathbf{r}_i}{dt}\cdot\frac{d}{dt}(\delta\mathbf{r}_i) = \tfrac{1}{2}\delta v_i^2 + v_i^2\frac{d}{dt}(\delta t).$$

When this is substituted in (54–2) we get

$$\frac{d}{dt}\left\{\sum_i\left(m_i\frac{d\mathbf{r}_i}{dt}\right)\cdot\delta\mathbf{r}_i\right\} = \delta(T - V) + 2T\frac{d}{dt}(\delta t)$$

$$= \delta(2T) + 2T\frac{d}{dt}(\delta t)$$

since $\delta V = -\,\delta T$. Integrating from the initial instant t_0 to the final instant t of the motion, remembering that $d\delta t = \delta dt$, we find

$$\left|\sum_i m_i\frac{d\mathbf{r}_i}{dt}\cdot\delta\mathbf{r}_i\right|_{t_0}^{t} = \int_{t_0}^{t}\{\delta(2T)dt + 2T\delta dt\}$$

$$= \delta\int_{t_0}^{t} 2Tdt.$$

As the varied paths considered have the same termini as the dynamical path, every $\delta\mathbf{r}_i$ vanishes at each terminus, and we have the *principle of least action*

$$\delta\int_{t_0}^{t} 2Tdt = 0. \qquad (55\text{–}1)$$

The time integral of twice the kinetic energy is called the *action* and will be designated by S. The principle of least action, then, states that the action has a stationary value for a dynamical path as compared with varied paths having the same termini and for which the total energy has the same constant value. In spite of the name of the principle, this stationary value is a minimum only in certain special cases. Although the principle of least action is historically older than Hamilton's principle, it is less useful in developing methods of solving dynamical problems.

As $\mathbf{v}_i\, dt$ is equal to a displacement $d\mathbf{r}_i$ along the dynamical path, we can express the action in either of the alternative forms

$$S = \int_{t_0}^{t} 2T\, dt = \sum_i \int_{r_{i_0}}^{r_i} m_i \mathbf{v}_i \cdot d\mathbf{r}_i. \qquad (55\text{–}2)$$

In the second the integrand represents the scalar product of the linear momentum of the ith particle by its displacement along the dynamical path.

Problem 55a. Show, from the principle of least action, that a particle subject to no forces moves in a straight line.

Problem 55b. A particle, constrained to move on the surface of a perfectly smooth sphere, is subject to no forces tangent to the surface. Show that the action S is proportional to the length of its path, and is a minimum for the dynamical path as compared with nearby adjacent paths provided the termini are less than 180° apart.

56. Lagrange's Equations. — In order to specify the positions of a number of unrelated particles relative to a set of axes XYZ fixed in an inertial system three times as many independent coordinates are needed as the number of particles. If, however, the coordinates of some of the particles are related, the number of independent coordinates required to specify their positions is reduced. In the case of a rigid body, where the distance between every pair of particles is invariable, the position of every particle in the body is completely specified by six independent coordinates such as the three coordinate distances specifying the position of the center of mass and the three angles specifying the orientation of the body relative to the center of mass. By the number of *degrees of freedom* of a system of particles is meant the number of independent coordinates necessary to specify completely the position of every one of the particles. The coordinates employed, which may be distances or angles or quantities of quite different physical dimensions, are termed *generalized coordinates* and are usually designated by the letter q with an appropriate subscript.

Consider a system of particles of f degrees of freedom corresponding to the f generalized coordinates $q_1, q_2, q_3, \ldots q_f$. Then the rectangular coordinates x_i, y_i, z_i of the ith particle may be expressed as functions of the q's, that is,

$$x_i = x_i(q_1 \ldots q_f), \quad y_i = y_i(q_1 \ldots q_f), \quad z_i = z_i(q_1 \ldots q_f).$$

The components of velocity of this particle along the axes XYZ are

$$\dot{x}_i = \frac{\partial x_i}{\partial q_1}\dot{q}_1 + \frac{\partial x_i}{\partial q_2}\dot{q}_2 + \frac{\partial x_i}{\partial q_3}\dot{q}_3 \ldots + \frac{\partial x_i}{\partial q_f}\dot{q}_f, \qquad (56\text{–}1)$$

and similar expressions for the two other components. The dot over a letter is used here and subsequently in this chapter to denote total differentiation with respect to the time.

This expression is a homogeneous linear function of the generalized velocities $\dot{q}_1, \dot{q}_2, \dot{q}_3 \ldots \dot{q}_f$ with coefficients which are functions of the q's. Therefore the kinetic energy

$$T = \sum_i \tfrac{1}{2} m_i (\dot{x}_i^2 + \dot{y}_i^2 + \dot{z}_i^2)$$

when written as a function of the $\dot{q}$'s and the q's is a homogeneous quadratic function of the former with coefficients which are, in general, functions of the latter. The potential energy V, on the other hand, is a function of the coordinates only, and therefore can be expressed in terms of the q's alone. In the remainder of this chapter we shall understand by T the kinetic energy expressed as a function of the q's and the $\dot{q}$'s, and by V the potential energy expressed as a function of the q's. For instance, if we use polar coordinates r and θ to describe the motion of the earth relative to the sun, we have

$$T = \tfrac{1}{2} m(\dot{r}^2 + r^2\dot{\theta}^2), \quad V = -\gamma\frac{mM}{r}.$$

Now the kinetic potential $L = T - V$ is a function of the q's and the $\dot{q}$'s. Therefore Hamilton's principle gives

$$\delta\int_{t_0}^{t}(T-V)dt = \int_{t_0}^{t}\left[\sum_s\left\{\frac{\partial(T-V)}{\partial q_s}\delta q_s + \frac{\partial(T-V)}{\partial \dot{q}_s}\delta\dot{q}_s\right\}\right]dt = 0, \qquad (56\text{–}2)$$

where q_s is one of the f generalized coordinates. If we replace $\mathbf{r}$ by q_s in (54–4), then, since $\delta t = 0$ for the variation involved in Hamilton's principle, it follows that

$$\delta\dot{q}_s = \delta\left(\frac{dq_s}{dt}\right) = \frac{d}{dt}(\delta q_s),$$

and, integrating by parts,

$$\int_{t_0}^{t}\left[\sum_s\frac{\partial(T-V)}{\partial\dot{q}_s}\delta\dot{q}_s\right]dt = \int_{t_0}^{t}\left[\sum_s\frac{\partial(T-V)}{\partial\dot{q}_s}\frac{d}{dt}(\delta q_s)\right]dt$$

$$= \left| \sum_s \frac{\partial(T-V)}{\partial \dot{q}_s} \delta q_s \right|_{t_0}^{t} - \int_{t_0}^{t} \left[\sum_s \frac{d}{dt}\left\{ \frac{\partial(T-V)}{\partial \dot{q}_s} \right\} \delta q_s \right] dt$$

$$= - \int_{t_0}^{t} \left[\sum_s \frac{d}{dt}\left\{ \frac{\partial(T-V)}{\partial \dot{q}_s} \right\} \delta q_s \right] dt,$$

since δq_s vanishes at the limits as the dynamical and the varied paths have the same termini. Substituting in (56–2)

$$\int_{t_0}^{t} \left[\sum_s \left\{ \frac{d}{dt} \frac{\partial(T-V)}{\partial \dot{q}_s} - \frac{\partial(T-V)}{\partial q_s} \right\} \delta q_s \right] dt = 0.$$

As the f variations $\delta q_1, \delta q_2, \delta q_3 \ldots \delta q_f$ are independent and arbitrary the term in the integrand corresponding to each subscript s must vanish. Therefore we have the f equations

$$\frac{d}{dt} \frac{\partial(T-V)}{\partial \dot{q}_s} - \frac{\partial(T-V)}{\partial q_s} = 0, \qquad s = 1, 2, 3 \ldots f, \qquad (56\text{–}3)$$

where we might have omitted V in the first term since the potential energy is not a function of the $\dot{q}$'s. Writing L for $T - V$

$$\frac{d}{dt} \frac{\partial L}{\partial \dot{q}_s} - \frac{\partial L}{\partial q_s} = 0, \qquad s = 1, 2, 3 \ldots f. \qquad (56\text{–}4)$$

These f equations are known as *Lagrange's equations*. The kinetic potential L, like T and V, must be expressed as a function of the q's and the $\dot{q}$'s in these equations.

Problem 56a. A mass m_1 is fastened to one end of a string passing over a fixed pulley. From the other end of the string is suspended a second pulley. Over the latter pulley passes a string to the ends of which are attached masses m_2 and m_3. Neglecting the masses of pulleys and strings find the acceleration of m_3 by the use of Lagrange's equations.

Ans. $\dfrac{4m_2m_3 + m_1(m_3 - 3m_2)}{4m_2m_3 + m_1(m_3 + m_2)} g.$

Problem 56b. A sphere of radius b (*a*) rolls (*b*) slides down a fixed sphere of radius a. If ϕ is the angle which the line joining the centers of the two spheres makes with the vertical, find $\ddot{\phi}$ for each case.

Ans. (*a*) $\dfrac{5}{7}\dfrac{g \sin \phi}{a + b}$, (*b*) $\dfrac{g \sin \phi}{a + b}$.

Problem 56c. A pendulum, instead of being supported by knife edges, is attached at the upper end to a cyclindrical rod of radius a with axis perpendicular to the plane in which the pendulum oscillates. The projecting ends of this rod roll back and forth on a horizontal plane. If m is the mass of the pendulum, l the distance of the center of mass from the axis of the supporting rod, k_c the radius of gyration about the center of mass and θ the angle which the pendulum makes with the vertical, find the kinetic potential L, and the period P for small oscillations.

$$Ans.\ L = \frac{m}{2}\left\{k_c^2 + (l - a)^2 + 2al\,(1 - \cos\theta)\right\}\dot{\theta}^2 - mgl\,(1 - \cos\theta),$$

$$P = 2\pi\sqrt{\frac{k_c^2 + (l - a)^2}{lg}}.$$

57. Canonical Equations. — In terms of the kinetic potential $L = T - V$ expressed as a function of the q's and the $\dot{q}$'s we define the *generalized momentum* p_s conjugate to the coordinate q_s by the relation

$$p_s = \frac{\partial L}{\partial \dot{q}_s} = \frac{\partial T}{\partial \dot{q}_s}, \qquad s = 1, 2, 3 \ldots f, \tag{57–1}$$

the second form being equivalent to the first since V is not a function of the $\dot{q}$'s. For instance, if we are using rectangular coordinates to describe the motion of a single particle,

$$T = \tfrac{1}{2}m(\dot{x}^2 + \dot{y}^2 + \dot{z}^2),$$

and $p_x = m\dot{x}$, $p_y = m\dot{y}$, $p_z = m\dot{z}$, are the components of linear momentum along the three axes, or, if we are using polar coordinates to describe the motion of a particle in a plane,

$$T = \tfrac{1}{2}m(\dot{r}^2 + r^2\dot{\theta}^2),$$

and $p_r = m\dot{r}$ is the linear momentum along the radius vector and $p_\theta = mr^2\dot{\theta}$ the angular momentum about the origin.

Since L and therefore $\dfrac{\partial L}{\partial \dot{q}_s}$ is a function of $q_1, \ldots q_f, \dot{q}_1, \ldots \dot{q}_f$, the f equations (57–1) give each p_s as a function of $q_1, \ldots q_f, \dot{q}_1 \ldots \dot{q}_f$. We can solve these equations for each of the generalized velocities $\dot{q}_1 \ldots \dot{q}_f$, so as to express it as a function of the q's and the p's, and by means of these relations we can express L as a function of the q's and the p's. Since T, expressed as a function of the $\dot{q}$'s, is a homogeneous quadratic function of these variables, each p_s as defined by

(57–1) is a homogeneous linear function of the $\dot{q}$'s. Therefore the part of L which represents the kinetic energy, when expressed as a function of the q's and the p's, is a homogeneous quadratic function of the p's.

To avoid confusion let us designate L when expressed as a function of the q's and p's by $L(q, p)$ and, when expressed as a function of the q's and the $\dot{q}$'s, as in Lagrange's equations, by $L(q, \dot{q})$. Now let us calculate the derivatives of $L(q, p)$ along a dynamical path. Remembering that each $\dot{q}_s$ is a function $\dot{q}_s(q, p)$ of the q's and the p's, we have, for the partial derivative of $L(q, p)$ with respect to q_r, the remaining q's and all the p's being held constant,

$$\frac{\partial L(q, p)}{\partial q_r} = \frac{\partial L(q, \dot{q})}{\partial q_r} + \sum_s \frac{\partial L(q, \dot{q})}{\partial \dot{q}_s} \frac{\partial \dot{q}_s(q, p)}{\partial q_r}$$

$$= \dot{p}_r + \sum_s p_s \frac{\partial \dot{q}_s(q, p)}{\partial q_r},$$

since

$$\frac{\partial L(q, \dot{q})}{\partial q_r} = \frac{d}{dt} \frac{\partial L(q, \dot{q})}{\partial \dot{q}_r} = \dot{p}_r$$

by Lagrange's equations, and

$$\frac{\partial L(q, \dot{q})}{\partial \dot{q}_s} = p_s$$

by definition. If we transpose the last term on the right of this equation and change signs we have

$$\frac{\partial}{\partial q_r}\left\{\sum_s p_s \dot{q}_s(q, p) - L(q, p)\right\} = -\dot{p}_r. \tag{57–2}$$

Next, differentiating $L(q, p)$ with respect to p_r, keeping the remaining p's and all the q's constant, we get

$$\frac{\partial L(q, p)}{\partial p_r} = \sum_s \frac{\partial L(q, \dot{q})}{\partial \dot{q}_s} \frac{\partial \dot{q}_s(q, p)}{\partial p_r}$$

$$= \sum_s p_s \frac{\partial \dot{q}_s (q, p)}{\partial p_r}.$$

But

$$\frac{\partial}{\partial p_r}\left\{\sum_s p_s \dot{q}_s(q, p)\right\} = \dot{q}_r + \sum_s p_s \frac{\partial \dot{q}_s (q, p)}{\partial p_r}.$$

Subtracting the preceding equation from this one,

$$\frac{\partial}{\partial p_r}\left\{\sum_s p_s\dot{q}_s(q, p) - L(q, p)\right\} = \dot{q}_r. \tag{57-3}$$

If, then, we introduce a function H of the p's and the q's defined by

$$H(p, q) \equiv \sum_s p_s\dot{q}_s\,(q, p) - L(q, p), \tag{57-4}$$

we have

$$\dot{q}_s = \frac{\partial H}{\partial p_s}, \quad \dot{p}_s = -\frac{\partial H}{\partial q_s}, \quad s = 1, 2, 3 \ldots f. \tag{57-5}$$

The function H is known as the *Hamiltonian function*, and equations (57–5) are called the *canonical equations*. Like Lagrange's equations, they must be satisfied if the motion is to be along a dynamical path. Except in special instances, we shall no longer indicate the variables in terms of which L and H are expressed, always understanding by L the kinetic potential expressed as a function of the q's and the $\dot{q}$'s as in Lagrange's equations, and by H a function of the p's and the q's as in the canonical equations.

It remains to find the physical significance of the Hamiltonian function H. By definition

$$H = \sum_s p_s\dot{q}_s - L = \sum_s \frac{\partial T}{\partial \dot{q}_s}\dot{q}_s - L. \tag{57-6}$$

Now as T is a homogeneous quadratic function of the $\dot{q}$'s,

$$T = \sum_{ij} a_{ij}\dot{q}_i\dot{q}_j$$

and

$$\frac{\partial T}{\partial \dot{q}_s} = \sum_j a_{sj}\dot{q}_j + \sum_i a_{is}\dot{q}_i,$$

where the first term comes from differentiating the first $\dot{q}$ in the product above and the second term from differentiating the second. So

$$\sum_s \frac{\partial T}{\partial \dot{q}_s}\dot{q}_s = \sum_{sj} a_{sj}\dot{q}_s\dot{q}_j + \sum_{is} a_{is}\dot{q}_i\dot{q}_s = 2T.$$

Substituting in (57–6)

$$H = 2T - L = T + V. \tag{57-7}$$

So the Hamiltonian function is the total energy expressed as a function of the coordinates $q_1 \ldots q_f$ and the momenta $p_1 \ldots p_f$.

The law of conservation of dynamical energy follows at once from the canonical equations, for

$$\frac{dH}{dt} = \sum_s \left\{\frac{\partial H}{\partial q_s}\dot{q}_s + \frac{\partial H}{\partial p_s}\dot{p}_s\right\} = \sum_s \left\{\frac{\partial H}{\partial q_s}\frac{\partial H}{\partial p_s} - \frac{\partial H}{\partial p_s}\frac{\partial H}{\partial q_s}\right\} = 0, \quad (57\text{–}8)$$

showing that the total energy does not change with the time.

Problem 57a. Obtain the equations of motion (30–1) and (30–2) of a particle subject to a gravitational force directed toward the origin (*a*) from Lagrange's equations, (*b*) from the canonical equations.

59. The Hamilton-Jacobi Equation. — We have seen that the total energy of a conservative dynamical system is given in terms of the momenta $p_1 \ldots p_f$ and the coordinates $q_1 \ldots q_f$ by the Hamiltonian function H. As the energy remains constant during the motion of such a system the equation

$$H(p_1 \ldots p_f, q_1 \ldots q_f) = \alpha_1 \text{ (a constant)} \quad (59\text{–}1)$$

must be satisfied.

Now the integral which appears in Hamilton's principle is

$$\int L dt = \int (\sum_s p_s \dot{q}_s - H) dt = \int (\sum_s p_s dq_s - H dt). \quad (59\text{–}2)$$

We are going to develop a method of solving dynamical problems applicable to cases where the integrand $\sum_s p_s dq_s - H dt$ of (59–2) is an exact differential, so that $\int L dt$ can be expressed as a function of $q_1 \ldots q_f, t$. Along a dynamical path H is equal to the constant α_1, and the last term on the right of (59–2) can be integrated immediately. If the entire integrand is to be an exact differential, then, the sum $\sum_s p_s dq_s$ must be an exact differential dS of some function S of $q_1 \ldots q_f$. Consequently

$$p_s = \frac{\partial S}{\partial q_s}, \quad s = 1, 2, 3 \ldots f, \quad (59\text{–}3)$$

and

$$\int L dt = S(q_1 \dots q_f) - \alpha_1 t. \tag{59–4}$$

Incidentally we observe from (59–2) that

$$S = \int \sum_s p_s dq_s = \int (L + H) dt = \int 2T dt$$

is the action defined in article 55.

On account of the relations (59–3), the function S must satisfy the partial differential equation obtained from (59–1) by replacing p_1 by $\frac{\partial S}{\partial q_1}$, p_2 by $\frac{\partial S}{\partial q_2}$, etc., that is,

$$H\left(\frac{\partial S}{\partial q_1} \dots \frac{\partial S}{\partial q_f}, q_1 \dots q_f\right) = \alpha_1. \tag{59–5}$$

This equation is known as the *Hamilton-Jacobi partial differential equation*. By solving it we can obtain the desired function S. Since it is a partial differential equation of the first order in f independent variables, the complete solution contains f arbitrary constants. However, as S appears in the equation only in the form of its derivatives, the solution is specified only to within an undetermined constant. So one of the constants of integration is additive. Discarding this constant and denoting the remaining $f - 1$ constants by $\alpha_2 \dots \alpha_f$, we get on solving the equation the function

$$S(q_1 \dots q_f, \alpha_1, \alpha_2 \dots \alpha_f). \tag{59–6}$$

Now we make use of Hamilton's principle to establish the equations of motion by comparing the dynamical path with paths between the same fixed termini formed by varying the f quantities $\alpha_1, \alpha_2 \dots \alpha_f$. This variation is to be carried out in such a way, however, that each $\delta\alpha_s$ as well as each δq_s is zero at the two termini of every varied path. Although each $d\alpha_s$ vanishes since the α's are constant along the dynamical path, $\delta d\alpha_s = d\delta\alpha_s$ does not necessarily do so. Therefore, in forming the complete differential of S, we must retain the terms in $d\alpha_1, d\alpha_2 \dots d\alpha_f$ until after we have performed the variation indicated in Hamilton's principle, writing

$$dS = \sum_s \frac{\partial S}{\partial q_s} dq_s + \sum_s \frac{\partial S}{\partial \alpha_s} d\alpha_s.$$

We know that $\dfrac{\partial S}{\partial q_s} = p_s$. Let us put $\dfrac{\partial S}{\partial \alpha_s} \equiv Q_s$. Then

$$dS = \sum_s p_s dq_s + \sum_s Q_s d\alpha_s,$$

and

$$\int_{t_0}^{t} (\sum_s p_s dq_s - Hdt) = -\int_{t_0}^{t} (\sum_s Q_s d\alpha_s + \alpha_1 dt) + \int_{t_0}^{t} dS.$$

Hamilton's principle requires that the variation of this integral shall vanish, that is,

$$-\delta \int_{t_0}^{t} (\sum_s Q_s d\alpha_s + \alpha_1 dt) + \delta \int_{t_0}^{t} dS = 0, \qquad (59\text{–}7)$$

the varied paths having the same termini and being described in the same time as the dynamical path. Now

$$\delta \int_{t_0}^{t} dS = \delta S_t(q, \alpha) - \delta S_{t_0}(q, \alpha) = 0$$

since the q's and the α's and therefore the function S are the same for the varied paths as for the dynamical path at each terminus. Hence, remembering that $\delta d\alpha_s = d\delta\alpha_s$, (59–7) reduces to

$$-\delta \int_{t_0}^{t} (\sum_s Q_s d\alpha_s + \alpha_1 dt) = -\int_{t_0}^{t} (\sum_s \delta Q_s d\alpha_s + \sum_s Q_s d\delta\alpha_s + \delta\alpha_1 dt)$$

$$= -\int_{t_0}^{t} \{\sum_s \delta Q_s d\alpha_s + d(\sum_s Q_s \delta\alpha_s) - \sum_s dQ_s \delta\alpha_s + \delta\alpha_1 dt\} = 0.$$

But

$$\int_{t_0}^{t} d(\sum_s Q_s \delta\alpha_s) = (\sum_s Q_s \delta\alpha_s)_t - (\sum_s Q_s \delta\alpha_s)_{t_0} = 0$$

as each $\delta\alpha_s$ vanishes at both termini, and therefore

$$\int_{t_0}^{t} \{-\sum_s \delta Q_s d\alpha_s + \sum_s dQ_s \delta\alpha_s - \delta\alpha_1 dt\} = 0.$$

Since each $d\alpha_s$ is everywhere zero along the path of integration, the first sum drops out. So, writing $\dot{Q}_s$ for $\frac{dQ_s}{dt}$, we are left with

$$\int_{t_0} \{(\dot{Q}_1 - 1)\delta\alpha_1 + \dot{Q}_2\delta\alpha_2 \ldots + \dot{Q}_f\delta\alpha_f\}dt = 0.$$

As $\delta\alpha_1, \delta\alpha_2 \ldots \delta\alpha_f$ are independent and arbitrary variations, this requires that $\dot{Q}_1 = 1, \dot{Q}_2 = 0, \ldots \dot{Q}_f = 0$, or $Q_1 = t + \beta_1$, $Q_2 = \beta_2, \ldots Q_f = \beta_f$, where $\beta_1, \beta_2 \ldots \beta_f$ are constants. Since Q_s was put for $\frac{\partial S}{\partial \alpha_s}$ we have then

$$\left.\begin{aligned} \frac{\partial S}{\partial \alpha_1} &= t + \beta_1, \\ \frac{\partial S}{\partial \alpha_s} &= \beta_s, \quad s = 2, 3 \ldots f. \end{aligned}\right\} \qquad (59\text{–}8)$$

Now S is a function of $q_1 \ldots q_f$ as well as of $\alpha_1 \ldots \alpha_f$, and the derivatives of S with respect to the α's are functions of the same arguments. So we have in (59–8) f relations between $q_1 \ldots q_f$, t and the $2f$ constants $\alpha_1 \ldots \alpha_f, \beta_1 \ldots \beta_f$. We may solve these for each q_s, obtaining

$$q_s = q_s(\alpha_1 \ldots \alpha_f, \beta_1 \ldots \beta_f, t), \quad s = 1, 2, 3 \ldots f. \qquad (59\text{–}9)$$

These are evidently the integrated equations of motion, the constants $\alpha_1 \ldots \alpha_f, \beta_1 \ldots \beta_f$ being determinable by the $2f$ initial coordinates and momenta. If we are interested only in the equations of the orbit of the dynamical system, we have these at once in the last $f - 1$ relations of (59–8), which are just the equations we would obtain by eliminating t from the f relations given in (59–9). While this method of solving dynamical problems is often more cumbersome than the elementary methods previously employed, it leads to a particularly elegant treatment of periodic motions, and in connection with the dynamics of the atom Sommerfeld remarks "it seems almost as if Hamilton's method were expressly created for treating the most important problems of physical mechanics."

So far we have developed no method of solving the partial differential equation (59–5). In general this equation can be solved only if the variables can be separated, one of the arbitrary constants $\alpha_2 \ldots \alpha_f$ being obtained as the result of each separation. In this method of solution we retain on the left-hand side of (59–5) all terms involving q_1 and $\frac{\partial S}{\partial q_1}$, the other variables and derivatives being carried over to the right-hand side of the equation, and then equate each side of the equation to a constant α_2, thus:

$$f_1\left(\frac{\partial S}{\partial q_1}, q_1, \alpha_1\right) = \Psi_1\left(\frac{\partial S}{\partial q_2} \cdots \frac{\partial S}{\partial q_f}, q_2 \ldots q_f, \alpha_1\right) = \alpha_2.$$

In this way we obtain two subsidiary equations:

$$f_1\left(\frac{\partial S}{\partial q_1}, q_1, \alpha_1\right) = \alpha_2, \tag{59–10}$$

$$\Psi_1\left(\frac{\partial S}{\partial q_2} \cdots \frac{\partial S}{\partial q_f}, q_2 \ldots q_f, \alpha_1\right) = \alpha_2. \tag{59–11}$$

Clearly any value of S which satisfies these subsidiary equations is a solution of the original equation. Now the first subsidiary equation is an ordinary differential equation and may be solved by the usual methods, giving

$$S = S_1(q_1, \alpha_1, \alpha_2).$$

Repeating the process of separation on (59–11) we get another ordinary differential equation of which the solution is

$$S = S_2(q_2, \alpha_1, \alpha_2, \alpha_3),$$

and so on. Adding all these solutions together we have for the solution of the Hamilton-Jacobi equation

$$S = S_1(q_1, \alpha_1, \alpha_2) + S_2(q_2, \alpha_1, \alpha_2, \alpha_3) \ldots . \tag{59–12}$$

Evidently this equation contains as many arbitrary constants $\alpha_1, \alpha_2 \ldots \alpha_f$ as there are variables, for the process of separation, repeated f–1 times, introduces f–1 constants in addition to the constant α_1 already present.

60. Keplerian Motion. — To illustrate the methods of the previous article we shall consider the motion of an electron of charge $-e$ revolving about an atomic nucleus of charge eZ. As the mass M of the nucleus is much greater than the mass m of the electron we may consider the nucleus to remain stationary without making any very appreciable error. Employing polar coordinates to specify the position of the electron relative to the nucleus, the kinetic energy is

$$T = \tfrac{1}{2}m(\dot{r}^2 + r^2\dot{\theta}^2), \tag{60–1}$$

and the potential energy

$$V = -\frac{e^2Z}{r}. \tag{60–2}$$

From (60–1) we have at once

$$p_r = m\dot{r}, \quad p_\theta = mr^2\dot{\theta}.$$

Therefore the Hamiltonian function is

$$H = \frac{1}{2m}\left(p_r^2 + \frac{1}{r^2}p_\theta^2\right) - \frac{e^2Z}{r}, \tag{60–3}$$

and the Hamilton-Jacobi partial differential equation takes the form

$$\frac{1}{2m}\left\{\left(\frac{\partial S}{\partial r}\right)^2 + \frac{1}{r^2}\left(\frac{\partial S}{\partial \theta}\right)^2\right\} - \frac{e^2Z}{r} = \alpha_1. \tag{60–4}$$

We can separate the variables by writing this equation in the form

$$\frac{\partial S}{\partial \theta} = \sqrt{2m\alpha_1 r^2 + 2me^2Zr - r^2\left(\frac{\partial S}{\partial r}\right)^2} = \alpha_2,$$

which gives us the two subsidiary equations

$$\frac{\partial S}{\partial \theta} = \alpha_2, \tag{60–5}$$

$$\frac{\partial S}{\partial r} = \sqrt{2m\alpha_1 + 2\frac{me^2Z}{r} - \frac{\alpha_2^2}{r^2}}. \tag{60–6}$$

The first tells us that the angular momentum p_θ is constant. In fact, whenever a coordinate such as θ in the present problem does not appear explicitly in the Hamilton-Jacobi equation, we can solve for the conjugate momentum and perform at least one separation of variables. Such a coordinate is known as a *cyclic* or *ignorable* coordinate. As a result of the separation effected in such a case the momentum conjugate to a cyclic coordinate is seen to be always constant.

Adding together the solutions of (60–5) and (60–6) we get for the action

$$S = \alpha_2\theta + \int\sqrt{2m\alpha_1 + 2\frac{me^2Z}{r} - \frac{\alpha_2{}^2}{r^2}}\,dr. \qquad (60\text{–}7)$$

The integrated equations of motion (59–8) are

$$\frac{\partial S}{\partial\alpha_1} = t + \beta_1, \quad \frac{\partial S}{\partial\alpha_2} = \beta_2$$

for this case. We shall evaluate only the second, which is the equation of the orbit. Differentiating (60–7) with respect to α_2,

$$\theta - \alpha_2\int\frac{dr}{r\sqrt{-\alpha_2{}^2 + 2me^2Zr + 2m\alpha_1r^2}} = \beta_2. \qquad (60\text{–}8)$$

The standard integral

$$\int\frac{dx}{x\sqrt{a + bx + cx^2}} = \frac{1}{\sqrt{-a}}\sin^{-1}\left(\frac{bx + 2a}{x\sqrt{b^2 - 4ac}}\right), \quad a < 0,$$

may be found in any table of integrals, such as Peirce's. Putting in the values of the constants appearing in (60–8) and solving for the reciprocal of the radius vector

$$\frac{1}{r} = \frac{me^2Z}{\alpha_2{}^2} + \sqrt{\frac{m^2e^4Z^2}{\alpha_2{}^4} + \frac{2m\alpha_1}{\alpha_2{}^2}}\cos(\theta - \beta_2'),\ \beta_2' \equiv \beta_2 - \frac{\pi}{2}. \qquad (60\text{–}9)$$

This is the equation of a conic section. Comparing it with the standard equation (30–6) we see that the eccentricity is

$$\epsilon = \sqrt{1 + \frac{2\alpha_1\alpha_2{}^2}{me^4Z^2}}, \qquad (60\text{–}10)$$

showing at once that the orbit is elliptic, parabolic or hyperbolic according as the energy α_1 is negative, zero or positive. In the first case, if we put W for the negative energy $-\alpha_1$, comparison with the standard equation (30–8) of the ellipse gives for the major axis

$$2a = \frac{e^2Z}{W}, \qquad (60\text{–}11)$$

showing that all elliptical orbits having the same major axes have the same energy irrespective of their eccentricities.

The results obtained in this article should be compared with those of article 30 where the same problem was treated by more elementary methods. To bring the results into consonance e^2Z must be replaced by γmM for the gravitational analog previously considered.

Problem 60a. Solve the problem of the projectile (article 23) by the method of article 59, finding the integrated equations of motion and the equation of the path.

Problem 60b. Express the kinetic energy of the top treated in article 43 in terms of the Eulerian angles θ, ψ, ϕ and find the momenta conjugate to these coordinates. Set up the Hamilton–Jacobi equation, separate the variables, show that certain of the momenta are constant, and discuss the libration limits of θ.

61. Phase Integrals and Angle Variables. — We shall now extend the methods developed in article 59 so as to adapt them particularly to the solution of problems in periodic motions. Suppose we have separated the variables in the Hamilton-Jacobi partial differential equation, obtaining

$$p_s = \frac{\partial S}{\partial q_s} = f_s(q_s, \alpha_1 \ldots \alpha_f). \quad s = 1, 2, 3 \ldots f.$$

We shall define the *phase integral* J_s conjugate to the coordinate q_s by the integral

$$J_s = \oint p_s dq_s = \oint f_s(q_s, \alpha_1 \ldots \alpha_f) dq_s. \tag{61–1}$$

In case q_s is a cyclic coordinate and therefore p_s is constant this integral is to be taken from 0 to 2π, otherwise it is to be taken over a cycle of values of the coordinate q_s. Thus if q_s is the radius vector r of an elliptical orbit it increases from a minimum value at perihelion to a maximum value at aphelion, and then decreases until it assumes its minimum value again at perihelion. The function f in such a case appears as a radical of the form

$$f = \pm a\sqrt{(r_2 - r)(r - r_1)},$$

showing that p_r is real only when r lies between the *libration limits* r_1 and r_2 corresponding to the values of the radius vector at perihelion and aphelion respectively. In this case the integral is to be taken from the minimum value of r to the maximum and then back to the minimum, the positive sign before the radical being used while

r is increasing and the negative sign while r is decreasing so that the product $p_r dr$ is always positive.

Integrating (61–1) we have

$$J_s = J_s(\alpha_1 \ldots \alpha_f), \quad s = 1, 2, 3 \ldots f, \tag{61–2}$$

since the definite integral evaluated here is not a function of q_s. We can solve these f equations for the α's, getting

$$\alpha_s = \alpha_s(J_1 \ldots J_f), \quad s = 1, 2, 3 \ldots f. \tag{61–3}$$

By means of these relations we can express the solution (59–6) of the Hamilton-Jacobi equation as a function

$$S = F(q_1 \ldots q_f, J_1 \ldots J_f) \tag{61–4}$$

of the q's and the J's. To avoid confusing (59–6) and (61–4) let us designate these two functions for the moment by $S(q, \alpha)$ and $S(q, J)$ respectively. Then, using (59–8) we have

$$\begin{aligned}\frac{\partial S(q, J)}{\partial J_s} &= \sum_k \frac{\partial S(q, \alpha)}{\partial \alpha_k} \frac{\partial \alpha_k}{\partial J_s} \\ &= (t + \beta_1) \frac{\partial \alpha_1}{\partial J_s} + \beta_2 \frac{\partial \alpha_2}{\partial J_s} \ldots + \beta_f \frac{\partial \alpha_f}{\partial J_s}.\end{aligned} \tag{61–5}$$

As the derivatives of the α's with respect to the J's are constants in the time, the right-hand side of this equation is a linear function of t. Hence, understanding $S(q, J)$ by S, we may write

$$\frac{\partial S}{\partial J_s} = \omega_s t + \delta_s, \quad s = 1, 2, 3 \ldots f, \tag{61–6}$$

where $\omega_s \equiv \dfrac{\partial \alpha_1}{\partial J_s}$ and δ_s are constants. Since the derivatives of S with respect to the J's are functions of $q_1 \ldots q_f$, we have here, as in (59–8), the integrated equations of motion of the dynamical system. If we wish, we can solve them for the q's, obtaining

$$q_s = q_s(J_1 \ldots J_f, \beta_1 \ldots \beta_f, t), \quad s = 1, 2, 3 \ldots f. \tag{61–7}$$

To remind ourselves of the fact that α_1 is the total energy of the system, we shall write $\overline{H}(J_1 \ldots J_f)$ for the energy α_1 expressed as a function of the phase integrals. Also we shall put w_s for the function $\frac{\partial S}{\partial J_s}$ of $q_1 \ldots q_f$ appearing in (61–6). Then the integrated equations of motion may be written

$$w_s = \omega_s t + \delta_s, \quad s = 1, 2, 3 \ldots f, \tag{61–8}$$

and, since $\dot{w}_s = \omega_s$ and $\overline{H} = \alpha_1$,

$$\dot{w}_s = \frac{\partial \overline{H}}{\partial J_s}, \quad s = 1, 2, 3 \ldots f. \tag{61–9}$$

Moreover, since $\overline{H}$ is not a function of $w_1 \ldots w_f$, and $J_1 \ldots J_f$ are not functions of t, we may write

$$\dot{J}_s = -\frac{\partial \overline{H}}{\partial w_s}, \quad s = 1, 2, 3 \ldots f, \tag{61–10}$$

for each side of each of these equations vanishes identically. We note, now, that (61–9) and (61–10) have the same form as the canonical equations (57–5), $\overline{H}$ like H representing the total energy, the J's replacing the momenta and the w's the coordinates. We say, then, that we have made a *canonical transformation* from the variables $p_1 \ldots p_f, q_1 \ldots q_f$ to the parameters $J_1 \ldots J_f, w_1 \ldots w_f$.

From the defining equation (61–1) of the phase integral it is clear that the function S increases by J_s when q_s goes through a cycle of values, all the other q's remaining constant. If we denote the initial and final values of S by S' and S''

$$S'' - S' = J_s. \tag{61–11}$$

Differentiating partially with respect to J_s

$$\frac{\partial S''}{\partial J_s} - \frac{\partial S'}{\partial J_s} = 1.$$

But $w_s = \frac{\partial S}{\partial J_s}$. Therefore

$$w''_s - w'_s = 1. \tag{61–12}$$

On the other hand, if we differentiate (61–11) partially with respect to some other phase integral, such as J_r,

$$w''_r - w'_r = 0. \tag{61–13}$$

So, when q_s goes through a cycle of values so as to return to its initial value, w_s increases by unity, all the other w's remaining unchanged. Therefore q_s is periodic in w_s with the period 1, and the quantities

$$\omega_s = \frac{\partial \overline{H}}{\partial J_s}, \quad s = 1, 2, 3 \ldots f, \tag{61–14}$$

are the fundamental frequencies of the motion. For instance, we might have

$$q_s = a \sin 2\pi w_s = a \sin 2\pi(\omega_s t + \delta_s),$$

where q_s resumes its initial value when w_s increases by unity, and ω_s is the frequency (true frequency, not angular frequency) of the oscillation in q_s. On account of these properties the w's are called *angle variables*.

Let us calculate the energy function $\overline{H}$ for the problem of an electron revolving about an atomic nucleus which was treated in article 60. From the equations (60–5) and (60–6) resulting from separation of the variables in the Hamilton-Jacobi equation we have

$$J_\theta = \oint \alpha_2 d\theta = 2\pi\alpha_2, \tag{61–15}$$

$$J_r = \oint \sqrt{2m\alpha_1 + 2\frac{me^2Z}{r} - \frac{\alpha_2{}^2}{r^2}}\, dr = \frac{2\pi me^2Z}{\sqrt{-2m\alpha_1}} - 2\pi\alpha_2, \tag{61–16}$$

the second integral being taken from any standard table of integrals such as Peirce's. Eliminating α_2 and solving for $\alpha_1 = \overline{H}$,

$$\overline{H}(J_\theta, J_r) = -\frac{2\pi^2 me^4Z^2}{(J_\theta + J_r)^2}. \tag{61–17}$$

The fundamental frequencies are

$$\omega_\theta = \frac{\partial \overline{H}}{\partial J_\theta} = \frac{4\pi^2 me^4 Z^2}{(J_\theta + J_r)^3} = \frac{\partial \overline{H}}{\partial J_r} = \omega_r. \tag{61–18}$$

As the two fundamental frequencies are the same the system is said to be *degenerate*. Substituting α_2 from (61–15) and α_1 from (61–16) in (60–10) the eccentricity of the orbit is seen to be

$$\epsilon = \sqrt{1 - \frac{J_\theta{}^2}{(J_\theta + J_r)^2}}, \tag{61–19}$$

and putting (61–17) for $-W$ in (60–11) the major axis takes the form

$$2a = \frac{(J_\theta + J_r)^2}{2\pi^2 me^2 Z}. \tag{61–20}$$

As a check on our results let us deduce Kepler's third law of planetary motion. Eliminating $(J_\theta + J_r)$ from (61–18) and (61–20)

$$\omega_\theta = \omega_r = \frac{1}{2\pi a^{3/2}}\sqrt{\frac{e^2 Z}{m}}.$$

Putting γmM for e^2Z to go over to the gravitational case and remembering that the period P is the reciprocal of the frequency

$$P = \frac{2\pi a^{3/2}}{\sqrt{\gamma M}},$$

which is identical with (30–19).

The importance of the expression (61–17) for the energy in terms of the phase integrals lies in the fact that in the Bohr theory the stationary states of the atom are determined by putting the phase integrals equal to integral multiples of Planck's constant h. This theory will be taken up in more detail in Chapter XV. It is to be noted that in obtaining (61–17) it was unnecessary to solve the Hamilton-Jacobi partial differential equation, as was done in article 60. In fact the procedure is very simple: first we set up the Hamilton-Jacobi equation for the particular mechanism under consideration; then we separate the variables obtaining the subsidiary equations (60–5) and (60–6); next the phase integrals are set up and integrated; and finally we eliminate the constant α_2 from these integrals and solve for the energy α_1.

Problem 61a. A particle of mass m is free to move in the XY plane under the action of two simple harmonic forces of restitution $-kx$ and $-ly$. Set up the Hamilton-Jacobi partial differential equation, find the energy as a function of the phase integrals and find the fundamental frequencies from (61–9).

$$\textit{Ans.}\ \overline{H} = \frac{1}{2\pi}\left\{J_x\sqrt{\frac{k}{m}} + J_y\sqrt{\frac{l}{m}}\right\},\quad \omega_x = \frac{1}{2\pi}\sqrt{\frac{k}{m}},\quad \omega_y = \frac{1}{2\pi}\sqrt{\frac{l}{m}}.$$

REFERENCES

AMES AND MURNAGHAN: *Theoretical Mechanics*, Ginn & Co., Boston.

WHITTAKER, E. T.: *Analytical Dynamics*, Cambridge University Press, Cambridge.

Part II

HYDRODYNAMICS

CHAPTER V

HYDRODYNAMICS OF PERFECT FLUIDS

62. Kinematical Preliminaries. — We shall treat a fluid as if its structure were continuous. Hence in dealing with differential elements we shall always assume that elements of volume, though very small, are large enough to contain a great many molecules. By a perfect fluid we mean one which cannot support a tangential stress. Therefore in the discussion of perfect fluids presented in the present chapter we ignore viscosity. In our analysis of the motion of a fluid we shall generally employ the Eulerian method of treatment in which attention is fixed on a particular point in the observer's inertial system and the velocity of the fluid, its density and its pressure at this point are determined as functions of the time.

Let $\mathbf{v}$ denote the linear velocity of the fluid at a point $P(x, y, z)$ at the time t, and $\mathbf{v} + d\mathbf{v}$ that at a neighboring point $Q(x + dx, y + dy, z + dz)$ at the time $t + dt$. Then if $\mathbf{v}$ is expressed as a function of x, y, z and t,

$$\left.\begin{aligned} d\mathbf{v} &= \frac{\partial \mathbf{v}}{\partial t} dt + \frac{\partial \mathbf{v}}{\partial x} dx + \frac{\partial \mathbf{v}}{\partial y} dy + \frac{\partial \mathbf{v}}{\partial z} dz \\ &= \frac{\partial \mathbf{v}}{\partial t} dt + d\mathbf{r}\cdot\nabla\mathbf{v}, \end{aligned}\right\} \tag{62–1}$$

where

$$d\mathbf{r} = \mathbf{i}dx + \mathbf{j}dy + \mathbf{k}dz$$

is the position vector of Q relative to P. Now if $d\mathbf{r} = \mathbf{v}dt$ the point Q is occupied at the time $t + dt$ by the particle of fluid which was at P at the time t. So

$$d\mathbf{v} = \frac{\partial \mathbf{v}}{\partial t} dt + \mathbf{v}\cdot\nabla\mathbf{v}dt$$

is the increase in velocity of this particle in the time dt, or

$$\frac{d\mathbf{v}}{dt} = \frac{\partial \mathbf{v}}{\partial t} + \mathbf{v}\cdot\nabla\mathbf{v} \tag{62–2}$$

is the acceleration of the fluid at P.

Let us consider the rotation of the neighboring fluid particles about P (x, y, z) at the instant t. Since the medium is not rigid different neighboring particles may have different angular velocities about P, and we cannot avail ourselves of the relation proved in article 13 between the angular velocity $\boldsymbol{\omega}$ and the curl of the linear velocity $\mathbf{v}$ for a rigid body. Nevertheless we can show that $\nabla \times \mathbf{v}$ at P represents both in magnitude and direction twice the *average* angular velocity about P of the fluid particles located in a small sphere (Fig. 70) with P as center. Consider an annular ring of radius

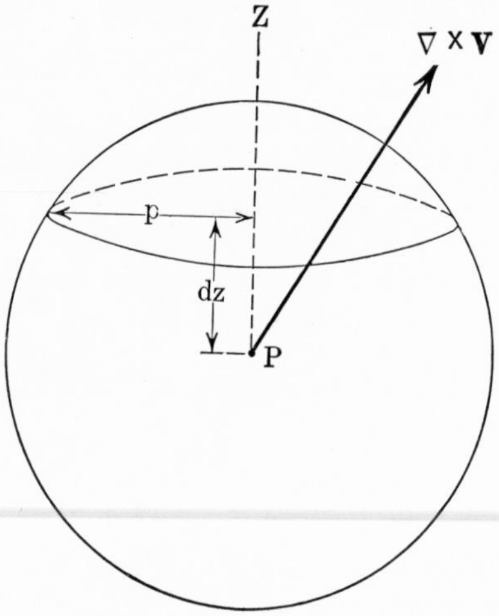

FIG. 70.

p about the Z axis at a distance dz from P. Applying Stoke's theorem to the area bounded by this ring,

$$\left\{ \left| \nabla \times \mathbf{v} \right|_z + \left| \frac{\partial}{\partial z} (\nabla \times \mathbf{v}) \right|_z dz \right\} \pi p^2 = \oint \mathbf{v} \cdot d\boldsymbol{\lambda}.$$

Now the tangential component of $\mathbf{v}$ averaged over this ring is

$$\bar{v}_\lambda = \frac{1}{2\pi p} \oint \mathbf{v} \cdot d\boldsymbol{\lambda},$$

and the mean angular velocity about the Z axis of the particles lying in it is

$$\omega_z = \frac{\bar{v}_\lambda}{p}.$$

Consequently

$$\left|\nabla \times \mathbf{v}\right|_z + \left|\frac{\partial}{\partial z}(\nabla \times \mathbf{v})\right|_z dz = 2\omega_z.$$

If we average this equation over two annular rings equidistant from P but on opposite sides, the term in dz disappears. Hence, as the volume of the sphere can be divided into such pairs of annular rings, we get $\left|\nabla \times \mathbf{v}\right|_z = 2\omega_z$ for the entire sphere. Since similar expressions hold for the other components, the mean angular velocity of the particles contained in a small sphere with P as center is

$$\boldsymbol{\omega} = \tfrac{1}{2}\nabla \times \mathbf{v}. \qquad (62\text{–}3)$$

If the mean angular velocity is everywhere zero $\mathbf{v}$ is an irrotational vector. In this case the motion is said to be *irrotational.* Now it was shown in article 17 that any irrotational vector may be expressed as the gradient of a scalar function of position in space. So if the motion of the fluid is irrotational we may write

$$\mathbf{v} = -\nabla\Phi. \qquad (62\text{–}4)$$

The scalar function of position Φ is known as the *velocity potential* since the velocity is obtained from it by the same mathematical operation as that used to get the force from the potential energy in the case of a conservative dynamical system.

A surface over which Φ is constant is known as an *equipotential surface.* The *stream lines* in the fluid are curves having everywhere the direction of the velocity $\mathbf{v}$. It was proved in article 11 in the introduction that $\nabla\Phi$ is perpendicular to the surface $\Phi(x, y, z) =$ constant. Therefore the stream lines are perpendicular to the equipotential surfaces. The differential equations of these lines are evidently

$$\frac{dx}{v_x} = \frac{dy}{v_y} = \frac{dz}{v_z}. \qquad (62\text{–}5)$$

Finally let us consider the boundary conditions at the surface of a solid with which a perfect fluid is in contact. As the fluid cannot support a tangential stress, its velocity tangent to the surface is not determined by that of the solid. On the other hand, its velocity normal to the surface must be the same as that of the solid so that it may maintain contact without penetration. Let AB (Fig. 71) represent the surface of a solid moving with velocity V in a direction making an angle θ with the normal N. Then, if l, m, n are the direction cosines of the normal, the components of velocity of a fluid in contact with the solid must satisfy the boundary condition

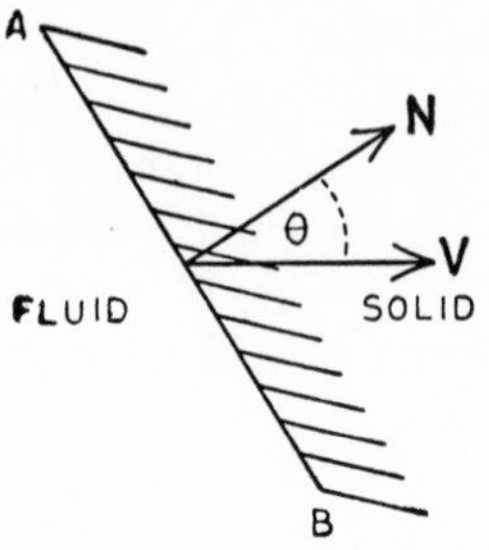

FIG. 71.

$$lv_x + mv_y + nv_z = V \cos \theta$$

at the surface AB.

63. Equation of Continuity. — The equation of continuity (12–2) was deduced in article 12. If ρ is the density of the fluid and $\mathbf{v}$ its velocity this equation takes the form

$$\frac{\partial \rho}{\partial t} + \nabla \cdot (\rho \mathbf{v}) = 0. \qquad (63\text{–}1)$$

Writing out the second term in expanded form

$$\frac{\partial \rho}{\partial t} + \frac{\partial}{\partial x}(\rho v_x) + \frac{\partial}{\partial y}(\rho v_y) + \frac{\partial}{\partial z}(\rho v_z) = 0,$$

or

$$\frac{\partial \rho}{\partial t} + v_x \frac{\partial \rho}{\partial x} + v_y \frac{\partial \rho}{\partial y} + v_z \frac{\partial \rho}{\partial z} = -\rho \left(\frac{\partial v_x}{\partial x} + \frac{\partial v_y}{\partial y} + \frac{\partial v_z}{\partial z} \right).$$

But the left-hand side of this equation is just the time rate of change of density $\frac{d\rho}{dt}$ of a particular element of the fluid followed in its motion relative to the axes XYZ. Therefore

$$\frac{d\rho}{dt} + \rho \nabla \cdot \mathbf{v} = 0. \qquad (63\text{–}2)$$

If the fluid is incompressible ρ is a constant and

$$\nabla \cdot \mathbf{v} = 0. \qquad (63\text{–}3)$$

If, in addition, the motion is irrotational, we obtain the equation

$$\nabla \cdot \nabla \Phi = 0 \qquad (63\text{–}4)$$

by substituting (62–4) into (63–3). The operator $\nabla \cdot \nabla$ is the Laplacian discussed in article 14 and (63–4) is known as *Laplace's equation.*

Frequently it is necessary to express the equation of continuity in terms of other than rectangular coordinates. We shall confine ourselves to curvilinear coordinates ξ, η, ζ which are orthogonal. Then, if λ, μ, ν are the functions of ξ, η, ζ by which we have to multiply $d\xi$, $d\eta$, $d\zeta$, respectively, in order to obtain the distances corresponding to these increments in the variables, it follows from (17.1–2) that the equation of continuity (63–1) assumes the form

$$\frac{\partial\rho}{\partial t}+\frac{1}{\lambda\mu\nu}\left\{\frac{\partial}{\partial\xi}(\mu\nu\rho v_\xi)+\frac{\partial}{\partial\eta}(\nu\lambda\rho v_\eta)+\frac{\partial}{\partial\zeta}(\lambda\mu\rho v_\zeta)\right\}=0 \qquad (63\text{–}5)$$

in the coordinates ξ, η, ζ.

Suppose that we wish to use spherical coordinates r, θ, ϕ. Then

$$\lambda = 1, \quad \mu = r, \quad \nu = r\sin\theta,$$

and the equation of continuity becomes

$$\frac{\partial\rho}{\partial t}+\frac{1}{r^2\sin\theta}\left\{\frac{\partial}{\partial r}(r^2\sin\theta\,\rho v_r)+\frac{\partial}{\partial\theta}(r\sin\theta\,\rho v_\theta)+\frac{\partial}{\partial\phi}(r\rho v_\phi)\right\}=0 \qquad (63\text{–}6)$$

where, if the motion is irrotational,

$$v_r = -\frac{\partial\Phi}{\partial r}, \quad v_\theta = -\frac{\partial\Phi}{r\partial\theta}, \quad v_\phi = -\frac{\partial\Phi}{r\sin\theta\partial\phi}. \qquad (63\text{–}7)$$

Again, if we use cylindrical coordinates r, θ, z,

$$\lambda = 1, \quad \mu = r, \quad \nu = 1,$$

and the equation of continuity is

$$\frac{\partial\rho}{\partial t}+\frac{1}{r}\left\{\frac{\partial}{\partial r}(r\rho v_r)+\frac{\partial}{\partial\theta}(\rho v_\theta)+\frac{\partial}{\partial z}(r\rho v_z)\right\}=0, \qquad (63\text{–}8)$$

where, if the motion is irrotational,

$$v_r = -\frac{\partial\Phi}{\partial r}, \quad v_\theta = -\frac{\partial\Phi}{r\partial\theta}, \quad v_z = -\frac{\partial\Phi}{\partial z}. \qquad (63\text{–}9)$$

The equation of continuity is very important in hydrodynamics, for the method of attacking most problems consists in finding a solution of this differential equation which satisfies the assigned boundary conditions.

64. Equation of Motion. — Consider a rectangular parallelopiped (Fig. 73) of volume $dx\ dy\ dz$ fixed relative to the axes XYZ. If we denote by p the pressure at the center P of the parallelopiped, the pressure on the surface $ABFE$ is

$$p - \frac{\partial p}{\partial x}\frac{dx}{2},$$

and that on $DCGH$ is

$$p + \frac{\partial p}{\partial x}\frac{dx}{2}.$$

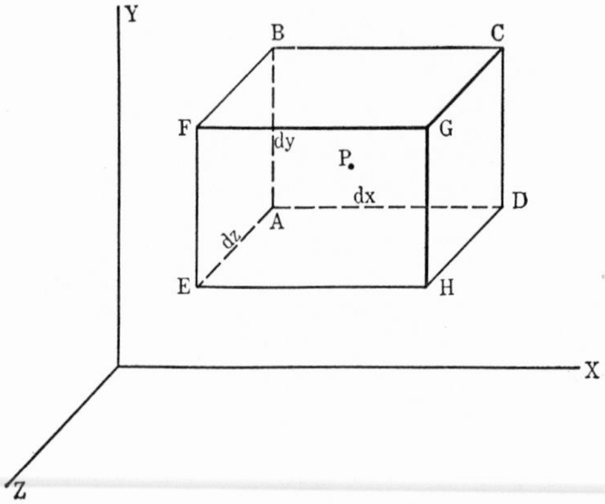

FIG. 73.

Therefore the force on the fluid inside the parallelopiped due to the pressure on $ABFE$ is

$$\left(p - \frac{\partial p}{\partial x}\frac{dx}{2}\right) dy\ dz$$

in the positive X direction, and that on $DCGH$

$$\left(p + \frac{\partial p}{\partial x}\frac{dx}{2}\right) dy\ dz$$

in the negative X direction. So the net force in the X direction due to the pressure on these two faces of the parallelopiped is

$$-\frac{\partial p}{\partial x}\, dx\ dy\ dz,$$

and similar expressions hold for the forces in the Y and Z directions on the pairs of faces perpendicular to these axes. Dividing by the volume $dx\,dy\,dz$ of the parallelopiped the force on a unit volume due to the pressure of the surrounding fluid is seen to be

$$-\mathbf{i}\frac{\partial p}{\partial x}-\mathbf{j}\frac{\partial p}{\partial y}-\mathbf{k}\frac{\partial p}{\partial z}=-\nabla p.$$

In addition to the force due to pressure there may be an external force acting on the elements of fluid, such as the force of gravity. Denoting by $\mathbf{F}$ the external force acting on a unit mass of the fluid and by ρ the density of the fluid, the total force per unit volume is $\rho\mathbf{F}-\nabla p$ and the equation of motion is

$$\rho\frac{d\mathbf{v}}{dt}=\rho\mathbf{F}-\nabla p. \tag{64–1}$$

If the external force is that of gravity, $\mathbf{F}=\mathbf{g}$.

Substituting (62–2) for the acceleration this equation becomes

$$\frac{\partial\mathbf{v}}{\partial t}+\mathbf{v}\cdot\nabla\mathbf{v}=\mathbf{F}-\frac{1}{\rho}\nabla p. \tag{64–2}$$

Generally the external force is derivable from a potential. In this case we can integrate the equation of motion (64–2) provided the motion is irrotational and the density ρ is a function of the pressure alone. Putting $-\nabla\Omega$ for $\mathbf{F}$ in (64–2) we have

$$\frac{\partial\mathbf{v}}{\partial t}+\mathbf{v}\cdot\nabla\mathbf{v}=-\nabla\Omega-\frac{1}{\rho}\nabla p. \tag{64–3}$$

As the motion is irrotational $\nabla\times\mathbf{v}$ vanishes and

$$(\nabla\times\mathbf{v})\times\mathbf{v}=\mathbf{v}\cdot\nabla\mathbf{v}-(\nabla\mathbf{v})\cdot\mathbf{v}=0,$$

the triple vector product on the left being expanded by the rule developed in article 7. Therefore

$$\mathbf{v}\cdot\nabla\mathbf{v}=(\nabla\mathbf{v})\cdot\mathbf{v}=\nabla(\tfrac{1}{2}v^2),$$

and if we put $-\nabla\Phi$ for $\mathbf{v}$ in the first term, (64–3) becomes

$$-\nabla\frac{\partial\Phi}{\partial t}+\nabla(\tfrac{1}{2}v^2)=-\nabla\Omega-\frac{1}{\rho}\nabla p. \tag{64–4}$$

If we pass from a point P in the fluid to a neighboring point Q, where $d\mathbf{r}$ is the position vector of Q relative to P,

$$d\left(\frac{\partial\Phi}{\partial t}\right) = \frac{\partial}{\partial x}\left(\frac{\partial\Phi}{\partial t}\right)dx + \frac{\partial}{\partial y}\left(\frac{\partial\Phi}{\partial t}\right)dy + \frac{\partial}{\partial z}\left(\frac{\partial\Phi}{\partial t}\right)dz = d\mathbf{r}\cdot\nabla\frac{\partial\Phi}{\partial t},$$

and similarly with the other terms in (64–4). So if we take the scalar product of $d\mathbf{r}$ by this equation

$$-d\left(\frac{\partial\Phi}{\partial t}\right) + d(\tfrac{1}{2}v^2) = -d\Omega - \frac{1}{\rho}dp.$$

Integrating we get

$$\int\frac{dp}{\rho} = \frac{\partial\Phi}{\partial t} - \Omega - \tfrac{1}{2}v^2, \tag{64–5}$$

since by hypothesis ρ is a function of p only. If the fluid is incompressible ρ is a constant and

$$\frac{p}{\rho} = \frac{\partial\Phi}{\partial t} - \Omega - \tfrac{1}{2}v^2 + F(t), \tag{64–6}$$

where the constant of integration $F(t)$ may be a function of the time since we are integrating with respect to the coordinates alone. If in addition the motion is steady, Φ is not a function of the time and

$$\frac{p}{\rho} = -\Omega - \tfrac{1}{2}v^2 + C, \tag{64–7}$$

where the constant C has the same value over all the region occupied by the fluid.

Problem 64a. Find the pressure at a distance r from the center of the earth due to gravitational attraction assuming the earth to be an incompressible fluid of spherical form without rotation and of density 5.6 gm/cm^3 throughout. What is the pressure at the center?

Ans. $p = \tfrac{1}{2}g\rho a\left(1 - \frac{r^2}{a^2}\right)$, 13,000 tons/in^2. Here ρ is the density and a the radius of the earth.

65. Bernoulli's Theorem for an Incompressible Liquid in Steady Flow. — From a narrow tube of flow bounded by stream lines (Fig. 74) take a section terminated by flat ends A and A' perpendicular to the axis of the tube. We shall use letters without primes to refer to values of quantities at the end A and with primes to refer to values at A'. If the cross-section of the tube is denoted by a the volume of fluid entering the end A in a unit time is av and that leaving A' is $a'v'$. Since the liquid is incompressible the masses entering and leaving in a unit time are the same, that is,

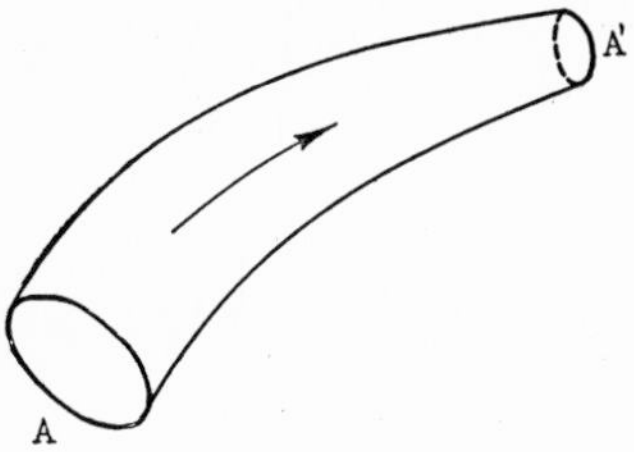

FIG. 74.

$$av\rho = a'v'\rho, \tag{65-1}$$

where ρ is the constant density of the fluid.

As before we shall suppose that the external force is derivable from a potential Ω. Then the energy possessed by the fluid entering A in a unit time is $av\rho(\frac{1}{2}v^2 + \Omega)$ and that possessed by the fluid leaving A' in a unit time is $a'v'\rho(\frac{1}{2}v'^2 + \Omega')$. Now the work done on the fluid in the tube at A by the pressure p is avp per unit time, and that done by the fluid at A' is $a'v'p'$. As the net work done must equal the increase in energy,

$$avp - a'v'p' = a'v'\rho(\tfrac{1}{2}v'^2 + \Omega') - av\rho(\tfrac{1}{2}v^2 + \Omega)$$

or

$$avp + av\rho(\tfrac{1}{2}v^2 + \Omega) = a'v'p' + a'v'\rho(\tfrac{1}{2}v'^2 + \Omega'). \tag{65-2}$$

Dividing (65–2) by (65–1),

$$\frac{p}{\rho} + \frac{1}{2}v^2 + \Omega = \frac{p'}{\rho} + \frac{1}{2}v'^2 + \Omega'.$$

This equation is true wherever the cross-sections A and A' may be taken on the tube of flow under consideration. Therefore the left-hand side of this equation has the same value at all points on the tube, that is,

$$\frac{p}{\rho} + \frac{1}{2}v^2 + \Omega = D, \tag{65-3}$$

where D is a constant for a given tube of flow. This relation is true whether the motion of the liquid is irrotational or not. The constant D, however, differs from C in (64–7) in that it may have different values for different tubes of flow. Only when the motion is irrotational is its value the same over the whole region occupied by the liquid.

As a first application of Bernoulli's theorem consider the steady flow of a liquid through a horizontal pipe of varying cross-section. As the pipe is horizontal the gravitational potential Ω is constant along its length. Therefore the pressure p is greatest where the velocity v is least, that is, where the pipe is widest, and *vice versa*.

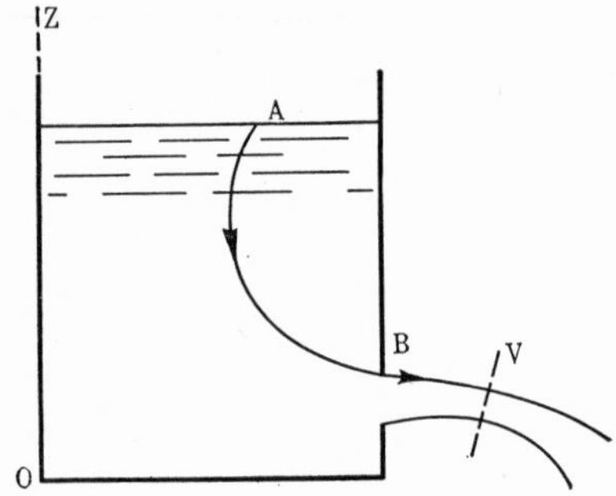

FIG. 75.

As another application we shall calculate the velocity of efflux of a liquid from an orifice B (Fig. 75) in a vessel which is kept filled to a constant level by the continual addition of fresh liquid. Take a stream line on the surface of the jet at B. It may be supposed to start from A. Then as Ω is the gravitational potential gz and p is atmospheric pressure P at both A and B,

$$\frac{P}{\rho} + gz_B + \tfrac{1}{2}v_B{}^2 = \frac{P}{\rho} + gz_A,$$

or

$$v_B{}^2 = 2g(z_A - z_B). \tag{65–4}$$

This is known as *Torricelli's law*. In general the stream lines converge in the neighborhood of the orifice B and consequently the pressure in the liquid is slightly greater than atmospheric pressure. At the *vena contracta* V, which is the narrowest portion of the jet, the stream lines are parallel and here the pressure in the liquid is equal to that of the air outside. So, strictly speaking, (65–4) should be written

$$v_V{}^2 = 2g(z_A - z_V). \tag{65–5}$$

If the orifice is a circular hole in a thin wall not provided with a mouthpiece the area of the *vena contracta* is about 0.62 that of the orifice.

66. Motion of a Sphere in an Incompressible Liquid of Infinite Extent. — We shall assume the motion of the liquid to be irrotational. Later on we shall justify this assumption by showing that if the motion is irrotational at the start it will remain irrotational for all future time. We shall consider the distant portions of the liquid to be at rest and in our preliminary discussion we shall suppose that there are no external forces such as gravity acting on the liquid particles.

Suppose a sphere of radius a to be moving through the liquid in the X direction (Fig. 76) with velocity V. Taking origin at the center of the sphere we shall employ spherical coordinates to locate a point P in the fluid. As the motion of the liquid is irrotational the velocity can be obtained from a velocity potential Φ, which symmetry shows to be a function of only r and θ. Therefore, since ρ is a constant, the equation of continuity (63–6) reduces to

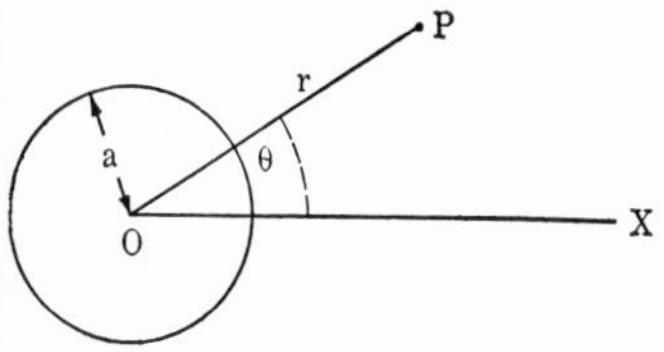

FIG. 76.

$$\frac{\partial}{\partial r}\left(r^2 \sin\theta \frac{\partial \Phi}{\partial r}\right) + \frac{\partial}{\partial \theta}\left(r \sin\theta \frac{\partial \Phi}{r\partial \theta}\right) = 0$$

when use is made of the components of velocity given by (63–7) for irrotational motion.

This equation may be written in the more convenient form

$$\frac{\partial}{\partial r}\left(r^2 \frac{\partial \Phi}{\partial r}\right) + \frac{1}{\sin\theta}\frac{\partial}{\partial \theta}\left(\sin\theta \frac{\partial \Phi}{\partial \theta}\right) = 0. \qquad (66\text{–}1)$$

We need a solution of (66–1) which satisfies the boundary conditions

$$-\left(\frac{\partial \Phi}{\partial r}\right)_{r=a} = V\cos\theta, \quad \left(\frac{\partial \Phi}{\partial r}\right)_{r=\infty} = 0. \qquad (66\text{–}2)$$

Try

$$\Phi = f(r)\cos\theta.$$

Substituting in (66–1) we find that the equation of continuity is satisfied provided

$$r^2 \frac{d^2f}{dr^2} + 2r \frac{df}{dr} - 2f = 0.$$

It is easily seen that this equation is satisfied by $f = cr^m$ for m equal to either 1 or -2. Therefore

$$\Phi = Ar \cos \theta + \frac{B}{r^2} \cos \theta,$$

where A and B are constants. Making use of the boundary conditions (66–2) it is found that

$$A = 0, \quad B = \tfrac{1}{2}Va^3.$$

Therefore

$$\Phi = \frac{Va^3}{2r^2} \cos \theta \tag{66–3}$$

is the velocity potential. The components of velocity of the fluid particles in the directions of increasing r and increasing θ respectively are

$$v_r = -\frac{\partial \Phi}{\partial r} = \frac{Va^3}{r^3} \cos \theta, \quad v_\theta = -\frac{\partial \Phi}{r\partial \theta} = \frac{Va^3}{2r^3} \sin \theta. \tag{66–4}$$

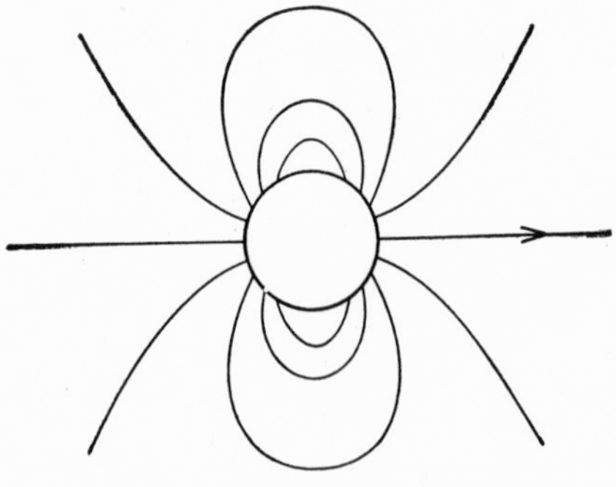

FIG. 77.

The stream lines are depicted in Fig. 77. Incidentally they are of the same form as the lines of force due to a small bar magnet.

To find the kinetic energy T of the liquid we have

$$v^2 = v_r^2 + v_\theta^2 = \left(\frac{Va^3}{r^3}\right)^2 (\cos^2\theta + \tfrac{1}{4}\sin^2\theta), \qquad (66\text{–}5)$$

and

$$T = \int_a^\infty \int_0^\pi \tfrac{1}{2}\rho v^2 2\pi r^2 \sin\theta \, d\theta \, dr$$

$$= \pi\rho V^2 a^6 \int_a^\infty \frac{dr}{r^4} \int_0^\pi (\cos^2\theta + \tfrac{1}{4}\sin^2\theta)\sin\theta \, d\theta$$

$$= \tfrac{1}{3}\pi a^3 \rho V^2 = \tfrac{1}{4}M'V^2,$$

where M' is the mass of the liquid displaced by the sphere. If M is the mass of the sphere the total kinetic energy of sphere and liquid together is

$$\tfrac{1}{2}(M + \tfrac{1}{2}M')V^2. \qquad (66\text{–}6)$$

The presence of the liquid is equivalent to an addition to the mass of the sphere of one-half the mass of the liquid displaced. A force applied to the sphere must increase the kinetic energy of the liquid as well as that of the sphere.

To get the pressure in the liquid from (64–6) we need Φ as a function of the time as well as of the coordinates. If we keep the origin O of the axes XYZ in Fig. 76 fixed relative to the inertial system from which observations are being made, but allow the origin of the spherical coordinates r and θ to move with the sphere, then when the sphere has moved a distance ξ in the X direction

$$r^2 = (x - \xi)^2 + y^2 + z^2,$$

$$\cos\theta = \frac{x - \xi}{\{(x - \xi)^2 + y^2 + z^2\}^{1/2}},$$

and

$$\Phi = \frac{Va^3(x - \xi)}{2\{(x - \xi)^2 + y^2 + z^2\}^{3/2}}.$$

Differentiating with respect to the time, remembering that

$$\frac{d\xi}{dt} = V,$$

it follows that

$$\frac{\partial\Phi}{\partial t} = \frac{V^2a^3}{2r^3}(3\cos^2\theta - 1) + \frac{a^3\cos\theta}{2r^2}\frac{dV}{dt}. \qquad (66\text{–}7)$$

Putting (66–5) and (66–7) in (64–6) and making the potential Ω zero we find for the pressure

$$\left.\begin{aligned}\frac{p}{\rho} &= \frac{V^2a^3}{2r^3}(3\cos^2\theta - 1) - \frac{V^2a^6}{2r^6}(\cos^2\theta + \tfrac{1}{4}\sin^2\theta)\\ &\quad + \frac{a^3\cos\theta}{2r^2}\frac{dV}{dt} + F,\end{aligned}\right\} \qquad (66\text{–}8)$$

where F is a function of the time only, which can be evaluated if the pressure is known at one point in the liquid. The back thrust R on the sphere is

$$R = \int_0^\pi p\cos\theta\, 2\pi a^2 \sin\theta\, d\theta,$$

where p in the integrand is the value of the pressure for $r = a$. Evidently all the terms in (66–8) will go out on integration over θ except the one in $\cos\theta$. Therefore

$$\left.\begin{aligned}R &= \pi a^3\rho\frac{dV}{dt}\int_0^\pi \cos^2\theta\sin\theta\, d\theta = \tfrac{2}{3}\pi a^3\rho\frac{dV}{dt}\\ &= \tfrac{1}{2}M'\frac{dV}{dt},\end{aligned}\right\} \qquad (66\text{–}9)$$

where M', as before, is the mass of the liquid displaced by the sphere. Therefore there is no resistance to motion with constant velocity of a solid sphere through a perfect fluid. The fluid moves aside in front of the sphere and closes in behind without exerting any resultant force on the sphere. Once the sphere is set in motion it will continue to move in a straight line with constant speed indefinitely, just as if the fluid were not present. If, however, a force K is applied to the sphere, causing it to accelerate, the fluid exerts the resistance (66–9). Therefore the equation of motion of the sphere is

$$K - R = M\frac{dV}{dt},$$

or

$$K = (M + \tfrac{1}{2}M')\frac{dV}{dt}. \qquad (66\text{–}10)$$

As in the case of its kinetic energy, here too the effective mass of the sphere is increased by an amount equal to half the mass of the liquid displaced.

So far we have supposed that no forces are acting on the fluid particles. To investigate the motion of a sphere falling through a perfect incompressible liquid we must take into account the force of gravity on the particles of liquid. If we take the X axis of Fig. 76 vertically downward, the potential due to gravity is

$$\Omega = -\, gr \cos \theta,$$

and the complete formula (64–6) contains $-\,\Omega$ in addition to the terms on the right of (66–8). The upward force R' on the sphere due to this added pressure is

$$\left.\begin{aligned} R' &= \int (-\,\rho\Omega) \cos \theta \; 2\pi a^2 \sin \theta \, d\theta \\ &= 2\pi a^3 \rho g \int_0^\pi \cos^2 \theta \sin \theta \, d\theta \\ &= \tfrac{4}{3}\pi a^3 \rho g = M' g. \end{aligned}\right\} \qquad (66\text{–}11)$$

This is the buoyant force equal to the weight of the liquid displaced which is given by Archimedes' principle. Now the equation of motion of the sphere becomes

$$K - R - R' = M \frac{dV}{dt},$$

or

$$K - R' = (M + \tfrac{1}{2}M') \frac{dV}{dt}. \qquad (66\text{–}12)$$

If the sphere is falling freely through the liquid, K is the force of gravity Mg. Putting this for K and (66–11) for R' equation (66–12) becomes

$$(M - M')g = (M + \tfrac{1}{2}M') \frac{dV}{dt},$$

or

$$\frac{dV}{dt} = \frac{M - M'}{M + \tfrac{1}{2}M'} g. \qquad (66\text{–}13)$$

If the solid sphere is of mean density σ this equation may be written

$$\frac{dV}{dt} = \frac{\sigma - \rho}{\sigma + \tfrac{1}{2}\rho} g. \qquad (66\text{–}14)$$

67. Kelvin's Circulation Theorem. — In our treatment of the motion of a sphere through a perfect liquid we assumed that the motion of the liquid is irrotational. We shall justify that assumption now by showing that if the initial motion of the liquid is irrotational it will remain irrotational forever after, provided the external force is derivable from a potential. The theorem we are going to prove in this article is not limited, however, to incompressible fluids. It is valid for any perfect fluid the density of which is a function of the pressure only.

Consider a closed curve λ lying in the fluid. The *circulation* along this curve is defined as the line integral

$$\oint \mathbf{v}\cdot\delta\boldsymbol{\lambda}$$

of the velocity taken around the closed circuit at a specified instant. We use $\delta\boldsymbol{\lambda}$ here to represent a displacement from one stream line to another, $d\boldsymbol{\lambda}$ being reserved for a displacement along a stream line. Now it was shown in article 15 that, if the line integral of a vector vanishes about every closed path, the vector is irrotational. Therefore the condition for irrotational motion of a fluid is that the circulation shall vanish everywhere.

If the external force is derivable from a potential the equation of motion (64–1) takes the form

$$\frac{d\mathbf{v}}{dt} = -\nabla\Omega - \frac{1}{\rho}\nabla p. \tag{67–1}$$

Moreover

$$\frac{d}{dt}(\mathbf{v}\cdot\delta\boldsymbol{\lambda}) = \frac{d\mathbf{v}}{dt}\cdot\delta\boldsymbol{\lambda} + \mathbf{v}\cdot\frac{d}{dt}(\delta\boldsymbol{\lambda}),$$

and

$$\mathbf{v}\cdot\frac{d}{dt}(\delta\boldsymbol{\lambda}) = \mathbf{v}\cdot\delta\left(\frac{d\boldsymbol{\lambda}}{dt}\right) = \mathbf{v}\cdot\delta\mathbf{v}$$

from (54–4), since $\delta t = 0$. So

$$\begin{aligned}\frac{d}{dt}(\mathbf{v}\cdot\delta\boldsymbol{\lambda}) &= \frac{d\mathbf{v}}{dt}\cdot\delta\boldsymbol{\lambda} + \mathbf{v}\cdot\delta\mathbf{v}\\ &= -\,\delta\boldsymbol{\lambda}\cdot\nabla\Omega - \frac{1}{\rho}\,\delta\boldsymbol{\lambda}\cdot\nabla p + \mathbf{v}\cdot\delta\mathbf{v}\\ &= -\,\delta\Omega - \frac{1}{\rho}\,\delta p + \delta(\tfrac{1}{2}v^2)\end{aligned}$$

on substituting (67–1) and recalling that

$$\delta\boldsymbol{\lambda}\cdot\nabla\Omega = \delta\Omega,$$

etc., as was shown in article 64. Therefore

$$\frac{d}{dt}\oint \mathbf{v}\cdot\delta\boldsymbol{\lambda} = -\oint \delta\Omega - \oint \frac{1}{\rho}\,\delta p + \oint \delta(\tfrac{1}{2}v^2). \qquad (67\text{–}2)$$

If the density ρ is constant or a function of the pressure p alone all the integrands on the right are exact differentials. But the integral of an exact differential about a closed path is zero. Therefore

$$\frac{d}{dt}\oint \mathbf{v}\cdot\delta\boldsymbol{\lambda} = 0. \qquad (67\text{–}3)$$

This equation tells us that, as the closed curve around which we are integrating is carried through the fluid by the motion of the particles of which it is the locus, the line integral of the velocity around this curve remains unchanged in value. So if the circulation is initially zero everywhere in the fluid it will remain zero for all time. As zero circulation is equivalent to irrotational motion, irrotational motion once established will persist indefinitely. Conversely an initial circulation or rotation of the fluid will never diminish in intensity. These conclusions are subject to the condition that the external force is derivable from a potential and that the density is a constant or a function of the pressure only, and of course they are true only for a perfect fluid free from viscosity. If an external force not derivable from a potential acts on the fluid particles or if there are frictional forces between the layers of fluid and the walls of a containing vessel a circulation may be set up in a fluid whose motion was initially irrotational.

If, now, the particles of a perfect liquid through which a sphere is allowed to fall are initially at rest the motion communicated to the liquid by the falling sphere is irrotational. Therefore we were justified in assuming irrotational motion of the fluid particles in the problem of the last article.

68. Vortex Motion. — Now we shall consider motion in which the fluid elements have an angular velocity. A *vortex line* is defined as a curve which has everywhere the direction of the axis of rotation of the fluid elements. If ω_x, ω_y, ω_z are the components of the angular velocity $\boldsymbol{\omega}$, the differential equations of a vortex line are

$$\frac{dx}{\omega_x} = \frac{dy}{\omega_y} = \frac{dz}{\omega_z}.$$

If vortex lines are drawn through every point on a small closed curve, the fluid contained in the tube so formed is said to constitute a *vortex* or *vortex filament*. The tube is taken so narrow that the angular velocity is practically the same for all points on any one cross-section. If a is the area of cross-section, the quantity ωa is defined as the *strength* of the vortex filament. We shall prove three fundamental laws of vortex motion in a fluid in which the external force is derivable from a potential and the density is a function of the pressure only.

Law I.— The same particles of fluid constitute a vortex filament at all times. To prove this take any open surface in the fluid which is the locus of vortex lines. Consider a closed curve S lying in this surface. As the vector $\boldsymbol{\omega} = \frac{1}{2}\nabla \times \mathbf{v}$ lies in the surface, the surface integral of $\nabla \times \mathbf{v}$ over the portion of the surface bounded by S vanishes. But this surface integral is equal to the line integral of $\mathbf{v}$ around S, that is, equal to the circulation around S, by Stokes' theorem. Therefore the circulation around S vanishes. After a lapse of time the surface under consideration will have been carried to a new position by the motion of the fluid. According to Kelvin's theorem the circulation around S is still zero and consequently the surface is still the locus of vortex lines. If two such surfaces are considered, their curve of intersection is initially a vortex line and remains one. Therefore vortex lines are carried along by the fluid particles in their motion.

Law II.— The strength ωa of a vortex filament is constant with respect to the time. To prove this consider a closed curve S encircling the filament. By Stokes' theorem the circulation around this curve is equal to the area a of the cross-section of the filament multiplied by the curl of the velocity $\mathbf{v}$. But the curl of $\mathbf{v}$ is twice the angular velocity $\boldsymbol{\omega}$. Therefore the circulation around S is equal to $2\omega a$. But Kelvin's theorem tells us that the circulation does not change with the time. Therefore the strength of the vortex filament is constant in time.

Law III. — The strength of a vortex filament is constant throughout the filament. Consider the circuit *ABCDEF* (Fig. 78) lying in the surface of the filament. As noted in the proof of the first law the circulation around any closed curve lying in a surface composed of vortex lines vanishes provided the curve does not encircle a vortex filament. Therefore the circulation around *ABCDEF* vanishes. Now the line integral of $\mathbf{v}$ along *FA* annuls that along *CD*. Therefore

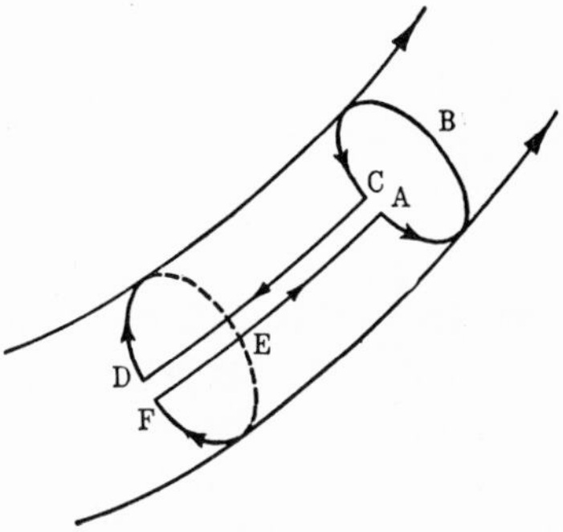

FIG. 78.

$$\int_{ABC} \mathbf{v}\cdot\delta\boldsymbol{\lambda} + \int_{DEF} \mathbf{v}\cdot\delta\boldsymbol{\lambda} = 0,$$

or

$$\int_{ABC} \mathbf{v}\cdot\delta\boldsymbol{\lambda} = \int_{FED} \mathbf{v}\cdot\delta\boldsymbol{\lambda},$$

as reversal of the sense in which the path of integration is described changes the sign of the integral. But it was shown in the proof of the second law that the circulation around a closed curve encircling a vortex filament is equal to twice the strength of the filament. Therefore the strength of the filament is the same at *D* as at *C*.

Every vortex must either form a closed tube or end in the surface of the fluid. For as the strength of a vortex filament is constant throughout its length the filament cannot end anywhere within the fluid.

Problem 68a. Prove the third law of vortex motion by applying Gauss' theorem to the surface integral of the angular velocity taken over a tubular surface with flat ends the curved portion of which coincides with the surface of the vortex filament.

69. Rectilinear Vortex in an Incompressible Liquid. — We shall consider a state of vortex motion in which the velocity of the fluid particles is perpendicular to the *Z* axis and a function of *x* and *y* only. Then the motion is the same in all planes normal to the *Z* axis and its determination becomes a problem in two dimensions.

Let *OAP* (Fig. 79) be the trace on the *XY* plane of a surface generated by a straight line parallel to the Z axis. Consider a strip of this surface of unit width extending from O to P. If

$$d\boldsymbol{\lambda} = \mathbf{i}dx + \mathbf{j}dy$$

is an element of the trace OAP, a rectangular element $d\mathbf{s}$ of the surface of the strip of length $d\boldsymbol{\lambda}$ is

$$d\mathbf{s} = \mathbf{k} \times d\boldsymbol{\lambda} = -\mathbf{i}dy + \mathbf{j}dx,$$

and the volume of fluid passing through the strip in a unit time is

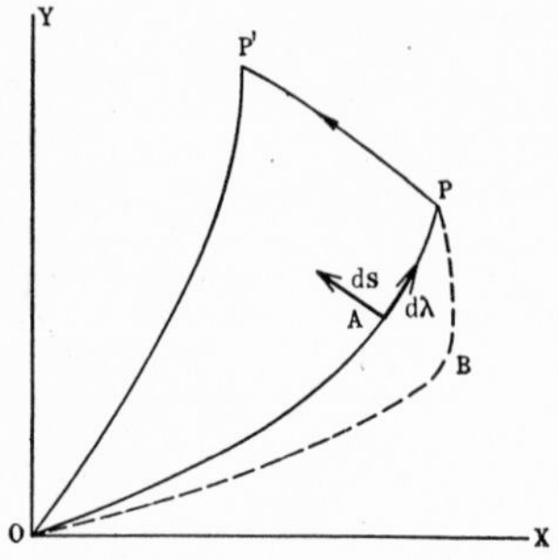

FIG. 79.

$$\Psi = \int \mathbf{v} \cdot d\mathbf{s} = \int_{OAP} (-v_x dy + v_y dx). \qquad (69\text{–}1)$$

As the fluid is assumed to be incompressible the same volume of fluid must pass in a unit time through any other strip of unit width extending from O to P, such as the strip OBP. Therefore if the initial point O of the trace of the strip is fixed, Ψ depends only upon the coordinates x, y of the end point P. So Ψ may be expressed as a function of the coordinates x, y of P and

$$d\Psi = -v_x dy + v_y dx$$

is an exact differential. Hence

$$v_x = -\frac{\partial \Psi}{\partial y}, \quad v_y = \frac{\partial \Psi}{\partial x}. \qquad (69\text{–}2)$$

The function Ψ is known as the *current function.* Equations (69–2) may also be obtained from the equation of continuity (63–3) for an incompressible fluid which takes the form

$$\frac{\partial v_x}{\partial x} + \frac{\partial v_y}{\partial y} = 0,$$

since $v_z = 0$. This equation is just the condition that $v_y dx - v_x dy$ shall be an exact differential $d\Psi$.

If PP' is a stream line no fluid flows through the surface perpendicular to the XY plane of which it is the trace. Therefore Ψ has the same value at P' as at P, and consequently the equation of a stream line is

$$\Psi = \text{constant}. \qquad (69\text{–}3)$$

As the linear velocity of the fluid has been assumed to be perpendicular to the Z axis, the angular velocity ω of the fluid elements is parallel to this coordinate axis and

$$2\omega = \frac{\partial v_y}{\partial x} - \frac{\partial v_x}{\partial y} = \frac{\partial^2 \Psi}{\partial x^2} + \frac{\partial^2 \Psi}{\partial y^2},$$

by (13–2) and (69–2).

Let us investigate the properties of a stationary vortex of circular cross-section with the same angular velocity throughout in a liquid of infinite extent the distant portions of which are at rest. If we take the Z axis as the axis of the vortex and a for its radius

$$\frac{\partial^2 \Psi}{\partial x^2} + \frac{\partial^2 \Psi}{\partial y^2} = 2\omega, \quad r < a, \tag{69–4}$$

$$\frac{\partial^2 \Psi}{\partial x^2} + \frac{\partial^2 \Psi}{\partial y^2} = 0, \quad r > a. \tag{69–5}$$

As symmetry requires that Ψ should be a function only of the radius vector r of polar coordinates in the XY plane, it is convenient to transform the coordinates in (69–4) and (69–5). As

$$r^2 = x^2 + y^2, \quad \frac{\partial r}{\partial x} = \frac{x}{r}, \quad \frac{\partial r}{\partial y} = \frac{y}{r},$$

it follows that

$$\frac{\partial \Psi}{\partial x} = \frac{d\Psi}{dr}\frac{\partial r}{\partial x} = \frac{x}{r}\frac{d\Psi}{dr}, \quad \frac{\partial \Psi}{\partial y} = \frac{d\Psi}{dr}\frac{\partial r}{\partial y} = \frac{y}{r}\frac{d\Psi}{dr}, \tag{69–6}$$

and

$$\frac{\partial^2 \Psi}{\partial x^2} = \frac{x^2}{r^2}\frac{d^2\Psi}{dr^2} + \frac{1}{r}\frac{d\Psi}{dr} - \frac{x^2}{r^3}\frac{d\Psi}{dr},$$

$$\frac{\partial^2 \Psi}{\partial y^2} = \frac{y^2}{r^2}\frac{d^2\Psi}{dr^2} + \frac{1}{r}\frac{d\Psi}{dr} - \frac{y^2}{r^3}\frac{d\Psi}{dr}.$$

Adding the last two equations

$$\frac{\partial^2 \Psi}{\partial x^2} + \frac{\partial^2 \Psi}{\partial y^2} = \frac{d^2\Psi}{dr^2} + \frac{1}{r}\frac{d\Psi}{dr} = \frac{1}{r}\frac{d}{dr}\left(r\frac{d\Psi}{dr}\right).$$

Therefore (69–4) and (69–5) become

$$\frac{1}{r}\frac{d}{dr}\left(r\frac{d\Psi}{dr}\right) = 2\omega, \quad r < a, \tag{69–7}$$

$$\frac{1}{r}\frac{d}{dr}\left(r\frac{d\Psi}{dr}\right) = 0, \quad r > a. \tag{69–8}$$

From (69–2) the radial velocity is

$$\frac{x}{r}v_x + \frac{y}{r}v_y = -\frac{x}{r}\frac{\partial\Psi}{\partial y} + \frac{y}{r}\frac{\partial\Psi}{\partial x} = 0, \tag{69–9}$$

if use is made of (69–6), and similarly the transverse velocity is

$$\frac{x}{r}v_y - \frac{y}{r}v_x = \frac{x}{r}\frac{\partial\Psi}{\partial x} + \frac{y}{r}\frac{\partial\Psi}{\partial y} = \frac{d\Psi}{dr}. \tag{69–10}$$

Solving (69–7) we have inside the vortex

$$\Psi_i = \tfrac{1}{2}\omega r^2 + A\log r + B.$$

Evidently $\Psi = 0$ when $r = 0$. Therefore $A = B = 0$ and

$$\Psi_i = \tfrac{1}{2}\omega r^2 \tag{69–11}$$

inside the vortex. Outside the vortex we get from (69–8)

$$\Psi_o = C\log r + D.$$

At the surface of the vortex the transverse velocity must have the same value whether obtained from Ψ_i or Ψ_o. Therefore

$$\omega a = \frac{C}{a}, \quad C = \omega a^2,$$

and

$$\Psi_o = \omega a^2 \log r + D.$$

Moreover Ψ_o must equal Ψ_i at the boundary of the vortex. Hence

$$D = \tfrac{1}{2}\omega a^2 - \omega a^2 \log a,$$

and

$$\Psi_o = \omega a^2 \log\frac{r}{a} + \tfrac{1}{2}\omega a^2. \tag{69–12}$$

If we put m for the strength $\pi a^2 \omega$ of the vortex

$$\Psi_i = \frac{mr^2}{2\pi a^2} \tag{69-13}$$

inside and

$$\Psi_o = \frac{m}{\pi} \log \frac{r}{a} + \frac{m}{2\pi} \tag{69-14}$$

outside the vortex. The transverse velocity is

$$v = \frac{d\Psi_i}{dr} = \frac{mr}{\pi a^2} \tag{69-15}$$

inside the vortex and

$$v = \frac{d\Psi_o}{dr} = \frac{m}{\pi r} \tag{69-16}$$

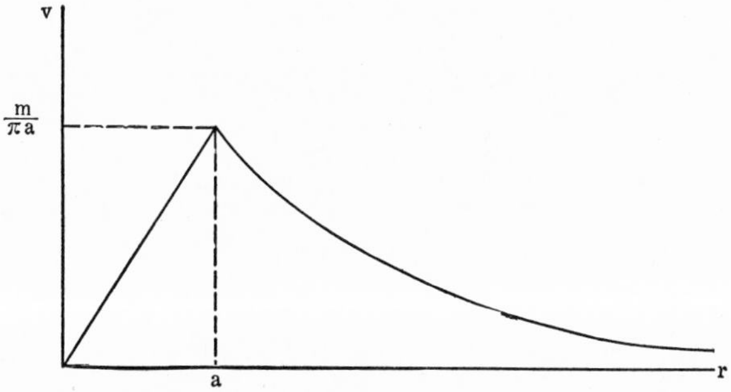

FIG. 80.

outside. Fig. 80 shows the graph of the velocity plotted against the distance r from the center of the vortex.

As the motion outside the vortex is irrotational we can obtain the pressure from (64–7) since the liquid is incompressible and the motion is steady. Since no external forces are acting on the fluid elements Ω vanishes and we get

$$\frac{p}{\rho} = C - \frac{m^2}{2\pi^2 r^2}$$

on substituting v from (69–16). If P is the pressure at infinity this becomes

$$\frac{p}{\rho} = \frac{P}{\rho} - \frac{m^2}{2\pi^2 r^2}. \tag{69-17}$$

The pressure decreases from infinity to the surface of the vortex where it is

$$\frac{p}{\rho} = \frac{P}{\rho} - \frac{m^2}{2\pi^2 a^2}. \tag{69–18}$$

Inside the vortex we cannot obtain the pressure from (64–7) as the motion is not irrotational. But if we take the component of the equation of motion (64–1) in the radial direction we have

$$-\rho\frac{v^2}{r} = -\frac{dp}{dr},$$

since **F** vanishes and the acceleration of the fluid particles consists entirely of the centripetal acceleration $-v^2/r$. Putting in the value of v from (69–15)

$$\frac{1}{\rho}\frac{dp}{dr} = \frac{m^2 r}{\pi^2 a^4},$$

and

$$\frac{p}{\rho} = \frac{P_0}{\rho} + \frac{m^2 r^2}{2\pi^2 a^4}, \tag{69–19}$$

where P_0 represents the pressure at the center of the vortex. Therefore the pressure continues to diminish as we pass from the surface to the center of the vortex. At the surface the pressure must be the same inside and out. Therefore

$$\frac{P_0}{\rho} = \frac{P}{\rho} - \frac{m^2}{\pi^2 a^2}.$$

If

$$P < \frac{m^2\rho}{\pi^2 a^2},$$

the pressure vanishes for some value of r greater than zero. In this case there is a cylindrical hollow inside the vortex. The graph in Fig. 81 shows p plotted against r for the case where the pressure

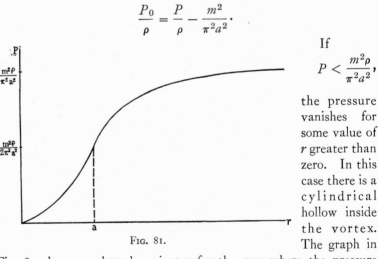

FIG. 81.

vanishes at the center of the vortex. There is a point of inflection at the surface of the vortex but no discontinuity in the slope of the curve. For this case

$$p = \frac{m^2\rho}{\pi^2 a^2}\left(1 - \frac{a^2}{2r^2}\right)$$

outside the vortex and

$$p = \frac{m^2\rho}{\pi^2 a^2} \cdot \frac{r^2}{2a^2}$$

inside. Vortices in the atmosphere constitute the most destructive feature of storms.

Problem 69a. Find the pressure outside the vortex by the same method that was used to determine the pressure inside.

70. Equilibrium Theory of the Tides. — In this preliminary investigation of tidal action we shall neglect the motion of the moon relative to the earth as well as the rotation of the earth on its axis. Let O (Fig. 82) be the center of the earth and C the center of the moon.

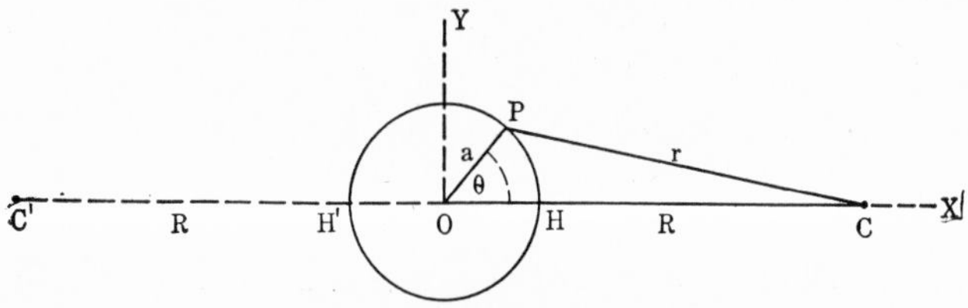

FIG. 82.

The acceleration $\mathbf{f}_0$ of a particle P on the surface of the earth relative to axes fixed in an inertial system is equal to the sum of the acceleration $\ddot{\boldsymbol{\rho}}$ of the center of the earth and the acceleration $\mathbf{f}$ of P relative to the center of the earth, that is,

$$\mathbf{f}_0 = \ddot{\boldsymbol{\rho}} + \mathbf{f}, \tag{70–1}$$

as was shown in article 32. If $\mathbf{K}_0$ is the force which the moon exerts on the earth as a whole

$$\mathbf{K}_0 \equiv \mathbf{i}\gamma \frac{ME}{R^2} = E\ddot{\boldsymbol{\rho}},$$

where M is the mass of the moon, E that of the earth and R the distance between centers. Therefore

$$\ddot{\boldsymbol{\rho}} = \mathbf{i}\frac{\gamma M}{R^2} \equiv -\nabla\Omega_0, \tag{70–2}$$

where the potential Ω_0 must be

$$\Omega_0 = -\frac{\gamma M}{R^2} x \tag{70-3}$$

in order to give the correct value for the force.

Now the potential at P due to the moon's attraction is

$$\Omega = -\frac{\gamma M}{r} = -\frac{\gamma M}{R\sqrt{1-2\frac{a}{R}\cos\theta + \frac{a^2}{R^2}}}$$

$$= -\frac{\gamma M}{R}\left\{1 - \frac{1}{2}\left(-2\frac{a}{R}\cos\theta + \frac{a^2}{R^2}\right) + \frac{3}{8}\left(4\frac{a^2}{R^2}\cos^2\theta \ldots\right)\ldots\right\}. \tag{70-4}$$

A particle at P is subject to the force of gravity as well as the attraction of the moon. If the potential due to the earth's gravitational field is denoted by Ψ, the total force due to both causes is $-\nabla(\Omega + \Psi)$. Therefore the equation of motion of a particle at P not subject to constraints is

$$\mathbf{f}_0 = -\nabla\Omega - \nabla\Psi,$$

and the acceleration $\mathbf{f}$ relative to a non-rotating earth is

$$\mathbf{f} = \mathbf{f}_0 - \ddot{\boldsymbol{\rho}} = -\nabla(\Omega - \Omega_0 + \Psi). \tag{70-5}$$

Consequently a particle at P has the same motion relative to the earth as if the earth were fixed and the particle acted upon by a field of potential

$$\left.\begin{aligned} \Omega' &= \Omega - \Omega_0 + \Psi = -\frac{\gamma M}{r} + \frac{\gamma M}{R^2} a\cos\theta + \Psi \\ &= -\frac{\gamma M}{R}\left\{1 - \frac{1}{2}\frac{a^2}{R^2}(1 - 3\cos^2\theta)\ldots\right\} + \Psi. \end{aligned}\right\} \tag{70-6}$$

If the earth is covered with water the surface of the liquid must be an equipotential surface for equilibrium to exist, for if it were not there would be a tangential force on the surface due to the effective field. The potential due to gravity is $\Psi = g\zeta$ where ζ is the elevation of the water above mean sea level. Therefore the equation of the surface is

$$\frac{\gamma M a^2}{2R^3}(1 - 3\cos^2\theta) + g\zeta = C \text{ (a constant)}$$

since the first term in the braces on the right of (70–6) is a constant, or the elevation above mean sea level is

$$\zeta = \frac{\gamma M a^2}{2gR^3}(3\cos^2\theta - 1) + \frac{C}{g}.$$

As the mass E of the earth is a^2g/γ this may be written

$$\zeta = \frac{1}{2}\frac{M}{E}\left(\frac{a}{R}\right)^3 a(3\cos^2\theta - 1) + \frac{C}{g}.$$

Since ζ is the elevation above mean sea level the average value of ζ over the surface of the earth must vanish. Therefore

$$\int_0^\pi \zeta 2\pi a^2 \sin\theta\, d\theta = 0.$$

Substituting the value of ζ above and integrating, it is seen that C is zero. Therefore

$$\zeta = \frac{1}{2}\frac{M}{E}\left(\frac{a}{R}\right)^3 a(3\cos^2\theta - 1). \tag{70–7}$$

The tide should be high, then, at H and H' and low at points on the great circle perpendicular to HH'. Actually, however, the tide is nearly low at H and H'. While the equilibrium theory accounts for two tides daily as actually observed, it gives a wrong phase to the tides. A closer approximation to the facts is given by the dynamical theory to be developed in article 72.

Problem 70a. Show that the potential (70–6) is the same as if the earth were at rest in an inertial system and two equidistant moons of mass $\frac{1}{2}M$ each were located at C and C' in Fig. 82.

Problem 70b. On the equilibrium theory of the tides find the elevation at high tide and the depression at low tide from mean sea level. The ratio of the masses of earth to moon is 80 and the ratio of the distance of the moon from the center of the earth to the radius of the earth is 60. *Ans.* 1.22 ft., 0.61 ft.

Problem 70c. What is the ratio of the height of the solar tide to that of the lunar tide? The ratio of the masses of sun to earth is 332,000 and the ratio of the distance of the sun from the earth to the radius of the earth is 23,200. *Ans.* 0.46.

71. Tidal Waves in an Incompressible Liquid. — Consider a long canal (Fig. 83) of depth h and unit width, the walls and bottom of the canal being perfectly smooth. Take the X axis along the canal and the Y axis vertical. By x and y we shall designate the coordinates of a liquid element when in its undisplaced position, denoting the components of its displacement parallel to the X and Y axes respectively by ξ and η. Thus the fluid element contained in the region $ABCD$ of dimensions dx, dy when no wave is passing through the

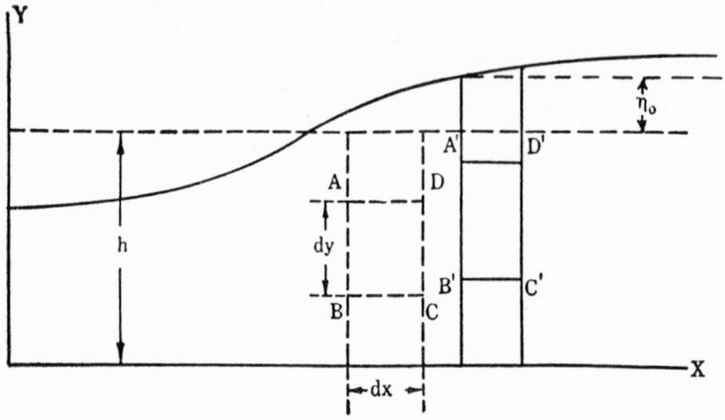

FIG. 83.

liquid becomes displaced to $A'B'C'D'$ as a result of the wave motion. Evidently

$$B'C' = dx + \frac{\partial \xi}{\partial x}dx, \qquad A'B' = dy + \frac{\partial \eta}{\partial y}dy,$$

and, as the differential coefficients are small, the area of $A'B'C'D'$ is

$$\left(dx + \frac{\partial \xi}{\partial x}dx\right)\left(dy + \frac{\partial \eta}{\partial y}dy\right) = dx\,dy\left(1 + \frac{\partial \xi}{\partial x} + \frac{\partial \eta}{\partial y}\right).$$

As the liquid is incompressible the displaced volume $A'B'C'D'$ of the element under consideration must equal the undisplaced volume $ABCD = dx\,dy$. Therefore

$$\frac{\partial \xi}{\partial x} + \frac{\partial \eta}{\partial y} = 0. \qquad (71\text{–}1)$$

If the wave length is long compared with the depth of the canal, so that the vertical motion of the fluid particles is small compared with the horizontal motion, the pressure at any point is essentially the static pressure due to depth below the surface. This static pressure on the side $C'D'$ of the fluid element is greater than that on the side $B'A'$ on account of the greater depth beneath the surface. If ξ_0, η_0 denote the components of displacement at the surface, this excess of pressure is evidently

$$\rho g \frac{\partial \eta_0}{\partial x} dx,$$

and the horizontal force due to it is

$$-\rho g \frac{\partial \eta_0}{\partial x} dx\, dy$$

in the X direction. Therefore the equation of motion of the rectangular fluid element under consideration is

$$(\rho\, dx\, dy) \frac{\partial^2 \xi}{\partial t^2} = -\rho g \frac{\partial \eta_0}{\partial x} dx\, dy \tag{71-2}$$

in so far as the motion in the horizontal direction is concerned. The acceleration in the vertical direction is so small as to be negligible.

Dividing by $\rho\, dx\, dy$ (71–2) becomes

$$\frac{\partial^2 \xi}{\partial t^2} = -g \frac{\partial \eta_0}{\partial x}. \tag{71-3}$$

This equation implies that the horizontal displacement ξ is the same at all depths and therefore not a function of y. Consequently we can integrate (71–1) getting

$$\eta = -y \frac{\partial \xi}{\partial x}, \tag{71-4}$$

since the constant of integration vanishes as there can be no vertical displacement at the bottom of the canal. At the surface y is equal to h and

$$\eta_0 = -h \frac{\partial \xi}{\partial x}.$$

Differentiating with respect to x and substituting in (71–3)

$$\frac{\partial^2 \xi}{\partial t^2} = gh \frac{\partial^2 \xi}{\partial x^2}, \tag{71-5}$$

which is the equation of a wave progressing with velocity

$$v = \sqrt{gh}. \tag{71-6}$$

If the wave is simple harmonic

$$\xi = A \cos \frac{2\pi}{\lambda}(x - vt),$$

and from (71–4)

$$\eta = \frac{2\pi y}{\lambda} A \sin \frac{2\pi}{\lambda}(x - vt).$$

Squaring the last two equations and eliminating $x - vt$, the path of a liquid particle is found to be the ellipse

$$\frac{\xi^2}{A^2} + \frac{\eta^2}{A^2\left(\frac{2\pi y}{\lambda}\right)^2} = 1. \qquad (71\text{–}7)$$

As y is always small compared with λ the vertical axis of the ellipse is shorter than the horizontal axis and diminishes to zero as the bottom of the canal is approached.

72. Dynamical Theory of the Tides. — On the dynamical theory the tides are attributed to a wave motion produced by the attraction of the moon. We shall not consider an earth covered with water but shall limit ourselves to the simpler case of a canal with perfectly smooth walls encircling the earth at the equator. As the centrifugal force due to the rotation of the earth is taken account of in the measured value of g and as the Coriolis force is negligible for the small relative velocities involved, we may consider the earth to be without rotation; the moon revolving around it in a little more than a day. The field acting on the water particles is then derivable from the potential function (70–6). Let O and C (Fig. 84) be the centers of earth and moon respectively, ϕ the longitude of a point P on the equator, and ω the westward angular velocity of the moon relative to a meridian fixed on the earth. As so defined ω is the excess of the eastward angular velocity of the earth relative to an inertial system over that of the moon. As

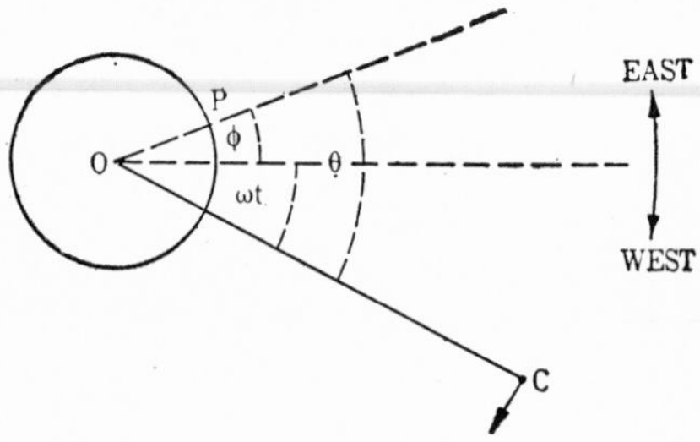

Fig. 84.

$$\theta = \omega t + \phi$$

the tangential force on a unit mass of water at P is

$$\left.\begin{aligned} -\frac{\partial\Omega'}{a\partial\phi} &= -\frac{\partial\Omega'}{a\partial\theta} = -\frac{3}{2}\frac{\gamma Ma}{R^3}\sin 2\theta \\ &= -\frac{3}{2}\frac{\gamma Ma}{R^3}\sin 2(\omega t + \phi) \end{aligned}\right\} \qquad (72\text{–}1)$$

from (70–6), as the term Ψ gives rise to a radial force only. This force has to be added to the force due to pressure on the right of (71–5) giving for the equation of motion

$$\frac{\partial^2\xi}{\partial t^2} = v^2\frac{\partial^2\xi}{a^2\partial\phi^2} - f\sin 2(\omega t + \phi), \qquad (72\text{–}2)$$

where $ad\phi$ has been put for the horizontal element of distance dx, v^2 for gh, and

$$f \equiv \frac{3}{2}\frac{\gamma Ma}{R^3}.$$

The forced wave due to the moon is given by a particular solution of this equation having the same frequency as the perturbing force due to the moon's attraction. Try

$$\xi = C\sin 2(\omega t + \phi).$$

Substituting in (72–2) we see that the differential equation is satisfied provided

$$-4\omega^2 C = -\frac{v^2}{a^2}4C - f, \quad C = -\frac{1}{4}\frac{fa^2}{v^2 - \omega^2 a^2},$$

and therefore the horizontal displacement is

$$\xi = -\frac{1}{4}\frac{fa^2}{v^2 - \omega^2 a^2}\sin 2(\omega t + \phi). \qquad (72\text{–}3)$$

Returning to (71–4) we get for the vertical displacement

$$\eta = -y\frac{\partial\xi}{a\partial\phi} = \frac{1}{2}\frac{fay}{v^2 - \omega^2 a^2}\cos 2(\omega t + \phi). \qquad (72\text{–}4)$$

These equations show that the frequency of the tides is double that of the apparent revolution of the moon. Therefore there are two tides a day, in agreement with the equilibrium theory. If $v^2 > \omega^2 a^2$ the tides are *direct*, that is, high tide is in phase with the moon, but if $v^2 < \omega^2 a^2$ the tides are *inverted*, that is, low tide is in phase with the moon.

In the case of the earth

$$\frac{v^2}{\omega^2 a^2} = \frac{g}{\omega^2 a}\frac{h}{a} = 311\frac{h}{a}, \tag{72-5}$$

so that unless the depth of the canal greatly exceeded such depths as are actually found in the ocean, the tides should be inverted. In fact for ordinary depths (10,000 ft.) v^2 is small compared with $\omega^2 a^2$. Making $y = h$ in (72–4), the height of the tide is seen to be

$$\eta_0 = \frac{1}{2}\frac{fah}{v^2 - \omega^2 a^2}\cos 2(\omega t + \phi). \tag{72-6}$$

As in the case of free waves the particles of water move in ellipses with the major axes horizontal.

Added to the particular solution of the equation of motion which represents the forced waves due to the attraction of the moon we may have solutions representing free waves such as were found in the last article.

Problem 72a. Find the amplitude of the horizontal and vertical displacements due to lunar tides in an equatorial canal of 2 miles depth. *Ans.* 165 ft., 0.16 ft.

Problem 72b. Find the depth at which the inverted tide would change to a direct tide. *Ans.* 13 miles.

Problem 72c. If $\omega = 0$, show that (72–6) agrees with (70–7).

73. Hyperbolic Functions. — As we shall have occasion to use these functions in the next article we shall digress from the subject of hydrodynamics for a moment in order to define these functions and to discuss their more important properties. The hyperbolic sine, cosine and tangent are defined by the three relations

$$\sinh x = \frac{e^x - e^{-x}}{2}, \quad \cosh x = \frac{e^x + e^{-x}}{2}, \quad \tanh x = \frac{\sinh x}{\cosh x}, \tag{73-1}$$

respectively, which should be compared with the relations

$$\sin x = \frac{e^{ix} - e^{-ix}}{2i}, \quad \cos x = \frac{e^{ix} + e^{-ix}}{2}, \quad \tan x = \frac{\sin x}{\cos x},$$

for the circular functions. It follows at once from their definitions that

$$\cosh^2 x - \sinh^2 x = 1. \tag{73-2}$$

Other elementary properties of the hyperbolic functions which follow at once from (73–1) are summarized in the following table.

$f(x)$	Value $x \doteq 0$	Value $x \doteq \infty$	Value $x \doteq -\infty$	$\frac{d}{dx} f(x)$	$\int f(x)dx$
sinh x	x	$\frac{1}{2}e^x$	$-\frac{1}{2}e^{-x}$	cosh x	cosh x
cosh x	1	$\frac{1}{2}e^x$	$\frac{1}{2}e^{-x}$	sinh x	sinh x
tanh x	x	1	-1		

In addition we have by definition csch $x = 1/\sinh x$, sech $x = 1/\cosh x$ and coth $x = 1/\tanh x$.

We note that, like their circular cousins, sinh x is an odd function and cosh x even. Now just as sin x and cos x are solutions of the differential equation

$$\frac{d^2y}{dx^2} + y = 0,$$

so it is clear from the table above that sinh x and cosh x are solutions of the equation

$$\frac{d^2y}{dx^2} - y = 0. \tag{73-3}$$

74. Gravity Waves. — In article 71 we discussed gravity waves of a length very great compared with the depth of water. Now we shall direct our attention to short gravity waves in an incompressible liquid, making the assumption, however, that the motion is irrotational. As before we shall treat the specific problem of waves running along a canal of depth h and unit width, the walls and bottom of which are perfectly smooth.

As the motion is irrotational a velocity potential exists and the equation of continuity (63–4) assumes the form

$$\frac{\partial^2\Phi}{\partial x^2} + \frac{\partial^2\Phi}{\partial y^2} = 0 \tag{74-1}$$

for the two-dimensional problem under consideration. We need a boundary condition at the bottom of the canal and at the free surface. The first is evidently

$$v_y = -\frac{\partial\Phi}{\partial y} = 0, \quad y = 0. \tag{74-2}$$

To get the second consider (64–6). As the velocity of the water particles is small we can neglect the term in v^2. The additive function $F(t)$ may be included in the as yet undetermined time derivative of Φ, and if we employ the notation of article 71 the potential due to gravity is

$$\Omega = g(y + \eta).$$

Therefore equation (64–6) becomes

$$\frac{p}{\rho} = \frac{\partial \Phi}{\partial t} - g(y + \eta),$$

or

$$\eta = \frac{1}{g}\frac{\partial \Phi}{\partial t} - y - \frac{p}{\rho g}.$$

Differentiating with respect to the time

$$v_y = \frac{\partial \eta}{\partial t} = \frac{1}{g}\frac{\partial^2 \Phi}{\partial t^2} - \frac{1}{\rho g}\frac{\partial p}{\partial t}. \tag{74–3}$$

At the surface p is the constant atmospheric pressure. So there

$$v_y = \frac{1}{g}\left(\frac{\partial^2 \Phi}{\partial t^2}\right)_{y=h},$$

or

$$\frac{\partial \Phi}{\partial y} = -\frac{1}{g}\frac{\partial^2 \Phi}{\partial t^2}, \quad y = h, \tag{74–4}$$

is the boundary condition which must be satisfied at the free surface.

To obtain a solution of the equation of continuity (74–1) which satisfies the boundary conditions let us try

$$\Phi = f(y) \cos \frac{2\pi}{\lambda}(x - vt).$$

Substituting in (74–1) we find that the equation of continuity is satisfied provided

$$\frac{d^2 f}{dy^2} - \left(\frac{2\pi}{\lambda}\right)^2 f = 0.$$

This equation is of the type (73–3). So its complete solution is

$$f = A \cosh \frac{2\pi y}{\lambda} + B \sinh \frac{2\pi y}{\lambda},$$

and

$$\Phi = \left(A \cosh \frac{2\pi y}{\lambda} + B \sinh \frac{2\pi y}{\lambda}\right) \cos \frac{2\pi}{\lambda}(x - vt) \qquad (74\text{–}5)$$

is the desired solution of the equation of continuity. Substituting in the boundary condition (74–2) at the bottom of the canal we see that $B = 0$ and the boundary condition (74–4) for the free surface gives in addition

$$\frac{2\pi}{\lambda} \sinh \frac{2\pi h}{\lambda} = \frac{1}{g}\left(\frac{2\pi v}{\lambda}\right)^2 \cosh \frac{2\pi h}{\lambda},$$

or

$$v^2 = \frac{g\lambda}{2\pi} \tanh \frac{2\pi h}{\lambda}. \qquad (74\text{–}6)$$

Two special cases are of interest.

Case I. — If the wave length is long compared with the depth of the canal

$$v^2 = \frac{g\lambda}{2\pi}\frac{2\pi h}{\lambda} = gh. \qquad (74\text{–}7)$$

This is the case of tidal waves treated in article 71. The velocity of propagation is independent of the wave length.

Case II. — If the wave length is short compared with the depth of the canal

$$v^2 = \frac{g\lambda}{2\pi}. \qquad (74\text{–}8)$$

This is the case of deep sea waves due to the wind. As the velocity is proportional to the square root of the wave length a high wind gives rise to longer waves than a gentle breeze.

To find the components of displacement of the water particles we have from (74–5)

$$\frac{\partial \xi}{\partial t} = -\frac{\partial \Phi}{\partial x} = \frac{2\pi A}{\lambda} \cosh \frac{2\pi y}{\lambda} \sin \frac{2\pi}{\lambda}(x - vt),$$

$$\frac{\partial \eta}{\partial t} = -\frac{\partial \Phi}{\partial y} = -\frac{2\pi A}{\lambda} \sinh \frac{2\pi y}{\lambda} \cos \frac{2\pi}{\lambda}(x - vt),$$

and integrating

$$\left.\begin{aligned}\xi &= \frac{A}{v}\cosh\frac{2\pi y}{\lambda}\cos\frac{2\pi}{\lambda}(x-vt),\\ \eta &= \frac{A}{v}\sinh\frac{2\pi y}{\lambda}\sin\frac{2\pi}{\lambda}(x-vt),\end{aligned}\right\} \tag{74–9}$$

whence the path of a fluid element is seen to be the ellipse

$$\frac{\xi^2}{\left(\dfrac{A}{v}\cosh\dfrac{2\pi y}{\lambda}\right)^2}+\frac{\eta^2}{\left(\dfrac{A}{v}\sinh\dfrac{2\pi y}{\lambda}\right)^2}=1 \tag{74–10}$$

with its major axis horizontal. As the hyperbolic sine and cosine approach the same limiting value for large values of the argument, this ellipse becomes a circle near the surface of deep water.

So far we have neglected the effect of surface tension. If T denotes the force per unit width acting along the surface, there is a vertical force on a length dx of a curved liquid surface which we can obtain from Fig. 63 in exactly the same way as we found the upward force (49–1) acting on a length dx of the stretched wire under discussion in article 49. If we replace S by T in (49–1) and divide by dx we get for the upward force on a unit area of the surface of the canal of unit width which we have been considering

$$T\frac{\partial^2\eta_0}{\partial x^2}. \tag{74–11}$$

Therefore the pressure in the water just under the surface must be less than atmospheric pressure by this amount, that is,

$$p = P - T\frac{\partial^2\eta}{\partial x^2}, \qquad y = h,$$

where P is the constant atmospheric pressure. Consequently

$$\frac{\partial p}{\partial t} = -T\frac{\partial^2}{\partial x^2}\frac{\partial\eta}{\partial t} = T\frac{\partial^2}{\partial x^2}\frac{\partial\Phi}{\partial y}, \quad y = h,$$

and (74–3) gives for the boundary condition at the free surface of the liquid

$$\frac{\partial\Phi}{\partial y} = -\frac{1}{g}\frac{\partial^2\Phi}{\partial t^2}+\frac{T}{\rho g}\frac{\partial^2}{\partial x^2}\frac{\partial\Phi}{\partial y}, \qquad y = h, \tag{74–12}$$

instead of (74–4). Substituting the solution (74–5) of the equation of continuity in (74–12), remembering that $B = 0$ in order to satisfy the boundary condition at the bottom of the canal,

$$\frac{2\pi}{\lambda}\sinh\frac{2\pi h}{\lambda} = \frac{1}{g}\left(\frac{2\pi v}{\lambda}\right)^2\cosh\frac{2\pi h}{\lambda} - \frac{T}{\rho g}\left(\frac{2\pi}{\lambda}\right)^3\sinh\frac{2\pi h}{\lambda},$$

or

$$v^2 = \left(\frac{g\lambda}{2\pi} + \frac{2\pi T}{\rho\lambda}\right)\tanh\frac{2\pi h}{\lambda}. \qquad (74\text{–}13)$$

In a deep sea the argument of the hyperbolic tangent is large and

$$v = \sqrt{\frac{g\lambda}{2\pi} + \frac{2\pi T}{\rho\lambda}}. \qquad (74\text{–}14)$$

We see from this expression that the velocity of long waves is determined almost entirely by gravity whereas for short waves surface tension plays the predominant role. Solving (74–14) for λ we get

$$\lambda = \frac{\pi v^2}{g}\left\{1 \pm \sqrt{1 - \frac{4Tg}{\rho v^4}}\right\}.$$

Therefore in general two sets of waves are produced by a given wind velocity. The shorter waves are called *ripples*. If v^4 is less than $4Tg/\rho$ the wave length becomes imaginary. Consequently there is a minimum velocity of the wind necessary to sustain waves. As the surface tension of water is about 75 dynes per centimeter this minimum velocity is about 23 centimeters per second corresponding to a wave length of 1.7 centimeters.

75. Group Velocity. — The velocity of wave propagation which has been dealt with in chapters III and V is more correctly known as the *phase velocity*. If *dispersion* exists in a medium through which waves are passing, that is, if the phase velocity is a function of the wave length, then one of two sets of waves of slightly different wave length travels faster than the other and reinforcement and interference take place as the one set gains on the other. The velocity with which the regions of reinforcement or interference advance is known as the *group velocity*. To find this velocity consider two trains of simple harmonic waves of the same amplitude but of slightly different wave length and frequency, such as

$$\eta_1 = A \sin \frac{2\pi}{\lambda_1} (x - v_1 t),$$

$$\eta_2 = A \sin \frac{2\pi}{\lambda_2} (x - v_2 t).$$

The resultant displacement η is

$$\eta = \eta_1 + \eta_2 = 2A \cos \pi \left\{ \left(\frac{1}{\lambda_1} - \frac{1}{\lambda_2} \right) x - \left(\frac{v_1}{\lambda_1} - \frac{v_2}{\lambda_2} \right) t \right\}$$

$$\sin \pi \left\{ \left(\frac{1}{\lambda_1} + \frac{1}{\lambda_2} \right) x - \left(\frac{v_1}{\lambda_1} + \frac{v_2}{\lambda_2} \right) t \right\}.$$

As the wave lengths and the velocities are only slightly different we may replace λ_1 and λ_2 by the mean wave length λ, and v_1 and v_2 by the mean velocity v in the second trigonometrical function, since here only sums of these quantities appear. Therefore,

$$\eta = \left[2A \cos \pi \left\{ d\left(\frac{1}{\lambda}\right) x - d\left(\frac{v}{\lambda}\right) t \right\} \right] \sin \frac{2\pi}{\lambda} (x - vt). \qquad (75\text{–}1)$$

This expression represents a wave traveling with phase velocity v with an amplitude given by the expression in brackets. At a given instant the amplitude plotted against x is represented by a cosine curve, the distance from one region of maximum amplitude to the next being the reciprocal $d(1/\lambda)$. Moreover this region of maximum amplitude is progressing in the positive X direction with the group velocity

$$U = \frac{d\left(\frac{v}{\lambda}\right)}{d\left(\frac{1}{\lambda}\right)} = \frac{\frac{\lambda dv - v d\lambda}{\lambda^2}}{-\frac{d\lambda}{\lambda^2}} = v - \lambda \frac{dv}{d\lambda}. \qquad (75\text{–}2)$$

Therefore we have a wave within a wave as represented in Fig. 85. The full-line wave curve advances with the phase velocity v whereas the broken-line curve advances with the group velocity U. If v increases with λ the phase wave travels more rapidly than the group wave. In this case the full-line waves pass through the group from rear to front, each crest disappearing at the front of the group while a new crest appears at the rear.

If instead of two isolated wave lengths we have a symmetrical band of wave lengths bunched about a mean value λ, we can com-

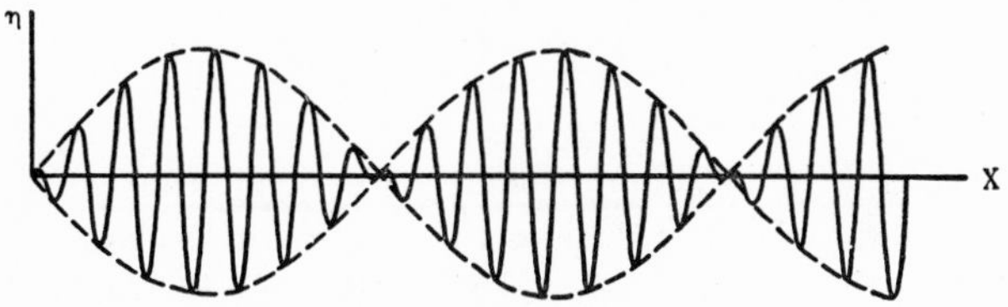

FIG. 85.

bine pairs of wave lengths of equal amplitude A so as to obtain for the resultant displacement

$$\eta = \left[\sum 2A \cos \pi \left\{ d\left(\frac{1}{\lambda}\right) x - d\left(\frac{v}{\lambda}\right) t \right\}\right] \sin \frac{2\pi}{\lambda}(x - vt) \quad (75\text{-}3)$$

summed up over the pairs considered. For a pair of wave lengths lying close together $d\left(\frac{1}{\lambda}\right)$ is small and hence the group wave is long, whereas for a pair of wave lengths farther apart $d\left(\frac{1}{\lambda}\right)$ is larger and the group wave is shorter. For all pairs, however, the group velocity is the same to the degree of approximation considered and is given by (75-2).

In the case of deep sea gravity waves considered in the previous article

$$v = \sqrt{\frac{g\lambda}{2\pi}},$$

and the group velocity is

$$U = v - \tfrac{1}{2}v = \tfrac{1}{2}v \quad (75\text{-}4)$$

which is only one-half the phase velocity.

REFERENCES

WEBSTER, A. G.: *The Dynamics of Particles and of Rigid, Elastic and Fluid Bodies*. B. G. Teubner, Leipzig.

LAMB, HORACE: *Hydrodynamics*, Cambridge University Press, Cambridge.

CHAPTER VI

HYDRODYNAMICS OF VISCOUS FLUIDS

76. Equation of Motion of a Viscous Fluid. — The dynamics of a viscous fluid is very similar to that of the elastic solid treated in chapter III, the main point of difference being that the shearing stress in a fluid is proportional to the time rate of change of strain instead of to the strain itself. If $\mathbf{v}$ is the velocity of the fluid at $P(x, y, z)$ and $\mathbf{v} + d\mathbf{v}$ that at a neighboring point Q at the same time, it follows from (62–1) that the velocity of the fluid at Q relative to that at P is

$$d\mathbf{v} = d\mathbf{r}\cdot\nabla\mathbf{v}, \tag{76–1}$$

where $d\mathbf{r}$ is the position vector of Q relative to P. The dyadic

$$\left.\begin{aligned}\nabla\mathbf{v} = \quad & \mathbf{ii}\frac{\partial v_x}{\partial x} + \mathbf{ij}\frac{\partial v_y}{\partial x} + \mathbf{ik}\frac{\partial v_z}{\partial x} \\ + \, & \mathbf{ji}\frac{\partial v_x}{\partial y} + \mathbf{jj}\frac{\partial v_y}{\partial y} + \mathbf{jk}\frac{\partial v_z}{\partial y} \\ + \, & \mathbf{ki}\frac{\partial v_x}{\partial z} + \mathbf{kj}\frac{\partial v_y}{\partial z} + \mathbf{kk}\frac{\partial v_z}{\partial z}\end{aligned}\right\} \tag{76–2}$$

is called the *rate of strain dyadic*. As before this dyadic can be written as the sum of two dyadics Φ and Ω, where $\Phi \equiv \frac{1}{2}\{\nabla\mathbf{v} + (\nabla\mathbf{v})_c\}$ is symmetric, and $\Omega \equiv \frac{1}{2}\{\nabla\mathbf{v} - (\nabla\mathbf{v})_c\}$ is skew-symmetric. So (76–1) becomes

$$d\mathbf{v} = d\mathbf{r}\cdot\Phi + d\mathbf{r}\cdot\Omega. \tag{76–3}$$

In the same way as in (47–5) we find

$$\begin{aligned} d\mathbf{r}\cdot\Omega &= \tfrac{1}{2}d\mathbf{r}\cdot\{\nabla\mathbf{v} - (\nabla\mathbf{v})_c\} \\ &= \tfrac{1}{2}\{d\mathbf{r}\cdot\nabla\mathbf{v} - \nabla\mathbf{v}\cdot d\mathbf{r}\} \\ &= \tfrac{1}{2}(\nabla\times\mathbf{v})\times d\mathbf{r} \\ &= \boldsymbol{\omega}\times d\mathbf{r}, \end{aligned} \tag{76–4}$$

where $\boldsymbol{\omega}$ is the mean angular velocity of the fluid at P. Therefore this portion of the relative velocity represents a rotation of the neighboring fluid particles about P with angular velocity $\boldsymbol{\omega}$. On the other hand the portion $d\mathbf{r}\cdot\Phi$ of the velocity of neighboring points relative to P represents the rate of change of pure strain. Written out in terms of its elements the dyadic Φ is

$$\left.\begin{aligned}\Phi = \mathbf{ii}\frac{\partial v_x}{\partial x} &+ \mathbf{ij}\frac{1}{2}\left(\frac{\partial v_y}{\partial x} + \frac{\partial v_x}{\partial y}\right) + \mathbf{ik}\frac{1}{2}\left(\frac{\partial v_x}{\partial z} + \frac{\partial v_z}{\partial x}\right)\\ &+ \mathbf{ji}\frac{1}{2}\left(\frac{\partial v_y}{\partial x} + \frac{\partial v_x}{\partial y}\right) + \mathbf{jj}\frac{\partial v_y}{\partial y} + \mathbf{jk}\frac{1}{2}\left(\frac{\partial v_z}{\partial y} + \frac{\partial v_y}{\partial z}\right)\\ &+ \mathbf{ki}\frac{1}{2}\left(\frac{\partial v_x}{\partial z} + \frac{\partial v_z}{\partial x}\right) + \mathbf{kj}\frac{1}{2}\left(\frac{\partial v_z}{\partial y} + \frac{\partial v_y}{\partial z}\right) + \mathbf{kk}\left(\frac{\partial v_z}{\partial z}\right),\end{aligned}\right\} \quad (76\text{–}5)$$

and if we put

$$\left.\begin{aligned} a &\equiv \frac{\partial v_x}{\partial x}, & b &\equiv \frac{\partial v_y}{\partial y}, & c &\equiv \frac{\partial v_z}{\partial z},\\ f &\equiv \frac{\partial v_z}{\partial y} + \frac{\partial v_y}{\partial z}, & g &\equiv \frac{\partial v_x}{\partial z} + \frac{\partial v_z}{\partial x}, & h &\equiv \frac{\partial v_y}{\partial x} + \frac{\partial v_x}{\partial y},\end{aligned}\right\} \quad (76\text{–}6)$$

it may be written

$$\left.\begin{aligned}\Phi = \quad & a\mathbf{ii} + \tfrac{1}{2}h\mathbf{ij} + \tfrac{1}{2}g\mathbf{ik}\\ &+ \tfrac{1}{2}h\mathbf{ji} + b\mathbf{jj} + \tfrac{1}{2}f\mathbf{jk}\\ &+ \tfrac{1}{2}g\mathbf{ki} + \tfrac{1}{2}f\mathbf{kj} + c\mathbf{kk}.\end{aligned}\right\} \quad (76\text{–}7)$$

As this dyadic is symmetric it may be put in the form

$$\Phi = a\mathbf{ii} + b\mathbf{jj} + c\mathbf{kk} \quad (76\text{–}8)$$

by a suitable orientation of the axes XYZ.

The stress dyadic Ψ is the same for a fluid as for a solid. As shown in article 47 this dyadic is symmetric and may be written

$$\Psi = P\mathbf{ii} + Q\mathbf{jj} + R\mathbf{kk} \quad (76\text{–}9)$$

if the axes are suitably oriented. As the fluid is isotropic it follows from symmetry that the same orientation of axes which brings the stress dyadic into the form (76–9) will bring the *rate of pure strain dyadic* Φ into the form (76–8).

Since P, Q, R in (76–9) are tensions it is clear that the mean pressure p is given by

$$P + Q + R = -3p. \tag{76–10}$$

If the fluid were not viscous P, Q, R would be individually equal to $-p$. Therefore it is the excess of each of these stresses over $-p$ which determines the rate of strain in a viscous fluid. For small rates of strain we should expect this excess to be a homogeneous linear function of the rates of pure strain a, b, c. This expectation is very exactly confirmed by experiment. Therefore, just as in the case of an elastic solid, we may write

$$P = -p + \lambda(a + b + c) + 2\mu a,$$

$$Q = -p + \lambda(a + b + c) + 2\mu b,$$

$$R = -p + \lambda(a + b + c) + 2\mu c.$$

Adding these three equations together and comparing with (76–10) we see that

$$\lambda = -\tfrac{2}{3}\mu. \tag{76–11}$$

Therefore as

$$a + b + c = \frac{\partial v_x}{\partial x} + \frac{\partial v_y}{\partial y} + \frac{\partial v_z}{\partial z} = \nabla \cdot \mathbf{v},$$

it follows that

$$\Psi = -(p + \tfrac{2}{3}\mu\nabla \cdot \mathbf{v})\mathbf{I} + 2\mu\Phi. \tag{76–12}$$

This relation is the analog of (47–16) for the case of an elastic solid. As it is an equation between dyadics it holds no matter how the axes to which Ψ and Φ are referred may be oriented. In general it is equivalent to nine scalar equations of which three are redundant on account of the symmetry of the dyadics involved. The coefficient μ is known as the *coefficient of viscosity*.

With the axes oriented so that Ψ and Φ have the more general forms (47–11) and (76–7) let us pick out the **ij** elements in equation (76–12). We get

$$U = \mu h.$$

Consider a fluid streaming in the X direction (Fig. 86), different layers of which are traveling with different velocities. As there is no component of velocity in the Y direction

$$U = \mu \frac{\partial v_x}{\partial y}. \tag{76–13}$$

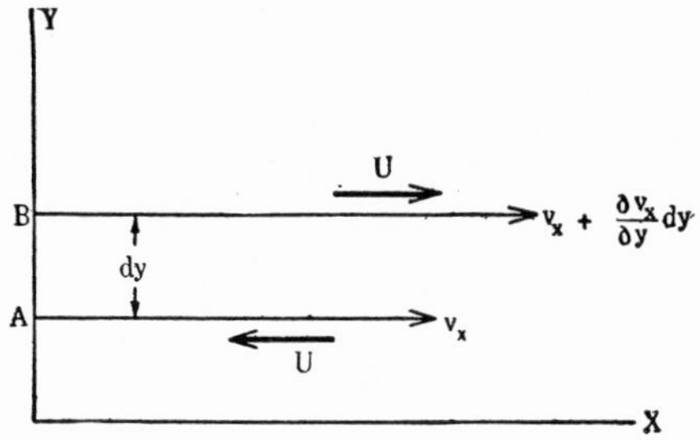

FIG. 86.

The layer of fluid between A and B is subject to a shearing stress in the X direction on its upper surface due to the more rapidly moving fluid above and in the $-X$ direction on its lower surface due to the more slowly moving fluid below.

The force per unit volume due to the stresses was shown to be $\nabla \cdot \Psi$ in article 52. From (76–12)

$$\nabla \cdot \Psi = -\nabla p - \tfrac{2}{3}\mu \nabla \nabla \cdot \mathbf{v} + 2\mu \nabla \cdot \Phi. \tag{76–14}$$

To express $\nabla \cdot \Phi$ in terms of $\mathbf{v}$ we proceed as in article 52. Since

$$\Phi = \tfrac{1}{2}\{\nabla \mathbf{v} + (\nabla \mathbf{v})_c\}$$

we have

$$\nabla \cdot \Phi = \tfrac{1}{2}(\nabla \cdot \nabla \mathbf{v} + \nabla \nabla \cdot \mathbf{v}).$$

Putting this in (76–14),

$$\nabla \cdot \Psi = -\nabla p + \tfrac{1}{3}\mu \nabla \nabla \cdot \mathbf{v} + \mu \nabla \cdot \nabla \mathbf{v}. \tag{76–15}$$

If in addition to the force due to the stresses there is an external force $\mathbf{F}$ acting on each unit mass of the fluid, the equation of motion is

$$\rho \frac{d\mathbf{v}}{dt} = \rho \mathbf{F} - \nabla p + \tfrac{1}{3}\mu \nabla \nabla \cdot \mathbf{v} + \mu \nabla \cdot \nabla \mathbf{v}. \tag{76–16}$$

By virtue of (62–2) we may write it in the form

Compare with M&F p.163, Eq. 2.3.20 for be[tter] analy[sis]

$$\rho \frac{\partial \mathbf{v}}{\partial t} + \rho \mathbf{v} \cdot \nabla \mathbf{v} = \rho \mathbf{F} - \nabla p + \tfrac{1}{3}\mu \nabla \nabla \cdot \mathbf{v} + \mu \nabla \cdot \nabla \mathbf{v}. \qquad (76\text{–}17)$$

If the fluid is incompressible the equation of continuity requires that $\nabla \cdot \mathbf{v}$ should vanish, making the third term on the right disappear. If in addition the velocity of the fluid elements is small we can neglect the term on the left in the square of $\mathbf{v}$. So for slow motion of an incompressible viscous fluid

$$\rho \frac{\partial \mathbf{v}}{\partial t} = \rho \mathbf{F} - \nabla p + \mu \nabla \cdot \nabla \mathbf{v}. \qquad (76\text{–}18)$$

The boundary conditions at the surface of a solid with which a viscous fluid is in contact are different from those for a perfect fluid since a viscous fluid sticks to the surface of a solid, and consequently the tangential as well as the normal component of velocity of adjacent fluid particles is the same as that of the solid.

77. Steady Flow of a Viscous Fluid through a Circular Pipe. — Take the axis of the pipe as the X coordinate axis (Fig. 87), the

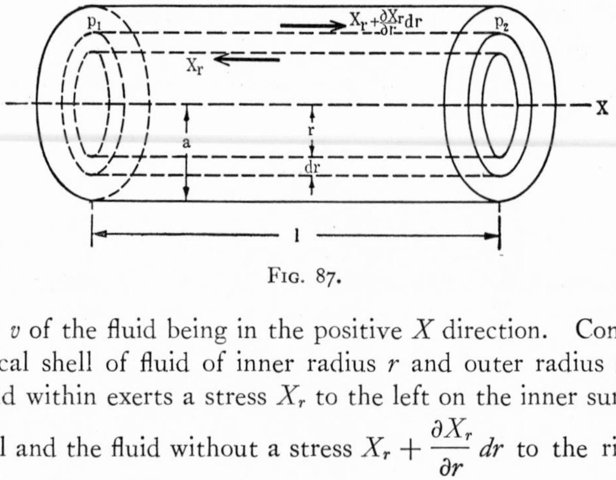

FIG. 87.

velocity v of the fluid being in the positive X direction. Consider a cylindrical shell of fluid of inner radius r and outer radius $r + dr$. The fluid within exerts a stress X_r to the left on the inner surface of the shell and the fluid without a stress $X_r + \frac{\partial X_r}{\partial r} dr$ to the right on the outer surface, where

$$X_r = \mu \frac{\partial v}{\partial r}$$

by (76–13). As the stress on the inner surface acts on an area $2\pi r l$ the force due to it is

$$X_r 2\pi r l = 2\pi r l \mu \frac{\partial v}{\partial r} \cdot$$

The net force to the right due to the stresses exerted on the cylindrical shell by the adjacent fluid is the excess of the force on the outer surface over that on the inner surface, that is,

$$\frac{\partial}{\partial r}\left\{2\pi r l \mu \frac{\partial v}{\partial r}\right\} dr.$$

If the fluid is unaccelerated this force must be balanced by an equal force to the left due to the difference between the pressure p_2 at the right end of the pipe and p_1 at the left end. As these pressures act on surfaces of area $2\pi r dr$ the net force to the left on the cylindrical shell due to the difference in pressure at the two ends is

$$(p_2 - p_1)2\pi r dr.$$

Equating this to the force to the right due to the shearing stresses produced by the unequal flow of the viscous fluid we have

$$\frac{\partial}{\partial r}\left\{2\pi r l \mu \frac{\partial v}{\partial r}\right\} = 2\pi r(p_2 - p_1).$$

Integrating once

$$2\pi r l \mu \frac{\partial v}{\partial r} = \pi r^2(p_2 - p_1) + A,$$

and a second integration gives

$$v = \frac{p_2 - p_1}{4\mu l} r^2 + \frac{A}{2\pi \mu l} \log r + B.$$

As the velocity is not infinite along the axis $A = 0$. The fluid in contact with the walls of the pipe is at rest. Therefore if a is the radius of the pipe v must vanish for $r = a$. Consequently

$$B = -\frac{p_2 - p_1}{4\mu l} a^2,$$

and the velocity at any distance r from the axis is

$$v = \frac{p_1 - p_2}{4\mu l}(a^2 - r^2). \qquad (77\text{–}1)$$

The volume of fluid passing any cross-section of the pipe in a unit time is then

$$\int_0^a v 2\pi r dr = \frac{\pi a^4}{8\mu} \frac{p_1 - p_2}{l}. \qquad (77\text{–}2)$$

This is known as *Poiseuille's formula.* It has been verified very exactly by him for the flow of water through capillary tubes. From a measurement of the pressure gradient $(p_1 - p_2)/l$, the radius a of the tube, and the volume of fluid passing through it, the coefficient of viscosity μ may be determined. As the volume of fluid emerging from a pipe line under a given pressure gradient is proportional to the fourth power of the radius halving the diameter of the pipe reduces the flow to one-sixteenth of its former value.

Problem 77a. A viscous fluid flows between two coaxial cylindrical pipes of radii a and b, where $b > a$. Show that the velocity at any distance r from the axis is

$$\frac{p_1 - p_2}{4\mu l \log \frac{b}{a}}\left[(b^2 - r^2)\log\frac{r}{a} - (r^2 - a^2)\log\frac{b}{r}\right]$$

and that the volume of fluid discharged per unit time is

$$\frac{\pi(b^2 - a^2)(p_1 - p_2)}{8\mu l}\left[(b^2 + a^2) - \frac{b^2 - a^2}{\log \frac{b}{a}}\right].$$

78. Motion of a Fluid between Rotating Cylinders. — Consider two coaxial cylinders (Fig. 88) of radii a_1 and a_2, respectively, the space between them being filled with the fluid under consideration. We

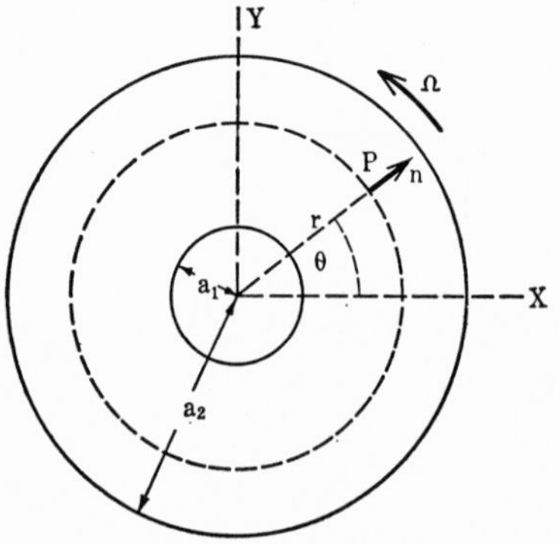

FIG. 88.

shall suppose the outer cylinder to rotate with angular velocity Ω while the inner one remains stationary. Let ω be the angular velocity of the fluid at a distance r from the axis. Taking the common axis of the cylinders for the Z coordinate axis, the linear velocity of the fluid at a point P (x, y) is

$$\mathbf{v} = \boldsymbol{\omega} \times \mathbf{r} = -\,\mathbf{i}\omega y + \mathbf{j}\omega x. \tag{78–1}$$

We want the shearing stress Θ_r on a surface normal to the radius vector, that is, the component along the unit vector $\boldsymbol{\theta}_1 = -\,\mathbf{i}\sin\theta + \mathbf{j}\cos\theta$ of the stress $\mathbf{S}_n$ on a surface normal to the unit vector $\mathbf{n}_1 = \mathbf{i}\cos\theta + \mathbf{j}\sin\theta$. From (47–10) this is

$$\begin{aligned}\Theta_r &= \mathbf{n}_1 \cdot \Psi \cdot \boldsymbol{\theta}_1\\ &= (-X_x + Y_y)\sin\theta\cos\theta - X_y\sin^2\theta + Y_x\cos^2\theta.\end{aligned} \tag{78–2}$$

Now from (76–12)

$$\begin{aligned}X_x &= -\,(p + \tfrac{2}{3}\mu\nabla\cdot\mathbf{v}) + 2\mu a,\\ Y_y &= -\,(p + \tfrac{2}{3}\mu\nabla\cdot\mathbf{v}) + 2\mu b,\\ X_y &= Y_x = \mu h,\end{aligned}$$

and therefore

$$\Theta_r = \mu\{2(b-a)\sin\theta\cos\theta + h(\cos^2\theta - \sin^2\theta)\}.$$

Since ω is a function of r only, we have from (78–1)

$$b - a = \frac{\partial v_y}{\partial y} - \frac{\partial v_x}{\partial x} = 2\frac{xy}{r}\frac{d\omega}{dr} = 2r\frac{d\omega}{dr}\sin\theta\cos\theta,$$

$$h = \frac{\partial v_y}{\partial x} + \frac{\partial v_x}{\partial y} = \frac{x^2 - y^2}{r}\frac{d\omega}{dr} = r\frac{d\omega}{dr}(\cos^2\theta - \sin^2\theta),$$

and

$$\begin{aligned}\Theta_r &= \mu r\frac{d\omega}{dr}\{4\sin^2\theta\cos^2\theta + (\cos^2\theta - \sin^2\theta)^2\}\\ &= \mu r\frac{d\omega}{dr}.\end{aligned} \tag{78–3}$$

The torque on a unit area of the fluid inside a cylinder of radius r due to the drag of the more rapidly rotating fluid outside is $r\,\Theta_r$, and if l is the length of the cylinders the total torque L is

$$L = 2\pi r l r\Theta_r = 2\pi\mu l r^3\frac{d\omega}{dr}. \tag{78–4}$$

As the motion is steady the torques on the hollow cylinder of fluid of radii r and $r + dr$ due to the forward drag of the fluid outside and the backward drag of the fluid inside must be equal, that is,

$$\frac{\partial}{\partial r}\left(2\pi\mu l r^3 \frac{d\omega}{dr}\right) = 0.$$

Therefore

$$r^3 \frac{d\omega}{dr} = -\ 2A(\text{a constant}),$$

and

$$\omega = \frac{A}{r^2} + B. \qquad (78\text{–}5)$$

The boundary conditions are that $\omega = 0$ when $r = a_1$ and $\omega = \Omega$ when $r = a_2$. So

$$\omega = \frac{a_2^{\,2}}{r^2}\,\frac{r^2 - a_1^{\,2}}{a_2^{\,2} - a_1^{\,2}}\,\Omega. \qquad (78\text{–}6)$$

To find the frictional couple L exerted by the outer cylinder on the fluid substitute (78–6) in (78–4) and make r equal to a_2. This gives

$$L = 4\pi\mu l\,\frac{a_1^{\,2}a_2^{\,2}}{a_2^{\,2}-a_1^{\,2}}\,\Omega. \qquad (78\text{–}7)$$

The couple exerted by the inner cylinder on the fluid is equal and opposite to this. By measuring the torque on the inner cylinder when the outer cylinder is rotated with a known angular velocity the coefficient of viscosity of the fluid may be measured. For water

$$\mu = 0.0101 \qquad \text{at } 20^\circ\ \text{C}.$$

and for air

$$\mu = 0.0001823 \text{ at } 23^\circ\ \text{C}.$$

The coefficient of viscosity of a gas is independent of the density, as will be shown in the chapter on kinetic theory.

If the inner cylinder is rotated and the outer cylinder kept fixed, a_1 and a_2 must be interchanged in (78–6) and (78–7).

79. Solution of Laplace's Equation. — Laplace's equation

$$\nabla \cdot \nabla \Phi = 0, \qquad (79\text{–}1)$$

which has already been encountered in article 63, is of great importance in theoretical physics. Not only in the next article shall we find it necessary to obtain a solution of this equation, but in the study of electrostatics and magnetostatics we shall meet it frequently. We shall now take up two theorems concerning solutions of this equation and shall then find a set of solutions for the case where Φ is a function of the radius vector r and the polar angle θ alone.

Theorem I. — If $\Phi_1, \Phi_2, \ldots \Phi_n$ are individually solutions of Laplace's equation, then

$$\Phi = A_1\Phi_1 + A_2\Phi_2 \ldots + A_n\Phi_n$$

is a solution where $A_1, A_2, \ldots A_n$ are any constants. For

$$\nabla\cdot\nabla\Phi = A_1\nabla\cdot\nabla\Phi_1 + A_2\nabla\cdot\nabla\Phi_2 \ldots + A_n\nabla\cdot\nabla\Phi_n = 0$$

as each term contains a vanishing factor.

Theorem II. — If Φ is a solution of Laplace's equation any partial derivative of Φ of any order with respect to the coordinates x, y, z is a solution. Writing out $\nabla\cdot\nabla$ in terms of partial derivatives with respect to x, y, z Laplace's equation takes the form

$$\frac{\partial^2\Phi}{\partial x^2} + \frac{\partial^2\Phi}{\partial y^2} + \frac{\partial^2\Phi}{\partial z^2} = 0,$$

and differentiating with respect to x

$$\frac{\partial^2}{\partial x^2}\left(\frac{\partial\Phi}{\partial x}\right) + \frac{\partial^2}{\partial y^2}\left(\frac{\partial\Phi}{\partial x}\right) + \frac{\partial^2}{\partial z^2}\left(\frac{\partial\Phi}{\partial x}\right) = 0.$$

Therefore if Φ is a solution of Laplace's equation $\dfrac{\partial\Phi}{\partial x}$ is also. In similar fashion it may be shown that $\dfrac{\partial\Phi}{\partial y}, \dfrac{\partial\Phi}{\partial z}, \dfrac{\partial^2\Phi}{\partial x^2}, \dfrac{\partial^2\Phi}{\partial x\partial y}$, etc. and also the vector $\nabla\Phi$ are solutions.

In many problems it is necessary to express Laplace's equation in spherical coordinates r, θ, ϕ. We have already seen how to do this in article 17.1. For the practice which it gives, we shall develop here a different method of obtaining the same result. Denoting by $\mathbf{r}_1$, $\boldsymbol{\theta}_1$, $\boldsymbol{\phi}_1$ unit vectors in the directions of increasing r, increasing θ, and increasing ϕ, respectively, as in article 19, we have

$$\nabla = \mathbf{r}_1 \frac{\partial}{\partial r} + \boldsymbol{\theta}_1 \frac{\partial}{r\partial\theta} + \boldsymbol{\phi}_1 \frac{\partial}{r \sin\theta\partial\phi}, \tag{79-2}$$

and

$$\nabla\cdot\nabla = \left(\mathbf{r}_1 \frac{\partial}{\partial r} + \boldsymbol{\theta}_1 \frac{\partial}{r\partial\theta} + \boldsymbol{\phi}_1 \frac{\partial}{r \sin\theta\partial\phi}\right)\cdot\left(\mathbf{r}_1 \frac{\partial}{\partial r} + \boldsymbol{\theta}_1 \frac{\partial}{r\partial\theta} + \boldsymbol{\phi}_1 \frac{\partial}{r \sin\theta\partial\phi}\right). \tag{79-3}$$

Referring to (19–7), (19–8) and (19–9) it is seen that

$$d\mathbf{r}_1 = \boldsymbol{\theta}_1 d\theta + \boldsymbol{\phi}_1 \sin\theta d\phi,$$

$$d\boldsymbol{\theta}_1 = -\mathbf{r}_1 d\theta + \boldsymbol{\phi}_1 \cos\theta d\phi,$$

$$d\boldsymbol{\phi}_1 = -\mathbf{r}_1 \sin\theta d\phi - \boldsymbol{\theta}_1 \cos\theta d\phi.$$

Therefore

$$\left.\begin{aligned}
&\frac{\partial \mathbf{r}_1}{\partial r} = 0, \quad \frac{\partial \mathbf{r}_1}{\partial \theta} = \boldsymbol{\theta}_1, \quad \frac{\partial \mathbf{r}_1}{\partial \phi} = \boldsymbol{\phi}_1 \sin\theta,\\
&\frac{\partial \boldsymbol{\theta}_1}{\partial r} = 0, \quad \frac{\partial \boldsymbol{\theta}_1}{\partial \theta} = -\mathbf{r}_1, \quad \frac{\partial \boldsymbol{\theta}_1}{\partial \phi} = \boldsymbol{\phi}_1 \cos\theta,\\
&\frac{\partial \boldsymbol{\phi}_1}{\partial r} = 0, \quad \frac{\partial \boldsymbol{\phi}_1}{\partial \theta} = 0, \quad \frac{\partial \boldsymbol{\phi}_1}{\partial \phi} = -\mathbf{r}_1 \sin\theta - \boldsymbol{\theta}_1 \cos\theta.
\end{aligned}\right\} \tag{79-4}$$

Expanding (79–3) then,

$$\left.\begin{aligned}
\nabla\cdot\nabla &= \frac{\partial^2}{\partial r^2} + \frac{1}{r}\frac{\partial}{\partial r} + \frac{1}{r^2}\frac{\partial^2}{\partial\theta^2} + \frac{1}{r}\frac{\partial}{\partial r} + \frac{\cot\theta}{r^2}\frac{\partial}{\partial\theta} + \frac{1}{r^2\sin^2\theta}\frac{\partial^2}{\partial\phi^2}\\
&= \frac{\partial^2}{\partial r^2} + \frac{2}{r}\frac{\partial}{\partial r} + \frac{1}{r^2}\frac{\partial^2}{\partial\theta^2} + \frac{\cot\theta}{r^2}\frac{\partial}{\partial\theta} + \frac{\csc^2\theta}{r^2}\frac{\partial^2}{\partial\phi^2}.
\end{aligned}\right\} \tag{79-5}$$

Thus if Φ is a function of r, θ, ϕ we may write

$$\nabla\cdot\nabla\Phi = \frac{1}{r^2}\left\{\frac{\partial}{\partial r}\left(r^2\frac{\partial\Phi}{\partial r}\right) + \frac{1}{\sin\theta}\frac{\partial}{\partial\theta}\left(\sin\theta\frac{\partial\Phi}{\partial\theta}\right) + \frac{1}{\sin^2\theta}\frac{\partial^2\Phi}{\partial\phi^2}\right\}, \tag{79-6}$$

and, if we put μ for $\cos\theta$, Laplace's equation (79–1) takes the form

$$\frac{\partial}{\partial r}\left(r^2\frac{\partial\Phi}{\partial r}\right) + \frac{\partial}{\partial\mu}\left\{(1-\mu^2)\frac{\partial\Phi}{\partial\mu}\right\} + \frac{1}{1-\mu^2}\frac{\partial^2\Phi}{\partial\phi^2} = 0. \tag{79-7}$$

At present we shall confine ourselves to solutions which are functions of r and θ only. Then the last term in (79–7) vanishes, and

$$\frac{\partial}{\partial r}\left(r^2\frac{\partial\Phi}{\partial r}\right)+\frac{\partial}{\partial\mu}\left\{(1-\mu^2)\frac{\partial\Phi}{\partial\mu}\right\}=0. \qquad (79\text{–}8)$$

To obtain a solution try

$$\Phi = A_n r^n P_n, \qquad (79\text{–}9)$$

where A_n is a constant and P_n is a function of μ alone. Substituting in (79–8) we get *Legendre's equation*

$$\frac{d}{d\mu}\left\{(1-\mu^2)\frac{dP_n}{d\mu}\right\}+n(n+1)P_n=0. \qquad (79\text{–}10)$$

Moreover if we substitute

$$\Phi = \frac{B_n}{r^{n+1}}P_n, \qquad (79\text{–}11)$$

where B_n is a constant, in (79–8) we are led to the same equation (79–10) again. Therefore both (79–9) and (79–11) are solutions of Laplace's equation (79–8) provided P_n satisfies Legendre's equation (79–10).

In order to solve (79–10) we assume a power series of the form

$$P_n = \sum_s a_s\mu^s.$$

Substituting in (79–10) and equating to zero the coefficient of each μ^s we get the recurrence formula

$$(s+1)(s+2)a_{s+2} - s(s+1)a_s + n(n+1)a_s = 0$$

or

$$(s+1)(s+2)a_{s+2} = \{s(s+1) - n(n+1)\}a_s. \qquad (79\text{–}12)$$

If $s+2 = 0$ or 1, a_s vanishes. Hence we have series beginning with a_0 and a_1, the successive coefficients being calculated from (79–12). Evidently only alternate powers of μ appear. When $s = n$, a_{s+2} vanishes and the series terminates with the term μ^n. Therefore the odd series reduces to a finite polynomial when n is odd, and the even series when n is even. We shall have occasion to consider only these polynomial solutions. The first four are as follows:

$$P_0 = 1,$$

$$P_1 = \mu,$$

$$P_2 = \tfrac{1}{2}(3\mu^2 - 1),$$

$$P_3 = \tfrac{1}{2}(5\mu^3 - 3\mu),$$

the arbitrary coefficients of the polynomials being conventional.

The corresponding solutions of Laplace's equation are

$$A_0, \quad \frac{B_0}{r}; \tag{79-13}$$

$$A_1 r \cos\theta, \quad \frac{B_1}{r^2}\cos\theta; \tag{79-14}$$

$$A_2 r^2(3\cos^2\theta - 1), \quad \frac{B_2}{r^3}(3\cos^2\theta - 1); \tag{79-15}$$

$$A_3 r^3(5\cos^3\theta - 3\cos\theta), \quad \frac{B_3}{r^4}(5\cos^3\theta - 3\cos\theta). \tag{79-16}$$

Further solutions may be obtained by this method or by differentiating the solutions already obtained with respect to one of the coordinates x, y, z. The functions P_n with an appropriate numerical coefficient attached are known as *Legendre's polynomials* and the solutions of Laplace's equation obtained above are called *zonal harmonics*.

Next we shall show that if Φ is given at all points on a surface surrounding a region in which Laplace's equation (79–1) holds, then a solution of this equation which satisfies the assigned boundary conditions is unique. Let Φ_1 be a solution of Laplace's equation satisfying the boundary conditions. Assume that another distinct solution Φ_2 exists which satisfies the same boundary conditions. We shall prove that Φ_2 must be identical with Φ_1. For let $\Phi \equiv \Phi_1 - \Phi_2$. Then Φ satisfies Laplace's equation in the region under consideration, since this equation is satisfied by Φ_1 and Φ_2 individually. Integrating the identity

$$(\nabla\Phi)\cdot(\nabla\Phi) = \nabla\cdot(\Phi\nabla\Phi) - \Phi\nabla\cdot\nabla\Phi$$

over the region τ in which Laplace's equation holds, we have

$$\int_\tau (\nabla\Phi)^2 d\tau = \int_\tau \nabla\cdot(\Phi\nabla\Phi)d\tau - \int_\tau \Phi\nabla\cdot\nabla\Phi d\tau.$$

As Φ satisfies Laplace's equation the integrand of the last term on the right vanishes throughout the region τ. The first term on the right may be transformed into a surface integral by Gauss' theorem. Hence

$$\int_\tau (\nabla\Phi)^2 d\tau = \int_\sigma (\Phi\nabla\Phi)\cdot d\boldsymbol{\sigma}.$$

But as $\Phi_1 = \Phi_2$ everywhere on the surface σ bounding the volume τ the right-hand side of this equation vanishes. Therefore as the integrand of the volume integral is a sum of squares it must vanish also, that is,

$$(\nabla\Phi)^2 = \left(\frac{\partial\Phi}{\partial x}\right)^2 + \left(\frac{\partial\Phi}{\partial y}\right)^2 + \left(\frac{\partial\Phi}{\partial z}\right)^2 = 0,$$

and

$$\frac{\partial\Phi}{\partial x} = 0, \quad \frac{\partial\Phi}{\partial y} = 0, \quad \frac{\partial\Phi}{\partial z} = 0.$$

Therefore Φ is a constant. But Φ vanishes at the boundary. Consequently this constant value of Φ is zero. Therefore

$$\Phi_2 = \Phi_1$$

and the two solutions of Laplace's equation are the same.

Suppose, now, that in solving a physical problem we find that a certain function Φ of the coordinates must satisfy Laplace's equation inside a region τ and have certain assigned values over a surface bounding this region. Then if we find a solution of Laplace's equation which satisfies the given boundary conditions we know that we have the correct solution of the problem. We need not ponder the possibility that there may exist some other solution of Laplace's equation which satisfies the assigned boundary conditions and also fulfills further necessary conditions which we have overlooked and which are not fulfilled by the first solution. For there is only one solution of Laplace's equation which can satisfy the given boundary conditions. In mathematical language Laplace's equation and the assigned boundary conditions are *sufficient* to determine the function Φ.

Problem 79a. If $x = r \cos\theta$ obtain the solutions (79–13), (79–14), (79–15), of Laplace's equation from (79–12) by successive partial differentiation with respect to x.

Problem 79b. If the distance of a point whose position vector is $\mathbf{R}$ from a fixed point whose position vector is $\mathbf{a}$ is denoted by $\mathbf{r}$ and the angle between $\mathbf{r}$ and $\mathbf{a}$ is θ, then

$$R = \sqrt{r^2 + 2ar\cos\theta + a^2}.$$

Expand the reciprocal of R by the binomial theorem both for the case $r < a$ and for the case $r > a$ and show that the successive terms in the expansion are zonal harmonics in each case.

Problem 79c. Show that

$$\frac{1}{r^{n+1}}(1 - \mu^2)^{m/2}\frac{d^m P_n}{d\mu^m}(A \sin m\phi + B\cos m\phi)$$

is a solution of Laplace's equation.

80. Slow Motion of a Sphere in an Incompressible Viscous Fluid of Infinite Extent. — Instead of assuming that the sphere is in motion relative to the observer and the distant portions of the fluid are at rest we shall find it more convenient to keep the sphere at rest at the origin and consider the fluid to be streaming by it in such a manner that distant portions have the constant velocity V in the X direction. Then by giving the fluid and sphere together a superposed constant velocity of translation V in the negative X direction we can go over to the case where the sphere has a velocity V and the distant portions of the fluid are at rest.

In our investigation of the motion of a sphere in a perfect liquid we neglected viscosity but took account of the inertia of the fluid; here we shall take the viscous forces into account but shall minimize the effects of inertia by assuming the motion to be very slow. On this assumption we can use for the equation of motion the approximate equation (76–18) which we shall further simplify by assuming that no external forces are acting on the fluid elements. Then we have

$$\rho\frac{\partial \mathbf{v}}{\partial t} = -\nabla p + \mu\nabla\cdot\nabla\mathbf{v}.$$

As the motion is steady $\mathbf{v}$ is not a function of the time and so

$$\nabla \cdot \nabla \mathbf{v} = \frac{1}{\mu} \nabla p. \tag{80–1}$$

Moreover as the fluid is incompressible the equation of continuity requires that

$$\nabla \cdot \mathbf{v} = 0. \tag{80–2}$$

Our problem consists in finding a solution of these two simultaneous equations which satisfies the assigned boundary conditions. First we take the curl of (80–1), obtaining

$$\nabla \cdot \nabla \nabla \times \mathbf{v} = 0,$$

since the curl of the gradient of p is identically zero, and since the operators $\nabla \cdot \nabla$ and $\nabla \times$ commute as both represent partial differentiation. But $\nabla \times \mathbf{v}$ is twice the mean angular velocity $\boldsymbol{\omega}$, giving

$$\nabla \cdot \nabla \boldsymbol{\omega} = 0. \tag{80–3}$$

The rectangular components of $\boldsymbol{\omega}$, then, are solutions of Laplace's equation. It is evident from symmetry, however, that the vortex lines are circles in planes perpendicular to the X axis with centers on this axis. Hence, if θ represents the angle with the X axis made by the radius vector r drawn from the center of the sphere, and if ϕ is the azimuth measured around the X axis from the XY plane,

$$\boldsymbol{\omega} = - \mathbf{j} f(r, \theta) \sin \phi + \mathbf{k} f(r, \theta) \cos \phi. \tag{80–4}$$

Substituting this in the complete form of Laplace's equation in spherical coordinates obtained by equating (79–6) to zero we find

$$\frac{\partial}{\partial r}\left(r^2 \frac{\partial f}{\partial r}\right) + \frac{1}{\sin \theta} \frac{\partial}{\partial \theta}\left(\sin \theta \frac{\partial f}{\partial \theta}\right) - \frac{f}{\sin^2 \theta} = 0,$$

whether we use the one or the other component of $\boldsymbol{\omega}$. Evidently the strength of the vortex filaments must be zero when θ is 0 or π, and must increase continuously as we pass from either of these limits to the equatorial plane $\theta = \pi/2$. Hence $f(r, \theta)$ may be expected to be of the form

$$f(r, \theta) = g(r) \sin \theta.$$

Putting this in the differential equation for $f(r, \theta)$ we get

$$\frac{d}{dr}\left(r^2\frac{dg}{dr}\right) - 2g = 0,$$

which is satisfied by either r or $1/r^2$. Since $\boldsymbol{\omega}$ must vanish for $r = \infty$, the boundary conditions of the physical problem demand the second solution, and (80–4) becomes

$$\boldsymbol{\omega} = -\mathbf{j}\frac{A}{r^2}\sin\theta\sin\phi + \mathbf{k}\frac{A}{r^2}\sin\theta\cos\phi, \tag{80–5}$$

where A is an arbitrary constant. We can write this in the form

$$\boldsymbol{\omega} = A\left(-\mathbf{j}\frac{z}{r^3} + \mathbf{k}\frac{y}{r^3}\right) = \nabla\times\left(\mathbf{i}\frac{A}{r}\right). \tag{80–6}$$

Consequently, as $\boldsymbol{\omega} = \frac{1}{2}\nabla\times\mathbf{v}$,

$$\mathbf{v} = \mathbf{i}\frac{2A}{r} + \nabla\Psi, \tag{80–7}$$

where Ψ is any scalar function of the coordinates. This vector function satisfies the conditions expressed in the equation of motion (80–1) and those imposed by symmetry. As it must also satisfy the equation of continuity (80–2),

$$\nabla\cdot\mathbf{v} = -2A\frac{\cos\theta}{r^2} + \nabla\cdot\nabla\Psi = 0,$$

since

$$\frac{\partial}{\partial x}\left(\frac{1}{r}\right) = -\frac{x}{r^3} = -\frac{\cos\theta}{r^2}.$$

Now

$$\nabla\cdot\nabla\cos\theta = -2\frac{\cos\theta}{r^2}$$

from (79–6), so the equation of continuity becomes

$$\nabla\cdot\nabla\{A\cos\theta + \Psi\} = 0,$$

showing that $\Psi = -A\cos\theta + \Phi$, where Φ is a solution of Laplace's equation. As the part of Ψ already obtained explicitly is linear in $\cos\theta$, the required solution of Laplace's equation must be linear in $\cos\theta$ also in order that we may be able to satisfy the boundary conditions at the surface of the sphere for all values of θ. Referring to the previous article, then, we see that Φ is limited to the two solutions $B\,r\cos\theta$ and $C\cos\theta/r^2$, where B and C are constant coefficients. Taking their sum for Φ we have

$$\mathbf{v} = \mathbf{i}\frac{2A}{r} - A\nabla\cos\theta + B\nabla(r\cos\theta) + C\nabla\left(\frac{\cos\theta}{r^2}\right) \qquad (80\text{–}8)$$

from (80–7). Consequently the components of velocity in the directions of increasing r and θ are

$$v_r = \left(B + \frac{2A}{r} - \frac{2C}{r^3}\right)\cos\theta,$$

$$v_\theta = -\left(B + \frac{A}{r} + \frac{C}{r^3}\right)\sin\theta.$$

For r infinite, the velocity of the fluid becomes the constant velocity V in the X direction, whereas for r equal to the radius a_0 of the stationary sphere the velocity of the fluid must be zero since a viscous fluid can have no motion relative to a solid with which it is in contact. The first boundary condition gives $B = V$ and the second $A = -\frac{3}{4}a_0V$, $C = -\frac{1}{4}a_0^3V$.

Hence

$$\left.\begin{aligned} v_r &= V\left(1 - \frac{3}{2}\frac{a_0}{r} + \frac{1}{2}\frac{a_0^3}{r^3}\right)\cos\theta, \\ v_\theta &= -V\left(1 - \frac{3}{4}\frac{a_0}{r} - \frac{1}{4}\frac{a_0^3}{r^3}\right)\sin\theta, \end{aligned}\right\} \qquad (80\text{–}9)$$

and from (80–5)

$$\omega = -\frac{3}{4}\frac{a_0V}{r^2}\sin\theta. \qquad (80\text{–}10)$$

Since we have satisfied all the boundary conditions of the problem we may be confident that the solution obtained is unique.

The kinematical portion of the problem being solved, the next step is to take up the dynamical part, that is, the calculation of the stresses at the surface of the sphere. The mean pressure is obtained at once from (80–1). As all save the second term in (80–8) are solutions of Laplace's equation,

$$\nabla p = \mu\nabla\cdot\nabla\mathbf{v} = -\mu A\nabla\cdot\nabla\nabla\cos\theta$$
$$= \tfrac{3}{4}\mu a_0 V\nabla\nabla\cdot\nabla\cos\theta,$$

and

$$p = \tfrac{3}{4}\mu a_0 V\nabla\cdot\nabla\cos\theta = -\tfrac{3}{2}\mu a_0 V\frac{\cos\theta}{r^2} \qquad (80\text{–}11)$$

to within an undetermined constant, which represents the pressure over the outer boundary of the fluid.

In finding the stresses it will simplify the analysis if we employ a set of rectangular axes so oriented that X is along the radius vector and Y at right angles to it in the direction of increasing θ. Then the stress on a surface perpendicular to the radius vector is

$$\mathbf{S}_r = \mathbf{S}_i = \mathbf{i}\cdot\Psi$$
$$= \mathbf{i}P + \mathbf{j}U,$$

from (47–11), since symmetry requires that the Z component of stress should vanish. To obtain P and U we need the rates of strain a and h. Now

$$\mathbf{v} = \mathbf{r}_1 v_r + \boldsymbol{\theta}_1 v_\theta.$$

Therefore it follows from (79–4) that

$$\frac{\partial\mathbf{v}}{\partial r} = \mathbf{r}_1\frac{\partial v_r}{\partial r} + \boldsymbol{\theta}_1\frac{\partial v_\theta}{\partial r}, \qquad (80\text{–}12)$$

$$\left.\begin{aligned}\frac{\partial\mathbf{v}}{r\partial\theta} &= \mathbf{r}_1\frac{\partial v_r}{r\partial\theta} + \frac{v_r}{r}\frac{\partial\mathbf{r}_1}{\partial\theta} + \boldsymbol{\theta}_1\frac{\partial v_\theta}{r\partial\theta} + \frac{v_\theta}{r}\frac{\partial\boldsymbol{\theta}_1}{\partial\theta}\\ &= \mathbf{r}_1\left(\frac{\partial v_r}{r\partial\theta} - \frac{v_\theta}{r}\right) + \boldsymbol{\theta}_1\left(\frac{\partial v_\theta}{r\partial\theta} + \frac{v_r}{r}\right).\end{aligned}\right\} \qquad (80\text{–}13)$$

Remembering that $\mathbf{r}_1$ is parallel to the X axis and $\boldsymbol{\theta}_1$ to the Y axis we have

$$a = \frac{\partial v_x}{\partial x} = \frac{\partial v_r}{\partial r},$$

$$h = \frac{\partial v_y}{\partial x} + \frac{\partial v_x}{\partial y} = \frac{\partial v_\theta}{\partial r} + \frac{\partial v_r}{r\partial\theta} - \frac{v_\theta}{r}.$$

Therefore we get from (80–9)

$$a = \frac{3}{2}\frac{a_0}{r^2}V\left(1 - \frac{a_0^2}{r^2}\right)\cos\theta, \tag{80–14}$$

$$\left.\begin{aligned} h &= -\frac{3}{4}\frac{a_0}{r^2}V\left(1+\frac{a_0^2}{r^2}\right)\sin\theta - \frac{1}{r}V\left(1-\frac{3}{2}\frac{a_0}{r}+\frac{1}{2}\frac{a_0^3}{r^3}\right)\sin\theta \\ &\quad + \frac{1}{r}V\left(1-\frac{3}{4}\frac{a_0}{r}-\frac{1}{4}\frac{a_0^3}{r^3}\right)\sin\theta \\ &= -\frac{3}{2}\frac{a_0^3}{r^4}V\sin\theta. \end{aligned}\right\} \tag{80–15}$$

As the fluid is incompressible $\nabla\cdot\mathbf{v}$ vanishes and (76–12) gives us

$$P = -p + 2\mu a,$$

$$U = \mu h.$$

To find the stresses at the surface of the sphere substitute a and h from (80–14) and (80–15), putting r equal to a_0. Then we get

$$P = -p = \frac{3}{2}\frac{\mu}{a_0}V\cos\theta$$

along the radius vector, and

$$U = -\frac{3}{2}\frac{\mu}{a_0}V\sin\theta$$

at right angles to the radius vector in the direction of increasing θ. The first is a tension and the second a shearing stress.

It is clear from symmetry that the resultant force K on the sphere is in the direction of the fluid's motion. Therefore

$$\left.\begin{aligned} K &= \int_0^\pi P\cos\theta\, 2\pi a_0^2\sin\theta d\theta - \int_0^\pi U\sin\theta\, 2\pi a_0^2\sin\theta d\theta \\ &= 2\pi\mu a_0 V + 4\pi\mu a_0 V \\ &= 6\pi\mu a_0 V. \end{aligned}\right\} \tag{80–16}$$

This is known as *Stokes' law*. Since the drag of the fluid on the sphere can depend only on the motion of the fluid relative to the sphere, the resistance offered by a stagnant fluid to a sphere moving through it with velocity V is also given by (80–16). As our calculation shows, one-third of the resistance is due to the difference of pressure on the two sides of the sphere and the remaining two-thirds to the shearing stresses. While our theory has been based on the assumption that the fluid is incompressible, the results are valid for a gas as well as a liquid if the motion is slow enough so that no appreciable differences in density exist.

To get the velocity of the fluid when the distant portions are at rest and the sphere is moving in the negative X direction with velocity V all we have to do is to add the components of $-\mathbf{i}V$ in the r and θ directions to the expressions (80–9). This gives

$$\left.\begin{aligned} v_r &= \left(-\frac{3}{2}\frac{a_0}{r} + \frac{1}{2}\frac{a_0^3}{r^3}\right) V \cos\theta, \\ v_\theta &= \left(\frac{3}{4}\frac{a_0}{r} + \frac{1}{4}\frac{a_0^3}{r^3}\right) V \sin\theta. \end{aligned}\right\} \qquad (80\text{–}17)$$

The stream lines are depicted in Fig. 89. It is to be noted that their configuration is quite different from that shown in Fig. 77 for a case of a sphere moving through a perfect fluid.

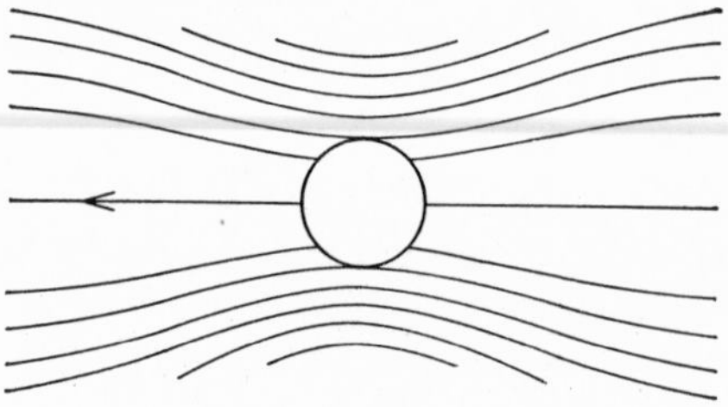

FIG. 89.

Consider a sphere of density σ falling under gravity in a stagnant fluid of density ρ. Acting on the sphere are the force of gravity

$$\tfrac{4}{3}\pi a_0^3 \sigma g,$$

the buoyant force

$$\tfrac{4}{3}\pi a_0^3 \rho g$$

given by Archimedes' principle, and the resistance of the fluid expressed by Stokes' law. So when a steady state is reached,

$$\tfrac{4}{3}\pi a_0^3 g(\sigma - \rho) = 6\pi\mu a_0 V,$$

and the velocity acquired by the sphere is

$$V = \frac{2}{9}\frac{\sigma - \rho}{\mu} a_0{}^2 g. \tag{80–18}$$

Problem 80a. Obtain the tension and shearing stresses on the sphere directly from (47–11) without changing the orientation of the axes.

Problem 80b. A sphere of radius a_0 immersed in a fluid of viscosity μ rotates about a diameter as axis with a very small angular velocity Ω. Show that at a distance $r > a_0$ from the center of the sphere the linear speed of the fluid particles is $\Omega a_0{}^3 \sin\theta/r^2$, where θ is the angle between the radius vector r and the axis of rotation, and that the retarding torque is $8\pi\mu a_0{}^3\Omega$ (Stokes' law for rotation).

81. Determination of the Charge of the Electron. — The most important application of Stokes' law is to the measurement of the charge of the electron. Consider oil drops of radii between $(10)^{-5}$ cm and $(10)^{-4}$ cm sprayed into the space between the horizontal plates of a parallel plate condenser (Fig. 90). On account of surface tension the drops assume a spherical form. If the air between the plates is ionized by a flash of X-rays or some other means, occasionally one or more ions will attach themselves to an oil drop, the motion of which can be observed through a microscope. By charging the condenser to a potential Φ, the oil drop may be subjected to an upward force eE, where e is the charge on the drop and E the electric intensity

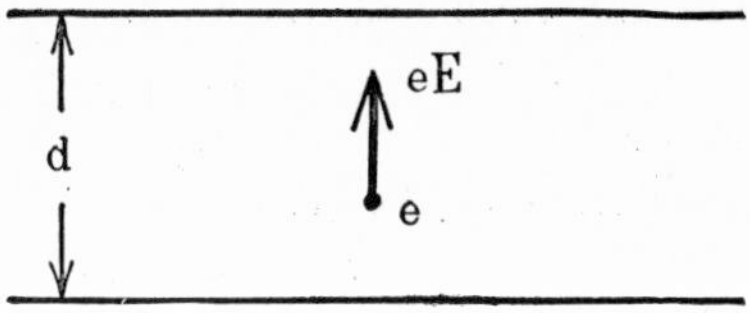

FIG. 90.

$$E = \frac{\Phi}{d}.$$

For simplicity we shall suppose that only a single electron is attached to the drop. Then e is the charge of the electron. If two electrons have been captured by the drop, the charge and hence the force due to the electric field is twice as great, and so on.

The forces acting on the drop are the downward force of gravity, the upward force due to the buoyancy of the air, and the upward force due to the electric field. So if we adjust the potential until the drop is in equilibrium,

$$\tfrac{4}{3}\pi a^3(\sigma - \rho)g = eE, \tag{81–1}$$

where a is the radius of the drop, σ the density of the oil of which it is composed, and ρ the density of the air. While σ, ρ and E are easily measured we cannot calculate e until we determine the radius a of the drop. To find the radius of the drop we remove the electric field and observe the rate at which the drop falls. Then from (80–18) we have

$$a = \sqrt{\frac{9}{2} \frac{\mu}{\sigma - \rho} \frac{V}{g}}. \tag{81–2}$$

Putting this in (81–1) and denoting the value of e calculated from the resulting equation by e_1 we get

$$e_1 = \frac{4\pi}{3}\left(\frac{9\mu}{2}\right)^{3/2}\left\{\frac{1}{g(\sigma - \rho)}\right\}^{1/2}\frac{V^{3/2}}{E}. \tag{81–3}$$

If the charge of the electron is computed from this formula it is found that the value obtained depends upon the pressure of the air and the radius of the drop. Evidently the drops are so close to molecular dimensions that the hydrodynamical assumption that the fluid has a continuous structure is no longer altogether valid. Consequently Stokes' law needs a correction factor, and we should expect to get more consistent results if we replace (80–18) by

$$V = \frac{2}{9} \frac{\sigma - \rho}{\mu} a^2 g \left(1 + A\frac{l}{a}\right), \tag{81–4}$$

where l is the mean free path of the air molecules and A an undetermined constant. If e is the charge of the electron as calculated from this modified formula, then, as e varies with a^3 according to (81–1), it follows that

$$e^{2/3} \propto a^2 \propto \frac{V}{1 + A\dfrac{l}{a}},$$

whereas

$$e_1^{2/3} \propto a^2 \propto V.$$

Consequently

$$e^{2/3} = \frac{e_1^{2/3}}{1 + A\dfrac{l}{a}}. \tag{81–5}$$

The correction to Stokes' law can be tested experimentally by varying the pressure of the air and carrying out measurements on drops of different sizes. If in each case e_1 is calculated from (81–3), then according to (81–5) the curve obtained by plotting $e_1^{2/3}$ against l/a should be a straight line (Fig. 91). This is found to be the case. By extending the straight line to the axis of ordinates $e^{2/3}$ is found. In this way the charge of the electron, first determined with accuracy by Millikan, is found to be

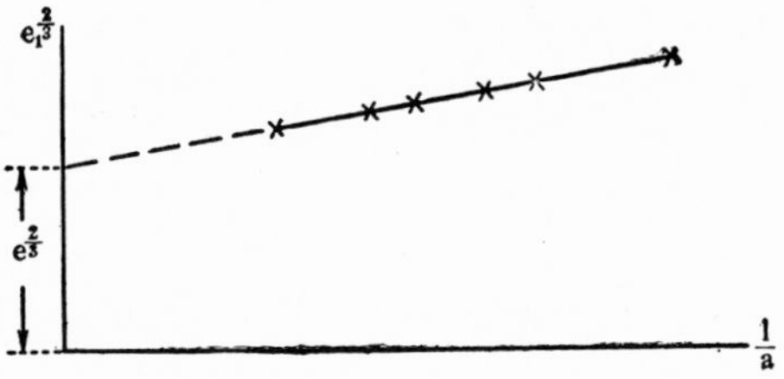

FIG. 91.

$$e = -\ 4.803\,(10)^{-10} e.s.u.$$

REFERENCE

LAMB, HORACE: *Hydrodynamics*, Cambridge University Press, Cambridge.

Part III

THERMODYNAMICS

CHAPTER VII

CLASSICAL THERMODYNAMICS

82. Definitions and Laws. — For the present we shall confine our attention to a single substance, whether existing in the solid, liquid or gaseous phase, or consisting of two coexisting phases, all parts of which are in thermal equilibrium with one another. Certain quantities with which we shall have to deal are proportional to the mass of the substance, such as the intrinsic energy U, volume V, heat Q taken in by the substance, work W done by the substance. These quantities are said to be *extensive*. If we wish to refer one of them to a unit mass of the substance we shall employ the corresponding small letter, writing u for the intrinsic energy per unit mass, v for the volume per unit mass or *specific volume*, and so forth. On the other hand such quantities as the pressure p and temperature T are independent of the mass of substance present. These are called *intensive*. For the moment we shall define temperature no more precisely than to say that two bodies are at the same temperature or in thermal equilibrium when a constant pressure gas thermometer gives the same volume reading when in contact with the one as when in contact with the other. If, on the other hand, the readings of the gas thermometer differ, the body for which the reading is larger is taken to be at the higher temperature. We notice that when two bodies at different temperatures are placed in contact, the temperature of the warmer decreases and that of the cooler increases. We ascribe this to a flow of heat from the warmer to the cooler body.

The state of a single substance is found to be completely determined by any two of the three quantities p, v, T. Therefore we may choose any two of these as independent variables. We make the fundamental assumption that the intrinsic energy u is a function of the two independent variables chosen to specify the state of the substance. If, for instance, we choose p and v as independent variables, then, if we allow these variables to go through a cycle returning ultimately to their original values, we come back at the same time to the original value of u. In mathematical language du is an exact differential in dv and dp.

The classical thermodynamics is based on the following two fundamental laws.

Law I. — *The increase dU in intrinsic energy of a substance during any transformation is equal to the heat δQ taken in less the work δW done by the substance*, that is

$$dU = \delta Q - \delta W. \tag{82–1}$$

This is merely the law of conservation of energy generalized so as to include heat as a form of energy.

Law II. — *No self-acting engine can transfer heat from a body of lower temperature to one of higher temperature.*

By a self-acting engine we mean one on which no work is done from outside and which is operated in such a manner as to take the working substance through one or more complete cycles. Then the final state of the working substance employed in the engine is the same as that existing at the start.

We define a *reversible transformation* as one which can be made to proceed in the opposite direction by an infinitesimal change in any one of the conditions determining the transformation. Thus, if a gas is expanding reversibly, an infinitesimal increase in the pressure to which it is subjected will cause it to contract, or, if heat is flowing reversibly from one body to another, an infinitesimal decrease in the temperature of the warmer body or increase in the temperature of the cooler body will reverse the direction of the heat flow. It is clear that any mechanism involved in a reversible transformation must be free from mechanical friction, and that the transformation of an actual substance must take place with great slowness. Therefore we are justified in concluding that during the course of such a transformation the different parts of a substance are in thermal equilibrium at every instant.

Two types of reversible transformation are of particular importance. An *isothermal transformation* is one during which the temperature remains constant and an *adiabatic transformation* one during which heat is neither taken in nor given out. A *cycle* is a succession of transformations which brings the working substance back to its initial state. A *Carnot cycle* is a cycle consisting of two isothermals and two adiabatics. This cycle is of great importance in thermodynamics because all the heat absorbed by the working substance is taken in at the single temperature of the isothermal expansion, and all the heat rejected is given out at the single temperature of the isothermal contraction. The only method of transferring heat reversibly from a reservoir of large capacity at temperature T_1 to a refrigerator of large capacity at temperature T_2 is by means of a reversible heat engine in which the working substance goes through a Carnot cycle with the isothermal expansion taking place at temperature T_1 and the isothermal contraction at temperature T_2. If, due to poor thermal contact, the working substance takes in heat at a temperature below T_1, or rejects heat at a temperature above T_2, the transfer is irreversible.

By the *efficiency* of a heat engine is meant the ratio of the work done by the engine when the working substance goes through a complete cycle to the heat taken in. If Q_1 is the heat taken in and Q_2 the heat rejected, the work performed is $Q_1 - Q_2$ and the efficiency is

$$E = \frac{W}{Q_1} = \frac{Q_1 - Q_2}{Q_1}. \qquad (82\text{–}2)$$

It is often convenient to represent reversible transformations and cycles by curves on the pressure-volume diagram. Consider the transformation represented by the curve *ab* in Fig. 92. The work done by the expanding substance per unit mass is

$$w = \int_a^b pdv.$$

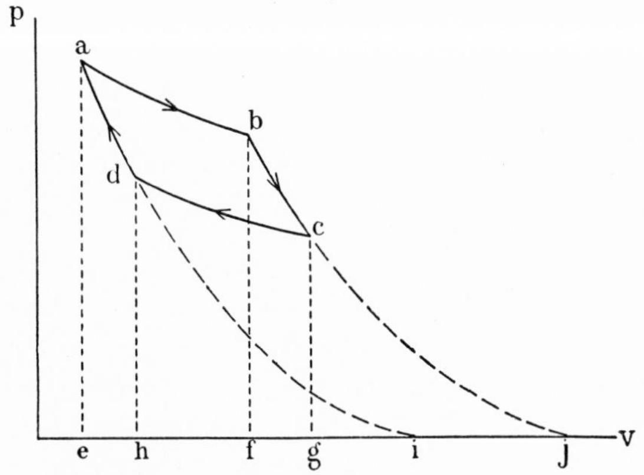

FIG. 92.

This is represented by the area *abfe*. Since this area depends upon the course of the path *ab* as well as on its termini, w is not a function of p and v and δw is not an exact differential in dv and dp. We shall use δ to designate a small quantity which is not an exact differential, reserving d for exact differentials. Since δw is not an exact differential it is clear from (82–1) that δq is not exact.

If ab and cd are isothermals connected by adiabatics bc and da the work done when the working substance goes through the Carnot cycle $abcd$ is given by the area

$$abfe + bcgf - cdhg - daeh = abcd$$

which is enclosed by the curve representing the cycle.

83. Carnot's Principle. — In this article we shall prove two theorems of fundamental importance based on the second law of thermodynamics.

Theorem I. — Consider a heat engine which takes in heat from a reservoir of large capacity at temperature T_1 and rejects heat to a refrigerator of large capacity at temperature T_2. We say, then, that the engine is working between the temperatures T_1 and T_2. The theorem we wish to prove asserts that no engine can have a greater efficiency than a reversible engine working between the same two temperatures. To prove this consider an irreversible engine E' (Fig. 93) which is driving a reversible engine E backwards. During a cycle E' takes an amount of heat Q'_1 from the reservoir T_1 and gives up an amount of heat Q'_2 to the refrigerator T_2, whereas E takes the heat Q_2 from the refrigerator and returns the heat Q_1 to the reservoir T_1. As E is reversible the heat Q_1 which it gives up to the reservoir per cycle is the same as the amount of heat it would take from the reservoir if it were running forward. Similar statements are true of Q_2 and the work W done on E per cycle. Therefore the efficiency of the reversible engine E is

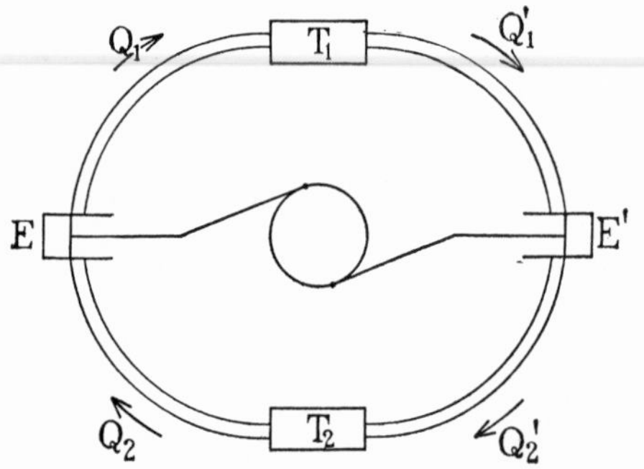

FIG. 93.

$$E = \frac{W}{Q_1},$$

and that of E' is

$$E' = \frac{W'}{Q'_1}.$$

But the work W' done by E' per cycle is equal to the work W done on E. Therefore

$$Q_1 - Q_2 = Q'_1 - Q'_2 \tag{83-1}$$

from the first law of thermodynamics, and

$$EQ_1 = E'Q'_1 \tag{83-2}$$

from the expressions for the efficiencies.

Now suppose $E' > E$. Then $Q_1 > Q'_1$ from (83–2) and $Q_2 > Q'_2$ from (83–1). So the two engines together transfer heat from the colder refrigerator T_2 to the hotter reservoir T_1. But the two engines taken together constitute a self-acting engine. Therefore we are led to a contradiction of the second law of thermodynamics. Hence we conclude that

$$E' \leq E. \tag{83-3}$$

Theorem II. — All reversible engines working between the same two temperatures have the same efficiency, irrespective of working substance. Consider two reversible engines of efficiencies E_1 and E_2 which employ different working substances. As both engines are reversible either one may take the place of E in the previous discussion, the other operating as E'. Therefore

$$E_1 \leq E_2,$$

$$E_2 \leq E_1,$$

which are satisfied only by

$$E_1 = E_2. \tag{83-4}$$

84. Kelvin's Thermodynamic Scale of Temperature. — In article 82 we defined equality of temperature. In order to devise a scale of temperature it is necessary first to select two fixed temperatures and assign to them arbitrary values. The two usually chosen are the freezing point and the boiling point of water at a standard atmospheric pressure sufficient to support a column of mercury 76 cm in height. On the Centigrade scale the first is assigned the value 0° C. and the second 100° C. Once these fixed points are marked on a thermometer stem of uniform bore any other temperature may be determined by simple proportion from the height of the thermometric liquid or gas when the thermometer takes on the desired temperature, provided we make the assumption that the volume of the thermometric substance varies linearly with the temperature. Unfortunately this assumption leads to different results with different thermometric substances. Thus mercury, alcohol and nitrogen thermometers agree only at the fixed points. Only those expansion thermometers using the simplest gases, such as hydrogen or helium, provide sensibly consistent temperature scales, which agree very closely with the theoretical scale which we are going to devise.

Carnot's principle, however, enables us to construct a scale of temperature which is entirely independent of the nature of the working substance. For suppose we measure the efficiency $E_0{}^{100}$ of a reversible engine which takes in heat at 100° C. and rejects heat at 0° C. If, now, we allow the engine to take in heat at 100° C. and reject heat at such a temperature that its efficiency is $\frac{n}{100} E_0{}^{100}$, we have a method of determining the lower temperature of the Carnot cycle through which it operates which is independent of the nature of the working substance, for it follows from Carnot's principle that all reversible engines, absorbing heat at the same temperature and showing the same efficiency, must reject heat at the same temperature. Making n equal to 1, 2, 3 . . . we establish temperatures of 99°, 98°, 97° . . . and so on down to 0° C. and below, the Centigrade temperature of the lower isothermal being in each case $t = 100° - n°$. As the experimentally determined value of $E_0{}^{100}$ is 100/373, the efficiency of a reversible engine working between the temperatures 100° C. and −273° C. is unity, since $n = 373$ in this case. Such an engine converts all the heat absorbed at 100° C. into mechanical work, rejecting none at the lower temperature. Evidently the number n has then attained the largest value it can assume, and −273° C. is the lower limit of temperature. This temperature is known as the *absolute zero*. If we denote the Centigrade temperature by t and the temperature measured from the absolute zero by T, then

$$T = t + 273°, \tag{84–1}$$

the size of the degree being the same on the two scales. The temperature T is called the *absolute thermodynamic temperature*. Unless otherwise specified we shall always understand by temperature the thermodynamic temperature, using t to refer to the Centigrade scale and T the absolute scale.

The process of establishing the thermodynamic scale of temperature is illustrated graphically on the pressure-volume diagram in Fig. 94. There *ae* and *bf* are two adiabatics, *ab* and *dc* being isothermals at the temperatures of boiling and freezing water respectively. The Carnot cycle described by the reversible heat engine operating between 100° C. and t is that included between the isothermal *ab*, the two adiabatics, and the isothermal corresponding to the temperature t. If q_1 is the heat taken in at 100° C. per unit mass of the working substance, the work performed is

$$w = q_1 E_t^{100} = n\left(\frac{q_1}{100} E_0^{100}\right),$$

which is proportional to n. Hence the area s between the two adiabatics *ae* and *bf* and any two isothermals one degree apart is the same. By constructing isothermals in such a way as to divide the area *abcd* into one hundred equal parts the temperature scale through the interval extending from 0° C. to 100° C. is established. Continuing the process of constructing isothermals including areas equal to s both above 100° C. and below 0° C., the temperature scale is extended to higher temperatures and down to the absolute zero. Evidently the isothermal of absolute zero is the v axis itself, for, if it lay above this axis, a state of the working substance corresponding to a yet lower temperature would exist. As the pressure is zero no work is done in passing along this isothermal from one point to another, and as already noted no heat is taken in or rejected. Therefore all points on the v axis represent states of the same intrinsic energy, which we may take to be zero. Returning to Fig. 92, consider a transformation along the adiabatic from i to a. As no heat is taken in or given out the intrinsic energy u_a of the substance in the state a is equal to the work done on the substance. Therefore u_a is represented by the area *iae*. Similarly u_b is represented by *jbf*. If we consider the transformation *ab* we have from the first law

$$q = w + u_b - u_a$$

and therefore the heat q taken in is represented by the area

$$abfe + jbf - iae = abji$$

included between *ab* and the two adiabatics *ai* and *bj*. Now, as all the areas between isothermals one degree apart in Fig. 94 have the same magnitude s, the area included between the isothermal of absolute temperature T_1 and the two adiabatics extending down to the v axis is $T_1 s$. But this represents the heat q_1 taken in by an engine

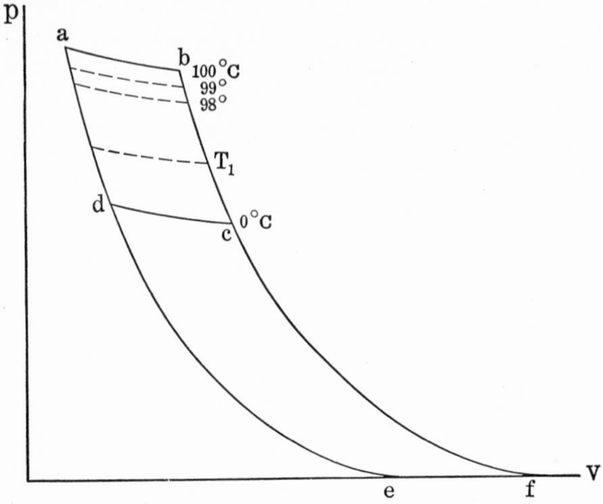

FIG. 94.

operating between the two adiabatics in the figure and receiving heat at this temperature. Similarly if the engine under consideration rejects heat at a temperature T_2, the heat q_2 rejected is represented by the area $T_2 s$. Therefore the efficiency of the engine is

$$E = \frac{w}{q_1} = \frac{q_1 - q_2}{q_1} = \frac{T_1 - T_2}{T_1} = 1 - \frac{T_2}{T_1}. \tag{84-2}$$

Furthermore we see from this equation that the ratio of the heat taken in to that rejected is equal to the ratio of the corresponding absolute temperatures, that is,

$$\frac{q_1}{T_1} = \frac{q_2}{T_2}. \tag{84-3}$$

85. Entropy. — Although the heat δQ taken in during a reversible transformation is not an exact differential in dV and dp, we can find a quantity whose increment is proportional to δQ which is a function of the variables defining the state of the substance. This quantity is known as *entropy*. We define the increase of entropy occurring when an amount of heat δQ is absorbed during the course of a reversible transformation as

$$dS = \frac{\delta Q}{T}, \tag{85-1}$$

and shall prove that dS is an exact differential. As it is proportional to the heat taken in, entropy is an extensive quantity. In accord with the notation adopted in article 82 we shall denote total entropy by S and entropy per unit mass by s.

Consider the change in entropy which takes place when a substance is carried around any reversible cycle $AaBbA$ (Fig. 95).

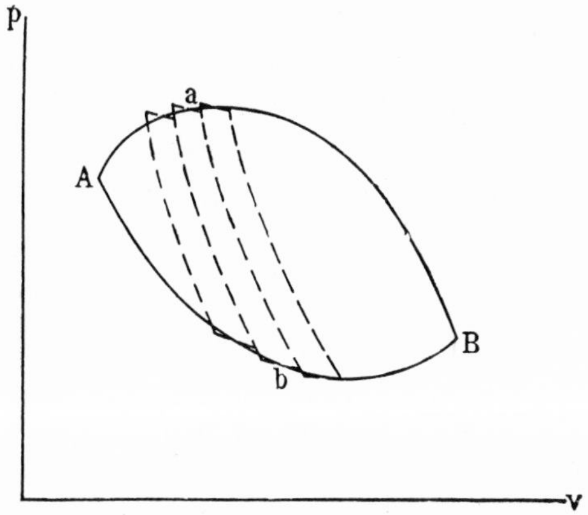

FIG. 95.

The area enclosed by the curve representing the cycle may be divided into a number of infinitesimal areas bounded by isothermals and adiabatics, such as those represented by broken lines in the figure. If the heat taken in along the isothermal at a is denoted by δq_1 and that given out along the isothermal at b by δq_2, then since the broken line cycle is an elementary Carnot cycle

$$\frac{\delta q_1}{T_1} = \frac{\delta q_2}{T_2}$$

by (84-3), where T_1 is the absolute temperature of the isothermal at a and T_2 that of the isothermal at b. If then we follow around the broken curve formed by isothermals and parts of adiabatics of the elementary Carnot cycles with which we have replaced the original cycle, the total change in entropy is

$$\Delta s = \sum \frac{\delta q_1}{T_1} - \sum \frac{\delta q_2}{T_2} = 0.$$

By making the elementary Carnot cycles narrow enough this broken curve can be made to coincide with the original curve as closely as desired. Therefore the change in entropy around any cycle vanishes.

Now the change of entropy around the cycle *AaBbA* consists of the change along *AaB* and that along *BbA*. So

$$\Delta s_{AaB} + \Delta s_{BbA} = 0.$$

But

$$\Delta s_{BbA} = - \Delta s_{AbB}.$$

Therefore

$$\Delta s_{AaB} = \Delta s_{AbB}.$$

This equation tells us that if we pass from A to B by a reversible transformation the change in entropy is independent of the path followed. Therefore the change in entropy depends only upon the coordinates of the termini A and B of the path. Consequently the entropy is a function of the specific volume and the pressure, and ds is an exact differential in dv and dp. It is this property of entropy which makes the quantity of such importance in thermodynamics. In all then du, ds and dT are exact differentials in dv and dp, while δq and δw are not exact. We may at will choose any two of the five variables u, s, T, v, p as independent variables for the purpose of describing the state of the substance, expressing the remaining three as functions of these two.

It must be remembered that (85–1) is valid for calculating the change of entropy only in the case of a reversible transformation. Suppose that a gas confined in a vessel at high pressure is allowed to escape into an evacuated vessel which is connected to the first vessel by a tube and stopcock. Although no heat is taken in during this irreversible transformation, the entropy of the gas changes by an amount which may be calculated by replacing the actual transformation by a reversible transformation connecting the same two end states and then using (85–1). The change in entropy is completely determined by the initial and final states, and is the same no matter whether the transformation by which the substance passes from the first to the second state is reversible or irreversible.

An exactly similar situation exists when we attempt to calculate the change in volume from the work done. Since $\delta W = pdV$ we have

$$dV = \frac{\delta W}{p} \tag{85-2}$$

in exact analogy with (85–1). In the case of a gas expanding irreversibly into an evacuated region such as was described in the last paragraph, no work is done, and hence (85–2), if valid for the calculation of the change of volume, would imply that there is no change of volume. But (85–2), like (85–1), is valid only for a reversible transformation. To calculate the change of volume occurring in an irreversible transformation from (85–2) it is necessary first to replace the actual transformation by a reversible transformation connecting the same two end states.

If now we replace δQ in the first law by TdS in accord with (85–1) and δW by pdV we have the combined first and second law

$$dU = TdS - pdV, \tag{85-3}$$

in which the differentials appearing are all exact. Referred to a unit mass this equation takes the form

$$du = Tds - pdv. \tag{85-4}$$

If u is expressed as a function of s and v it follows that

$$T = \left(\frac{\partial u}{\partial s}\right)_v, \quad p = -\left(\frac{\partial u}{\partial v}\right)_s, \tag{85-5}$$

since du is an exact differential. The subscript appended to the derivative indicates which variable is kept constant in the process of differentiation.

We can now define an adiabatic transformation as one in which the entropy remains constant. If then we use T and s as independent variables the curve representing Carnot's cycle takes the form of a rectangle.

Consider two bodies, the first at a temperature T_1 and the second at a lower temperature T_2. Let the two together be surrounded by a rigid adiabatic envelope, so as to limit transfers of energy to a flow of heat from the one body to the other. If a quantity of heat δQ

flows from the hotter to the cooler body the change in entropy of the first is

$$dS_1 = -\frac{\delta Q}{T_1},$$

and that of the second

$$dS_2 = \frac{\delta Q}{T_2}.$$

Therefore the total increase in entropy is

$$dS = dS_1 + dS_2 = \frac{\delta Q(T_1 - T_2)}{T_1 T_2} > 0.$$

Consequently heat flows in such a direction as to increase the entropy of an isolated system of bodies. For thermal equilibrium the entropy must be a maximum, subject to the condition of constant total energy. Therefore the conditions of stable equilibrium may be written

$$dS = 0, \quad d^2S < 0,$$
$$dU = 0,$$
$$dV = 0.$$

Problem 85a. The pressure on a perfect reflector due to radiation of energy u per unit volume is $p = \frac{1}{3}u$. Show that the energy density of radiation in equilibrium with matter at temperature T is proportional to the fourth power of the absolute temperature. This is known as the *Stefan-Boltzmann law.* (*Hint:* The energy density u is a function of T only. Make use of the fact that dS is an exact differential.)

86. Calorimetric, Thermometric and Thermoelastic Coefficients. — In this article we shall list certain coefficients of importance in thermodynamics and deduce relations between some of them. The following six are known as calorimetric coefficients:

$$\eta_v = \left(\frac{\delta q}{\partial p}\right)_v = \text{heat of compression at constant volume,}$$

$$\lambda_p = \left(\frac{\delta q}{\partial v}\right)_p = \text{heat of expansion at constant pressure,}$$

$$c_v = \left(\frac{\delta q}{\partial T}\right)_v = \text{specific heat at constant volume,}$$

$$c_p = \left(\frac{\delta q}{\partial T}\right)_p = \text{specific heat at constant pressure,}$$

$$h_t = \left(\frac{\delta q}{\partial p}\right)_t = \text{latent heat of change of pressure,}$$

$$l_t = \left(\frac{\delta q}{\partial v}\right)_t = \text{latent heat of change of volume.}$$

In each case the subscript indicates the quantity which is kept constant. If L denotes the latent heat of change of state, that is, the heat necessary to change the state of a unit mass of the substance from solid to liquid or from liquid to gas, then

$$L = l_t(v_2 - v_1)_t$$

where v_1 is the specific volume before the change of state and v_2 that after.

Now

$$\delta q = \eta_v dp + \lambda_p dv = c_p dT + h_t dp = c_v dT + l_t dv, \qquad (86\text{–}1)$$

and

$$(c_p - c_v)dT + h_t dp - l_t dv = 0.$$

If $dv = 0$,

$$c_v = c_p + h_t \left(\frac{\partial p}{\partial T}\right)_v, \qquad (86\text{–}2)$$

or if $dp = 0$

$$c_p = c_v + l_t \left(\frac{\partial v}{\partial T}\right)_p, \qquad (86\text{–}3)$$

As a functional relation exists between v, p and T we may write

$$f(v, p, T) = 0.$$

Therefore

$$dv = \left(\frac{\partial v}{\partial p}\right)_t dp + \left(\frac{\partial v}{\partial T}\right)_p dT, \qquad (86\text{–}4)$$

$$dp = \left(\frac{\partial p}{\partial T}\right)_v dT + \left(\frac{\partial p}{\partial v}\right)_t dv, \qquad (86\text{–}5)$$

$$dT = \left(\frac{\partial T}{\partial v}\right)_p dv + \left(\frac{\partial T}{\partial p}\right)_v dp. \qquad (86\text{–}6)$$

If $dp = 0$ in the second of these

$$\left(\frac{\partial p}{\partial v}\right)_t = -\frac{\left(\frac{\partial p}{\partial T}\right)_v}{\left(\frac{\partial v}{\partial T}\right)_p}. \qquad (86\text{–}7)$$

The thermometric coefficients are

$$\alpha_v = \frac{1}{p}\left(\frac{\partial p}{\partial T}\right)_v = \text{coefficient of change of pressure at constant volume,}$$

$$\alpha_p = \frac{1}{v}\left(\frac{\partial v}{\partial T}\right)_p = \text{coefficient of dilatation at constant pressure,}$$

and the thermoelastic coefficients are

$$E_t = -v\left(\frac{\partial p}{\partial v}\right)_t = \text{modulus of elasticity for isothermal change,}$$

$$E_s = -v\left(\frac{\partial p}{\partial v}\right)_s = \text{modulus of elasticity for adiabatic change.}$$

If we make δq zero in (86–1)

$$\left(\frac{\partial p}{\partial v}\right)_s = -\frac{\lambda_p}{\eta_v} = -\frac{\left(\frac{\delta q}{\partial v}\right)_p}{\left(\frac{\delta q}{\partial p}\right)_v}. \qquad (86\text{–}8)$$

Dividing this by (86–7),

$$\frac{\left(\frac{\partial p}{\partial v}\right)_s}{\left(\frac{\partial p}{\partial v}\right)_t} = \frac{\left(\frac{\delta q}{\partial v}\right)_p\left(\frac{\partial v}{\partial T}\right)_p}{\left(\frac{\delta q}{\partial p}\right)_v\left(\frac{\partial p}{\partial T}\right)_v} = \frac{\left(\frac{\delta q}{\partial T}\right)_p}{\left(\frac{\delta q}{\partial T}\right)_v} = \frac{c_p}{c_v}. \qquad (86\text{–}9)$$

So the ratio of the slope of an adiabatic on the pressure-volume diagram to that of an isothermal is equal to the ratio of the specific heat at constant pressure to that at constant volume. This ratio

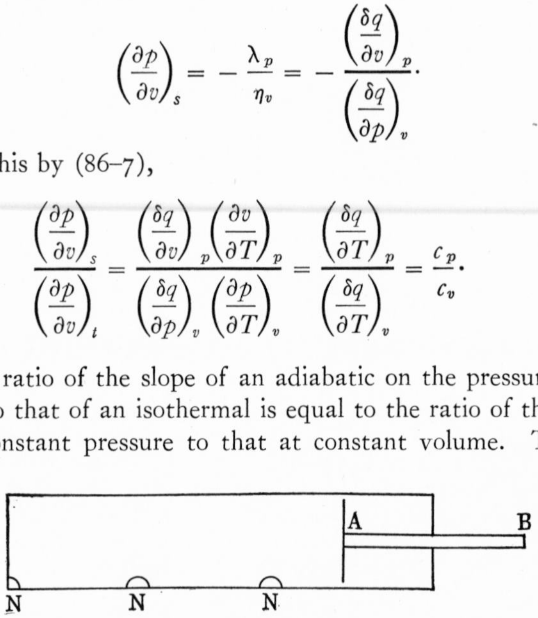

FIG. 96.

of the specific heats we shall denote by γ. Its value for a gas may be determined very simply by means of Kundt's tube. This apparatus consists of a tube (Fig. 96) of adjustable length. To one end the metal rod *AB* is firmly fastened at its middle point. The end *A* of this rod carries a light diaphragm which fits loosely in the tube. When the rod is set in longitudinal vibration standing waves are produced in the gas inside the tube provided the closed end is made to coincide with a node. If dust is put in the tube it will collect at the nodes *N* and in this way indicate their positions. As the distance between successive nodes is a half wave length, the wave length λ may be measured easily. If then the frequency of vibration of the metal rod is measured or calculated from its elastic constants and length, the velocity of the waves in the gas may be computed. But it was shown in article 52 that the velocity of sound in an ideal gas is given by

$$v = \sqrt{\gamma \frac{p}{D}},$$

where D is the density of the gas. Therefore the ratio of specific heats can be calculated from the formula

$$\gamma = v^2 \frac{D}{p}. \qquad (86\text{–}10)$$

The method is more generally used to compare the ratios of specific heats of different gases at the same pressure. Then

$$\frac{\gamma}{\gamma'} = \frac{\lambda^2}{\lambda'^2} \frac{D}{D'}, \qquad (86\text{–}11)$$

where the unprimed letters refer to the one gas and the primed letters to the other. For air $\gamma = 1.403$.

87. Gibbs' Functions and Maxwell's Relations. — We have already expressed the combined first and second law of thermodynamics in the form

$$du = Tds - pdv, \qquad (87\text{–}1)$$

and noted that

$$T = \left(\frac{\partial u}{\partial s}\right)_v, \quad p = -\left(\frac{\partial u}{\partial v}\right)_s, \qquad (87\text{–}2)$$

since du is an exact differential. Therefore

$$\left(\frac{\partial T}{\partial v}\right)_s = -\left(\frac{\partial p}{\partial s}\right)_v. \qquad (87\text{–}3)$$

This is the first* of *Maxwell's relations.*

Gibbs' ψ function is defined by $\psi = u - Ts$. Therefore

$$d\psi = du - Tds - sdT = - sdT - pdv \qquad (87\text{–}4)$$

on account of (87–1). As $d\psi$ is an exact differential we have

$$s = - \left(\frac{\partial\psi}{\partial T}\right)_v, \quad p = - \left(\frac{\partial\psi}{\partial v}\right)_t, \qquad (87\text{–}5)$$

and Maxwell's second relation

$$\left(\frac{\partial s}{\partial v}\right)_t = \left(\frac{\partial p}{\partial T}\right)_v. \qquad (87\text{–}6)$$

Now, for a change in state,

$$\left(\frac{\partial s}{\partial v}\right)_t = \frac{1}{T}\left(\frac{\delta q}{\partial v}\right)_t = \frac{l_t}{T} = \frac{L}{T(v_2 - v_1)_t}.$$

So (87–6) may be written

$$L = T\left(\frac{\partial p}{\partial T}\right)(v_2 - v_1)_t, \qquad (87\text{–}7)$$

the subscript v being omitted from the derivative of p with respect to T since the pressure at which change of state occurs is a function of the temperature only.

This is known as *Clapeyron's equation.* By measuring the latent heat L of vaporization of water, the specific volume v_1 of water and the specific volume v_2 of steam at the boiling point, and the change in pressure per unit change in temperature at constant volume of a mixture of water and steam, the absolute thermodynamic temperature T of the boiling point of water can be calculated. However, as it is difficult to measure v_2 accurately, Clapeyron's equation is generally used to calculate v_2, the absolute temperature of the boiling point being determined by methods to be described later. The increase in pressure per unit increase in temperature at constant volume is accurately known from Regnault's experiments.

Writing Clapeyron's equation in the form

$$\left(\frac{\partial T}{\partial p}\right) = \frac{T(v_2 - v_1)_t}{L},$$

*Maxwell's relations are numbered differently by some authors.

we see that increase in pressure raises the temperature at which the change in state takes place if $v_2 > v_1$ and lowers it if $v_2 < v_1$, since T and L are always positive. Thus, as ice contracts on melting, increase in pressure lowers the freezing point of water. On the other hand water expands on boiling and increase in pressure raises the boiling point.

Gibbs' χ function is defined by $\chi = u + pv$. Hence

$$d\chi = du + pdv + vdp = Tds + vdp, \tag{87–8}$$

giving the third of Maxwell's relations

$$\left(\frac{\partial T}{\partial p}\right)_s = \left(\frac{\partial v}{\partial s}\right)_p. \tag{87–9}$$

Finally we have Gibbs' ζ function defined by $\zeta = u - Ts + pv$. Here

$$d\zeta = du - Tds - sdT + pdv + vdp = -sdT + vdp, \tag{87–10}$$

from which is obtained Maxwell's fourth relation

$$\left(\frac{\partial s}{\partial p}\right)_t = -\left(\frac{\partial v}{\partial T}\right)_p. \tag{87–11}$$

Problem 87a. For a mixture of water and steam at atmospheric pressure $\left(\frac{\partial p}{\partial T}\right) = 2.68$ cm of mercury per 1° C., $L = 538.7$ cal/gm, $T = 373°$ absolute, $v_1 = 1$ cm³/gm. Find the specific volume of steam. *Ans.* 1686 cm³/gm.

Problem 87b. Find the depression of the freezing point of water for an increase in pressure of one atmosphere. $L = 80$ cal/gm, $T = 273°$ absolute, $v_1 = 1.09$ cm³/gm, $v_2 = 1.00$ cm³/gm. *Ans.* 0.0073° C./atmos.

Problem 87c. A wire expands on being heated. Show that if a tension stress F is applied adiabatically the temperature falls. (*Hint:* Use the function $\chi = U - Fx$. Why?)

Problem 87d. Prove Maxwell's second relation graphically, both from the p–v diagram and the T–s diagram.

88. Gibbs-Helmholtz Equation for a Reversible Cell. — We wish to investigate the variation with temperature of the electromotive force $\mathcal{E}$ of a reversible cell, such as a storage cell.

Let the cell C (Fig. 97) run a frictionless motor M which does a very small amount of external work. The speed of the motor, then, is such as to produce a back electromotive force nearly equal to that of the cell, and the current i is very small. Consequently, if R is the resistance of the circuit, the rate Ri^2 of irreversible dissipation of energy in the production of heat in the circuit is negligible compared even with the small rate $i\mathcal{E}$ at which work is done by the cell. Hence we can treat the circuit as reversible. If, instead of allowing the motor to do work, a small amount of work is done on it, the speed will be increased a little, the back electromotive force will slightly exceed that of the cell, and the current will reverse its direction so as to charge the cell in place of discharging it.

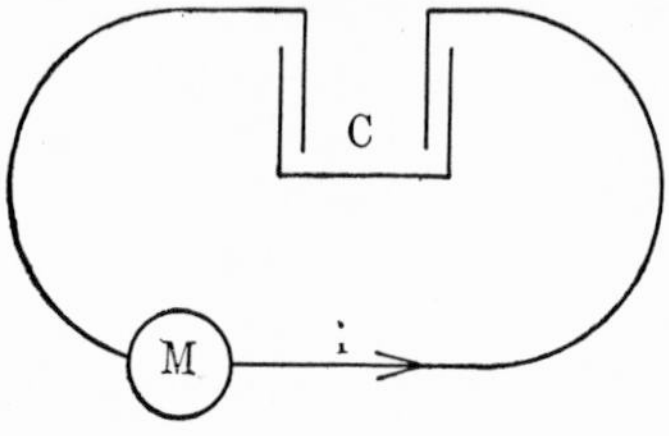

FIG. 97.

Now let a quantity de of electricity pass through the cell in the direction of discharge, the volume of the cell being maintained constant. Denoting by U the intrinsic energy of the cell, the combined first and second law (85–3) takes the form

$$dU = TdS - \mathcal{E}de, \tag{88–1}$$

where the work $\mathcal{E}de$ done by the cell takes the place of pdV. The increase in the Ψ function is

$$d\Psi = d(U - TS) = -SdT - \mathcal{E}de,$$

and as $d\Psi$ is an exact differential

$$\left(\frac{\partial \mathcal{E}}{\partial T}\right)_e = \left(\frac{\partial S}{\partial e}\right)_t. \tag{88–2}$$

Now (88–1) can be written in the form

$$\left(\frac{\partial S}{\partial e}\right)_t = \frac{1}{T}\left\{\left(\frac{\partial U}{\partial e}\right)_t + \mathcal{E}\right\}. \tag{88–3}$$

Comparing (88–2) and (88–3)

$$-\left(\frac{\partial U}{\partial e}\right)_t = \mathcal{E} - T\left(\frac{\partial \mathcal{E}}{\partial T}\right)_e. \qquad (88\text{–}4)$$

This is the *Gibbs-Helmholtz equation.* The left-hand member represents the loss of energy of the cell when a unit quantity of electricity passes through it, the temperature being kept constant. If the chemical reaction taking place in the cell when a current passes through it should occur without the performance of external work this energy would be dissipated as heat. Therefore the heat liberated by the chemical reaction corresponding to that taking place when a unit charge passes through the cell is given by the right-hand side of (88–4). If F is Faraday's constant 96490 coulombs necessary for the reaction of a gram-equivalent of the active substances contained in the cell, the heat H of formation of one gram-equivalent of the active substances is

$$H = F\left\{\mathcal{E} - T\left(\frac{\partial \mathcal{E}}{\partial T}\right)_e\right\} \qquad (88\text{–}5)$$

The quantities on the right-hand side of this equation are easily measured, and it affords by far the most accurate method of determining the heats of formation of chemical reactions.

Since $\mathcal{E}$ in (88–4) represents the work done by the cell during the passage of a unit charge, we note that if $\left(\frac{\partial \mathcal{E}}{\partial T}\right)_e$ is positive the work done is greater than the decrease in intrinsic energy, and consequently heat must be supplied to the cell to maintain a constant temperature. On the other hand, if $\left(\frac{\partial \mathcal{E}}{\partial T}\right)_e$ is negative, the decrease in intrinsic energy is greater than the work done, and heat is evolved.

Problem 88a. In a $Pb - HgCl$ cell the reaction taking place when a current passes through the cell is

$$Pb + 2HgCl = PbCl_2 + 2Hg.$$

Find the heat of formation of one gram-equivalent of the active substances contained in the cell at a temperature of 298.1° absolute if $\mathcal{E} = 0.5357$ volt, $\left(\frac{\partial \mathcal{E}}{\partial T}\right)_e = 0.000145$ volt/1° C. *Ans.* 11,360 cal.

Problem 88b. The pressure in a gas cell is maintained constant. Using the ζ function, show that in this case

$$-\left(\frac{\partial \chi}{\partial e}\right)_t = \mathcal{E} - T\left(\frac{\partial \mathcal{E}}{\partial T}\right)_p,$$

where $\chi = U + pV$

89. The Ideal Gas. — From the experimental point of view an ideal gas is defined as one which obeys Boyle's law that the product of pressure by volume is constant at constant temperature and Joule's law that the intrinsic energy is a function of the temperature alone. From Boyle's law the equation of an isothermal is

$$pv = A \text{ (a constant)}, \quad T \text{ constant}, \tag{89–1}$$

and the slope of an isothermal on the pressure-volume diagram is

$$\left(\frac{\partial p}{\partial v}\right)_t = -\frac{p}{v}. \tag{89–2}$$

From the first law of thermodynamics and Joule's law

$$\delta q = du + pdv = \frac{du}{dT}dT + pdv.$$

Comparing with (86–1) we see that

$$c_v = \frac{du}{dT}, \quad l_t = p$$

So Maxwell's second relation becomes

$$\left(\frac{\partial p}{\partial T}\right)_v = \frac{p}{T}. \tag{89–3}$$

Therefore we get from (89–2) and (89–3)

$$dp = \frac{p}{T}dT - \frac{p}{v}dv.$$

or

$$\frac{dp}{p} + \frac{dv}{v} = \frac{dT}{T}.$$

The integral of this equation is

$$pv = RT. \tag{89–4}$$

This is the gas law, or characteristic equation of an ideal gas.

Now, from (86–8),

$$c_p - c_v = l_t\left(\frac{\partial v}{\partial T}\right)_p = R. \qquad (89\text{–}5)$$

We have shown that the ratio of the slope of an adiabatic on the pressure-volume diagram to that of an isothermal is equal to the ratio γ of the specific heats. As the slope of an isothermal is given by (89–2) that of an adiabatic is

$$\left(\frac{\partial p}{\partial v}\right)_s = -\gamma\frac{p}{v}.$$

The specific heats are found to be constant except at very low temperatures. Therefore the equation of an adiabatic is

$$pv^\gamma = B \text{ (a constant)}, \quad s \text{ constant}. \qquad (89\text{–}6)$$

The work done by the gas during an isothermal expansion is

$$w = \int_{v_1}^{v_2} pdv = RT\int_{v_1}^{v_2}\frac{dv}{v} = RT\log\frac{v_2}{v_1}. \qquad (89\text{–}7)$$

As the intrinsic energy u is a function of the temperature alone it remains constant during an isothermal transformation. Therefore the heat q taken in is equal to the work w done by the gas.

Similarly the work done during an adiabatic expansion is

$$\left.\begin{aligned} w &= \int_{v_1}^{v_2} pdv = B\int_{v_1}^{v_2}\frac{dv}{v^\gamma} = \frac{B}{\gamma - 1}\left\{\frac{1}{v_1^{\gamma-1}} - \frac{1}{v_2^{\gamma-1}}\right\} \\ &= \frac{1}{\gamma - 1}(p_1v_1 - p_2v_2). \end{aligned}\right\} \qquad (89\text{–}8)$$

Consider a Carnot cycle such as is depicted in Fig. 92. As *ab* and *cd* are isothermals, and *bc* and *da* adiabatics

$$p_av_a = p_bv_b,$$

$$p_bv_b^\gamma = p_cv_c^\gamma,$$

$$p_cv_c = p_dv_d,$$

$$p_dv_d^\gamma = p_av_a^\gamma.$$

Multiplying these four equations together we get

$$\frac{v_b}{v_a} = \frac{v_c}{v_d}, \tag{89-9}$$

showing that the expansion ratio is the same for the two isothermals.

The work done along the adiabatics is

$$\frac{1}{\gamma - 1}\{(p_b v_b - p_c v_c) - (p_a v_a - p_d v_d)\} = 0,$$

on account of Boyle's law. Therefore the entire work done by the gas in going around the cycle is that done along the isothermals. It is

$$\left.\begin{aligned} w &= RT_1 \log \frac{v_b}{v_a} - RT_2 \log \frac{v_c}{v_d} \\ &= R(T_1 - T_2) \log \frac{v_b}{v_a}, \end{aligned}\right\} \tag{89-10}$$

on account of (89–9), where T_1 is the temperature of the upper isothermal and T_2 that of the lower. The heat q_1 taken in is equal to the work done on the upper isothermal, that is,

$$q_1 = RT_1 \log \frac{v_b}{v_a}, \tag{89-11}$$

and the efficiency of the cycle is

$$E = \frac{w}{q_1} = \frac{T_1 - T_2}{T_1}, \tag{89-12}$$

in agreement with (84–2).

To calculate the entropy of the gas we have from (86–1)

$$\delta q = c_v dT + l_t dv = c_v dT + p dv.$$

Therefore, using the gas law to eliminate p,

$$ds = \frac{\delta q}{T} = c_v \frac{dT}{T} + R \frac{dv}{v}.$$

As c_v and R are both constants the excess of the entropy over that in some standard state of temperature T_0 and specific volume v_0 is seen to be

$$s - s_0 = c_v \log \frac{T}{T_0} + R \log \frac{v}{v_0}. \tag{89–13}$$

Eliminating T by means of the gas law we have

$$s - s_0 = c_v \log \frac{p}{p_0} + c_p \log \frac{v}{v_0}, \tag{89–14}$$

in view of (89–5), or eliminating v

$$s - s_0 = c_p \log \frac{T}{T_0} - R \log \frac{p}{p_0}. \tag{89–15}$$

Problem 89a. Find the height h of a mountain as a function of the pressure p on the top of the mountain and the pressure p_0 at sea level, (*a*) on the assumption that the atmosphere is isothermal, (*b*) on the assumption that the atmosphere is adiabatic. Calculate the height of the atmosphere on the second assumption if $c_p = 0.2375$ cal/gm 1° C. and $T_0 = 300°$ absolute at sea level.

Ans. (*a*) $h = \frac{RT}{g} \log \frac{p_0}{p}$, (*b*) $h = \frac{c_p T_0}{g} \left\{ 1 - \left(\frac{p}{p_0} \right)^{\frac{\gamma - 1}{\gamma}} \right\}$, 19 miles.

90. Joule's Free Expansion Experiment. — This experiment, performed by Joule in 1845, consists in allowing gas to escape from a vessel *A* into an evacuated vessel *B*. After the gas in the two connected vessels has come into equilibrium as regards both pressure and temperature, the temperature is measured and compared with the original temperature of the gas confined in *A*. As no external work is done and no heat is added, the intrinsic energy of the gas remains unchanged. Joule was unable to detect any change in temperature, and therefore concluded that the intrinsic energy of a gas is a function of its temperature only. This is one of the two laws from which we deduced the characteristic equation of an ideal gas in article 89.

Recently N. I. Adams, Jr. has shown that a slight cooling occurs as the result of the free expansion of an actual gas. From the measurement of this cooling the corrections which must be applied to the readings of a constant volume gas thermometer to obtain thermodynamic temperatures may be determined. We shall not discuss these corrections, but shall turn our attention to a slightly different type of expansion in which the small temperature change is more easily measured and from which the corrections to the constant pressure gas thermometer may be found.

Problem 90a. Two vessels A and B of equal volumes are connected by a tube with a stopcock. Vessel A contains a mass m of ideal gas at pressure p and temperature T and vessel B is empty. Calculate the change in entropy which occurs when the stopcock is opened by substituting for the irreversible transformation actually taking place a reversible transformation leading to the same end state. Show that the result obtained agrees with that calculated from (89–13). *Ans.* $\Delta S = mR \log 2$.

91. Joule-Thomson Porous Plug Experiment. — This experiment consists in measuring the cooling experienced by a gas flowing through a porous plug P (Fig. 98) from a region of pressure p_1 to a region of slightly lower pressure p_2. It is of great importance because the absolute thermodynamic temperature can be calculated from the measurements obtained and the corrections determined necessary to reduce the readings of the constant pressure gas thermometer to thermodynamic temperatures.

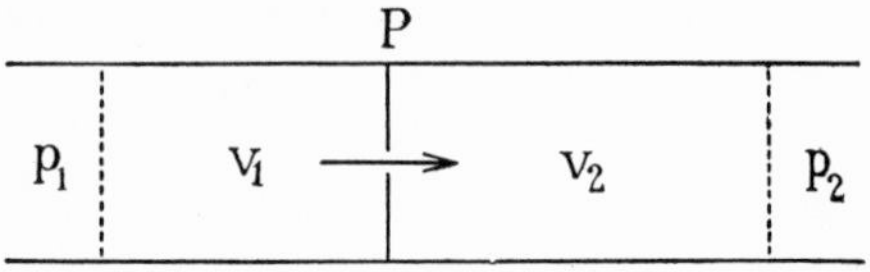

FIG. 98.

Consider the passage of a unit mass of gas through the plug. If v_1 is the specific volume of the gas at pressure p_1 and v_2 that at pressure p_2, the work done on the gas by that behind in pushing it through the volume v_1 is p_1v_1, whereas the work it does in displacing the gas in front of it on the other side of the plug through the volume v_2 is p_2v_2. Therefore the total work done by the unit mass of gas is

$$\delta w = p_2v_2 - p_1v_1 = d(pv).$$

As no heat is taken in it follows from the first law of thermodynamics that

$$\delta q = du + \delta w = du + d(pv) = d\chi = 0.$$

So the function χ remains unchanged by the passage of the gas through the plug. Therefore in accord with (87–8)

$$d\chi = Tds + vdp = 0.$$

As s may be expressed as a function of T and p

$$ds = \left(\frac{\partial s}{\partial T}\right)_p dT + \left(\frac{\partial s}{\partial p}\right)_t dp.$$

Hence

$$d\chi = T\left(\frac{\partial s}{\partial T}\right)_p dT + \left\{T\left(\frac{\partial s}{\partial p}\right)_t + v\right\}dp = 0. \qquad (91\text{–}1)$$

Now, for any reversible transformation at constant pressure,

$$T\left(\frac{\partial s}{\partial T}\right)_p = \left(\frac{\delta q}{\partial T}\right)_p = c_p.$$

Substituting this in (91–1) and making use of the fourth of Maxwell's relations (87–11) we have

$$c_p dT + \left\{v - T\left(\frac{\partial v}{\partial T}\right)_p\right\} dp = 0,$$

whence

$$c_p\left(\frac{\partial T}{\partial p}\right)_\chi = T\left(\frac{\partial v}{\partial T}\right)_p - v. \qquad (91\text{–}2)$$

Now $\left(\frac{\partial T}{\partial p}\right)_\chi$ is the fall in temperature per unit fall in pressure occurring when the gas escapes through the porous plug. Most gases suffer a cooling although hydrogen heats up slightly at temperatures above the *inversion temperature* $-80°$ C. The cooling becomes very large at low temperatures and is made use of in liquefying gases.

Introducing the coefficient of dilatation at constant pressure and solving (91–2) for T we have

$$T = \frac{1}{\alpha_p}\left\{1 + \rho c_p\left(\frac{\partial T}{\partial p}\right)_\chi\right\}, \qquad (91\text{–}3)$$

where the density ρ of the gas has been put for the reciprocal of the specific volume v. As the coefficient of dilatation or expansion α_p at constant pressure can be measured very accurately and the second term in the braces is merely a small correction term, the absolute thermodynamic temperature of the freezing point of water or of any other fixed point can be calculated to a high degree of precision from this formula, using the values of α_p, ρ and c_p measured at the temperature and pressure considered. By this method the thermodynamic temperature of the freezing point of water is found to be 273.18° absolute.

Over a considerable range of temperatures it is found from experiment that

$$c_p\left(\frac{\partial T}{\partial p}\right)_\chi = \frac{n}{T^2},$$

where n is a constant. Putting this in (91–2)

$$T\left(\frac{\partial v}{\partial T}\right)_p = v + \frac{n}{T^2},$$

or

$$\frac{Tdv - vdT}{T^2} = n\frac{dT}{T^4}, \qquad p \text{ constant.}$$

Integrating

$$\frac{v}{T} = -\frac{n}{3T^3} + C, \; p \text{ constant.} \qquad (91\text{–}4)$$

If v_0 is the specific volume of the gas at the temperature T_0 of the freezing point of water this becomes

$$\frac{v}{T} - \frac{v_0}{T_0} = \frac{n}{3}\left(\frac{1}{T_0{}^3} - \frac{1}{T^3}\right), \qquad p \text{ constant.}$$

Putting x for the right-hand side of this equation we have

$$\frac{v}{v_0} = \frac{T}{T_0} + \frac{x}{v_0}T,$$

or

$$\left.\begin{aligned}\frac{v - v_0}{v_0} &= \frac{T - T_0}{T_0} + \frac{x}{v_0}T = \frac{T - T_0}{T_0}\left\{1 + \frac{x}{v_0}\frac{TT_0}{T - T_0}\right\}\\ &= \frac{T - T_0}{T_0}\left\{1 + \frac{np_0}{3T_0{}^2}\left(1 + \frac{T_0}{T} + \frac{T_0{}^2}{T^2}\right)\right\}.\end{aligned}\right\} \qquad (91\text{–}5)$$

provided the pressure is maintained constant. Now if θ is the Centigrade temperature determined by a constant pressure gas thermometer on the assumption that the gas expands uniformly

$$\theta = 100\frac{v - v_0}{v_{100} - v_0} = \frac{v - v_0}{\alpha v_0}, \qquad (91\text{–}6)$$

where v_{100} is the specific volume at the boiling point of water and α is the mean coefficient of expansion at constant pressure, that is,

$$\alpha = \frac{v_{100} - v_0}{100 v_0}.$$

From (91–5) and (91–6) it follows that

$$\theta = \frac{T - T_0}{\alpha T_0}\left\{1 + \frac{n p_0}{3 T_0^2}\left(1 + \frac{T_0}{T} + \frac{T_0^2}{T^2}\right)\right\}. \qquad (91\text{–}7)$$

From this formula the error in the constant pressure gas thermometer at any temperature can be calculated.

From the characteristic equation (89–4) of an ideal gas we see that

$$T\left(\frac{\partial v}{\partial T}\right)_p = \frac{RT}{p} = v.$$

Comparing with (91–2) it appears that such a gas shows no change in temperature on passing through a porous plug to a region of lower pressure. Therefore n vanishes in (91–7) and a constant pressure thermometer employing an ideal gas as thermometric substance reads the thermodynamic temperature without correction.

If we assume that actual gases approximate more closely to an ideal gas the higher the temperature we can obtain from (91–4) a characteristic equation for real gases. For at very high temperatures the first term on the right of (91–4) becomes negligible and

$$\frac{v}{T} = C, \quad p \text{ constant}.$$

Comparing this with the ideal gas equation

$$\frac{v}{T} = \frac{R}{p}$$

we see that the constant C is equal to R/p. Therefore the desired equation is

$$pv = RT - \frac{np}{3T^2}. \qquad (91\text{–}8)$$

Actual gases follow an equation of this form very closely.

Problem 91a. At 0° C. and 1 atmosphere pressure the coefficient of dilatation at constant pressure of nitrogen is 0.003673/1° C., the density is 1.2507 gm/liter, the specific heat at constant pressure is 0.2350 cal/gm 1° C. and the drop in temperature when passed through a porous plug is 0.255° C. per atmosphere drop in pressure. Find the absolute thermodynamic temperature of the freezing point of water. *Ans.* 273.1°.

Problem 91b. Taking $T_0 = 273.18°$ and $\alpha = 0.0036690$, find the error in the constant pressure nitrogen thermometer at 50° C., and at −150° C. Determine n by making the gas temperature agree with the thermodynamic temperature at the boiling point of water. *Ans.* +0.01°, −0.90°.

Problem 91c. By using Maxwell's second relation, show that the expression corresponding to (91–3) for the free expansion of a gas is

$$T = \frac{1}{\alpha_v}\left\{1 - \frac{c_v}{p}\left(\frac{\partial T}{\partial v}\right)_u\right\}.$$

92. Van der Waals' Equation. — Van der Waals' characteristic equation is

$$\left(p + \frac{a}{v^2}\right)(v - b) = RT, \tag{92–1}$$

where a and b are constants. The term a/v^2 is added to the pressure to compensate for the diminution in the pressure of a real gas due to the attractions of the molecules for one another, and the constant b is subtracted from the volume to take account of the space actually filled by the molecules. While this equation does not describe the behavior of actual gases as well as the equation (91–8) deduced from the results of the porous plug experiment, it has the advantage of applying to both the gaseous and liquid phases.

Writing Van der Waals' equation in powers of v

$$v^3 - \left(b + \frac{RT}{p}\right)v^2 + \frac{a}{p}v - \frac{ab}{p} = 0. \tag{92–2}$$

This is a cubic in v. The critical point is that point whose pressure p_c and temperature T_c are such as to make the three roots equal. Above the critical point the equation has only one real root; below it has three. If v_c is the specific volume at the critical point,

$$(v - v_c)^3 = v^3 - 3v_cv^2 + 3v_c^2v - v_c^3 = 0 \tag{92–3}$$

in order that the three roots may be equal. Comparing with (92–2)

$$3v_c = b + \frac{RT_c}{p_c}, \quad 3v_c^2 = \frac{a}{p_c}, \quad v_c^3 = \frac{ab}{p_c}$$

or

$$v_c = 3b, \quad p_c = \frac{a}{27b^2}, \quad T_c = \frac{8a}{27bR}, \tag{92–4}$$

If we solve for a, b, R

$$a = 3v_c^2 p_c, \quad b = \frac{v_c}{3}, \quad R = \frac{8p_c v_c}{3T_c}. \tag{92–5}$$

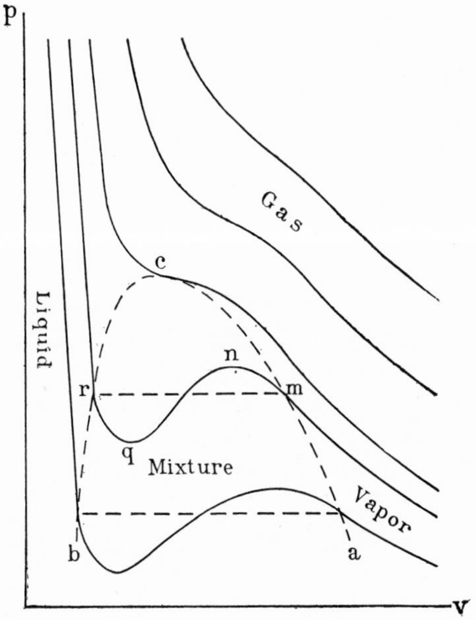

FIG. 99.

By means of these relations a, b and R may be determined from the critical constants v_c, p_c and T_c. In Fig. 99 are sketched isothermals in the neighborhood of the critical point c. The liquid line is represented by bc and the saturated vapor line by ac. Only inside the curve acb may the liquid and vapor exist together in equilibrium. The portion of the isothermal extending from m to n represents supersaturation and that from n to q a region of instability. Only under special conditions are the portions mn and qr realizable experimentally, the isothermal ordinarily following the horizontal line from m to r.

If we substitute the values of a, b, R given by (92–5) in Van der Waals' equation (92–1) we get

$$\left(\frac{p}{p_c} + 3\frac{v_c^2}{v^2}\right)\left(\frac{v}{v_c} - \frac{1}{3}\right) = \frac{8}{3}\frac{T}{T_c},$$

and if we take the critical constants as our units of pressure, specific volume and temperature by putting

$$p' \equiv \frac{p}{p_c}, \quad v' \equiv \frac{v}{v_c}, \quad T' \equiv \frac{T}{T_c},$$

then

$$\left(p' + \frac{3}{v'^2}\right)\left(v' - \frac{1}{3}\right) = \frac{8}{3}T', \tag{92–6}$$

which is independent of the characteristics of the particular substance under consideration.

Van der Waals' equation leads, at least qualitatively, to an explanation of the inversion temperature (art. 91) of an expanding gas. From (92–2) we find

$$T\left(\frac{\partial v}{\partial T}\right)_p - v = \frac{2av - bpv^2 - 3ab}{pv^2 - a + 2\dfrac{ab}{v}}.$$

Neglecting the term in ab in the numerator in comparison with those in a and b, and the terms in a and ab in the denominator in comparison with that in pv^2, we have from (91–2)

$$c_p\left(\frac{\partial T}{\partial p}\right)_\chi = \frac{2a}{pv} - b.$$

Replacing pv by RT this becomes

$$c_p\left(\frac{\partial T}{\partial p}\right)_\chi = \frac{2a}{RT} - b. \qquad (92\text{–}7)$$

This equation indicates a normal cooling with drop in pressure for temperatures less than $2a/bR$ but a heating for higher temperatures.

Problem 92a. Find as a function of T and v the entropy of a gas obeying Van der Waals' equation, assuming c_v to be constant.

$$\textit{Ans.}\ s - s_0 = c_v \log \frac{T}{T_0} + R \log \frac{v - b}{v_0 - b}.$$

93. Lagrange's Method of Undetermined Multipliers. — In the next article and frequently in the next chapter we shall be required to find the values of $x_1, x_2 \ldots x_f$ for which a function $f(x_1, x_2 \ldots x_f)$ has a stationary value, subject to one or more equations of condition between the variables. Evidently the desired stationary value occurs at those values of $x_1, x_2 \ldots x_f$ for which

$$\frac{\partial f}{\partial x_1} dx_1 + \frac{\partial f}{\partial x_2} dx_2 \ldots + \frac{\partial f}{\partial x_f} dx_f = 0 \qquad (93\text{–}1)$$

for *any* values of the increments $dx_1, dx_2 \ldots dx_f$ which are consistent with the equations of condition. Suppose the latter are

$$g(x_1, x_2 \ldots x_f) = 0, \quad h(x_1, x_2 \ldots x_f) = 0. \qquad (93\text{–}2)$$

Differentiating these, we have

$$\frac{\partial g}{\partial x_1} dx_1 + \frac{\partial g}{\partial x_2} dx_2 \ldots + \frac{\partial g}{\partial x_f} dx_f = 0, \qquad (93\text{–}3)$$

$$\frac{\partial h}{\partial x_1} dx_1 + \frac{\partial h}{\partial x_2} dx_2 \ldots + \frac{\partial h}{\partial x_f} dx_f = 0. \qquad (93\text{–}4)$$

Now, (93–3) and (93–4) impose limitations on the values which may be assigned to $dx_1, dx_2 \ldots dx_f$ in (93–1). Effectively they reduce the number of independent increments in (93–1) from f to $f - 2$, so that we must consider two of the increments to be functions of the remaining ones. We can, however, use (93–3) and (93–4) to eliminate two of the increments from (93–1), in which event the remaining increments are independent and can be assigned any values at will.

To do this, multiply (93–3) by a constant α and (93–4) by a constant β and add the equations so obtained to (93–1). Then we have

$$\left(\frac{\partial f}{\partial x_1} + \alpha \frac{\partial g}{\partial x_1} + \beta \frac{\partial h}{\partial x_1}\right) dx_1 + \left(\frac{\partial f}{\partial x_2} + \alpha \frac{\partial g}{\partial x_2} + \beta \frac{\partial h}{\partial x_2}\right) dx_2$$

$$+ \left(\frac{\partial f}{\partial x_3} + \alpha \frac{\partial g}{\partial x_3} + \beta \frac{\partial h}{\partial x_3}\right) dx_3 \ldots + \left(\frac{\partial f}{\partial x_f} + \alpha \frac{\partial g}{\partial x_f} + \beta \frac{\partial h}{\partial x_f}\right) dx_f = 0.$$

Let us take dx_1 and dx_2 as the two increments which are expressed as functions of the remaining independent increments by (93–3) and (93–4). Then if the constants α and β are chosen so as to make the coefficients of dx_1 and dx_2 vanish for the values of $x_1, x_2 \ldots x_f$ at which $f(x_1, x_2 \ldots x_f)$ has its stationary value, we are left with the equation

$$\left(\frac{\partial f}{\partial x_3} + \alpha \frac{\partial g}{\partial x_3} + \beta \frac{\partial h}{\partial x_3}\right) dx_3 \ldots + \left(\frac{\partial f}{\partial x_f} + \alpha \frac{\partial g}{\partial x_f} + \beta \frac{\partial h}{\partial x_f}\right) dx_f = 0.$$

in which all the increments are independent. As we can make all of them zero except dx_3, we see that the coefficient of dx_3 must vanish, and so on. Hence the stationary value of $f(x_1, x_2 \ldots x_f)$, subject to the condition equations (93–2), occurs for those values of $x_1, x_2 \ldots x_f$ for which

$$\frac{\partial f}{\partial x_s} + \alpha \frac{\partial g}{\partial x_s} + \beta \frac{\partial h}{\partial x_s} = 0, \quad s = 1, 2 \ldots f. \qquad (93\text{–}5)$$

These equations are just sufficient in number to determine $x_1, x_2 \ldots x_f$ in terms of α and β. Then, substituting back in the two condition equations (93–2), we can evaluate the constants α and β. Evidently the method described applies whatever the number of condition equations may be.

The constants α and β in the example discussed are known as *undetermined multipliers*.

Problem 93a. The space rate of increase of a scalar function Φ in the direction specified by the direction cosines l, m, n is

$$l\frac{\partial\Phi}{\partial x} + m\frac{\partial\Phi}{\partial y} + n\frac{\partial\Phi}{\partial z},$$

where l, m, n satisfy the condition equation $l^2 + m^2 + n^2 = 1$. Show, by Lagrange's method of undetermined multipliers, that the greatest space rate of increase of Φ is given by the gradient of Φ.

94. Gibbs' Phase Rule. — So far we have limited our discussion to a single substance. Now we shall consider a *complex* or mixture of substances in chemical and thermal equilibrium.

The number of *components* in a complex is the smallest number of independently variable constituents needed to define the composition of every phase in the system. Thus in the mixture $PCl_5 + Cl_2 + PCl_3$ we have only two components on account of the relation $PCl_3 + Cl_2 \rightleftarrows PCl_5$. Again, a complex consisting of water and its vapor in equilibrium with each other contains but a single component.

A *phase* is a homogeneous substance in equilibrium. Thus ice, water, steam are three phases of a single substance. A mixture of PCl_5, Cl_2, PCl_3 contains two components in three phases.

Consider a mixture of n components existing in ϕ different phases. The *chemical potential* μ_i of a phase is defined as the increase in energy of that phase when a unit mass of the ith component is added to it, the entropy S and the volume V being held constant. Confining attention to a single phase, then, the increase in energy when S, V and the mass of each component is increased is

$$dU = TdS - pdV + \mu_1 dm_1 \ldots + \mu_n dm_n. \qquad (94\text{–}1)$$

Let us build up the phase under consideration from nothing to the final state. In doing so we increase the extensive quantities S, V, $m_1 \ldots m_n$ by bringing from outside additional increments $dm_1 \ldots dm_n$ of each component at the temperature T and pressure p of the completed phase. We shall add these increments of mass at such rates that, at any stage of the process, the masses of all components are the same fraction x of their final values. Then, if we understand by S, V, $m_1 \ldots m_n$ the final entropy, volume, and masses of the various components constituting the phase, the values of the entropy, volume and masses at any state of the process are xS, xV, $xm_1 \ldots xm_n$, and the increments added simultaneously are Sdx, Vdx, $m_1dx \ldots m_ndx$. Evidently the addition of new increments of the components at the temperature and pressure of the substance already present will not change the temperature and pressure. Moreover, the chemical potentials of the various components can at most be functions of T, p and the relative masses of these components. Hence, as we are keeping T, p and the relative masses constant, the μ's will remain constant during the construction of the phase. Consequently we have from (94–1) for the energy of the completed phase

$$U = (TS - pV + \mu_1 m_1 \ldots + \mu_n m_n)\int_0^1 dx$$

$$= TS - pV + \mu_1 m_1 \ldots + \mu_n m_n. \qquad (94\text{–}2)$$

For equilibrium the total entropy must be maximum subject to constant total energy, total volume and total mass of each component. So, if we distinguish the different phases by accents, we have from (94–1)

$$dS' + dS'' \ldots = \frac{dU'}{T'} + \frac{dU''}{T''} \ldots + \frac{p'}{T'}dV' + \frac{p''}{T''}dV'' \ldots$$

$$- \frac{\mu_1'}{T'}dm_1' - \frac{\mu_1''}{T''}dm_1'' \ldots - \frac{\mu_n'}{T'}dm_n' - \frac{\mu_n''}{T''}dm_n'' \ldots = 0,$$

subject to

$$dU' + dU'' \ldots = 0,$$

$$dV' + dV'' \ldots = 0,$$

$$dm_1' + dm_1'' \ldots = 0,$$

$$\cdot \quad \cdot \quad \cdot \quad \cdot$$

$$dm_n' + dm_n'' \ldots = 0.$$

Multiplying the condition equations by α, β, $\gamma_1 \ldots \gamma_n$ respectively and adding to the first equation we get by Lagrange's method of undetermined multipliers,

$$\frac{1}{T'} + \alpha = 0, \qquad \frac{1}{T''} + \alpha = 0, \ldots$$

$$\frac{p'}{T'} + \beta = 0, \qquad \frac{p''}{T''} + \beta = 0, \ldots$$

$$-\frac{\mu_1'}{T'} + \gamma_1 = 0, \quad -\frac{\mu_1''}{T''} + \gamma_1 = 0, \ldots$$

$$\cdot \quad \cdot \quad \cdot \quad \cdot$$

$$-\frac{\mu_n'}{T'} + \gamma_n = 0, \quad -\frac{\mu_n''}{T''} + \gamma_n = 0, \ldots$$

From the first set of equations we see that $T' = T'' = \ldots$, from the second that $p' = p'' = \ldots$, and from the remaining ones that $\mu_1' = \mu_1'' = \ldots, \ldots, \mu_n' = \mu_n'' = \ldots$ So for equilibrium the temperature, the pressure and each chemical potential must be the same in every phase.

Let us consider a small variation from the state of equilibrium. Subtracting (94–1) from the complete differential of (94–2) we have for any phase

$$SdT - Vdp + m_1 d\mu_1 \ldots + m_n d\mu_n = 0. \qquad (94\text{–}3)$$

If there are ϕ phases present in the complex we have ϕ equations of condition of the form (94–3) between the $(n + 2)$ intensive variables T, p, $\mu_1 \ldots \mu_n$ in terms of which the state of the heterogeneous substance of n components is described. The number of independent variables is then $(n + 2) - \phi$. This number is called the number of *degrees of freedom* of the complex or the *variance*, and will be denoted by f. Therefore

$$f = (n + 2) - \phi. \qquad (94\text{–}4)$$

This is the *phase rule of* Gibbs'. The number of components n is often referred to as the *order* of the complex and the number of phases ϕ as its *degree*.

Consider a complex of order *one* such as water. If it exists in the form of steam alone its degree is *one* and its variance is

$$f = (1 + 2) - 1 = 2.$$

This is known as a *bivariant* system. Its state is determined by the two independent intensive variables T and p.

On the other hand a mixture of water and steam, or of ice and water, is of order *one* and degree *two*. Its variance is

$$f = (1 + 2) - 2 = 1.$$

This is a *univariant* system, its state being determined by a single independent variable, either T or p.

Finally a mixture of three phases ice, water and steam in equilibrium with one another constitutes a system of order *one* and degree *three* with variance

$$f = (1 + 2) - 3 = 0.$$

Such a system is said to be *invariant*. The three phases can coexist at only a single point known as the triple point. The temperature of the triple point of water is 0.0072° C. and the pressure 0.46 cm of mercury.

REFERENCES

PLANCK, MAX: *Treatise on Thermodynamics*, Longmans, Green & Co., London.

SAHA AND SRIVASTAVA: *A Text Book of Heat*, The India Press, Allahabad.

LEWIS AND RANDALL: *Thermodynamics*, McGraw-Hill Book Co., New York.

GIBBS, J. W.: *Collected Works*, Vol. I, Longmans, Green & Co., New York.

CHAPTER VIII

STATISTICAL MECHANICS

95. Thermodynamic Probability. — Consider N particles, such as gas molecules, all of the same type and each having f degrees of freedom. The state of the substance composed of these N particles is specified microscopically at any instant by the f generalized coordinates q and the f generalized momenta p of each particle; in all by $2f$ independent variables. If we use these $2f$ variables as the coordinates in a $2f$ dimensional representative space the state of each individual particle is determined by a point in this space. This $2f$ dimensional representative space is known as *state space* or *phase space*. As time goes on the position of the point representing a particular particle changes; the path described by this point is known as a *phase path*.

Now we shall divide the $2f$ dimensional representative space into small boxes or cells of equal size. These cells are known as *elements of state space*, or *elements of extension-in-phase*. If we know in which cell each individual particle lies, we have a complete microscopic specification of the state of the substance within the limits imposed by the finite but small dimensions of an individual cell. From the point of view of thermodynamics, however, we are not interested in the microscopic state of the substance. All we are concerned with is the specification of such quantities as pressure, density, temperature, which are determined by the number of particles whose representative points lie in each element of extension-in-phase irrespective of which particles these may be. In other words we are concerned only with the macroscopic state of the substance.

A *complexion* is defined as a specified arrangement of particles among the elements of extension-in-phase. For instance, if we have ten particles numbered 1 to 10, and seven elements of extension-in-phase, then if the squares in Fig. 100 represent elements of extension-in-phase and the dots representative points of particles, the arrangement illustrated represents a complexion. If we interchange particles 4 and 7 we have another complexion and another microscopic state, but the same macroscopic state. Clearly many different complexions or microscopic states correspond to the same macroscopic state. As it is only the macroscopic state with which we are concerned in statistical mechanics we shall use the word "state" in this sense in future. Now the state of equilibrium is the state which the substance tends to assume and retain; therefore it is the most probable state. We shall make the assumption that in the absence of any restricting conditions the chance that the representa-

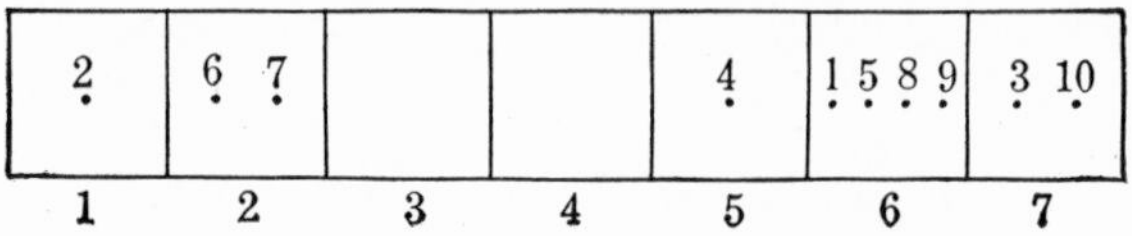

Fig. 100.

tive point of a particle lies in any one element of extension-in-phase is as good as the chance that it lies in any other. This is a natural assumption to make since we have made all the elements of extension-in-phase of the same size. Then the most probable state is the one to which the greatest number of complexions corresponds.

Our present concept of the state of equilibrium differs in one important respect from that of the classical thermodynamics. There it is supposed that once the state of equilibrium has been attained, it will persist indefinitely provided the substance remains undisturbed. Here, however, we recognize that all complexions consistent with the specified energy of the substance are equally probable, and that the only reason that the state of equilibrium appears to persist is that the number of complexions corresponding to states differing appreciably from this state is extremely small compared with the number corresponding to it or to states very close to it. Nevertheless, there exists a remote but finite chance that a glass of water may spontaneously boil at the top and freeze at the bottom. That this phenomenon is too unlikely to be worth watching for, will be appreciated after the reader has solved problem 96*b*.

We define the *thermodynamic probability W* of a given state as the number of complexions which give that state. Consider the state to which the complexion illustrated in Fig. 100 corresponds. The number of permutations of ten particles in a row is 10!, for the first place in the row may be filled in 10 different ways and after it is filled the second place may be filled in 9 different ways by the nine remaining particles, and so on. But the permutations of the two particles in the second cell, the four in the sixth cell and the two in the seventh cell do not lead to new complexions. Therefore the total number of complexions corresponding to the state under consideration is

$$W = \frac{10!}{1!\,2!\,0!\,0!\,1!\,4!\,2!} = 37{,}800,$$

where unity is to be understood by factorial 0. In general, then, if we have N particles, the thermodynamic probability of the state in which N_1 particles are in element of extension-in-phase 1, N_2 in 2, N_3 in 3, and so on, is

$$W = \frac{N!}{N_1!\,N_2!\,N_3!\ldots} = \frac{N!}{\prod\limits_{e} N_e!}. \tag{95–1}$$

From the point of view of probability the state of equilibrium is the most probable state, whereas from the point of view of the classical thermodynamics it is the state of maximum entropy. Therefore we suspect an intimate connection between entropy and thermodynamic probability. Now entropies are additive, whereas the probability of the simultaneous existence of specified states of two different substances is the product of the probabilities of the individual states. Since, however,

$$\log (W_1 W_2) = \log W_1 + \log W_2$$

the logarithms of the probabilities are additive. So let us consider the function

$$S = k \log W, \tag{95–2}$$

where k is a universal positive constant. We shall show later that if the value of k is suitably chosen the function S is identical with the entropy of classical thermodynamics to within an additive constant.

Putting (95–1) in (95–2)

$$S = k \log N! - k\sum_{c} \log N_e! \tag{95–3}$$

To evaluate $\log N!$ for the case where N is large consider the curve $y = \log x$ depicted in Fig. 101. As

$$\frac{dy}{dx} = \frac{1}{x}$$

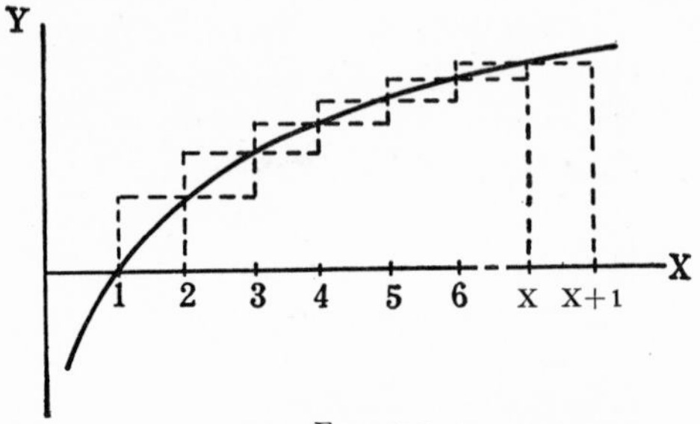

Fig. 101.

the curve approaches parallelism with the X axis for very large values of x, whereas y becomes ever greater. Now

$$\log x! = \log 2 + \log 3 \ldots + \log x$$

is equal to either the area under the upper step-like broken-line curve extending from 1 to x or the area under the lower step-like curve extending from 2 to $x + 1$. But the first is greater than the area under the portion of the logarithmic curve extending from 1 to x, and the second less than that under the portion of the logarithmic curve extending from 1 to $x + 1$, that is,

$$\int_1^x \log x\, dx < \log x! < \int_1^{x+1} \log x\, dx.$$

Evaluating the integrals, we find, for the case where x is a large integer,

$$x \log x - x + 1 < \log x! < (x + 1) \log (x + 1) - (x + 1) + 1$$
$$< (x + 1) \log x + (x + 1) \log \left(1 + \frac{1}{x}\right) - x$$
$$< \left(1 + \frac{1}{x}\right) x \log x - x + 1 + \frac{1}{2x} + \ldots$$

where, in the right-hand member of the inequality, we have neglected terms in the square and higher powers of $1/x$. We see, then, that we may write

$$\log x! = x \log x - x \qquad (95\text{–}4)$$

with a fractional error of the order of only $1/x$.

We are concerned only with material substances containing a vast number of molecules. Therefore N and many of the N_e's in (95–3) are large enough so that (95–4) is a sufficiently good approximation. Others of the N_e's may be so small that (95–4) is a poor approximation, but they will contribute so little to the sum in (95–3) that a large fractional error in the terms in which they occur will have a negligible effect on the error of the entire sum. Hence we may use (95–4) in calculating all the terms in (95–3). Let us put

$$w_e = \frac{N_e}{N}$$

a priori probability

for the mathematical probability that the representative point of a particle lies in element of extension-in-phase e. Obviously

$$\sum_e w_e = 1.$$

Then (95–3) becomes

$$\left.\begin{aligned} S &= k\{N \log N - N - \sum_e N_e \log N_e + \sum_e N_e\} \\ &= kN\{\log N - \sum_e w_e \log N_e\} \\ &= kN\{\sum_e w_e \log N - \sum_e w_e \log N_e\} \\ &= -kN\sum_e w_e \log w_e. \end{aligned}\right\} \qquad (95\text{–}5)$$

If U_e is the energy associated with element of extension-in-phase e, the energy of the N_e particles whose representative points lie in this element of extension-in-phase is $N_eU_e = NU_ew_e$ and the total energy of the substance is

$$U = N\sum_e U_e w_e. \qquad (95\text{–}6)$$

Finally it follows from the definition of the mathematical probability w_e that

$$N = N\sum_e w_e. \qquad (95\text{–}7)$$

Problem 95a. Find the percentage error of the approximate formula

$$\log x! = x \log x - x + 1$$

for $x = 10$ and for $x = 20$. *Ans.* 7.2 per cent, 3.4 per cent.

96. The State of Equilibrium. — From our present viewpoint the state of equilibrium is the state of maximum probability. As the maximum of the logarithm comes at the same point as that of its argument, this state is the one for which the function S is a maximum.

isolated system 1.)

If, then, we consider a group of molecules surrounded by a rigid adiabatic envelope so that no energy can be communicated from outside either in the form of heat or of work, a necessary condition for equilibrium is that $dS = 0$ subject to $dU = 0$ and $dN = 0$. The last requirement is imposed by the fact that the number of molecules must remain constant in any variation of the state. So long as the number of elements of extension-in-phase remains constant it is equivalent to the condition $\sum_e dw_e = 0$. Therefore

$$dS = -kN\sum_e(\log w_e + 1)dw_e = 0,$$

$$dU = N\sum_e U_e\, dw_e = 0,$$

$$N\sum_e dw_e = 0,$$

from (95–5), (95–6) and (95–7). We shall solve these equations by the method of Lagrange described in article 93. Multiplying the second equation by the undetermined constant $-k\beta$ and the third by $-k\lambda$, adding, and equating the coefficient of each dw_e to zero, we have

$$\log w_e + \beta U_e + \lambda + 1 = 0, \qquad (96\text{–}1)$$

or

$$w_e = \alpha e^{-\beta U_e}, \qquad (96\text{–}2)$$

where

$$\log \alpha \equiv -(\lambda + 1).$$

To show that this stationary value is a maximum, let $w'_e = w_e + \epsilon_e$ be the mathematical probability that the representative point of a particle lies in element of extension-in-phase e for a state of the same energy differing slightly from the state of equilibrium. Then

$$N\sum_e U_e\epsilon_e = 0, \qquad (96\text{–}2.1)$$

$$N\sum_e \epsilon_e = 0. \qquad (96\text{–}2.2)$$

As $\epsilon_e << w_e$ for every element of extension-in-phase, the S function for the new state is

$$\begin{aligned} S' &= -kN\sum_e w'_e \log w'_e \\ &= -kN\sum_e (w_e + \epsilon_e)\left\{\log w_e + \log\left(1 + \frac{\epsilon_e}{w_e}\right)\right\} \\ &= -kN\sum_e\left\{w_e \log w_e + \epsilon_e(\log w_e + 1) + \frac{\epsilon_e^2}{2w_e} + \ldots\right\}. \end{aligned}$$

Since w_e satisfies (96–1), this may be written

$$S' = S + kN\sum_e(\beta U_e + \lambda)\epsilon_e - \frac{1}{2}kN\sum_e \frac{\epsilon_e^2}{w_e} + \ldots$$

and, with the use of (96–2.1) and (96–2.2),

$$S' = S - \frac{1}{2}kN\sum_e \frac{\epsilon_e^2}{w_e} + \ldots . \qquad (96\text{–}2.3)$$

Therefore $S > S'$ no matter whether the ϵ_e's are positive or negative.

If the constant β is positive, as will be shown to be the case later, equation (96–2) shows us that the probability of the representative point of a particle lying in an element of extension-in-phase of large energy is less than the probability of it lying in an element of extension-in-phase of small energy.

Next we shall consider two substances separated by a rigid partition impervious to the passage of particles of either substance but transparent to heat, the two substances together being surrounded by a rigid adiabatic envelope so as to preclude the communication of energy from outside. In this case the condition for constancy of energy applies only to the total energy of the two substances and not to the energy of each individually. So if we refer to the first substance by letters without primes and to the second by letters with primes,

$$S = -kN\sum_e w_e \log w_e - kN'\sum_e{}' w'_e \log w'_e,$$

$$U = N\sum_e U_e w_e + N'\sum_e{}' U'_e w'_e,$$

$$N = N\sum_e w_e,$$

$$N' = N'\sum_e{}' w'_e.$$

Applying Lagrange's method of undetermined multipliers as before we are led to

$$\log w_e + \beta U_e + \lambda + 1 = 0, \quad \log w'_e + \beta U'_e + \lambda' + 1 = 0,$$

or

$$w_e = \alpha e^{-\beta U_e}, \quad w'_e = \alpha' e^{-\beta U'_e}. \qquad (96\text{–}3)$$

Here we are dealing with a case where the two substances, even though they may be at different pressures, are in thermal equilibrium and therefore at the same temperature. But the only constant in the two equations (96–3) which is the same for the two substances is β. Therefore β must be a function of the temperature alone.

Finally we shall consider a single substance which is confined in

isolated system 3.)

an adiabatic flexible envelope subject to a constant external pressure p. For equilibrium

$$dS = -\,kN\sum_e(\log w_e + 1)dw_e - kN\frac{\partial}{\partial V}\{\sum_e w_e \log w_e\}dV = 0, \quad (96\text{–}4)$$

$$dU = N\sum_e U_e dw_e + N\frac{\partial}{\partial V}\{\sum_e U_e w_e\}dV = -\,pdV, \quad (96\text{–}5)$$

$$N\sum_e dw_e + N\frac{\partial}{\partial V}\{\sum_e w_e\}dV = 0. \quad (96\text{–}6)$$

Lagrange's method of undetermined multipliers gives us

$$\log w_e + \beta U_e + \lambda + 1 = 0, \quad (96\text{–}7)$$

as before, and in addition the relation

$$N\frac{\partial}{\partial V}\{\sum_e(w_e \log w_e + \beta U_e w_e + \lambda w_e)\} = -\,\beta p. \quad (96\text{–}8)$$

Instead of a static state of equilibrium let us now consider a reversible transformation in which the substance absorbs heat and does external work. We may suppose that such a transformation consists of infinitesimal steps, each of which involves a slight departure from the state of equilibrium followed by reestablishment of equilibrium. Now the increment in S for a small deviation from the state of equilibrium is

$$dS = -\,kN\sum_e(\log w_e + 1)dw_e - kN\frac{\partial}{\partial V}\{\sum_e w_e \log w_e\}dV,$$

where the coefficients of the dw_e's and of dV satisfy (96–7) and (96–8). Therefore

$$\begin{aligned} dS &= kN\sum_e(\beta U_e + \lambda)dw_e + kN\frac{\partial}{\partial V}\{\sum_e(\beta U_e w_e + \lambda w_e)\}dV + k\beta pdV \\ &= k\beta\Big[N\sum_e U_e dw_e + N\frac{\partial}{\partial V}\{\sum_e U_e w_e\}dV\Big] \\ &\quad + k\lambda\Big[N\sum_e dw_e + N\frac{\partial}{\partial V}\{\sum_e w_e\}dV\Big] + k\beta pdV. \end{aligned}$$

The expression in the first brackets is equal to dU by (96–5) and that in the second vanishes by (96–6) since no change in the number of particles takes place during the transformation. Therefore

$$dS = k\beta(dU + pdV).$$

But the principle of conservation of energy requires that

$$dU = \delta Q - pdV.$$

Therefore

$$dS = k\beta\delta Q. \tag{96–9}$$

In this equation k is a universal constant, β a function of the temperature alone, and dS an exact differential in dU and dV. But we know from classical thermodynamics that the only exact differential proportional to a function of the temperature multiplied by δQ is the product of the change in entropy $\delta Q/T$ by an arbitrary constant. For consider an infinitesimal Carnot cycle. If

$$\frac{\delta Q}{T} f(T)$$

is an exact differential

$$\frac{\delta Q_1}{T_1} f(T_1) = \frac{\delta Q_2}{T_2} f(T_2),$$

where the subscript 1 refers to the upper isothermal and 2 to the lower isothermal. But this equation is consistent with

$$\frac{\delta Q_1}{T_1} = \frac{\delta Q_2}{T_2}$$

only if $f(T)$ is a constant. Therefore if the constant k in (96–9) is suitably chosen,

$$\beta = \frac{1}{kT}, \tag{96–10}$$

and dS is the change in entropy. Hence the function S is the entropy of classical thermodynamics to within an additive constant.

If we put (96–10) in (96–2) we find for the probability that the representative point of a particular particle lies in an element of extension-in-phase of energy U_e

$$w_e = \alpha e^{-U_e/kT}. \tag{96–11}$$

when the substance is in the equilibrium state. Therefore the number of particles in this element of extension-in-phase is

$$N_e = Nw_e = N\alpha e^{-U_e/kT}. \tag{96–12}$$

Problem 96a. If a rigid adiabatic box containing a group of particles is in uniform motion relative to the observer's inertial system, we have additional equations of condition expressing the constancy of the three components of linear momentum. Show that the equilibrium condition (96–2) still holds, if we understand by U_e the energy relative to the inertial system of the box.

Problem 96b. A cubic centimeter of air at normal pressure and temperature containing $2(10)^{19}$ molecules is in a state in which w'_e for each element of extension-in-phase differs from the value w_e for the equilibrium state by one tenth of one percent. Find the ratio of the probability W of the equilibrium state to that of the specified state.

Ans. $e^{(10)^{13}} = (10)^{4,342,944,819,032}$

97. Entropy and ψ Function. — Putting (96–11) in (95–5) we find for the entropy of a substance in the equilibrium state

$$S = -kN\sum_e w_e\left(\log\alpha - \frac{U_e}{kT}\right)$$

$$= kN\log\frac{1}{\alpha} + \frac{U}{T},$$

since

$$\sum_e w_e = 1, \quad N\sum_e U_e w_e = U.$$

Now

$$\sum_e w_e = \alpha\sum_e e^{-U_e/kT} = 1,$$

and

$$S = kN\log\sum_e e^{-U_e/kT} + \frac{U}{T}. \tag{97–1}$$

The ψ function is given by the somewhat simpler expression

$$\left.\begin{aligned}\Psi &= U - TS\\ &= -kNT\log\sum_e e^{-U_e/kT}.\end{aligned}\right\} \tag{97–2}$$

We shall now evaluate the definite integral

$$J \equiv \int_0^\infty e^{-x^2}\,dx$$

and related integrals which we shall meet in the next and later articles. Considering x and y as independent variables,

$$J^2 = \int_0^\infty e^{-x^2}\,dx \int_0^\infty e^{-x^2y^2}\,x\,dy = \int_0^\infty\int_0^\infty e^{-x^2(1+y^2)}\,x\,dx\,dy$$

$$= \int_0^\infty dy \int_0^\infty e^{-x^2(1+y^2)}\,x\,dx$$

$$= \frac{1}{2}\int_0^\infty \frac{dy}{1+y^2} = \frac{1}{2}\Big|\tan^{-1}y\Big|_0^\infty = \frac{\pi}{4}.$$

Therefore

$$J = \tfrac{1}{2}\sqrt{\pi}.$$

Also

$$\int_0^\infty e^{-\alpha x^2}\,dx = \frac{1}{\sqrt{\alpha}}\int_0^\infty e^{-\alpha x^2}\,d(\sqrt{\alpha}x) = \frac{1}{2}\sqrt{\frac{\pi}{\alpha}}, \qquad (97\text{–}3)$$

$$\int_{-\infty}^\infty e^{-\alpha x^2}\,dx = 2\int_0^\infty e^{-\alpha x^2}\,dx = \sqrt{\frac{\pi}{\alpha}}. \qquad (97\text{–}4)$$

Differentiate (97–3) with respect to α. Then

$$\int_0^\infty x^2 e^{-\alpha x^2}\,dx = \frac{1}{4}\sqrt{\frac{\pi}{\alpha^3}}, \qquad (97\text{–}5)$$

$$\int_{-\infty}^\infty x^2 e^{-\alpha x^2}\,dx = 2\int_0^\infty x^2 e^{-\alpha x^2}\,dx = \frac{1}{2}\sqrt{\frac{\pi}{\alpha^3}}. \qquad (97\text{–}6)$$

98. Principle of Equipartition of Energy. — Consider a group of particles each of which has f degrees of freedom in a state of thermal equilibrium inside a rigid adiabatic envelope. The kinetic energy T_e of a particle whose representative point lies in the eth element of extension-in-phase is a homogeneous quadratic function of the f generalized momenta $p_{1e}, p_{2e} \ldots p_{fe}$ corresponding to this particular element of extension-in-phase. This homogeneous quadratic function of the p's can always be expressed as a sum of squares by a suitable transformation. However, we shall be concerned only with cases in which the kinetic energy appears as a sum of squares *ab initio*. Therefore we shall write at once

$$T_e = c_1 p_{1e}^2 + c_2 p_{2e}^2 \ldots + c_f p_{fe}^2, \qquad (98\text{–}1)$$

where the c's may be functions of the generalized coordinates $q_1, q_2 \ldots q_f$. We may speak of $c_i p_{ie}^2$, then, as the kinetic energy associated with the ith degree of freedom. In view of (96–2) the energy associated with the ith degree of freedom of all the N_e particles in the eth element of extension-in-phase is

$$N_e c_i p_{ie}^2 = N\alpha e^{-\beta U_e} c_i p_{ie}^2,$$

and the mean kinetic energy associated with this degree of freedom averaged over all the particles in the substance is

$$\overline{T}_i = \frac{N\alpha \sum\limits_e e^{-\beta U_e} c_i p_{ie}^2}{N\alpha \sum\limits_e e^{-\beta U_e}}, \tag{98–2}$$

the denominator of the fraction being merely the total number of particles.

The summation expressed by $\sum\limits_e$ in (98–2) is a multiple sum analogous to a multiple integral. First we sum up over p_1 from $-\infty$ to ∞, then over p_2 between the same limits, and so on for all the p's. Then we sum up over q_1 between limits determined by the volume or other dimensions of the system, over q_2 and the rest of the q's. Let us separate the summation into two parts, designating by $\sum\limits_e{}'$ the summation over all the p's except p_i and over all the q's, and by $\sum\limits_e{}''$ the summation over p_i alone. Since the potential energy is a function of the q's alone, it is clear from (98–1) that $U_e - c_i p_{ie}^2$ does not contain p_{ie}. Therefore we may write (98–2) in the form

$$\overline{T}_i = \frac{\sum\limits_e{}' e^{-\beta(U_e - c_i p_{ie}^2)} \sum\limits_e{}'' e^{-\beta c_i p_{ie}^2} c_i p_{ie}^2}{\sum\limits_e{}' e^{-\beta(U_e - c_i p_{ie}^2)} \sum\limits_e{}'' e^{-\beta c_i p_{ie}^2}}. \tag{98–3}$$

On the classical theory we assume that a particle may have any energy. Therefore the elements of extension-in-phase fill up the whole of the phase space. Moreover it is clear that in order to obtain an accurate description of the state of the substance we should make the elements of extension-in-phase very small. Hence we can replace the sums in (98–3) by integrals. We shall need to do this only with the sum over p_{ie}. Multiplying both numerator and denominator of (98–3) by dp_i we have

$$\overline{T_i} = \frac{\sum_e' e^{-\beta(U_e - c_i p_{ie}^2)} \int_{-\infty}^{\infty} e^{-\beta c_i p_i^2} c_i p_i^2 dp_i}{\sum_e' e^{-\beta(U_e - c_i p_{ie}^2)} \int_{-\infty}^{\infty} e^{-\beta c_i p_i^2} dp_i}.$$

Now

$$\int_{-\infty}^{\infty} e^{-\beta c_i p_i^2} c_i p_i^2 dp_i = \frac{1}{\sqrt{c_i}} \int_{-\infty}^{\infty} e^{-\beta c_i p_i^2} c_i p_i^2 d(\sqrt{c_i} p_i) = \frac{1}{2\sqrt{c_i}} \sqrt{\frac{\pi}{\beta^3}}$$

by (97–6), and

$$\int_{-\infty}^{\infty} e^{-\beta c_i p_i^2} dp_i = \frac{1}{\sqrt{c_i}} \int_{-\infty}^{\infty} e^{-\beta c_i p_i^2} d(\sqrt{c_i} p_i) = \frac{1}{\sqrt{c_i}} \sqrt{\frac{\pi}{\beta}}$$

by (97–4). Therefore, as β is a constant,

$$\overline{T_i} = \frac{1}{2\beta} \frac{\sum_e' e^{-\beta(U_e - c_i p_{ie}^2)} \frac{1}{\sqrt{c_i}}}{\sum_e' e^{-\beta(U_e - c_i p_{ie}^2)} \frac{1}{\sqrt{c_i}}} = \frac{1}{2\beta}. \tag{98–4}$$

Hence, as β is independent of the particular degree of freedom under consideration, the mean kinetic energy associated with every degree of freedom is the same. Writing β in terms of the absolute thermodynamic temperature T in accord with (96–10) we have the *principle of equipartition of energy*:

$$\left. \begin{array}{c} \text{Mean kinetic energy associated} \\ \text{with each degree of freedom} \end{array} \right\} = \tfrac{1}{2} kT. \tag{98–5}$$

We shall see later that k is the gas constant per molecule and equal to 1.380 $(10)^{-16}$ erg/1°C. Equation (98–5) throws a new light on the meaning of temperature. Except for a factor of proportionality which can be made unity by the choice of a degree of suitable size, the absolute thermodynamic temperature of a group of particles in thermal equilibrium is nothing more than the mean kinetic energy associated with each degree of freedom of the particles. Absolute zero is the temperature at which the kinetic energy vanishes and all the particles have come to rest relative to one another.

Consider a solid composed of linear simple harmonic oscillators which are free to take on various energies of oscillation but which are constrained so as to be unable to acquire a velocity of translation.

In article 26 it was shown that the mean potential energy of such an oscillator is equal to the mean kinetic energy. Therefore the mean total energy $\bar{U}$ is twice the mean kinetic energy, or

$$\bar{U} = kT \tag{98–6}$$

in terms of the temperature.

99. Quantum Principle of Partition of Energy. — In this article we shall confine our attention to a group of linear simple harmonic oscillators of frequency ν. As shown in article 26 the energy of such an oscillator is

$$U = \tfrac{1}{2}mv^2 + \tfrac{1}{2}kx^2 = \frac{p^2}{2m} + 2\pi^2 m\nu^2 q^2.$$

Therefore the phase path in the pq representative space is an ellipse of semi-axes

$$a = \sqrt{2mU}, \quad b = \sqrt{\frac{U}{2\pi^2 m\nu^2}},$$

and area

$$A = \pi ab = \frac{U}{\nu}. \tag{99–1}$$

On the quantum theory we assume that an oscillator cannot have any arbitrary energy, but that its energy is limited to a number of discrete values U_1, U_2, etc., the energy of the oscillator passing from one of these values to another by a discontinuous jump. Therefore the elements of extension-in-phase do not fill phase space but are separated from one another by vacant spaces. If we assume the vacant spaces between phase paths to be all of the same area h, then, denoting by U_n the energy associated with the nth phase path,

$$\frac{U_{n+1}}{\nu} - \frac{U_n}{\nu} = h,$$

and, except for a possible additive constant,

$$U_n = nh\nu. \tag{99–2}$$

Therefore the mean energy of an oscillator is

$$\bar{U} = \frac{N\alpha\sum_n e^{-n\beta h\nu}nh\nu}{N\alpha\sum_n e^{-n\beta h\nu}} = h\nu\frac{\sum_n ne^{-n\beta h\nu}}{\sum_n e^{-n\beta h\nu}}. \tag{99–3}$$

Now

$$\sum_{n=0}^{\infty} ne^{-nx} = e^{-x} + 2e^{-2x} + 3e^{-3x} + \ldots$$

$$= e^{-x}\{1 + 2e^{-x} + 3e^{-2x} + \ldots\}$$

$$= \frac{e^{-x}}{(1 - e^{-x})^2} = \frac{1}{(1 - e^{-x})(e^{x} - 1)},$$

$$\sum_{n=0}^{\infty} e^{-nx} = 1 + e^{-x} + e^{-2x} + \ldots = \frac{1}{1 - e^{-x}}.$$

So (99–3) becomes

$$\bar{U} = \frac{h\nu}{e^{\beta h\nu} - 1},$$

or, in terms of the absolute thermodynamic temperature T,

$$\bar{U} = \frac{h\nu}{e^{h\nu/kT} - 1}. \qquad (99\text{–}4)$$

Unlike the corresponding expression (98–6) on the classical theory, here the mean energy depends upon the frequency of the oscillators as well as upon the temperature of the group. At very high temperatures or very low frequencies

$$e^{h\nu/kT} - 1 = \left(1 + \frac{h\nu}{kT} + \ldots\right) - 1 = \frac{h\nu}{kT}$$

to a sufficient degree of approximation and (99–4) reduces to the classical expression (98–6).

We shall return to the results of this and the previous article when we take up the study of radiation in chapter XII.

REFERENCES

Planck, Max: *The Theory of Heat Radiation*, P. Blakiston's Son & Co., Philadelphia.

Gibbs, J. W.: *Collected Works*, Vol. II, *Statistical Mechanics*, Longmans, Green & Co., New York.

CHAPTER IX

KINETIC THEORY OF GASES

100. Ideal Monatomic Gas. — From the point of view of the kinetic theory we define an ideal gas as one in which (*a*) there are no forces between molecules, (*b*) the molecules fill no appreciable portion of the space occupied by the gas. If in addition the gas is monatomic the molecules may be treated as mathematical points incapable of rotation. The only degrees of freedom they possess are the three associated with motion of translation.

We wish to calculate the ψ function for an ideal monatomic gas from (97–2) using the classical theory. Denoting the mass of a molecule by m we have

$$U_e = \tfrac{1}{2}m(\dot{x}^2 + \dot{y}^2 + \dot{z}^2) = \frac{1}{2m}(p_x^2 + p_y^2 + p_z^2),$$

since there are no forces between molecules and consequently the energy is entirely kinetic. If g denotes the size of an element of extension-in-phase,

$$g = dp_x\, dp_y\, dp_z\, dx\, dy\, dz,$$

for the space projection of the phase space coincides with the volume V occupied by the gas since no appreciable portion of this volume is actually filled by the gas molecules themselves. Therefore

$$\sum_e e^{-U_e/kT} = \frac{1}{g}\int\!\!\int\!\!\int\!\!\int\!\!\int\!\!\int e^{-\frac{p_x^2+p_y^2+p_z^2}{2mkT}}\, dp_x\, dp_y\, dp_z\, dx\, dy\, dz$$

$$= \frac{1}{g}\int_{-\infty}^{\infty} e^{-\frac{p_x^2}{2mkT}}dp_x \int_{-\infty}^{\infty} e^{-\frac{p_y^2}{2mkT}}dp_y \int_{-\infty}^{\infty} e^{-\frac{p_z^2}{2mkT}}dp_z \int\!\!\int\!\!\int dx\, dy\, dz$$

$$= \frac{V}{g}(2\pi mkT)^{3/2}$$

by (97–4), and

$$\Psi = -kNT\log\left\{\frac{V}{g}(2\pi mkT)^{3/2}\right\} \qquad (100\text{–}1)$$

from (97–2). Hence, remembering that the capital letters we are using here refer to the entire mass of gas, equations (87–5) give us for the pressure

$$p = -\left(\frac{\partial \Psi}{\partial V}\right)_T = \frac{kNT}{V},$$

or

$$pV = kNT, \tag{100–2}$$

and for the intrinsic energy of the gas

$$\left.\begin{aligned} U &= \Psi + TS = \Psi - T\left(\frac{\partial \Psi}{\partial T}\right)_V \\ &= \tfrac{3}{2}kNT. \end{aligned}\right\} \tag{100–3}$$

The first of these equations is the gas law (89–4). Since k is a universal constant the same for all gases, (100–2) also expresses Avogadro's law that equal volumes of different gases at the same pressure and temperature contain equal numbers of molecules. The second equation accords with Joule's law that the intrinsic energy is a function of the temperature alone, although it is more specific in that it shows that the intrinsic energy is directly proportional to the absolute thermodynamic temperature. Equation (100–3) might have been obtained directly from the principle of equipartition of energy. For as each molecule has three degrees of freedom the mean kinetic energy of a molecule is $\tfrac{3}{2}kT$ and that of the entire assemblage of molecules $\tfrac{3}{2}kNT$. This is the total energy since the molecules have no potential energy on account of the absence of inter-molecular forces.

If we write n for the number of molecules per unit mass equations (100–2) and (100–3) may be referred to a unit mass of the gas in the forms

$$pv = knT, \tag{100–4}$$

$$u = \tfrac{3}{2}knT. \tag{100–5}$$

Comparing the first with (89–4) we see that

$$R = kn. \tag{100–6}$$

Therefore k is the gas constant per molecule. To get the specific heats of an ideal monatomic gas we have

$$c_v = \left(\frac{\partial u}{\partial T}\right)_v = \frac{3}{2} kn = \frac{3}{2} R,$$

$$c_p = c_v + R = \frac{5}{2} R,$$

showing that the specific heats are constants. The ratio of the specific heats is

$$\gamma = \frac{c_p}{c_v} = \frac{5}{3} = 1.667.$$

Experiment gives the following values of γ at room temperature for the monatomic gases listed in the table.

Gas	γ Observed
Mercury Vapor............	1.666
Argon....................	1.667
Krypton..................	1.666
Helium...................	1.652

These agree very well with the theoretical value. At low temperatures diatomic gases act like monatomic gases, the value of c_v for both being equal to $3/2R$.

101. Ideal Polyatomic Gas. — The molecule of this gas differs from that of a monatomic gas in that it may have other degrees of freedom in addition to the three associated with motion of translation. Let U'_e denote the translatory energy of a molecule whose representative point lies in the eth element of extension-in-phase and U''_e the internal energy associated with the other degrees of freedom. Then as there are no inter-molecular forces or associated potential energy

$$U'_e = \frac{1}{2m} (p_x^2 + p_y^2 + p_z^2),$$

as in the case of a monatomic gas, and the projection of an element of extension-in-phase on the p_x, p_y, p_z, x, y, z space is

$$g' = dp_x \, dp_y \, dp_z \, dx \, dy \, dz.$$

Therefore

$$\sum_e e^{-U_e/kT} = \sum_e{}' e^{-U'_e/kT} \sum_e{}'' e^{-U''_e/kT}$$

$$= \frac{V}{g'} (2\pi mkT)^{3/2} \sum_e{}'' e^{-U''_e/kT},$$

just as in the case of a monatomic gas. Hence

$$\psi = -kNT \log \left\{ \frac{V}{g'} (2\pi mkT)^{3/2} \right\} - kNT \log \sum_e{}'' e^{-U''_e/kT}. \qquad (101\text{–}1)$$

The second term, though it contains the temperature, is not a function of the volume. Therefore

$$p = -\left(\frac{\partial \psi}{\partial V}\right)_T = \frac{kNT}{V},$$

or

$$pV = kNT, \qquad (101\text{–}2)$$

and the gas law and Avogadro's law hold in the same form as in the case of a monatomic gas.

The intrinsic energy is obtained most easily from the principle of equipartition of energy. If we assume the energy to be entirely kinetic and denote by ν the number of internal degrees of freedom

minimum for x, y, z coord.

$$U = \frac{3+\nu}{2} kNT. \qquad (101\text{–}3)$$

Referred to a unit mass (101–2) and (101–3) become

$$pv = knT, \qquad (101\text{–}4)$$

$$u = \frac{3+\nu}{2} knT. \qquad (101\text{–}5)$$

As before $R = kn$ and

$$\left.\begin{aligned} c_v &= \frac{3+\nu}{2} kn = \frac{3+\nu}{2} R, \\ c_p &= \frac{5+\nu}{2} kn = \frac{5+\nu}{2} R, \\ \gamma &= \frac{5+\nu}{3+\nu} = 1 + \frac{2}{3+\nu}. \end{aligned}\right\} \qquad (101\text{–}6)$$

The greater the number of degrees of freedom the smaller γ becomes, approaching unity as a limit.

In the case of a diatomic molecule two degrees of freedom of rotation about axes perpendicular to the line joining the two atoms would be expected in addition to the three degrees of freedom of translatory motion. Therefore $\nu = 2$ and $\gamma = 1.400$. In the following table are shown measured values of γ at room temperature for some diatomic gases:

Gas	γ Observed	Gas	γ Observed
Air	1.401	O_2	1.400
H_2	1.41	CO	1.401
N_2	1.41	NO	1.394

For gases with more than two atoms to the molecule this simple theory does not give results agreeing so well with experiment.

No matter how complicated the structure of the molecule, the kinetic energy of translation of the N molecules constituting an ideal gas is $3/2\ kNT$. So if we denote by G the square root of the mean value of the square of the velocity of a molecule, and by M the mass of gas under consideration,

$$\tfrac{1}{2}MG^2 = \tfrac{3}{2}kNT. \tag{101–7}$$

Therefore (101–2) may be written

$$pV = \tfrac{1}{3}MG^2,$$

or if ρ is the density of the gas

$$p = \tfrac{1}{3}\rho G^2. \tag{101–8}$$

This equation shows that the root-mean-square velocity G at a specified pressure varies inversely with the square root of the density. From (101–8) G may be calculated if the density is known.

Problem 101a. Show that the gas constant R referred to a gram-molecule, that is, a number of grams equal to the molecular weight, is the same for all gases, and calculate this constant if the specific volume of nitrogen (molecular weight 28) is 800.4 cm³/gm at 0° C. and 1 atmos. pressure. *Ans.* $8.316(10)^7$ erg/1° C.

Problem 101b. Calculate c_p for argon (molecular weight 39.9) and nitrogen and compare with the experimental values 0.123 cal/gm 1° C. for argon and 0.235 cal/gm 1° C. for nitrogen. *Ans.* 0.125 and 0.248.

Problem 101c. From the value $4.803(10)^{-10}$ e.s.u. for the electronic charge and Faraday's constant 96490 coulombs per gram-equivalent calculate the number A of molecules per gram-molecule (Avogadro's constant) and the number L of molecules per cm^3 of an ideal gas at 0° C. and a pressure of 1 atmos. (Loschmidt's constant). From Avogadro's constant calculate the value of k. *Ans.* $A = 6.02(10)^{23}$ molecules/gm-molecule, $L = 2.69(10)^{19}$ molecules/cm^3, $k = 1.38(10)^{-16}$ erg/1° C.

Problem 101d. Compute the mass of a hydrogen atom. The density of hydrogen at 0° C. and 1 atmos. pressure is 0.0899 gm/liter. *Ans.* $1.65(10)^{-24}$ gm.

Problem 101e. Find the root-mean-square velocity G of the hydrogen molecule at 0° C. and 1 atmos. pressure and explain why so little hydrogen is found in the earth's atmosphere. *Ans.* 1.14 mi/sec.

102. Maxwell's Law of Distribution of Molecular Velocities. — If we express the energy U_e of a molecule of an ideal gas as the sum of the kinetic energy of translation U'_e and the internal energy U''_e, the mathematical probability that its representative point lies in the eth element of extension-in-phase is

$$w_e = \alpha e^{-U''_e/kT} e^{-U'_e/kT}.$$

Denoting the projection of an element of extension-in-phase on the p_x, p_y, p_z space by $g'_p = dp_x dp_y dp_z = m^3 dv_x dv_y dv_z$ and replacing U'_e by $\frac{1}{2}mv^2$,

$$w_e = \frac{m^3\alpha}{g'_p} e^{-U''_e/kT} e^{-mv^2/2kT} dv_x dv_y dv_z.$$

To find the probability w'_e that the molecule has a velocity whose components lie between v_x and $v_x + dv_x$, v_y and $v_y + dv_y$, v_z and $v_z + dv_z$, whatever its internal energy may be, we must sum up over all dimensions in phase space except those corresponding to v_x, v_y, v_z. Denoting this summation by a double accent

$$w'_e = \left\{ \frac{m^3\alpha}{g'_p} \sum_e{}'' e^{-U''_e/kT} \right\} e^{-mv^2/2kT} dv_x dv_y dv_z,$$

and if the constant inside the braces is denoted by α'

$$w'_e = \alpha' e^{-mv^2/2kT} dv_x dv_y dv_z.$$

To find the value of α' we have

$$\sum_e{}' w'_e = \alpha' \int_{-\infty}^{\infty} e^{-mv_x^2/2kT} dv_x \int_{-\infty}^{\infty} e^{-mv_y^2/2kT} dv_y \int_{-\infty}^{\infty} e^{-mv_z^2/2kT} dv_z = 1.$$

Using (97–4)

$$\alpha' = \left(\frac{m}{2\pi kT}\right)^{3/2},$$

and

$$w_e' = \left(\frac{m}{2\pi kT}\right)^{3/2} e^{-mv^2/2kT}\, dv_x dv_y dv_z.$$

Therefore the number of molecules with velocities whose components lie between v_x and $v_x + dv_x$, v_y and $v_y + dv_y$, v_z and $v_z + dv_z$ is

$$dN = N\left(\frac{m}{2\pi kT}\right)^{3/2} e^{-mv^2/2kT}\, dv_x dv_y dv_z. \qquad (102\text{–}1)$$

This is *Maxwell's law*. It may be written in two additional forms. In terms of the mean kinetic energy $\overline{U}$ of translation of a single molecule

$$dN = N\left(\frac{3m}{4\pi \overline{J}}\right)^{3/2} e^{-3mv^2/4\overline{U}}\, dv_x dv_y dv_z, \qquad (102\text{–}2)$$

from the principle of equipartition of energy, and if we put

$$h \equiv \frac{3}{4\overline{U}} = \frac{1}{2kT}, \qquad (102\text{–}3)$$

then

$$dN = N\left(\frac{hm}{\pi}\right)^{3/2} e^{-hmv^2}\, dv_x dv_y dv_z. \qquad (102\text{–}4)$$

Evidently h, like T and $\overline{U}$, is the same for all gases in equilibrium with one another.

If we keep v_y and v_z constant and allow v_x alone to vary

$$dN = Ae^{-hmv_x^2} dv_x,$$

where A is a constant. Plotting $\frac{dN}{dv_x}$, the number of molecules per unit range of the velocity component v_x, against v_x, we get the well-known error curve depicted in Fig. 102. It is symmetrical with respect to the axis of ordinates and approaches the axis of abscissae asymptotically in both directions. It is clear from the graph that for any assigned values of v_y and v_z more molecules have an X component of velocity equal to zero than equal to any other value.

Next let us find the number of molecules having speeds between

v and $v + dv$ irrespective of direction. To do this we must replace the element of volume $dv_x dv_y dv_z$ of the v_x, v_y, v_z representative space

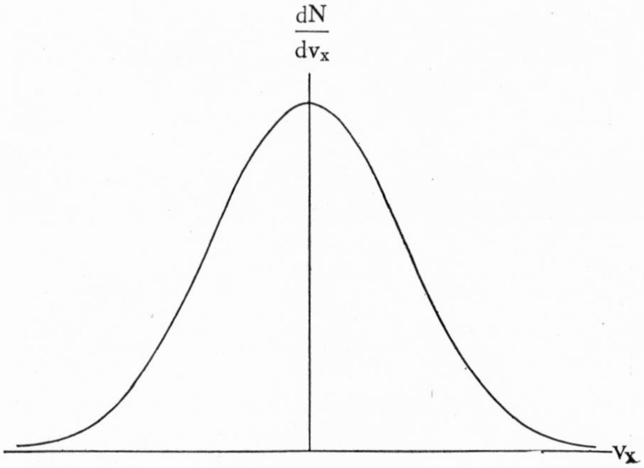

FIG. 102.

by the volume included between spheres of radii v and $v + dv$, that is, by $4\pi v^2 dv$. Therefore (102–4) becomes

$$dN = 4N\sqrt{\frac{h^3m^3}{\pi}}\, e^{-hmv^2}\, v^2 dv. \qquad (102\text{–}5)$$

To find the arithmetic mean speed Ω,

$$\left.\begin{aligned} \Omega &= \frac{1}{N}\int_0^\infty v\,dN = 4\sqrt{\frac{h^3m^3}{\pi}}\int_0^\infty e^{-hmv^2}\, v^3 dv \\ &= 2\sqrt{\frac{h^3m^3}{\pi}}\int_0^\infty e^{-hmx}\, x\,dx = \frac{2}{\sqrt{\pi hm}}. \end{aligned}\right\} \qquad (102\text{–}6)$$

The most probable speed W is that which a specified molecule is most likely to possess. As the probability that a molecule has a speed between v and $v + dv$ is

$$w = \frac{dN}{N} = 4\sqrt{\frac{h^3m^3}{\pi}}\, e^{-hmv^2}\, v^2 dv,$$

the condition for maximum w is

$$\frac{dw}{dv} = 4\sqrt{\frac{h^3m^3}{\pi}}\left\{-\, hmv^2 e^{-hmv^2} + e^{-hmv^2}\right\} dv = 0$$

and

$$W = \frac{1}{\sqrt{hm}}. \qquad (102\text{–}7)$$

Figure 103 shows the curve obtained by plotting $\frac{dN}{dv}$ against v in (102–5). The most probable speed W comes at the highest point of the curve, the arithmetic mean speed Ω a little farther out, and the

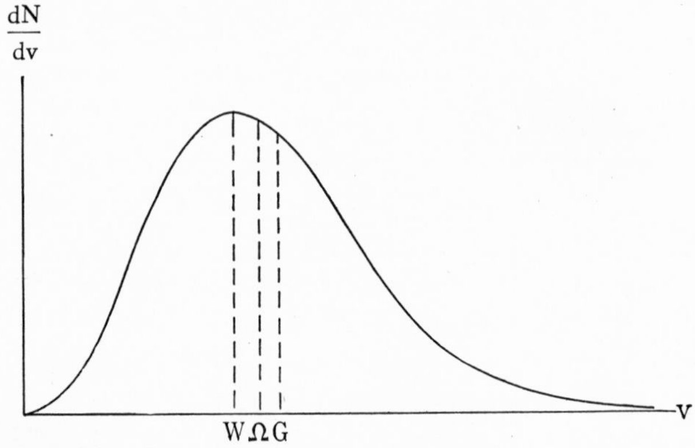

FIG. 103.

root-mean-square speed G still farther out. The curve has zero ordinate at the origin, and after passing through its maximum it comes down asymptotically to the v axis.

Each of the three speeds indicated on the curve may be expressed in terms of T, $\bar{U}$ or h. From (101–7) and (102–3)

$$G = \sqrt{\frac{3kT}{m}} = \sqrt{\frac{2\bar{U}}{m}} = \sqrt{\frac{3}{2hm}}, \qquad (102\text{–}8)$$

and similarly

$$\Omega = 4\sqrt{\frac{kT}{2\pi m}} = 4\sqrt{\frac{\bar{U}}{3\pi m}} = \frac{2}{\sqrt{\pi hm}}, \qquad (102\text{–}9)$$

$$W = 2\sqrt{\frac{kT}{2m}} = 2\sqrt{\frac{\bar{U}}{3m}} = \frac{1}{\sqrt{hm}}. \qquad (102\text{–}10)$$

Therefore

$$W : \Omega : G = \sqrt{\frac{2}{3}} : \sqrt{\frac{8}{3\pi}} : 1 = 0.8165 : 0.9213 : 1.$$

For air, oxygen, nitrogen, hydrogen at 0° C. G, Ω, W in meters per second are:

	G	Ω	W
Air	484.9	446.7	395.9
O_2	461.2	424.9	376.6
N_2	491.7	453.0	401.4
H_2	1838.2	1693.6	1500.9

Problem 102a. Given 1000 molecules of hydrogen in thermal equilibrium at 0° C. find the number with speeds between 0 and 500 meter/sec, 500 and 1000 meter/sec, 1000 and 1500 meter/sec, 1500 and 2000 meter/sec, 2000 and 2500 meter/sec, 2500 and 3000 meter/sec, 3000 and 3500 meter/sec, 3500 and 4000 meter/sec, above 4000 meter/sec. *Ans.* 26, 147, 256, 260, 180, 88, 32, 9, 2.

Problem 102b. If a gas is in motion as a whole relative to the observer's inertial system, show from the result of problem 96*a* that the velocity appearing in Maxwell's law must be replaced by the velocity relative to the center of mass.

103. Collision Frequency and Mean Free Path. — In discussing collisions we shall treat the molecules of a gas as if they were spheres of radius a. Then if the center of a molecule comes within a distance $s = 2a$ of the center of another molecule the two will collide. In the equilibrium state the collisions between molecules must, on the whole, be elastic; for if they were inelastic, energy would be transferred at collisions from the degrees of freedom of translatory motion to the internal degrees of freedom in contradiction to the principle of equipartition of energy.

The sphere of radius s described about the center of a molecule is known as its *sphere of influence*. If the molecule is moving with velocity v its sphere of influence describes a cylinder of volume $\pi s^2 vt$ in a time t. Provided they are at rest, all other molecules whose centers lie within this cylinder will be struck by the molecule under consideration. If, however, the molecules collided with are in motion, we have to consider the cylinder described by the original molecule due to its velocity relative to the molecules which are struck. If we denote the velocity of the first molecule by v and confine our attention to collisions with molecules having the velocity v', the relative velocity V is

$$V = \sqrt{(v_x - v'_x)^2 + (v_y - v'_y)^2 + (v_z - v'_z)^2},$$

and the molecules struck in a time t are those whose centers lie in a cylinder of volume $\pi s^2 V t$.

Following Clausius we shall treat the molecules as if they were all moving with the arithmetic mean speed Ω. Then if the original molecule is moving in the X direction

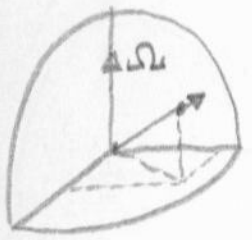

$$v_x = \Omega, \quad v_y = 0, \quad v_z = 0,$$

and using spherical coordinates with polar axis along X, the components of velocity of the molecules collided with are

$$v'_x = \Omega \cos\theta, \quad v'_y = \Omega \sin\theta \cos\phi, \quad v'_z = \Omega \sin\theta \sin\phi.$$

Therefore

$$V = \Omega\sqrt{(1 - \cos\theta)^2 + \sin^2\theta\cos^2\phi + \sin^2\theta\sin^2\phi} = 2\Omega\sin\theta/2,$$

and the volume of the cylinder described by the sphere of influence due to the relative velocity is

$$\pi s^2 V t = 2\pi s^2 \Omega \sin\theta/2 \cdot t.$$

If n is the number of molecules per unit volume, the number whose velocities make angles between θ and $\theta + d\theta$ with the X axis is

$$dn = \tfrac{1}{2} n \sin\theta d\theta,$$

and the number of collisions $d\Gamma$ per unit time with this species of molecule is

$$d\Gamma = \pi s^2 V dn = \pi n s^2 \Omega \sin\theta/2 \sin\theta d\theta.$$

Summing up over θ the total number of collisions made by a single molecule per unit time is on the average

$$\left.\begin{aligned}\Gamma &= \pi n s^2 \Omega \int_0^\pi \sin\theta/2 \sin\theta d\theta = 4\pi n s^2 \Omega \int_0^\pi \sin^2\theta/2 \cos\theta/2\, d\theta/2 \\ &= \tfrac{4}{3}\pi n s^2 \Omega = 1.33\pi n s^2 \Omega.\end{aligned}\right\} \quad (103\text{–}1)$$

In obtaining this result we have not taken into account any deviation of the original molecule from its initial path due to collisions with other molecules. No apprehension need be felt on this score, however, since for every molecule which is knocked out of a given course by collision another molecule is thrown into this course. Therefore the resultant effect is the same for the average molecule as if it had continued undeviated in its initial path.

Assuming that each collision involves two molecules only, the total number of collisions per second per unit volume is

$$\frac{n\Gamma}{2} = \frac{2}{3}\pi n^2 s^2 \Omega. \qquad (103\text{–}2)$$

A more rigorous calculation of the collision frequency, based on Maxwell's law of distribution of velocities, gives

$$\Gamma = \sqrt{2}\pi n s^2 \Omega = 1.41\pi n s^2 \Omega \qquad (103\text{–}3)$$

in place of (103–1).

As there are no attractions or repulsions between the molecules of an ideal gas, each molecule moves in a straight line between collisions. Therefore the path of a particular molecule is a broken line. The *mean free path* l is defined as the average distance between collisions. If, then, $l_1, l_2, l_3, \ldots l_f$ are successive free paths described in a long time t,

$$l = \frac{l_1 + l_2 + l_3 \ldots + l_f}{f} = \frac{\Omega t}{\Gamma t} = \frac{\Omega}{\Gamma},$$

since the speed of a single molecule averaged over a long period of time is equal to the average speed of a large number of molecules at a single instant. Therefore

$$l = \frac{3}{4\pi n s^2} \qquad (103\text{–}4)$$

if we make use of (103–1), or

$$l = \frac{1}{\sqrt{2}\pi n s^2} \qquad (103\text{–}5)$$

if we use the more accurate expression (103–3). As means for computing the number of molecules n per unit volume have already been described, we can calculate s from this formula and thence the radius of the molecule provided we find a method of determining the mean free path l. We shall see in the next article that l may be obtained from measurements of the viscosity of a gas.

Let us now find the probability that a molecule may travel a distance between x and $x + dx$ before making a collision. Let $e^{-\alpha}$ be the probability that a molecule may travel a unit distance without collision. Then $e^{-2\alpha}$ is the probability that it will travel two units distance, and $e^{-\alpha x}$ the probability that it will travel a distance x without collision.

Consider N molecules starting out together. Then $Ne^{-\alpha x}$ go a distance x without collision, and $Ne^{-\alpha(x+dx)}$ a distance $x + dx$. Therefore those that collide after traversing a distance between x and $x + dx$ number

$$Ne^{-\alpha x} - Ne^{-\alpha(x+dx)} = Ne^{-\alpha x}\, \alpha dx.$$

The total distance traversed by the N molecules together before collision is

$$N\int_0^\infty e^{-\alpha x}\, \alpha x dx = \frac{N}{\alpha},$$

and the average distance covered by a single molecule between successive collisions is $1/\alpha$. But this is just the mean free path l. Therefore the number of molecules which suffer a collision after a free path of length between x and $x + dx$ is

$$Ne^{-\alpha x}\, \alpha dx = Ne^{-x/l}\frac{dx}{l}, \tag{103-6}$$

and the probability of an individual molecule having a free path between x and $x + dx$ is

$$e^{-\alpha x}\, \alpha dx = e^{-x/l}\frac{dx}{l}. \tag{103-7}$$

Furthermore the probability of a molecule having a free path equal to or greater than x is

$$e^{-\alpha x} = e^{-x/l}. \tag{103-8}$$

104. Coefficient of Viscosity. — Consider a gas streaming in the X direction in such a manner that different layers have different velocities as in the case of the fluid illustrated in Fig. 86. The shearing stress X_y is given by

$$X_y = \mu\frac{\partial v_x}{\partial y}, \tag{104-1}$$

where μ is the coefficient of viscosity. We explain the viscosity of a gas as due to the passage of the faster moving molecules in the upper layers down into the lower layers which are thereby accelerated, and to the passage of the slower moving molecules in the lower layers up into the upper layers which are thereby retarded.

We shall assume the thermal velocities of all the molecules to be the same and equal to the arithmetic mean velocity Ω just as in our calculation of the collision frequency Γ. If we direct our attention to two layers of the gas a distance y apart, the molecules in the lower layer have the translational velocity v_x superposed on the thermal velocity Ω, while those in the upper layer have the translational velocity $v_x + \frac{\partial v_x}{\partial y} y$. We shall assume that v_x is very small compared with Ω.

Take origin at the center of the unit area perpendicular to the Y axis on which we wish to calculate the shearing stress (Fig. 104), and consider the molecules whose free paths originate in the volume element $dx\ dy\ dz$ at P. If n denotes the number of molecules per unit volume, there are $n\ dx\ dy\ dz$ molecules inside this element of volume, and these make $\Gamma n\ dx\ dy\ dz$ collisions per unit time. Therefore in each unit of time $\Gamma n\ dx\ dy\ dz$ molecules start out on a fresh free path, and of these $e^{-r/l}\ \Gamma n\ dx\ dy\ dz$ travel a distance $r = PO$ before making a collision. As the unit area at O subtends a solid angle $\cos\theta/r^2$ at P, only $\cos\theta/(4\pi r^2)$ of these molecules are directed so as to pass through the unit area at O. Consequently a number

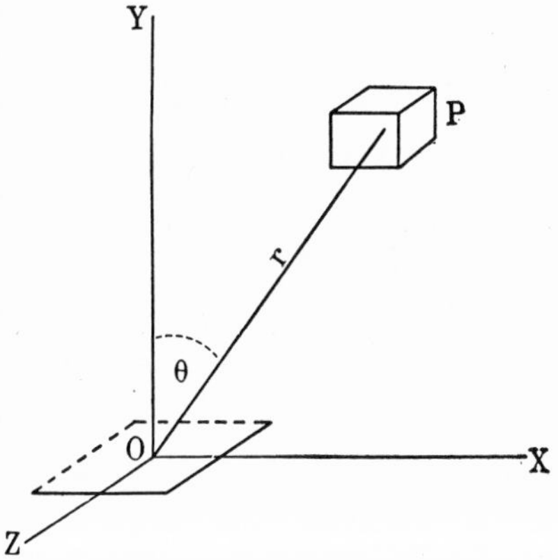

FIG. 104.

$$\frac{dN}{dt} = \frac{\Gamma n}{4\pi r^2} e^{-r/l} \cos\theta\ dx\ dy\ dz \qquad (104\text{–}2)$$

of molecules whose free paths originate in the volume element at P pass through the unit area at O per unit time.

Now if dM/dt is the aggregate mass of these molecules, the force necessary to reduce their translational velocity to that of the gas in the layer at $y = 0$ is

$$F_x = \frac{dM}{dt}\left\{v_x - \left(v_x + \frac{\partial v_x}{\partial y} y\right)\right\} = -\frac{dM}{dt}\frac{\partial v_x}{\partial y} r\cos\theta$$

from (35–4), and the equal reaction on the gas below the XZ plane is

$$dX_y = \frac{dM}{dt}\frac{\partial v_x}{\partial y} r\cos\theta.$$

If m is the mass of a single molecule

$$\frac{dM}{dt} = m\frac{dN}{dt} = \frac{\Gamma nm}{4\pi r^2} e^{-r/l} \cos\theta \cdot 2\pi r^2 \sin\theta d\theta\, dr$$

from (104–2), where we have replaced $dx\,dy\,dz$ by the volume $2\pi r^2 \sin\theta d\theta dr$ of an annular element. Consequently

$$X_y = \tfrac{1}{2}\Gamma nm \frac{\partial v_x}{\partial y}\int_0^\infty e^{-r/l}\, rdr \int_0^\pi \cos^2\theta \sin\theta d\theta$$

$$= \tfrac{1}{3}\Gamma nml^2 \frac{\partial v_x}{\partial y}.$$

As $\Omega = \Gamma l$ this equation may be written

$$X_y = \tfrac{1}{3}nm\Omega l \frac{\partial v_x}{\partial y}. \qquad (104\text{–}3)$$

Comparing with (104–1) we see that the coefficient of viscosity is

$$\mu = \tfrac{1}{3}\rho\Omega l, \qquad (104\text{–}4)$$

since nm is the density ρ. A more exact calculation, based on Maxwell's law of distribution of molecular velocities, gives

$$\mu = 0.30967\rho\Omega l. \qquad (104\text{–}5)$$

As the coefficient of viscosity can be measured by the methods discussed in chapter VI the mean free path l can be computed from these equations and once it is known the molecular radius can be calculated from (103–4) or (103–5). If we eliminate l from (103–4) and (104–4) we get

$$\mu = \frac{\rho\Omega}{4\pi n s^2} = \frac{m\Omega}{4\pi s^2}. \qquad (104\text{–}6)$$

Now Ω, like G, depends only on the temperature. So we reach the remarkable conclusion that the coefficient of viscosity of a gas is independent of the pressure, a result which is well verified by experiment. This fact was first pointed out by Maxwell, who showed by measurements on the viscosity of air that μ is constant for pressures ranging from one-sixtieth of an atmosphere to one atmosphere. Since G and therefore Ω varies with the square root of the absolute temperature, the coefficient of viscosity is proportional to $\sqrt{T}$.

If we solve (104–6) for s we get

$$s = \sqrt{\frac{\rho\Omega}{4\pi n\mu}} = \sqrt{\frac{0.250\rho\Omega}{\pi n\mu}}, \qquad (104\text{–}7)$$

or using the more exact formulae (103–5) and (104–5) based on Maxwell's law

$$s = \sqrt{\frac{0.30967\rho\Omega}{\sqrt{2}\pi n\mu}} = \sqrt{\frac{0.219\rho\Omega}{\pi n\mu}}, \qquad (104\text{–}8)$$

which differs very little from (104–7). Below is a table of measured coefficients of viscosity at 0° C. and molecular radii a computed from a formula differing slightly from (104–8) in that it takes into account the persistence of translatory velocity as well as the Maxwellian distribution of thermal velocities.

Gas	μ Observed, 0° C.	$a = \frac{1}{2}s$ Calculated
H_2	0.0000864	1.23 $(10)^{-8}$ cm
He	0.000188	1.09
H_2O	0.000090	2.04
N_2	0.000166	1.75
Air	0.000171	1.73
CO_2	0.000139	2.09

It is seen that the molecular radii of simple inorganic molecules differ very little one from another, ranging in value from about $(10)^{-8}$ cm to about $2(10)^{-8}$ cm.

Problem 104a. Calculate from the results of the approximate theory developed in the preceding articles the mean free path l and the collision frequency Γ of the hydrogen molecule at 0° C. at (*a*) one atmosphere pressure, (*b*) a pressure of 1 mm of mercury. *Ans.* (*a*) $1.70(10)^{-5}$ cm, $1.00(10)^{10}$/sec. (*b*) $1.28(10)^{-2}$ cm, $1.31(10)^{7}$/sec.

Problem 104 b. Calculate the radius of the hydrogen molecule.

105. Thermal Transpiration. — Consider a gas in a box divided into two parts by a horizontal rigid adiabatic partition containing a small hole. We want to investigate the quasi-equilibrium existing when the upper compartment is maintained at a temperature T_1 and the lower compartment at a different temperature T_2.

For a steady state to exist, the number of molecules passing through the hole in the partition from above to below per unit time must equal the number passing from below to above. If, for simplicity, we take the area of the hole as unity and differentiate the gases in the upper and lower compartments by the subscripts 1 and 2, we have for the first number

$$\frac{dN_1}{dt} = \frac{\Gamma_1 n_1}{2}\int_0^\infty e^{-r/l_1}\,dr\int_0^{\pi/2}\cos\theta\sin\theta d\theta = \tfrac{1}{4}\Gamma_1 n_1 l_1 = \tfrac{1}{4}n_1\Omega_1$$

from (104–2), the volume element $dx\,dy\,dz$ having been replaced by $2\pi r^2 \sin\theta d\theta dr$.

As n_1 represents the number of molecules per unit volume, the gas law (101–4) becomes

$$n_1 = \frac{p_1}{kT_1},$$

and from (102–9)

$$\Omega_1 = 4\sqrt{\frac{kT_1}{2\pi m}}.$$

Therefore

$$\frac{dN_1}{dt} = \frac{1}{\sqrt{2\pi mk}}\frac{p_1}{\sqrt{T_1}}. \qquad (105\text{–}1)$$

As a similar expression holds for the equal number of molecules of the gas in the lower compartment which pass through the hole per unit time,

$$\frac{p_1}{p_2} = \sqrt{\frac{T_1}{T_2}} \qquad (105\text{–}2)$$

in the steady state. As the density ρ of a gas is proportional to p/T we have also

$$\frac{\rho_1}{\rho_2} = \sqrt{\frac{T_2}{T_1}}. \qquad (105\text{–}3)$$

An interesting application is to the free electrons in a metallic conductor the ends of which are maintained at different temperatures. Evidently the pressure of the electron gas at the hotter end is greater than that at the cooler end, whereas the density is less. Therefore the hotter end should be charged positively and the cooler end negatively, indicating the presence of an electromotive force in the conductor directed from the end at lower temperature toward that at higher temperature. This phenomenon, first predicted by Thomson (Lord Kelvin), is known as the *Thomson effect.*

Problem 105a. Find the heat transferred per unit time per unit area of the hole in the partition.

$$\textit{Ans.}\ c_v \sqrt{\frac{m}{2\pi k}} \frac{p_1}{\sqrt{T_1}} (T_1 - T_2).$$

106. Radius of Molecule from Van der Waals' Equation. — The radius of the molecule may be determined from the constant b in Van der Waals' equation (92–1). This constant represents the portion of the volume occupied by the gas which has to be excluded from phase space on account of the size of the molecule. We shall find the relation between it and the radius a of the molecule on the assumption that simultaneous collisions of three or four molecules are so rare that we make no appreciable error in proceeding as if all collisions occur between two molecules alone. If two molecules collide, their centers get no nearer than the distance $2a$. So a space $\frac{4}{3}\pi(2a)^3 = \frac{32}{3}\pi a^3$ must be omitted from the volume v on account of a pair of colliding molecules, or $\frac{16}{3}\pi a^3$ for each molecule. Therefore, if N is the number of molecules in a volume v,

$$b = \frac{16}{3}\pi a^3 N, \tag{106–1}$$

which is four times the space actually filled by the N molecules. As b can be determined from data on the critical point and N is known a may be calculated.

In addition to the methods heretofore described an upper limit to the radius of the molecule may be obtained from the maximum density assumed by the substance of which it is a part. For the quotient of the specific volume by the number of molecules in a unit mass gives an upper limit to the volume of the molecule. Finally the molecular volume can be calculated from the specific inductive capacity of a dielectric. All these methods give fairly concordant results. For the purpose of comparison the molecular radii of three gases computed from the coefficient of viscosity μ, Van der Waal's constant b and the limiting density ρ are tabulated below.

Gas	*a* from μ	*a* from *b*	*a* from ρ
H_2	1.23 $(10)^{-8}$ cm	1.16 $(10)^{-8}$ cm	1.96 $(10)^{-8}$ cm
N_2	1.75	1.76	1.48
CO_2	2.09	1.70	2.21

REFERENCES

MEYER, O. E.: *The Kinetic Theory of Gases*, Longmans, Green & Co., London.
JEANS, J. H.: *The Dynamical Theory of Gases*, Cambridge University Press, Cambridge.

Part IV

ELECTROMAGNETISM

ELECTRICAL QUANTITIES

Table of Equivalents in Heaviside-Lorentz Units (h.l.u.), and Gaussian Units (g.u.).

	h.l.u.	g.u.
Charge,	q_l	$\sqrt{4\pi}\, q_g$
Current,	i_l	$\sqrt{4\pi}\, i_g$
Electric Intensity,	E_l	$\frac{1}{\sqrt{4\pi}} E_g$
Magnetic Intensity,	H_l	$\frac{1}{\sqrt{4\pi}} H_g$
Polarization,	P_l	$\sqrt{4\pi}\, P_g$
Magnetization,	I_l	$\sqrt{4\pi}\, I_g$
Electric Displacement,	D_l	$\frac{1}{\sqrt{4\pi}} D_g$
Magnetic Induction,	B_l	$\frac{1}{\sqrt{4\pi}} B_g$
Conductivity,	σ_l	$4\pi\, \sigma_g$
Resistance,	R_l	$\frac{1}{4\pi} R_g$
Capacitance,	C_l	$4\pi\, C_g$
Self-Inductance,	L_l	$\frac{1}{4\pi} L_g$

CHAPTER X

ELECTROSTATICS AND MAGNETOSTATICS

109. Coulomb's Law of Force between Charges. — In electrostatics we are concerned only with charges at rest relative to the observer. Coulomb showed in 1785 that two like electric charges at rest repel each other or two unlike charges attract each other with a force which is inversely proportional to the square of the distance between them. His method consisted in placing one charge on a small conducting sphere attached to the end of the horizontal arm of a sensitive torsion balance and bringing up a second charge to a point at a predetermined distance from the original position of the first charge. The angle through which the torsion head had to be rotated in order to restore the first charge to its original position measured the torque on the balance arm and hence the force between the two charges at this distance apart.

If, then, we choose as unit of charge one, which, placed at a distance of one centimeter from a like equal charge *in vacuo*, repels it with a force of one dyne, the force between two charges q_1 and q_2 a distance r apart *in vacuo* is

$$F = \frac{q_1 q_2}{r^2}. \qquad (109\text{–}1)$$

A positive value of F indicates repulsion, a negative value attraction. The unit of charge defined above and the c.g.s. units of all quantities which are based upon equation (109–1) are known as *electrostatic units* and designated by the abbreviation e.s.u.

An *electric field* is a region in which a charge, placed anywhere in the field, would experience an electrical force. The *electric intensity* **E** at a point in an electric field is the force that would be exerted on a unit positive charge at rest relative to the observer at the point in question. Therefore if a charge q is placed at a point where the electric intensity is **E** the force experienced by it is

$$\mathbf{F} = q\mathbf{E}. \qquad (109\text{–}2)$$

As the forces between charges at rest are attractions or repulsions depending only on the distances between them, it follows from article 22 that the force and therefore the electric intensity is derivable from a potential. As the increase dV in potential corresponding to the displacement $d\mathbf{r}$ is the work done against the field in moving a unit positive charge through this distance,

$$dV = -\mathbf{E}\cdot d\mathbf{r}. \tag{109-3}$$

Giving $d\mathbf{r}$ successively the values $\mathbf{i}dx$, $\mathbf{j}dy$, $\mathbf{k}dz$ we see that

$$E_x = -\frac{\partial V}{\partial x}, \quad E_y = -\frac{\partial V}{\partial y}, \quad E_z = -\frac{\partial V}{\partial z},$$

or

$$\mathbf{E} = -\nabla V, \tag{109-4}$$

and, as shown in article 11, the component of $\mathbf{E}$ in any direction is equal to the space rate of decrease of potential in that direction.

Let us calculate the potential at a distance R from a point charge q. At any distance r from q

$$\mathbf{E} = \frac{q}{r^3}\mathbf{r} \tag{109-5}$$

by Coulomb's law, and

$$dV = -\frac{q}{r^3}\mathbf{r}\cdot d\mathbf{r} = -q\frac{dr}{r^2}$$

from (109-3). If then we take as the zero of potential that at an infinite distance from the charge

$$V = -q\int_\infty^R \frac{dr}{r^2} = \frac{q}{R}. \tag{109-6}$$

Consequently the potential due to a group of point charges q_1, q_2, q_3, etc., at distances r_1, r_2, r_3, etc., respectively, is

$$V = \frac{q_1}{r_1} + \frac{q_2}{r_2} + \frac{q_3}{r_3} + \ldots = \sum \frac{q}{r}. \tag{109-7}$$

If a charge of density ρ per unit volume is distributed continuously through a volume τ, the charge in a volume element $d\tau$ is $\rho d\tau$ and the potential due to such a distribution is

$$V = \int_\tau \frac{\rho d\tau}{r}. \tag{109-8}$$

As the potential is a scalar it is more easily calculated from the assigned distribution of charge than is the electric intensity. Once the potential has been found as a function of the coordinates the electric intensity may be obtained from (109–4).

110. Gauss' Law. — The *electric flux dN* through an element of surface $d\mathbf{s}$ is defined as the product of the component of the electric intensity normal to the surface by the area of the surface, that is,

$$dN = \mathbf{E}\cdot d\mathbf{s}. \qquad (110\text{–}1)$$

Consider the flux through the closed surface s (Fig. 107) due to

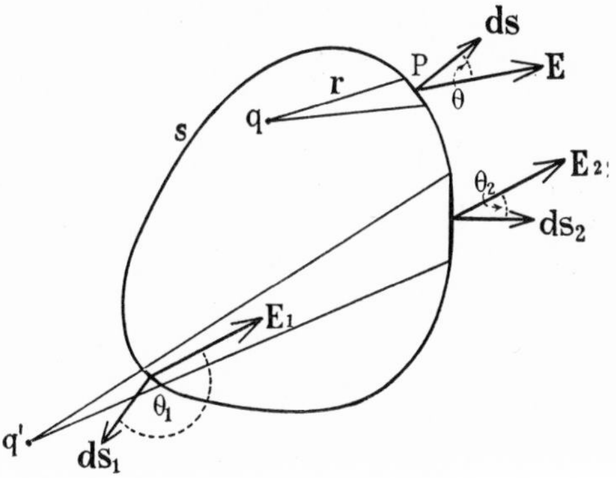

FIG. 107.

the point charge q inside. The flux through the element of surface $d\mathbf{s}$ at P is

$$dN = E\,ds\cos\theta = q\frac{ds\cos\theta}{r^2}.$$

But the solid angle subtended at q by ds is

$$d\Omega = \frac{ds\cos\theta}{r^2}.$$

Therefore

$$dN = q\,d\Omega.$$

Summing up, the entire flux out through the closed surface is

$$N = 4\pi q. \qquad (110\text{–}2)$$

On the other hand the total flux through the surface due to a point charge q' outside the surface is zero, for if we divide the surface into pairs of elements subtending the same solid angle at q', such as $d\mathbf{s}_1$ and $d\mathbf{s}_2$, the positive outward flux through $d\mathbf{s}_2$ is annulled by the equal negative inward flux through $d\mathbf{s}_1$.

Therefore the total outward electric flux through any closed surface is equal to 4π times the charge enclosed by the surface. This is *Gauss' law*, which should not be confused with Gauss' theorem proved in article 16 of the introduction. If the charge is distributed continuously in the volume τ surrounded by the closed surface

$$N = 4\pi \int_\tau \rho d\tau. \tag{110–3}$$

By definition the flux N through the closed surface s is the surface integral

$$N = \int_s \mathbf{E} \cdot d\mathbf{s}.$$

Therefore (110–3) may be written

$$\int_s \mathbf{E} \cdot d\mathbf{s} = 4\pi \int_\tau \rho d\tau. \tag{110–4}$$

Applying Gauss' theorem to the left-hand member

$$\int_\tau \nabla \cdot \mathbf{E} d\tau = 4\pi \int_\tau \rho d\tau.$$

As this is true for every volume τ, however small, the integrands must be equal. Therefore the differential form of Gauss' law corresponding to the integral form (110–4) is

$$\nabla \cdot \mathbf{E} = 4\pi\rho. \tag{110–5}$$

Moreover, as $\mathbf{E}$ is expressible as the gradient of a scalar potential,

$$\nabla \times \mathbf{E} = 0 \tag{110–6}$$

from (14–4). By integrating (110–6) over an arbitrary surface, and converting the surface integral into a line integral around the periphery l of the surface by means of Stokes' theorem, we obtain the integral form

$$\oint \mathbf{E} \cdot d\mathbf{l} = 0 \tag{110–7}$$

of (110–6), the path of integration being *any* closed curve. This line integral is known as the *electromotive force* around the specified curve. In an electrostatic field the electromotive force around any closed curve is zero.

It was proved in article 17.4 that a well-behaved vector function of the coordinates which vanishes at infinity is completely determined if both its divergence and its curl are known everywhere. Therefore an electrostatic field is as completely described by (110–5) and (110–6), or by their equivalents (110–4) and (110–7), as by Coulomb's law (109–1). Equation (110–5) tells us that the electric intensity is a solenoidal vector at all points where no charge is present. In regions containing charge the electric intensity has a divergence equal to 4π times the charge per unit volume. Furthermore (110–6) shows that the electric intensity in an electrostatic field is an irrotational vector everywhere, whether charge is present or not.

Combining (109–4) with (110–5) we get *Poisson's equation*

$$\nabla \cdot \nabla V = -4\pi\rho, \tag{110–8}$$

which must be satisfied everywhere by the potential function V. In regions where no charge is present this reduces to *Laplace's equation*

$$\nabla \cdot \nabla V = 0. \tag{110–9}$$

Gauss' law provides us with a powerful method of solving problems in which symmetry allows us to construct a surface normal to $\mathbf{E}$ at all points of which the electric intensity has the same magnitude. Suppose, for instance, that we wish to find the electric intensity at a point P (Fig. 108) distant r from the center O of a spherical distribution of charge in which the charge density ρ is a function of the radius vector only. Construct a spherical surface of radius r about O as center. Then $\mathbf{E}$ is everywhere perpendicular to this surface and has the same magnitude at all points of it. Therefore the flux through it is $4\pi r^2 E$ and according to Gauss' law

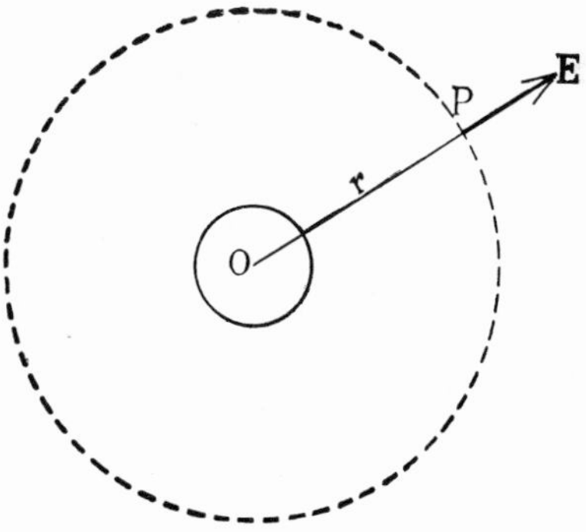

FIG. 108.

$$4\pi r^2 E = 4\pi Q,$$

where Q is the total charge inside the sphere. Hence the electric intensity

$$E = \frac{Q}{r^2} \qquad (110\text{–}10)$$

is the same as if the charge Q were concentrated at the point O. If the sphere of radius r lies inside the charged region, Q represents only the portion of the total charge inside the sphere. The part of the charge outside the sphere gives rise to no field at the point P.

Next consider an electrically charged conductor. As a conductor cannot support a difference of potential the electric intensity in its interior must vanish everywhere. Therefore the divergence of the electric intensity is zero, and in consequence of (110–5) no charge is present. Hence the charge on a conductor resides entirely on its surface.

Problem 110a. By applying Gauss' law find the electric intensity (*a*) at a distance $r > a$ from the axis of an infinite cylinder of radius a with a uniform charge λ per unit length, (*b*) in the neighborhood of an infinite plane with a uniform charge σ per unit area, (*c*) between and outside of two infinite parallel planes of which one has the uniform charge σ per unit area and the other the uniform charge $-\sigma$ per unit area.

Ans. (*a*) $\frac{2\lambda}{r}$, (*b*) $2\pi\sigma$, (*c*) $4\pi\sigma$, 0.

Problem 110b. Find the electric intensity at a distance $r < a$ (*a*) from the center of a uniformly charged sphere of radius a with total charge Q, (*b*) from the axis of a uniformly charged infinite cylinder of radius a with total charge λ per unit length.

Ans. $\frac{Q}{a^3}r$, $\frac{2\lambda}{a^2}r$.

Problem 110c. Show from Gauss' law that the field vanishes inside a uniformly charged spherical shell.

111. Lines of Electric Force and Equipotential Surfaces.— *Lines of electric force* are lines drawn in an electric field so as to have everywhere the direction of the electric intensity **E**. A bundle of M lines of force, where M is a very large number arbitrarily chosen, is called a *tube of force*. Lines of force are drawn in such density that the number of tubes of force per unit cross-section is everywhere equal to the magnitude of the electric intensity. By taking M large enough we are provided with a representation of an electric field which is as nearly continuous as may be desired, even in the weakest fields.

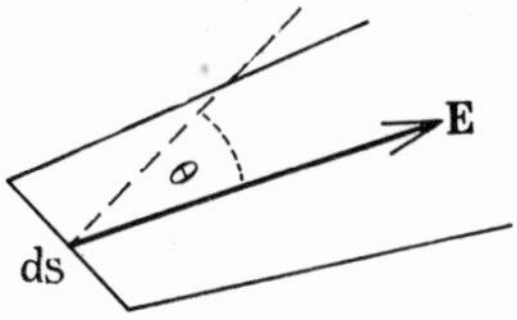

FIG. 109.

Suppose that dN tubes of force pass through a small surface ds (Fig. 109) at an angle θ with the normal to the surface. The cross-section of the group of tubes is $ds \cos \theta$ and therefore the electric intensity is

$$E = \frac{dN}{ds \cos \theta}.$$

Consequently the electric flux through ds is

$$Eds \cos \theta = dN,$$

equal to the number of tubes of force passing through it.

Furthermore, as $E \cos \theta = dN/ds$, the component of the electric intensity normal to a surface element ds is equal to the number of tubes of force per unit area passing through it.

We shall now prove two theorems regarding lines of force.

Theorem I. — In regions containing no charge lines of force are continuous. Consider a tubular region (Fig. 110) bounded by lines of force and terminated by the cross-sections s_1 and s_2. According to Gauss' law the flux into the end s_1 must equal that out of the end s_2 since no charge is contained in the region under consideration. But we have just shown that the number of tubes of force passing through a surface is equal to the flux through that surface. Therefore as many tubes of force enter the end s_1 as leave the end s_2. Hence lines of force are continuous in the region between s_1 and s_2 and therefore in any region containing no charge. This geometrical result is equivalent to the analytical statement contained in (110–5) to the effect that the divergence of **E** vanishes where no charge is present.

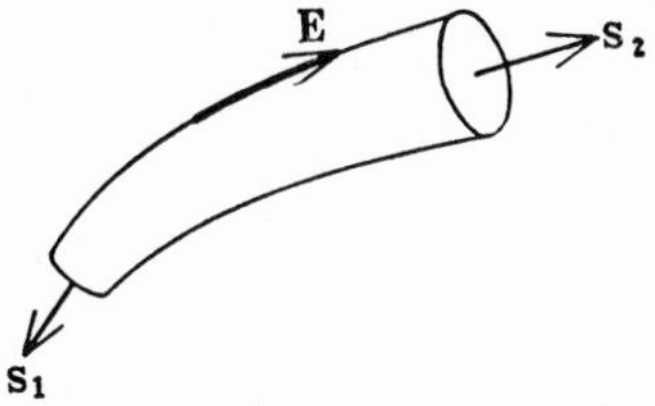

FIG. 110.

Theorem II. — The number of tubes of force diverging from a positive charge q or converging on a negative charge is equal to $4\pi q$. Since the flux through any closed surface surrounding the charge is equal to the number of tubes of force diverging from the charge, this follows at once from Gauss' law (110–2).

An equipotential surface is a surface all points of which are at the same potential. Clearly no two equipotential surfaces can intersect. Now lines of force have the direction of **E**, which is related to the potential by the equation $\mathbf{E} = -\nabla V$. But it was proved in article 11 that the vector ∇V is perpendicular to the surface $V =$ constant. Therefore lines of force and equipotential surfaces intersect at right angles. Furthermore, as $-\nabla V$ represents the greatest space rate of decrease of potential, lines of force are directed from equipotential surfaces of higher potential toward those of lower potential and are more dense the closer together the equipotential surfaces.

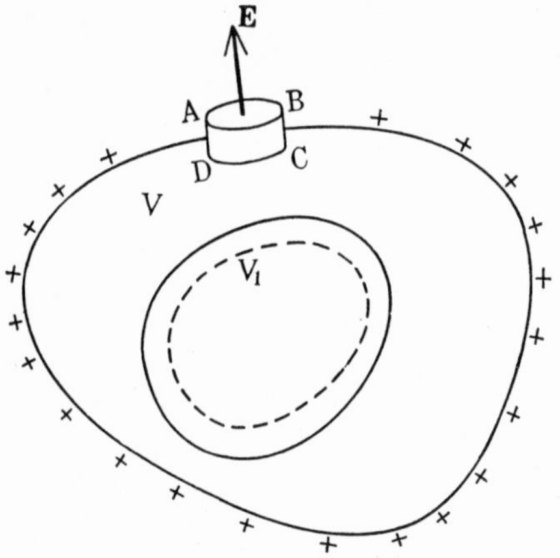

FIG. 111.

Consider a charged conductor (Fig. 111) with an empty cavity inside. As a conductor cannot support a difference of potential all parts of the conductor must be at the same potential V. Therefore the inner surface of the conductor is an equipotential surface of potential V. Let V_1 be the potential of an equipotential surface inside the cavity adjacent to the inner surface of the conductor. If V_1 is greater than V the electric intensity is everywhere directed from V_1 toward V and therefore the flux through the equipotential surface V_1 is positive. But this contradicts Gauss' law since no charge is present inside the cavity. A similar contradiction is reached if V_1 is less than V. Therefore V_1 must equal V and the same must be true throughout the cavity. Consequently there is no field inside the cavity. Now if there were a charge on the inner surface of the conductor the lines of force originating on the charge would have to pass either into the cavity or into the body of the conductor. But no field exists in either. Therefore there can be no charge on the inner surface of the conductor. Consequently all the charge is located on the outer surface.

Let us calculate the field just outside the outer surface of the conductor. As the outer surface is an equipotential surface **E** is perpendicular to it. Describe a pill-box shaped surface $ABCD$ of altitude small compared with its diameter about an element ds of the surface of the conductor. As there is no field inside the body of the conductor there is no flux through the base DC of the pill-box. Therefore the total flux is Eds through the base AB. If then the charge per unit area of the surface of the conductor is denoted by σ,

$$Eds = 4\pi\sigma ds$$

by Gauss' law, and

$$E = 4\pi\sigma \qquad (111\text{–}1)$$

immediately outside the surface.

Finally we shall calculate the tension S on the surface of the conductor. Strictly speaking the charge does not lie on a mathematical surface but occupies a thin layer extending a short distance into the conductor. Let us describe in this layer a number of surfaces parallel to the surface of the conductor so spaced that the charge $d\sigma'$ per unit area included between each pair of adjacent surfaces is the same. Then since lines of force originate on charges, the electric intensity increases by a constant amount in passing from each surface to the next, starting from zero at the innermost surface. If σ' is the charge per unit area between a given surface and the innermost surface the electric intensity at the former is

$$E = \frac{\sigma'}{\sigma} 4\pi\sigma = 4\pi\sigma'.$$

Therefore the tension stress on the surface of the conductor is

$$S = \int_0^\sigma E d\sigma' = 4\pi \int_0^\sigma \sigma' d\sigma' = 2\pi\sigma^2. \qquad (111\text{–}2)$$

As σ appears squared in this expression the stress on the surface is always a tension, no matter whether the charge is positive or negative.

112. Density of Charge in a Polarized Medium. — As regards their electrical properties material media may be classified roughly as either *conductors or dielectrics.* The former contain charges free to move through the body of the conductor under the influence of an electric field. Therefore the charges on a conductor do not attain static equilibrium until sufficient electricity has been transported to the surface of the conductor to annul the electric field at all points in the interior of the body. The free charges in a conductor not an electrolyte are ascribed to electrons which are free to move among the atoms under the influence of an applied electric field. As the free electrons originate in the normally uncharged atoms of the body, the atom cores remaining are positively charged. But as the atom is much more massive than the electron, the positively charged atom cores remain comparatively immobile in the body of the conductor, the free electrons moving in the spaces between them and being hindered in their effort to follow the field by collisions with them.

Although a dielectric contains no free electrons it is not altogether unaffected by the presence of an electric field. In the first place the center of the positive electricity in a neutral atom or molecule in its normal state may not coincide with the center of the negative electricity. If the distance of the one center from the other is invariable, that is, unaffected by an impressed electric field, the configuration of charges constitutes a *permanent electric dipole,* which we may represent by two point charges q and $-q$ a fixed distance l apart. As the positive end of the dipole tends to move in the direction of the electric intensity and the negative end in the opposite direction, an impressed electric field tends to turn the dipole until its axis is parallel to $\mathbf{E}$. Again, although the center of the positive electricity in an atom or molecule may coincide with that of the negative electricity in the absence of a field, the one center may become displaced relative to the other when an electric field is impressed on the medium. The dipole produced in this case is called an *induced electric dipole.* In an isotropic dielectric its axis is parallel to the electric intensity existing in the medium. A single particle of the dielectric may, of course, exhibit both permanent and induced dipoles under the action of an impressed field. When permanent dipoles are oriented from their random directions, or induced dipoles are created, the dielectric is said to be *polarized.*

Let us calculate the field due to an electric dipole — whether permanent or induced — at a distance from its center large compared with the distance of separation of the two charges. Denoting the two charges by q and $-q$ (Fig. 112) and the distance between them by l, the potential at a point P distant r from the center O of the dipole is

$$V = \frac{q}{r_1} - \frac{q}{r_2} = \frac{q}{r - l/2 \cos\theta} - \frac{q}{r + l/2 \cos\theta}$$

to a sufficient degree of approximation. Expanding the denominators in terms of the small quantity l/r

$$V = \frac{q}{r}\left(1 + \frac{l}{2r}\cos\theta \ldots - 1 + \frac{l}{2r}\cos\theta \ldots\right) = \frac{ql}{r^2}\cos\theta.$$

The product ql of the positive charge by the distance of separation is known as the *electric moment* of the dipole. Evidently it is a vector quantity, its direction being determined by that of the line l. We shall denote it by $\mathbf{p}$ and take for its positive sense that of the line drawn from $-q$ to q. Then

$$V = \frac{p}{r^2}\cos\theta = \frac{\mathbf{p}\cdot\mathbf{r}}{r^3}, \quad (112\text{–}1)$$

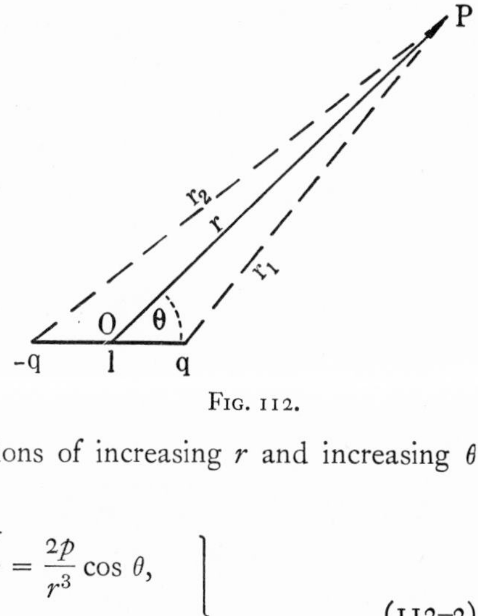

FIG. 112.

and the components of the electric intensity in the directions of increasing r and increasing θ are respectively

$$\left.\begin{aligned} E_r &= -\frac{\partial V}{\partial r} = \frac{2p}{r^3}\cos\theta, \\ E_\theta &= -\frac{\partial V}{r\partial\theta} = \frac{p}{r^3}\sin\theta. \end{aligned}\right\} \quad (112\text{–}2)$$

Next consider a permanent dipole of moment $\mathbf{p}$ placed in an external electric field with its axis making an angle θ with the lines of force. If V is the potential at the negative charge $-q$ that at the positive charge q is $V + \mathbf{l}\cdot\nabla V$, where $\mathbf{l}$ is the vector distance of q from $-q$. Therefore the energy of the dipole due to its position in the field is

$$\begin{aligned} U &= -qV + q(V + \mathbf{l}\cdot\nabla V) = \mathbf{p}\cdot\nabla V \\ &= -\mathbf{p}\cdot\mathbf{E} = -pE\cos\theta. \end{aligned} \quad (112\text{–}3)$$

since $\mathbf{E} = -\nabla V$. Similarly the force acting on the dipole as a whole is

$$\mathbf{F} = -q\mathbf{E} + q(\mathbf{E} + \mathbf{l}\cdot\nabla\mathbf{E}) = \mathbf{p}\cdot\nabla\mathbf{E}, \tag{112-4}$$

from the form of which it is evident that $\mathbf{F}$ vanishes if the field is uniform. Finally let us calculate the torque $\mathbf{L}$ on the dipole about any point O as origin. If $\mathbf{r}$ is the position vector of its center and if we neglect terms in l^2,

$$\begin{aligned}\mathbf{L} &= \left(\mathbf{r} - \frac{\mathbf{l}}{2}\right) \times \{-q\mathbf{E}\} + \left(\mathbf{r} + \frac{\mathbf{l}}{2}\right) \times \{q(\mathbf{E} + \mathbf{l}\cdot\nabla\mathbf{E})\} \\ &= q\mathbf{l} \times \mathbf{E} + \mathbf{r} \times (q\mathbf{l}\cdot\nabla\mathbf{E}) \\ &= \mathbf{p} \times \mathbf{E} + \mathbf{r} \times \mathbf{F}.\end{aligned} \tag{112-5}$$

The first term is the turning couple and the second represents the torque of the translational force (112–4). The former is proportional to $\sin\theta$, and the latter is small if the field is nearly constant in the region occupied by the dipole.

The electric moment of a dipole induced in an isotropic particle is always in the direction of and proportional to $\mathbf{E}$. So in this case $\mathbf{p} = \alpha\mathbf{E}$, where α is a constant. The energy of the dipole is the work done in producing it, that is,

$$U = \int E dp = \tfrac{1}{2}\alpha E^2. \tag{112-6}$$

The force on the dipole is still given by (112–4), which becomes $\mathbf{F} = \alpha\mathbf{E}\cdot\nabla\mathbf{E}$ in this case. But, as $\nabla \times \mathbf{E}$ vanishes,

$$(\nabla \times \mathbf{E}) \times \mathbf{E} \equiv \mathbf{E}\cdot\nabla\mathbf{E} - \tfrac{1}{2}\nabla E^2 = 0.$$

Hence

$$\mathbf{F} = \tfrac{1}{2}\alpha\nabla E^2. \tag{112-7}$$

Since the axis of an induced dipole is parallel to $\mathbf{E}$, it is subject to no turning couple in an external field.

As all matter is constructed of atoms, which in turn are built up of positively and negatively charged particles of dimensions extremely minute compared with those of the atom itself, the structure of material bodies is, in the microscopic sense, far from continuous. For many purposes, however, we are interested merely in the mean density of charge or mean electric intensity averaged up over a volume of dimensions small compared with those we can measure by ordinary methods but yet large enough to contain a very great number of atoms, and not in the fluctuations in charge density or electric intensity which occur as we pass from particle to particle. We shall now calculate the average density of charge in such a small volume τ of dimensions Δx, Δy, Δz (Fig. 113) due to the polarization of the medium.

In the unpolarized state the permanent dipoles in the dielectric are oriented so that as many have their axes pointing in one direction

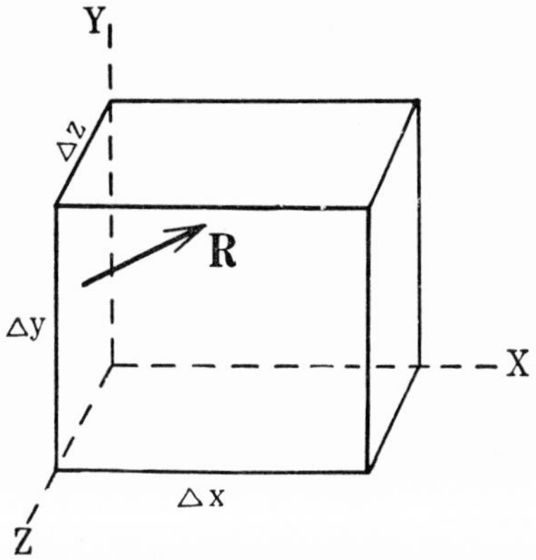

FIG. 113.

as in any other, and no induced dipoles are present. Therefore the net charge inside the volume τ under consideration is zero. The polarization of the medium, however, gives rise to a displacement of charge, whether due to the rotation of permanent dipoles or to the separation of positive from negative charge as in the production of induced dipoles. This displacement causes charges to pass through the surfaces bounding the volume τ, destroying the balance between the positive and negative electricity in its interior. Let ρ_1 be the positive charge per unit volume of the dipoles in the medium and let **R** be the mean displacement experienced by this charge. Then the quantity of positive charge which passes into τ through the left-hand face perpendicular to the X axis when the medium is polarized is that originally contained in a thin layer of thickness R_x and cross-section $\Delta y \Delta z$, that is,

$$\rho_1 R_x \Delta y \Delta z.$$

Similarly the positive charge passing out through the right-hand face is

$$\left\{\rho_1 R_x + \frac{\partial}{\partial x}(\rho_1 R_x)\Delta x\right\}\Delta y \Delta z,$$

giving a net gain of charge equal to

$$-\frac{\partial}{\partial x}(\rho_1 R_x)\Delta x \Delta y \Delta z.$$

If $\mathbf{R}'$ is the mean displacement of the negative charge $-\rho_1$ per unit volume of the dipoles in the medium, the net gain of charge inside τ due to the passage of this charge through the two faces perpendicular to the X axis is

$$-\frac{\partial}{\partial x}(-\rho_1 R_x')\Delta x \Delta y \Delta z.$$

Adding the last two expressions we have for the total gain of charge

$$-\frac{\partial}{\partial x}\left\{\rho_1(R_x - R_x')\right\}\Delta x \Delta y \Delta z.$$

Now $\rho_1(\mathbf{R} - \mathbf{R}')$ is the mean electric moment per unit volume. This vector quantity is called the *polarization*, and is denoted by $\mathbf{P}$. So adding to the expression above corresponding expressions for the charge entering τ through the pairs of boundary surfaces perpendicular to the Y and Z axes, and dividing by the volume $\Delta x \Delta y \Delta z$ of the element τ, the net charge per unit volume produced by the polarization of the medium is seen to be

$$\rho_P = -\left(\frac{\partial P_x}{\partial x} + \frac{\partial P_y}{\partial y} + \frac{\partial P_z}{\partial z}\right) = -\nabla \cdot \mathbf{P}. \qquad (112\text{–}8)$$

We note that in a region where $\mathbf{P}$ is uniform, and therefore the derivatives of $\mathbf{P}$ are zero, the polarization charge ρ_P vanishes. At the surface between a dielectric and empty space, or at the surface between one dielectric and another, we may consider that we have a thin transition layer in which $\mathbf{P}$ and its derivatives change rapidly but continuously from their values on one side of the surface to those on the other. Then we need not deduce a separate expression for the polarization charge on the surface of a dielectric, but can apply (112–8) everywhere. This is the point of view we shall adopt in developing the general theory of dielectrics.

In making the calculations required in specific problems, however, it is convenient to have a separate expression for the polarization charge σ_P per unit area on the surface of a dielectric. We shall assume the region outside the dielectric to be empty space. Describing a small pill-box shaped surface *ABCD* (Fig. 114) about a unit area of the transition layer at the surface of the dielectric and integrating (112–8) over the volume enclosed by this surface, we have

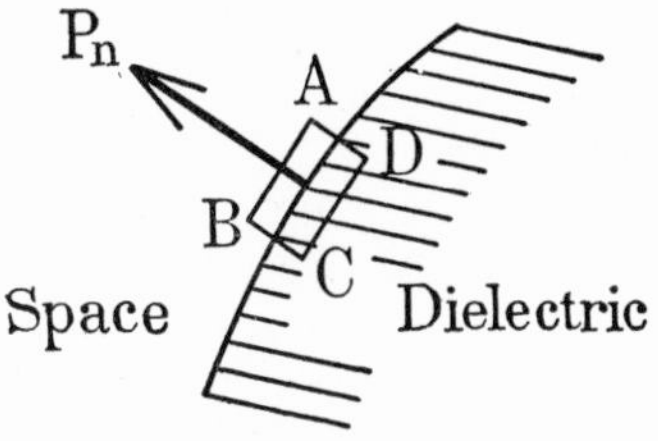

FIG. 114.

$$\sigma_P = \int_{ABCD} \rho_P d\tau = -\int_{ABCD} \nabla \cdot \mathbf{P} d\tau,$$

and applying Gauss' theorem

$$\sigma_P = -\int_{ABCD} \mathbf{P} \cdot d\mathbf{s}.$$

The surface integral over the base *AB* of the pill-box vanishes as *AB* is in the region outside the dielectric where **P** is zero. Moreover by making the pill-box short enough the integral over the curved surface whose traces are *AD* and *BC* becomes negligible. Therefore the only portion of the integral which survives is that over the unit area *CD*. If P_n is the component of the polarization inside the dielectric perpendicular to its surface in the direction of the outward drawn normal, the integral over *CD* is $-P_n$ and

$$\sigma_P = P_n. \tag{112–9}$$

So a polarized dielectric may be considered to have a charge P_n per unit area on the surface and a charge $-\nabla \cdot \mathbf{P}$ per unit volume in the interior. For this distribution of charge the potential may be calculated by (109–8) and the electric intensity obtained from it by (109–4).

113. Gauss' Law for Charges in a Dielectric. — Gauss' law states that the total electric flux through any closed surface is 4π times the charge enclosed by the surface. If there is a dielectric inside the surface, the total charge enclosed consists of the charge q on the charged bodies present plus the charges in the medium due to the irregular polarization of the dielectric. It has been shown that the latter gives rise to a mean charge $-\nabla \cdot \mathbf{P}$ per unit volume. So if τ is the region surrounded by the closed surface s over which the flux is to be evaluated and $\mathbf{E}$ is the mean electric intensity in the medium,

$$\int_s \mathbf{E}\cdot d\mathbf{s} = 4\pi\left\{q - \int_\tau \nabla\cdot\mathbf{P}d\tau\right\}$$

$$= 4\pi\left\{q - \int_s \mathbf{P}\cdot d\mathbf{s}\right\}$$

by Gauss' theorem. Therefore

$$\int_s (\mathbf{E} + 4\pi\mathbf{P})\cdot d\mathbf{s} = 4\pi q.$$

The *electric displacement* $\mathbf{D}$ is defined by the relation

$$\mathbf{D} \equiv \mathbf{E} + 4\pi\mathbf{P}.$$

So Gauss' law takes the form

$$\int_s \mathbf{D}\cdot d\mathbf{s} = 4\pi q, \tag{113-1}$$

or, if the charge is distributed continuously in the volume τ surrounded by the surface s,

$$\int_s \mathbf{D}\cdot d\mathbf{s} = 4\pi\int_\tau \rho d\tau. \tag{113-2}$$

If the *flux of displacement* through an element of surface $d\mathbf{s}$ is defined as the product of the component of the electric displacement $\mathbf{D}$ normal to the surface by ds, then the left-hand member of (113–2) is just the total outward flux of displacement through the closed surface s. So Gauss' law for a region in which dielectrics are present may be expressed by the statement that the total outward flux of displacement through any closed surface is equal to 4π times the sum of the *free charges* enclosed within the surface, where the term *free charges* designates all charges except those due to the polarization of the medium. In this form of the law the charges due to polarization are included in the left-hand member of the equation instead of in the right-hand member. If no dielectric is present, $\mathbf{P} = 0$, $\mathbf{D} = \mathbf{E}$, and equation (113–2) reverts to the original form of Gauss' law expressed in (110–4).

Following the same procedure as that used to obtain (110–5) from (110–4) we get

$$\nabla \cdot \mathbf{D} = 4\pi\rho. \qquad (113\text{–}3)$$

Therefore the electric displacement is a solenoidal vector everywhere in a dielectric or in the transition layer between two dielectrics except where free charges are present. Following the reasoning of theorem I, article 111, we see that lines of electric displacement, although not lines of electric force, are continuous when we pass from one dielectric to another, provided no free charge resides on the surface of separation.

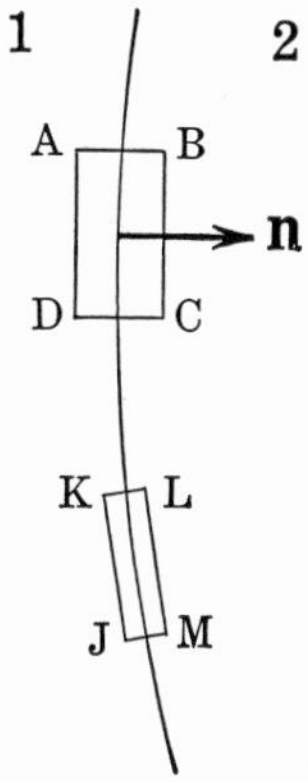

FIG. 115.

Finally we must investigate the boundary conditions at the surface separating two dielectrics. Referring to Fig. 115 and supposing that the surface represented there separates a dielectric 1 on the left from a dielectric 2 on the right, we integrate (113–2) over the pill-box *ABCD* with bases parallel to the surface of separation. If no free charge resides in the transition layer separating the two dielectrics, $\rho = 0$ and

$$\int_{ABCD} \mathbf{D} \cdot d\mathbf{s} = 0.$$

As the integral over the curved portion of the surface of the pill-box is negligible, this gives

$$D_{2n} = D_{1n} \qquad (113\text{–}4)$$

at the surface of separation of the two dielectrics, the subscript n designating the component of $\mathbf{D}$ in the direction of the normal $\mathbf{n}$. Hence *the normal component of* $\mathbf{D}$ *remains unchanged when we pass from one dielectric to another through a surface on which no free charge resides.*

A second boundary condition which is obviously required is that the potential V shall be continuous as we pass from the one dielectric to the other, that is,

$$V_2 = V_1 \qquad (113\text{–}5)$$

at the surface. As $\mathbf{E}$ is the negative gradient of V, it follows that the components of $\mathbf{E}$ tangential to the surface must be the same on both sides, a relation which can be proved directly by integrating (110–7) over a rectangle such as $JKLM$. Unlike (113–4), the boundary condition (113–5) must be satisfied even if free charge resides on the surface of separation.

In article 110 we found that the fundamental equations of electrostatics may be put in the form

$$\nabla \cdot \mathbf{E} = 4\pi\rho, \quad \nabla \times \mathbf{E} = 0. \tag{113–6}$$

While these equations are valid, even in dielectrics, if we understand by ρ the total charge per unit volume, including polarization charge as well as free charge, we have seen in this article that they may be replaced by

$$\nabla \cdot \mathbf{D} = 4\pi\rho, \quad \nabla \times \mathbf{E} = 0, \tag{113–7}$$

where ρ represents the density of free charge alone. The latter equations, however, are not sufficient by themselves to describe the field, for a relation between **D** and **E** is lacking. In the next article we shall obtain such a relation for the case of a homogeneous isotropic dielectric.

It should be noted that the theory developed in this article is applicable to a region containing dielectrics of any type whatsoever, whether homogeneous and isotropic or not.

114. Homogeneous Isotropic Dielectrics. — Since the polarization **P** is produced by the electric field it would be expected that **P** should be proportional to **E** in an isotropic medium. If we write

$$\mathbf{P} = \epsilon\mathbf{E}$$

the *electric susceptibility* ϵ is found to be practically constant for isotropic media in steady fields. Hence

$$\mathbf{D} = (1 + 4\pi\epsilon)\mathbf{E},$$

or writing

$$\kappa \equiv 1 + 4\pi\epsilon,$$

the relation between **D** and **E** becomes

$$\mathbf{D} = \kappa\mathbf{E}. \tag{114–1}$$

The number κ is known as the *permittivity*, *specific inductive capacity*, or *dielectric constant*.

Consider a region in the interior of a homogeneous isotropic dielectric in which there are no free charges. Since κ is a constant, Gauss' law (113–3) becomes $\kappa\nabla\cdot\mathbf{E} = 0$, and, as κ is not zero, $\nabla\cdot\mathbf{E} = 0$. But, from the relation defining $\mathbf{D}$ it follows that $\nabla\cdot\mathbf{D} = \nabla\cdot\mathbf{E} + 4\pi\nabla\cdot\mathbf{P}$. Hence, as both $\nabla\cdot\mathbf{E}$ and $\nabla\cdot\mathbf{D}$ vanish, $\nabla\cdot\mathbf{P}$ is zero. Consequently (112–8) requires that $\rho_P = 0$. Therefore there can be no polarization charge in the interior of the dielectric. The polarization charge must reside entirely on its surface. If the region outside the dielectric is empty space, it follows from (112–9) and (114–1) that the charge per unit area on the surface is

$$\sigma_P = P_n = \frac{\kappa - 1}{4\pi} E_n, \qquad (114\text{–}2)$$

where E_n is the normal component of the electric intensity just inside the surface, taken in the sense of the outward drawn normal to the surface of the dielectric. Furthermore, as $\nabla\cdot\mathbf{E} = 0$ and $\mathbf{E} = -\nabla V$ in the interior of the dielectric, $\nabla\cdot\nabla V = 0$. Therefore the potential inside the dielectric must be a solution of Laplace's equation.

Consider the field due to a point charge q immersed in a dielectric of permittivity κ. To obtain $\mathbf{E}$ at a distance r from the charge, describe a spherical surface of radius r with q as center and apply Gauss' law (113–1). From symmetry it is clear that $\mathbf{D}$ is everywhere radial and has the same magnitude all over the spherical surface. Therefore the total flux of displacement through the spherical surface is $4\pi r^2 D$ and Gauss' law requires that

$$4\pi r^2 D = 4\pi q,$$

or

$$D = \frac{q}{r^2}.$$

Therefore, as $D = \kappa E$,

$$E = \frac{q}{\kappa r^2}, \qquad (114\text{–}3)$$

and, as $\mathbf{E} = -\nabla V$, the potential is

$$V = \frac{q}{\kappa r}. \qquad (114\text{–}4)$$

For a group of point charges immersed in a dielectric this becomes

$$V = \sum \frac{q}{\kappa r}. \qquad (114\text{–}5)$$

The reader must be warned that this expression cannot be applied in general to calculate the potential of an extended distribution of charge surrounded by a homogeneous isotropic dielectric. It is, however, valid for conductors immersed in such a medium, as will now be shown.

The field just outside the surface of a charged conductor which is surrounded by a homogeneous isotropic dielectric may be found by the method of article 111. Applying Gauss' law (113–2) to the pill-box shaped surface *ABCD* in Fig. 111 we get $D = 4\pi\sigma$ in place of $E = 4\pi\sigma$ and therefore

$$E = \frac{4\pi\sigma}{\kappa}. \qquad (114\text{–}6)$$

Immersing charged conductors in a homogeneous isotropic dielectric, then, merely reduces the field strength in the ratio $1/\kappa$.

Problem 114a. A sphere immersed in a homogeneous isotropic dielectric is charged in such a way that the charge density is a function of the distance from the center only. Show that (114–3) holds for the field anywhere outside the sphere. Calculate the polarization charge on the surface of the cavity in the dielectric in which the sphere lies, and show that (114–3) is obtained directly from (110–10) if the polarization charge is taken into account as well as the free charge on the sphere.

Problem 114b. If θ_1 and θ_2 are the angles made by a line of force with the normal to the surface of separation of two dielectrics of permittivities κ_1 and κ_2 respectively, show that the law of refraction of lines of force is

$$\frac{\tan\theta_1}{\tan\theta_2} = \frac{\kappa_1}{\kappa_2}.$$

115. Mean Electric Intensity in a Dielectric. — The average electric intensity **E** inside the region occupied by a single atom may be separated into two parts; the portion $\mathbf{E}_1$ due to the external field and to the other atoms of the medium, and the portion $\mathbf{E}_2$ due to the atom under consideration itself. If the medium is isotropic we can assume the region occupied by a single atom to be spherical in form and of a volume equal to the reciprocal of the number of atoms per unit volume n. Now consider a charge q (Fig. 116) displaced a distance **R** in the X direction from the center O of this sphere. The average electric intensity inside this volume is obtained by integrating the field due to q over the region occupied by the sphere and then

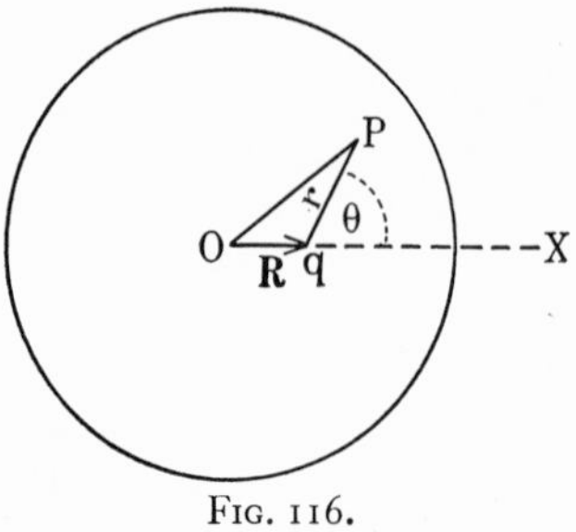

FIG. 116.

dividing by the volume $1/n$. As it is clear from symmetry that the average values of the Y and Z components of the field vanish, it is necessary to calculate the average value of the X component only. We have from the figure

$$E_{2x} = n \int\int \frac{q}{r^2} \cos \theta \, 2\pi r^2 \sin \theta d\theta dr$$

$$= 2\pi nq \int\int \cos \theta \sin \theta d\theta dr. \qquad (115\text{–}1)$$

The limits of θ are zero and π, the lower limit of r is zero and if b is the radius of the sphere the upper limit is given by

$$b^2 = R^2 + 2rR \cos \theta + r^2,$$

or

$$r = -R \cos \theta + \sqrt{R^2 \cos^2 \theta + b^2 - R^2},$$

where the plus sign has been taken before the radical since r is a positive quantity. Integrating (115–1) with respect to r and substituting in the limits

$$E_{2x} = -\, 2\pi nq \left\{ R \int_0^\pi \cos^2 \theta \sin \theta d\theta \right.$$

$$\left. + \frac{1}{2} \int_0^\pi \sqrt{R^2 \cos^2 \theta + b^2 - R^2} d(\cos^2 \theta) \right\}.$$

Since $\cos^2 \theta$ has the same value at both limits the second integral vanishes and

$$E_{2x} = -\frac{4\pi}{3} nqR,$$

or, since $\mathbf{E}_2$ and $\mathbf{R}$ have the same direction,

$$\mathbf{E}_2 = -\frac{4\pi}{3} nq\mathbf{R}. \qquad (115\text{–}2)$$

Now the atom contains equal amounts of positive and negative electricity separated from one another so as to form a dipole. For the moment we shall assume that the positive electricity q is concentrated at a point whose vector distance from the center of the atom is $\mathbf{R}_1$ and the negative electricity $-q$ at a point whose position vector relative to O is $\mathbf{R}_2$. Then

$$\mathbf{E}_2 = -\frac{4\pi}{3} nq(\mathbf{R}_1 - \mathbf{R}_2). \qquad (115\text{–}3)$$

But $\mathbf{R}_1 - \mathbf{R}_2$ is the vector displacement of the positive electricity relative to the negative electricity. Therefore $q(\mathbf{R}_1 - \mathbf{R}_2)$ is the electric moment of the atom. So $\mathbf{E}_2$ depends only upon the number of atoms per unit volume n and the electric moment of each atom. It is quite independent of the position of the somewhat vaguely defined center of the atom O. This origin may be taken anywhere so long as the two charges constituting the dipole lie inside the sphere of volume $1/n$ described about O without affecting the calculated value of $\mathbf{E}_2$. Finally, if instead of two point charges constituting a single dipole we have any arbitrarily assigned distribution of positive and negative electricity inside the sphere taken to represent the volume occupied by the atom, then, provided equal amounts of positive charge and of negative charge are present, it is possible to pair off equal elements of charge of opposite sign to form a multitude of dipoles each of which gives rise to an average field proportional to its electric moment. So if we denote by $\mathbf{p}$ the resultant electric moment of all the dipoles contained in the atom, (115–3) becomes

$$\mathbf{E}_2 = -\frac{4\pi}{3} n\mathbf{p}.$$

Now if we designate by $\bar{\mathbf{p}}$ the mean electric moment obtained by averaging over a large number of atoms, the polarization $\mathbf{P}$ is given by $n\bar{\mathbf{p}}$, so that the mean $\mathbf{E}_2$ is

$$\mathbf{E}_2 = -\frac{4\pi}{3} \mathbf{P}. \qquad (115\text{–}4)$$

The field which tends to align the permanent dipole of the atom or molecule, or which produces an induced dipole, is the field $\mathbf{E}_1$, due to the combined effect of external causes and the repulsions and attractions of neighboring polarized particles. In an isotropic dielectric we would expect the polarization $\mathbf{P}$ to be proportional to the mean value of $\mathbf{E}_1$. Hence

$$\mathbf{P} = \sigma\mathbf{E}_1. \qquad (115\text{–}5)$$

But

$$\mathbf{E}_1 = \mathbf{E} - \mathbf{E}_2 = \mathbf{E} + \frac{4\pi}{3}\mathbf{P},$$

and consequently

$$\mathbf{P} = \sigma\left(\mathbf{E} + \frac{4\pi}{3}\mathbf{P}\right),$$

or

$$\mathbf{P} = \frac{\sigma}{1 - \frac{4}{3}\pi\sigma}\mathbf{E}.$$

Therefore

$$\left.\begin{aligned} \epsilon &= \frac{\sigma}{1 - \frac{4}{3}\pi\sigma}, \\ \kappa &= \frac{1 + \frac{8}{3}\pi\sigma}{1 - \frac{4}{3}\pi\sigma}. \end{aligned}\right\} \qquad (115\text{–}6)$$

We may write the last equation in the form

$$\frac{\kappa - 1}{\kappa + 2} = \frac{4}{3}\pi\sigma. \qquad (115\text{–}7)$$

In the next article we shall attempt to calculate σ for a dielectric containing permanent dipoles, and in the succeeding article for one the polarization of which is due to induced dipoles.

116. Polarization Due to Permanent Dipoles. — We shall treat specifically the case of a homogeneous isotropic fluid dielectric, although the results obtained may be applied as a first approximation to many solid dielectrics. The field $\mathbf{E}_1$ to which an elementary dipole is subject tends to turn the dipole into line with itself; this organizing effect we shall suppose to be opposed only by the disorganizing effect of thermal agitation. Denoting the permanent electric moment of an elementary dipole by $\mathbf{p}_0$, the energy of the dipole in the external field E_1 is $-p_0E_1 \cos\theta$ by (112–3), where θ is the angle between $\mathbf{p}_0$ and $\mathbf{E}_1$. As the number dn of dipoles per unit volume whose axes make angles between θ and $\theta + d\theta$ with $\mathbf{E}_1$ is evidently proportional to the conical angle $2\pi \sin\theta d\theta$, we have, on substituting $-p_0E_1 \cos\theta$ for U_e in (96–11),

$$dn = Ae^{p_0E_1 \cos\theta/kT} \sin\theta d\theta,$$

where the constant A is to be determined by making the integral of dn over all directions equal to the total number n of elementary dipoles per unit volume.

Evidently the polarization **P** has the direction of the mean field $\mathbf{E}_1$. Hence, if we put $x \equiv p_0E_1/kT$, $\mu \equiv \cos\theta$,

$$P = \int p_0 \cos\theta dn = Ap_0\int_0^{\pi} e^{x\cos\theta} \cos\theta \sin\theta d\theta$$

$$= Ap_0\int_{-1}^{1} e^{x\mu} \mu d\mu.$$

But, integrating the expression for dn,

$$n = A\int_0^{\pi} e^{x\cos\theta} \sin\theta d\theta = A\int_{-1}^{1} e^{x\mu} d\mu.$$

Consequently

$$P = np_0 \frac{\int_{-1}^{1} e^{x\mu} \mu d\mu}{\int_{-1}^{1} e^{x\mu} d\mu} = np_0 \frac{\frac{d}{dx}\int_{-1}^{1} e^{x\mu} d\mu}{\int_{-1}^{1} e^{x\mu} d\mu}$$

$$= np_0 \frac{d}{dx} \log \int_{-1}^{1} e^{x\mu} d\mu.$$

Now

$$\int_{-1}^{1} e^{x\mu} d\mu = \frac{1}{x}\{e^x - e^{-x}\} = 2\frac{\sinh x}{x}$$

and hence

$$P = np_0\left\{\frac{\cosh x}{\sinh x} - \frac{1}{x}\right\}. \qquad (116\text{–}1)$$

For very large fields, that is large x, the ratio of cosh x to sinh x approaches unity and $1/x$ approaches zero. Hence the polarization approaches the saturation value np_0 corresponding to complete alignment of the elementary dipoles with the field. At room temperature, however, x is very small compared with unity even for the largest fields available in the laboratory. Therefore

$$\frac{\cosh x}{\sinh x} - \frac{1}{x} = \frac{e^x + e^{-x}}{e^x - e^{-x}} - \frac{1}{x} = \frac{1}{3}x$$

to a first approximation, and

$$P = \frac{1}{3}\frac{np_0^2}{kT}E_1, \qquad (116\text{–}2)$$

giving for the constant σ in (115–5)

$$\sigma = \frac{1}{3}\frac{np_0^2}{kT}. \tag{116–3}$$

Hence, substituting in (115–7), the ratio

$$\frac{\kappa - 1}{\kappa + 2} = \frac{4\pi}{9}\frac{np_0^2}{kT} \tag{116–4}$$

should vary inversely with the absolute temperature in the case of a dielectric whose properties are due to permanent dipoles alone.

117. Polarization Due to Induced Dipoles. — In this case the elementary particle has no electric moment in its normal state. If the dielectric is isotropic, no matter whether it is fluid or solid, we should expect each atom or molecule to acquire an electric moment $\mathbf{p}$ proportional to $\mathbf{E}_1$ when a field is impressed. Hence we may write

$$\mathbf{p} = \alpha\mathbf{E}_1,$$

where α is an atomic or molecular constant. If, then, there are n elementary particles per unit volume, the polarization is

$$\mathbf{P} = n\mathbf{p} = n\alpha\mathbf{E}_1. \tag{117–1}$$

Consequently

$$\sigma = n\alpha \tag{117–2}$$

and

$$\frac{\kappa - 1}{\kappa + 2} = \frac{4}{3}\pi n\alpha. \tag{117–3}$$

Combining this expression with (116–4), we find for a dielectric whose polarization is due to both permanent and induced dipoles,

$$\frac{\kappa - 1}{\kappa + 2} = \frac{4}{3}\pi n\left(\alpha + \frac{p_0^2}{3kT}\right). \tag{117–4}$$

As both α and p_0^2 are atomic or molecular constants, and n represents the number of particles per unit volume, this equation tells us that the ratio of $\kappa - 1$ to $\kappa + 2$ at constant temperature is proportional to the density. That this is the case has been verified for a number of gases. Moreover, by varying the temperature at constant density, we can separate the portion of the effect due to permanent dipoles from that due to induced dipoles. Plotting

$(\kappa - 1)/(\kappa + 2)$ against $1/kT$ (Fig. 117) a straight line AB is obtained. If this line is horizontal, no permanent dipoles are present, whereas if it passes through the origin, the entire effect is due to permanent dipoles. From the intercept on the vertical axis $n\alpha$ can be calculated, and from the slope np_0^2 can be obtained.

In order to calculate a rough value of σ for induced polarization we shall replace the electrons in the atom by a sphere of negative elec-

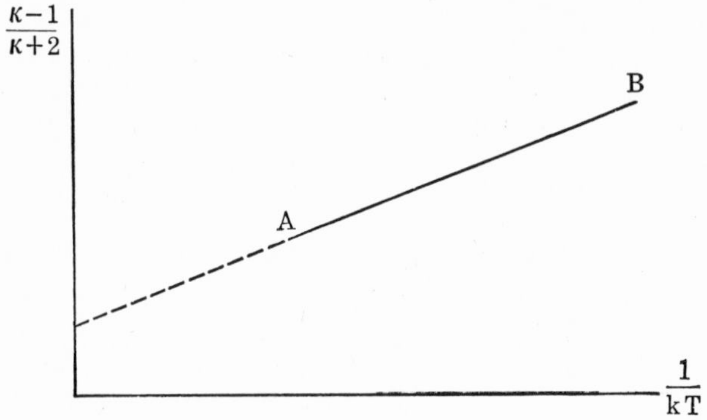

FIG. 117.

tricity of uniform charge density. If the center of this sphere is displaced a distance $\mathbf{R}$ relative to the positive nucleus of the atom, the force drawing the positive and negative charges together is that exerted on the positive nucleus by the portion of the negative charge inside a sphere of radius R described about the center of the atom from the result of problem 110*c*. If a is the radius of the atom, N the number of electrons in the atom, and $-e$ the charge on each, this charge is

$$-\left(\frac{R}{a}\right)^3 Ne,$$

and the force of attraction between it and the positive nucleus is

$$F = -\frac{1}{R^2}\left(\frac{R}{a}\right)^3 Ne \cdot Ne = -\frac{N^2e^2}{a^3} R.$$

In addition to this simple harmonic force of restitution the positive nucleus is subject to the electrical force NeE_1. Therefore for equilibrium

$$\mathbf{E}_1 = \frac{Ne}{a^3}\mathbf{R} = \frac{1}{a^3}\mathbf{p}. \qquad (117\text{–}5)$$

Consequently the ratio α of $\mathbf{p}$ to $\mathbf{E}_1$ is equal to a^3 and $\sigma = na^3$ from (117–2). So (117–3) becomes

$$\frac{\kappa - 1}{\kappa + 2} = \frac{4}{3}\pi n a^3 \qquad (117\text{–}6)$$

for a dielectric whose polarization is due to induced dipoles alone. As n is the number of particles per unit volume and a the radius of a particle, the right-hand side of (117–6) represents the space actually filled by matter per unit volume of the dielectric. By measuring the dielectric constant of a gas, the radii of gaseous molecules can be calculated by means of the formula. Such computations lead to results in fair agreement with those obtained from kinetic theory considerations.

118. Stresses in a Homogeneous Isotropic Dielectric. — According to (112–4) the force on a single dipole of electric moment $\mathbf{p}$ is $\mathbf{p}\cdot\nabla\mathbf{E}$. So if $\mathbf{P}$ is the polarization, the mean force per unit volume on the dipoles in a dielectric is

$$\mathbf{F}_P = \mathbf{P}\cdot\nabla\mathbf{E} = \frac{1}{4\pi}(\mathbf{D}\cdot\nabla\mathbf{E} - \mathbf{E}\cdot\nabla\mathbf{E}), \qquad (118\text{–}1)$$

and, in the homogeneous regions of an isotropic dielectric where $\mathbf{D} = \kappa\mathbf{E}$,

$$\mathbf{F}_P = \frac{\kappa - 1}{4\pi}\mathbf{E}\cdot\nabla\mathbf{E}.$$

It was shown in obtaining (112–7) that $\mathbf{E}\cdot\nabla\mathbf{E} = \frac{1}{2}\nabla E^2$ in any electro static field. Hence

$$\mathbf{F}_P = \frac{\kappa - 1}{8\pi}\nabla E^2,$$

and the resultant force $\mathbf{K}_P$ on a volume τ of the dielectric is

$$\mathbf{K}_P = \frac{\kappa - 1}{8\pi}\int_\tau \nabla E^2 d\tau.$$

But, by Gauss' theorem,

$$\int_\tau \nabla E^2 d\tau = \mathbf{i}\int_\tau \nabla\cdot(\mathbf{i}E^2)d\tau + \ldots = \mathbf{i}\int_s E^2\mathbf{i}\cdot d\mathbf{s} + \ldots$$

$$= \int_s E^2 d\mathbf{s}, \qquad (118\text{–}2)$$

where s is the closed surface surrounding τ. Therefore

$$\mathbf{K}_P = \frac{\kappa - 1}{8\pi} \int_s E^2 d\mathbf{s}, \tag{118-3}$$

showing that the body force on any region τ is equivalent to a tension stress

$$S = \frac{\kappa - 1}{8\pi} E^2 \tag{118-4}$$

over the surface bounding τ. As the dielectric is supposed to be in equilibrium, this tension must be opposed by a mechanical pressure in the medium of equal magnitude. As the formula shows, this pressure is proportional to the square of the field strength **E** and therefore is greatest where the field is most intense.

If conductors or other bodies with free charges are immersed in the dielectric, we have the additional force per unit volume

$$\mathbf{F}_F = \rho \mathbf{E} = \frac{1}{4\pi} \mathbf{E} \nabla \cdot \mathbf{D} \tag{118-5}$$

from Gauss' law (113–3). Adding this to (118–1), which is valid even in regions where the dielectric is not homogeneous, and replacing $\mathbf{E} \cdot \nabla \mathbf{E}$ by its equal $\frac{1}{2} \nabla E^2$, the total force per unit volume is seen to be

$$\mathbf{F}' = \frac{1}{4\pi} \nabla \cdot (\mathbf{DE}) - \frac{1}{8\pi} \nabla E^2.$$

Integrating, as before, over an arbitrary volume τ, the resultant force $\mathbf{K}'$ on the charged bodies and the portion of the dielectric inside τ is

$$\mathbf{K}' = \frac{1}{4\pi} \int_\tau \nabla \cdot (\mathbf{DE}) d\tau - \frac{1}{8\pi} \int_\tau \nabla E^2 d\tau.$$

We have seen how to convert the second integral into a surface integral. Applying Gauss' theorem to the first,

$$\int_\tau \nabla \cdot (\mathbf{DE}) d\tau = \mathbf{i} \int_\tau \nabla \cdot (\mathbf{D} E_x) d\tau + \ldots = \mathbf{i} \int_s E_x \mathbf{D} \cdot d\mathbf{s} + \ldots$$
$$= \int_s \mathbf{ED} \cdot d\mathbf{s}. \tag{118-6}$$

So, altogether

$$\mathbf{K}' = \frac{1}{4\pi}\int_s \mathbf{ED}\cdot d\mathbf{s} - \frac{1}{8\pi}\int_s E^2 d\mathbf{s}. \qquad (118\text{–}7)$$

This expression gives the total *electrical* force on the charged bodies and dielectric lying inside the surface *s*. We shall suppose the surface *s* to lie wholly in the dielectric. If, then, we add the negative of (118–3) to (118–7) we will get the resultant of this electrical force and the force due to the mechanical pressure in the dielectric. Putting $\mathbf{D} = \kappa\mathbf{E}$ this gives

$$\mathbf{K} = \frac{\kappa}{4\pi}\int_s \mathbf{EE}\cdot d\mathbf{s} - \frac{\kappa}{8\pi}\int_s E^2 d\mathbf{s}. \qquad (118\text{–}8)$$

If now, we wish to find the force on a conductor or other charged body immersed in a homogeneous isotropic dielectric, we must integrate (118–8) over a surface lying in the dielectric just outside the body.

In the case of a charged conductor, **E** just outside the conductor is normal to the surface and the two integrals in (118–8) can be combined, giving

$$\mathbf{K} = \frac{\kappa}{8\pi}\int_s E^2 d\mathbf{s}.$$

From this we see that the stress on the surface of a conductor immersed in a homogeneous isotropic dielectric is the simple tension

$$S = \frac{\kappa E^2}{8\pi} = \tfrac{1}{2}\,\sigma E = \frac{2\pi\sigma^2}{\kappa}, \qquad (118\text{–}9)$$

the expressions in terms of the charge σ per unit area being obtained with the aid of (114–6).

In general we can get the stresses X_x, Y_x, Z_x in the dielectric from the integrand of (118–8) by letting *ds* be a surface of unit area perpendicular to the X axis, etc. This gives for the stress dyadic

$$\begin{aligned}\Psi = \frac{\kappa}{4\pi}\{&\mathbf{ii}\tfrac{1}{2}(E_x^2 - E_y^2 - E_z^2) + \mathbf{ij}E_xE_y + \mathbf{ik}E_xE_z\\ &+ \mathbf{ji}E_yE_x + \mathbf{jj}\tfrac{1}{2}(E_y^2 - E_z^2 - E_x^2) + \mathbf{jk}E_yE_z\\ &+ \mathbf{ki}E_zE_x + \mathbf{kj}E_zE_y + \mathbf{kk}\tfrac{1}{2}(E_z^2 - E_x^2 - E_y^2)\}\cdot \qquad (118\text{–}10)\end{aligned}$$

Although these stresses have been obtained for an electrostatic field only, we shall see later that the same electrical stresses exist in any electromagnetic field.

As a first application we shall calculate the force on a charged conductor immersed in a homogeneous isotropic fluid dielectric. The resultant field **E** just outside an element *ds* of the surface of the conductor consists of the impressed field $\mathbf{E}_0$ and the field due to the charge on the conductor and on the adjacent surface of the cavity in the dielectric in which it lies. The latter field we shall divide into two parts; the field $\mathbf{E}''$ due to the charge on the element *ds* of the surface and the field $\mathbf{E}'$ due to the charge on the remainder of the surface. Then

$$\mathbf{E}_0 + \mathbf{E}' + \mathbf{E}'' = \mathbf{E}. \tag{118–11}$$

Just inside the element *ds* the field due to the charge on this element is of the same magnitude but in the opposite direction. Here, however, the resultant field vanishes. Hence

$$\mathbf{E}_0 + \mathbf{E}' - \mathbf{E}'' = 0. \tag{118–12}$$

Eliminating $\mathbf{E}''$ between (118–11) and (118–12),

$$\mathbf{E} = 2(\mathbf{E}_0 + \mathbf{E}').$$

From (118-9), then, the resultant force on the conductor is

$$\mathbf{K} = \int \tfrac{1}{2}\sigma \mathbf{E} ds = \int \sigma \mathbf{E}_0 ds + \int \sigma \mathbf{E}' ds = \int \sigma \mathbf{E}_0 ds, \tag{118–13}$$

since the second integral must vanish as it represents the force on the conductor due to its own field. Therefore the resultant force on a charged conductor, immersed in a homogeneous isotropic fluid dielectric, including the force due to the mechanical pressure in the dielectric as well as the directly electrical forces, is the same as the force that would be exerted on it by the impressed field $\mathbf{E}_0$ if the dielectric were absent.

Consider two small charged conductors immersed in a dielectric at a distance r apart large compared with their linear dimensions. Effectively each is a point charge. If q and q' are the respective charges, the electric intensity at the second due to the first is $q/\kappa r^2$ by (114–3), and the force between them is

$$F = \frac{qq'}{\kappa r^2} \tag{118–14}$$

by (118–13).

Finally consider a slab of dielectric with its parallel faces normal to a uniform impressed field of magnitude E_0 outside the dielectric. Inside the dielectric the electric intensity is E_0/κ by (113–4). If we take the X axis parallel to the lines of force it follows from (118–10) that the stresses in the dielectric consist of a tension

$$X_x = \frac{\kappa}{8\pi} E^2 = \frac{E_0{}^2}{8\pi\kappa}$$

along the lines of force and an equal pressure at right angles. Outside there is a tension

$$X_{0x} = \frac{1}{8\pi} E_0{}^2$$

along the lines of force. Hence the dielectric is subject to a stretching force per unit area of its surface equal to

$$X_{0x} - X_x = \frac{\kappa - 1}{8\pi\kappa} E_0{}^2. \qquad (118\text{–}15)$$

This tendency of a dielectric to stretch in the direction of the lines of force is known as *electrostriction*.

119. Isolated Conductor or Condenser. — We define the *capacitance* of an isolated conductor as the charge which must be put on it to raise its potential by one unit. Consider, for instance, an isolated spherical conductor of radius a immersed in a dielectric of permittivity κ on which a charge Q has been placed. Applying Gauss' law (113–1) to a spherical surface of radius greater than a described about the center of the conductor we see that the field outside the conductor is the same as if the charge Q were located at its center. Therefore the potential at its surface is

$$V = \frac{Q}{\kappa a}$$

from (114–4), and the capacitance of the conductor is

$$C = \frac{Q}{V} = \kappa a. \qquad (119\text{–}1)$$

As κ is a pure number the electrostatic unit of capacitance is the same as the c.g.s. unit of distance, that is, the centimeter.

To find the energy of a charged conductor we must calculate the work done in charging it. Let q be the charge on the conductor and v its potential at any time during the process of charging. Then if the capacitance of the conductor is C the work dU necessary to bring up an additional charge dq is

$$dU = vdq = \frac{q}{C}dq,$$

and if Q and V are the final charge and potential respectively, the entire work done in charging the conductor is

$$U = \frac{1}{C}\int_0^Q q\,dq = \frac{1}{2}\frac{Q^2}{C} = \frac{1}{2}QV = \frac{1}{2}CV^2. \qquad (119\text{–}2)$$

A condenser consists of two conductors separated by a dielectric. One of the conductors is charged, while the other is usually connected to earth so as to keep its potential zero. The capacitance of a condenser is defined as the charge on the first conductor per unit difference of potential between the two. We can consider the charging as produced by a transfer of electricity from the one conductor to the other. If q is the charge on the first and v the difference of potential between the two at any time during the process of charging, the work necessary to transfer an additional charge dq is given by the same expression as that found above for the work necessary to bring up a charge dq to an isolated conductor, and the energy is given by the same formula (119–2).

Problem 119a. Find the capacitance of (*a*) a spherical condenser of radii a and b, (*b*) a cylindrical condenser of radii a and b, (*c*) a parallel plate condenser consisting of two plates a distance d apart.

Ans. (*a*) $\frac{\kappa ab}{b-a}$, (*b*) $\frac{\kappa}{2\log b/a}$ per unit length, (*c*) $\frac{\kappa}{4\pi d}$ per unit area.

Problem 119b. Find the single capacitance equivalent to n capacitances connected in parallel and to n capacitances connected in series.

Ans. $C = C_1 + C_2 \ldots + C_n$, $\frac{1}{C} = \frac{1}{C_1} + \frac{1}{C_2} \cdots + \frac{1}{C_n}$.

Problem 119c. Two spherical condensers of capacitances C_1 and C_2, far enough apart so as not to influence each other, are connected in series, the outer coating of C_1 being grounded. If C'_2 is the capacitance of the outer coating of the second relative to ground, show that the capacitance C of the combination is given by

$$\frac{1}{C} = \frac{1}{C_2} + \frac{1}{C_1 + C'_2}.$$

Problem 119d. Find the capacitance of a multiple parallel plate condenser of n plates.

$$\textit{Ans.}\ (n - 1)\frac{\kappa}{4\pi d}\ \text{per unit area.}$$

Problem 119e. A parallel plate condenser has only a slab of dielectric of thickness t between the plates, which are a distance d apart. Find the capacitance per unit area.

$$\textit{Ans.}\ \frac{\kappa}{4\pi\{\kappa(d - t) + t\}}.$$

120. Energy of a Number of Charged Conductors. — Consider n conductors at rest relative to the observer. Let $p_{11}, p_{21}, \ldots p_{n1}$ be the potentials of conductors 1, 2 . . . n when a unit charge is placed on conductor 1, all the remaining conductors being uncharged. Since the potential due to a point charge is proportional to the magnitude of the charge in accord with (114–5), it is evident that doubling the charge on conductor 1 will double the potentials of all the conductors. So if conductor 1 is given a charge Q_1, the potentials of the n conductors will be $p_{11}Q_1, p_{21}Q_1 \ldots p_{n1}Q_1$. Similarly, if conductor 2 alone is charged with charge Q_2, the n conductors will assume potentials $p_{12}Q_2, p_{22}Q_2 \ldots p_{n2}Q_2$. So, the potentials $V_1, V_2 \ldots V_n$ of the n conductors when they possess charges $Q_1, Q_2 \ldots Q_n$ respectively are

$$\left.\begin{aligned} V_1 &= p_{11}Q_1 + p_{12}Q_2 \ldots + p_{1n}Q_n, \\ V_2 &= p_{21}Q_1 + p_{22}Q_2 \ldots + p_{2n}Q_n, \\ &\cdot\quad\cdot\quad\cdot\quad\cdot\quad\cdot\quad\cdot\quad\cdot\quad\cdot \\ V_n &= p_{n1}Q_1 + p_{n2}Q_2 \ldots + p_{nn}Q_n, \end{aligned}\right\} \qquad (120\text{–}1)$$

where the positive geometrical coefficients p_{11}, p_{12} etc. are known as *coefficients of potential.*

We wish to find the energy U of the system of conductors when they have acquired charges $Q_1, Q_2 \ldots Q_n$ and potentials $V_1, V_2 \ldots V_n$. Let us bring up charges to the various conductors at such a rate that the charges at any instant are $q_1 = xQ_1,\ q_2 = xQ_2, \ldots q_n = xQ_n$, where x is a variable which increases from 0 to 1 during the process of charging. Then the potentials at the instant considered are $v_1 = xV_1$, $v_2 = xV_2$, $\ldots$ $v_n = xV_n$. The energy, measured by the work done in charging the conductors, is

$$\begin{aligned} U &= \int (v_1 dq_1 + v_2 dq_2 \ldots + v_n dq_n) \\ &= (V_1 Q_1 + V_2 Q_2 \ldots + V_n Q_n) \int_0^1 x\,dx \\ &= \tfrac{1}{2}\{Q_1 V_1 + Q_2 V_2 \ldots + Q_n V_n\}. \end{aligned} \tag{120–2}$$

We can eliminate the potentials from this expression by means of (120–1), getting for the energy as a function of the charges

$$\left.\begin{aligned} U_Q = \tfrac{1}{2}\{&p_{11}Q_1^2 + p_{12}Q_1Q_2 \ldots + p_{1n}Q_1Q_n \\ &+ p_{21}Q_2Q_1 + p_{22}Q_2^2 \ldots + p_{2n}Q_2Q_n. \\ &\cdot \quad \cdot \quad \cdot \quad \cdot \quad \cdot \quad \cdot \quad \cdot \quad \cdot \quad \cdot \\ &+ p_{n1}Q_nQ_1 + p_{n2}Q_nQ_2 \ldots + p_{nn}Q_n^2\}. \end{aligned}\right\} \tag{120–3}$$

Now consider the change in energy which occurs when Q_1 increases by dQ_1, all the other Q's remaining constant. If we use the expression (120–3) for the energy as a function of the charges, it follows from the definition of potential that

$$V_1 = \frac{\partial U_Q}{\partial Q_1} = p_{11}Q_1 + \tfrac{1}{2}(p_{12} + p_{21})Q_2 \ldots + \tfrac{1}{2}(p_{1n} + p_{n1})Q_n.$$

But

$$V_1 = p_{11}Q_1 + p_{12}Q_2 \ldots + p_{1n}Q_n.$$

Hence as $Q_1, Q_2 \ldots Q_n$ may be given any values at will,

$$p_{21} = p_{12}, \quad p_{31} = p_{13}, \ldots p_{n1} = p_{1n},$$

and in general

$$p_{ji} = p_{ij}. \tag{120–4}$$

If we solve the set of equations (120–1) for the Q's we find

$$\left.\begin{aligned} Q_1 &= c_{11}V_1 + c_{12}V_2 \ldots + c_{1n}V_n, \\ Q_2 &= c_{21}V_1 + c_{22}V_2 \ldots + c_{2n}V_n, \\ &\cdot \quad \cdot \quad \cdot \quad \cdot \quad \cdot \quad \cdot \quad \cdot \\ Q_n &= c_{n1}V_1 + c_{n2}V_2 \ldots + c_{nn}V_n, \end{aligned}\right\} \tag{120–5}$$

where the geometrical coefficients c_{11}, $c_{22} \ldots c_{nn}$ are known as *coefficients of capacitance*, and c_{12}, $c_{13} \ldots c_{21}$, $c_{23} \ldots$ as *coefficients of induction*. It may be shown that the former are always positive and the latter always negative. Substituting (120–5) in (120–2) we find

$$\left.\begin{aligned} U_V = \tfrac{1}{2}\{&c_{11}V_1^2 + c_{12}V_1V_2 \ldots + c_{1n}V_1V_n \\ &+ c_{21}V_2V_1 + c_{22}V_2^2 \ldots + c_{2n}V_2V_n \\ &\cdot \quad \cdot \quad \cdot \quad \cdot \quad \cdot \quad \cdot \quad \cdot \quad \cdot \quad \cdot \\ &+ c_{n1}V_nV_1 + c_{n2}V_nV_2 \ldots + c_{nn}V_n^2\} \end{aligned}\right\} \qquad (120\text{–}6)$$

for the energy of the system of conductors as a function of their potentials.

Now differentiating (120–2)

$$2dU = Q_1dV_1 + Q_2dV_2 \ldots + Q_ndV_n + V_1dQ_1 + V_2dQ_2 \ldots + V_ndQ_n.$$

But

$$dU = V_1dQ_1 = V_2dQ_2 \ldots + V_ndQ_n.$$

Subtracting

$$dU = Q_1dV_1 + Q_2dV_2 \ldots + Q_ndV_n.$$

Therefore

$$Q_1 = \frac{\partial U_V}{\partial V_1}, \quad Q_2 = \frac{\partial U_V}{\partial V_2}, \ldots Q_n = \frac{\partial U_V}{\partial V_n}.$$

So (120–6) gives us

$$Q_1 = \frac{\partial U_V}{\partial V_1} = c_{11}V_1 + \tfrac{1}{2}(c_{12} + c_{21})V_2 \ldots + \tfrac{1}{2}(c_{1n} + c_{n1})V_n.$$

Comparing with (120–5)

$$c_{21} = c_{12}, \quad c_{31} = c_{13}, \ldots c_{n1} = c_{1n},$$

and in general

$$c_{ji} = c_{ij}. \qquad (120\text{–}7)$$

Problem 120a. Find the p's and c's for a spherical condenser of inner radius a and outer radius b, the inner conductor being taken as 1 and the outer conductor as 2 and $\kappa = 1$. Considered as a condenser show that the capacitance is greater if the inner conductor is earthed and the outer charged than if connected in the usual way.

$$\textit{Ans.}\ c_{11} = \frac{ab}{b-a}, \quad c_{12} = c_{21} = -\frac{ab}{b-a}, \quad c_{22} = \frac{b^2}{b-a}.$$

Problem 120b. Two spherical conductors of radii 2 cm and 3 cm are placed with their centers 20 cm apart. Neglecting the slight non-uniformity in distribution of the charge of each due to the presence of the other, calculate the p's and c's. If the first conductor has a charge of 400 e.s.u. and the second is connected to earth find the potential of each and the charge on the second, taking $\kappa = 1$. *Ans.* $V_1 = 197$ e.s.u., $V_2 = 0$, $Q_2 = -60$ e.s.u.

Problem 120c. Three conductors have charges Q_1, Q_2, Q_3. The second, which is connected to earth, completely surrounds the first. The third is outside the second. Show from (120–5) that the electrical condition of the first is entirely independent of that of the third and *vice versa.*

121. Forces and Torques on Conductors. — In this article we shall limit ourselves to two conductors for the sake of simplicity. Let F be the component of the electrical force on conductor 1 in the direction of increasing ξ, and let this conductor move a distance $d\xi$ under the action of this force, the other conductor remaining stationary. Then the work done by the electrostatic forces is $Fd\xi$.

Case I. — Let the charges on the conductors remain constant. Then no energy is added to the conductors and

$$dU_Q = -Fd\xi$$

or

$$F = -\frac{\partial U_Q}{\partial \xi}. \tag{121–1}$$

Here we are differentiating the p's with respect to ξ, keeping the Q's constant.

Case II. — Let the potentials be the same after the motion as before. First let the motion take place with the charges constant. As

$$U_Q = \tfrac{1}{2}(p_{11}Q_1^2 + 2p_{12}Q_1Q_2 + p_{22}Q_2^2),$$

$$dU_Q = \frac{1}{2}\left(\frac{\partial p_{11}}{\partial \xi}Q_1^2 + 2\frac{\partial p_{12}}{\partial \xi}Q_1Q_2 + \frac{\partial p_{22}}{\partial \xi}Q_2^2\right)d\xi = -Fd\xi.$$

To restore the potentials to their initial values we must add charges dQ_1 and dQ_2 given by

$$dV_1 = p_{11}dQ_1 + p_{12}dQ_2 + \left(\frac{\partial p_{11}}{\partial \xi}Q_1 + \frac{\partial p_{12}}{\partial \xi}Q_2\right)d\xi = 0,$$

$$dV_2 = p_{12}dQ_1 + p_{22}dQ_2 + \left(\frac{\partial p_{12}}{\partial \xi}Q_1 + \frac{\partial p_{22}}{\partial \xi}Q_2\right)d\xi = 0,$$

from (120–1), and thereby increase the energy by

$$\begin{aligned}\delta U &= V_1 dQ_1 + V_2 dQ_2 \\ &= Q_1(p_{11}dQ_1 + p_{12}dQ_2) + Q_2(p_{12}dQ_1 + p_{22}dQ_2) \\ &= -\left(\frac{\partial p_{11}}{\partial \xi} Q_1^2 + 2\frac{\partial p_{12}}{\partial \xi} Q_1 Q_2 + \frac{\partial p_{22}}{\partial \xi} Q_2^2\right) d\xi \\ &= -2dU_Q.\end{aligned}$$

Therefore the total change in energy is

$$dU_V = dU_Q + \delta U = -dU_Q = Fd\xi, \qquad (121\text{–}2)$$

and

$$F = \frac{\partial U_V}{\partial \xi}. \qquad (121\text{–}3)$$

Here we are differentiating the c's with respect to ξ, keeping the V's constant. It is apparent from (121–2) that the energy of the conductors increases by an amount equal to the work done by the electrical forces. Therefore the sources of potential supply an amount of energy double the work done by the field.

If we are dealing with rotation instead of translation we must replace F by the torque L and $d\xi$ by the angular displacement $d\theta$ in the direction of the torque, getting

$$L = -\frac{\partial U_Q}{\partial \theta} \qquad (121\text{–}4)$$

for the case where the charges are kept constant, and

$$L = \frac{\partial U_V}{\partial \theta} \qquad (121\text{–}5)$$

for the case where the potentials remain unchanged.

122. Electrometers. — An electrometer is an instrument designed to measure differences of potential. We shall take up the theory of two types of electrometer.

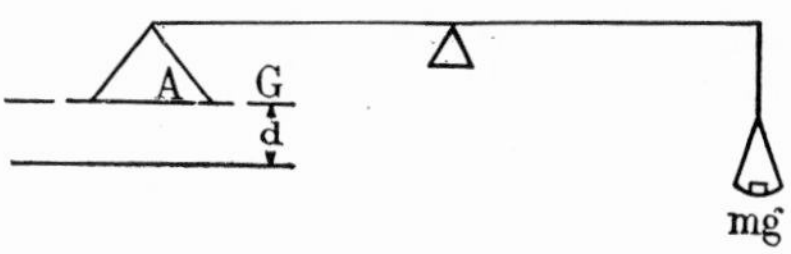

Fig. 118.

I. Kelvin's Absolute Electrometer. — In this instrument (Fig. 118) a circular disk A cut out of the upper plate of a horizontal parallel plate condenser is suspended from one arm of a beam balance. When the condenser is charged the field exerts a downward stress on the upper plate equal to $2\pi\sigma^2$ by (111–2), where σ is the charge per unit area. Therefore the downward force on the suspended disk of area A is $2\pi\sigma^2 A$. This force is balanced by the weight mg placed in the balance pan on the right. Then

$$2\pi\sigma^2 A = mg.$$

If V is the difference in potential of the two plates and d their separation

$$\frac{V}{d} = E = 4\pi\sigma.$$

Therefore

$$V = d\sqrt{\frac{8\pi mg}{A}}. \tag{122–1}$$

We have tacitly assumed that the field between the plates is the uniform field of a condenser of infinite extent. To insure that this shall be the case the *guard ring* G, placed around the circular plate A, is connected electrically to it. The instrument is called an absolute electrometer in that absolute values of the potential difference can be measured by means of formula (122–1).

II. Quadrant Electrometer. — This instrument is shown in plan in the upper part of Fig. 119 and in elevation in the lower part of the figure. It consists of a flat needle N suspended by a torsion fibre F so as to lie inside a pill-box shaped metal box divided into four quadrants. Opposite quadrants are electrically connected, one pair being charged to a potential V_1 and the other pair to a potential V_2. The needle is charged to a potential V_3. The energy of the system of three conductors expressed as a function of their potentials is

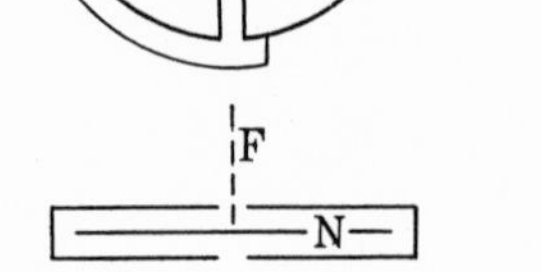

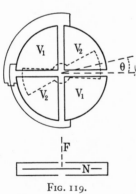

Fig. 119.

$$U_V = \tfrac{1}{2}\{c_{11}V_1^2 + c_{22}V_2^2 + c_{33}V_3^2 + 2c_{12}V_1V_2 + 2c_{13}V_1V_3 + 2c_{23}V_2V_3\}, \tag{122–2}$$

where the subscripts 1 and 2 refer to the two pairs of quadrants and 3 to the needle. The torque on the needle is given by (121–5). To calculate it we need to know how each of the c's varies with the deflection θ of the needle.

From (120–5) it appears that the coefficient c_{33} represents the charge on the needle per unit potential on the needle, both quadrants being grounded. As the slits between quadrants are so narrow as to be negligible, the quadrants, when grounded, form a closed surface of zero potential surrounding the needle and it is evident from symmetry that c_{33} is independent of the position of the needle. The charge on quadrants 1 per unit potential on quadrants 2, both 1 and 3 being grounded, is given by c_{12}. As this charge is proportional to the number of tubes of force passing from the pair of quadrants 2 to the pair 1, it is determined by the field in the neighborhood of the slits between quadrants. Since the needle is usually about 60° wide, and in practice the deflection is rarely more than 6° or 7°, the edge of the needle never comes near the slits. Hence the field in their neighborhood is virtually independent of the position of the needle, and c_{12} is constant in θ for small deflections.

Now suppose that the two pairs of quadrants are connected and charged to a unit potential, the needle being uncharged. Since the whole region inside the quadrants is at unit potential, the needle can be oriented to any position without affecting the electrical condition of the quadrants. From symmetry each pair will have the same constant charge Q. Hence, (120–5) gives

$$c_{11} + c_{12} + c_{13} = Q,$$

$$c_{12} + c_{22} + c_{23} = Q,$$

$$c_{13} + c_{23} + c_{33} = 0.$$

Differentiating with respect to θ, remembering that c_{33}, c_{12} and Q are constants,

$$\frac{\partial c_{11}}{\partial \theta} + \frac{\partial c_{13}}{\partial \theta} = 0,$$

$$\frac{\partial c_{22}}{\partial \theta} + \frac{\partial c_{23}}{\partial \theta} = 0,$$

$$\frac{\partial c_{13}}{\partial \theta} + \frac{\partial c_{23}}{\partial \theta} = 0.$$

Now c_{13}, being the charge on quadrants 1 per unit potential on the needle when both pairs of quadrants are grounded, is proportional to the number of tubes of force passing from the needle to quadrants 1 under these circumstances. Therefore it is proportional to the area of the needle inside quadrants 1, that is, to θ. So, if we put k for the constant value of the derivative of c_{13} with respect to θ, the equations above give

$$k = \frac{\partial c_{13}}{\partial \theta} = -\frac{\partial c_{23}}{\partial \theta} = -\frac{\partial c_{11}}{\partial \theta} = \frac{\partial c_{22}}{\partial \theta}. \tag{122–3}$$

Differentiating (122–2) with respect to θ we get for the torque (121–5)

$$L = \frac{\partial U_V}{\partial \theta} = \tfrac{1}{2}\{-kV_1^2 + kV_2^2 + 2kV_1V_3 - 2kV_2V_3\}$$

$$= k(V_1 - V_2)\left\{V_3 - \frac{V_1 + V_2}{2}\right\}. \tag{122–4}$$

When the electrometer is used heterostatically, V_3 is given a constant value much greater than either V_1 or V_2 and

$$L = kV_3(V_1 - V_2). \tag{122–5}$$

In this case the deflection is proportional to the difference between the potentials of the two pairs of quadrants.

When the instrument is used idiostatically, the needle is connected to one pair of quadrants, say the first pair. Then $V_3 = V_1$ and

$$L = \tfrac{1}{2}k(V_1 - V_2)^2. \tag{122–6}$$

Although the idiostatic method of using the electrometer is much less sensitive than the heterostatic, it has the advantage of being able to measure an alternating potential difference, since the deflection is proportional to the square of $V_1 - V_2$.

While the quadrant electrometer is not an absolute instrument, it can be made very much more sensitive than Kelvin's absolute electrometer. In the most precise measurements it is used as a null instrument. As an example of this method of employing the electrometer we shall describe Kelvin's bridge method of comparing capacitances. In Fig. 120, C_3 and C_4 are condensers of known capacitances, C_2 a calibrated condenser of variable capacitance, C_1 a condenser whose capacitance is to be measured, E a quadrant electrometer, and $\mathcal{E}$ a battery or other source of constant potential difference.

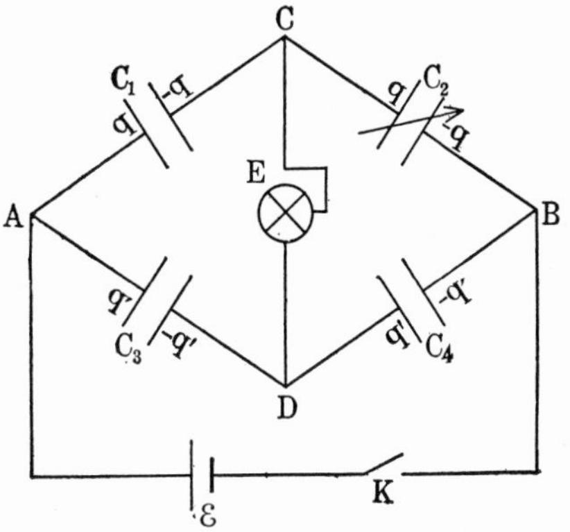

FIG. 120.

We adjust the variable condenser C_2 until the electrometer shows no deflection when the key K is pressed. Then

$$V_C = V_D.$$

But

$$V_A - V_C = \frac{q}{C_1},$$

$$V_C - V_B = \frac{q}{C_2},$$

$$V_A - V_D = \frac{q'}{C_3},$$

$$V_D - V_B = \frac{q'}{C_4}.$$

Therefore

$$\frac{q}{C_1} = \frac{q'}{C_3}, \quad \frac{q}{C_2} = \frac{q'}{C_4},$$

and

$$\frac{C_1}{C_2} = \frac{C_3}{C_4}. \tag{122-7}$$

Problem 122a. Obtain (122–1) by calculating U_V and using (121–3).

123. Laplace's Equation. — We shall devote the remainder of the space allotted to electrostatics to a consideration of methods of solving electrostatic problems, particularly those in which we are given a system of conductors at assigned potentials and wish to find the electric intensity in the surrounding medium and the density of charge on the surfaces of the conductors. We shall limit our discussion to the case where the conductors under consideration are immersed in a homogeneous isotropic dielectric, including the special case where the medium is empty space, that is, $\kappa = 1$. We proved in article 114 that no polarization charge can be present in the interior of a homogeneous isotropic dielectric and that the potential must satisfy Laplace's equation. So the problem of determining the field at all points in the region between and surrounding the conductors consists in finding a solution $V(x, y, z)$ of Laplace's equation which becomes, at the surface of each conductor, equal to the potential of that conductor, and which satisfies the assigned boundary conditions at infinity. Once the potential function has been found the electric intensity is obtained immediately from (109–4), and the charge per unit area on any conducting surface is given in terms of the electric intensity just outside by (114–6), which may be written

$$\sigma = \frac{\kappa}{4\pi} E = -\frac{\kappa}{4\pi} \frac{\partial V}{\partial n}, \qquad (123\text{–}1)$$

where the derivative represents the space rate of increase of potential along the outward normal to the surface.

As an example of the procedure just developed for solving elec-

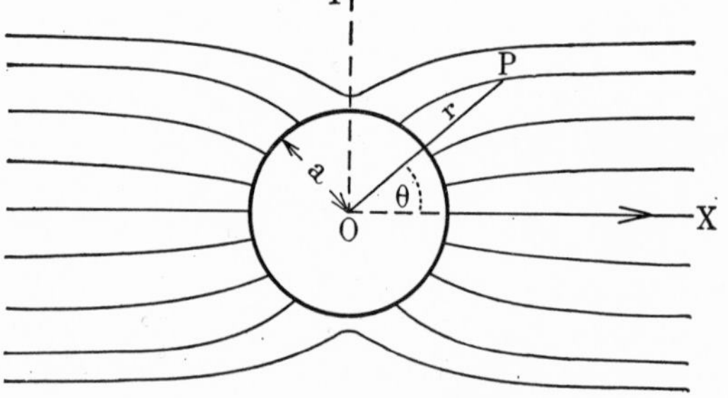

FIG. 121.

trostatic problems we shall take up the case of an earthed conducting sphere of radius a (Fig. 121) placed in a uniform field $\mathbf{E}_0$ parallel to the

X axis. Taking origin at the center of the sphere, the boundary condions are

$$\left.\begin{aligned} V &= 0, & r &= a; \\ V &= -E_0 x = -E_0 r \cos\theta, & r &= \infty. \end{aligned}\right\} \qquad (123\text{–}2)$$

We see at once that we need the first solution (79–13) of Laplace's equation in order to satisfy the condition at infinity, and in addition the second solution (79–13) in order to satisfy the boundary condition at the surface of the sphere for all values of θ. Therefore let us put

$$V = Ar\cos\theta + \frac{B}{r^2}\cos\theta.$$

To satisfy the boundary condition at infinity we must have $A = -E_0$, and to satisfy that at the surface of the sphere $B = -a^3A = a^3E_0$. Therefore

$$V = -E_0 r\cos\theta\left(1 - \frac{a^3}{r^3}\right). \qquad (123\text{–}3)$$

The components of electric intensity at any point P outside the sphere are

$$E_r = -\frac{\partial V}{\partial r} = E_0\left(1 + 2\frac{a^3}{r^3}\right)\cos\theta \qquad (123\text{–}4)$$

in the direction of increasing r, and

$$E_\theta = -\frac{\partial V}{r\partial\theta} = -E_0\left(1 - \frac{a^3}{r^3}\right)\sin\theta \qquad (123\text{–}5)$$

in the direction of increasing θ. Finally the charge per unit area on the surface of the sphere is

$$\sigma = -\frac{\kappa}{4\pi}\left(\frac{\partial V}{\partial r}\right)_{r=a} = \frac{3\kappa E_0\cos\theta}{4\pi}, \qquad (123\text{–}6)$$

showing that the sphere has a positive charge on the right-hand half and a symmetrically distributed negative charge on the left-hand half of its surface.

Our solution applies only in the region outside the sphere. Inside the potential is zero.

If, instead of being earthed, the sphere has a net charge Q, the potential at any point outside is

$$V = -E_0 r \cos\theta\left(1 - \frac{a^3}{r^3}\right) + \frac{Q}{\kappa r}, \qquad (123\text{–}7)$$

obtained by superposing the field of a uniformly charged sphere on that specified by (123–3).

Problem 123a. Show how the field of an infinite charged conducting plane with a hemispherical boss of radius a can be obtained from the problem just solved, and find the charge per unit area on the plane.

$$\textit{Ans.}\ \sigma = \frac{\kappa E_0}{4\pi}\left(1 - \frac{a^3}{r^3}\right).$$

Problem 123b. A dielectric sphere of permittivity κ is placed in a uniform electric field E_0, the permittivity of the medium outside the sphere being unity. Find the potential and radial and transverse components of electric intensity both outside and inside the sphere, taking the potential at the center of the sphere to be zero. Show that when $\kappa = \infty$ the results obtained reduce to those found for a conducting sphere.

$$\textit{Ans.}\ V = -E_0 r\cos\theta\left(1 - \frac{\kappa - 1}{\kappa + 2}\frac{a^3}{r^3}\right) \text{ outside,}$$

$$V = -\frac{3}{\kappa + 2} E_0 r \cos\theta \text{ inside.}$$

Problem 123c. In two dimensions Laplace's equation is

$$\frac{\partial^2 V}{\partial x^2} + \frac{\partial^2 V}{\partial y^2} = 0.$$

Show that

$$r\cos\theta, \quad \frac{\cos\theta}{r},$$

are solutions. A cylindrical conductor of infinite length is placed in a uniform field E_0 with its axis at right angles to the lines of force. Taking the potential of the conductor as zero find the potential and components of electric intensity outside the conductor, and the charge per unit area on the surface of the conductor.

$$\textit{Ans.}\ V = -E_0 r\cos\theta\left(1 - \frac{a^2}{r^2}\right), \quad \sigma = \frac{2\kappa E_0 \cos\theta}{4\pi}.$$

124. Point Images. — Consider two equal charges q and $-q$ of opposite sign placed at O and O' (Fig. 122) respectively. If $\kappa = 1$ the potential at any point P due to the two charges is

$$V = \frac{q}{r} - \frac{q}{r'}.$$

Hence at all points of the plane *AB* which bisects perpendicularly the line *O'O* the potential is zero. So a plane conducting surface connected to earth and placed so as to coincide with *AB* has no effect on the field. If after the conducting surface has been placed in position the charge at *O'* is removed, the field to the left of *AB* disappears, the field to the right remaining unaltered. Therefore the field between a point charge *q* and a conducting plane is identical with the portion in front of the plane of the field produced by *q* and a charge $-q$ placed at a point on the perpendicular dropped from *q* to the plane as far behind the plane as *q* is in front. The charge $-q$ at *O'* is called the *electrical image* of the charge *q* at *O*.

If the distance of *q* from the plane is $d/2$, the potential at any point *P* is

$$V = \frac{q}{r} - \frac{q}{\sqrt{r^2 + 2rd\cos\theta + d^2}}, \qquad (124\text{–}1)$$

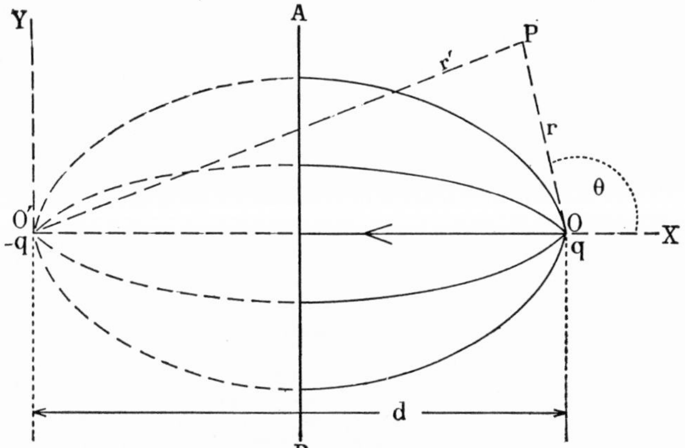

FIG. 122.

and the components of electric intensity in the directions of increasing *r* and increasing θ are respectively

$$E_r = -\frac{\partial V}{\partial r} = \frac{q}{r^2} - \frac{q(r + d\cos\theta)}{(r^2 + 2rd\cos\theta + d^2)^{3/2}}, \qquad (124\text{–}2)$$

$$E_\theta = -\frac{\partial V}{r\partial\theta} = \frac{qd\sin\theta}{(r^2 + 2rd\cos\theta + d^2)^{3/2}}. \qquad (124\text{–}3)$$

The charge per unit area of the conducting plane is

$$\sigma = -\frac{1}{4\pi}\frac{\partial V}{\partial n} = \frac{1}{4\pi}(E_r \cos\theta - E_\theta \sin\theta), \quad r = r',$$

that is,

$$\sigma = -\frac{qd}{4\pi r^3}. \tag{124-4}$$

The total negative charge on the plane is

$$-\int_{\pi/2}^{\pi} \sigma\, 2\pi r^2 \tan\theta\, d\theta = -q\int_{\pi/2}^{\pi} \sin\theta\, d\theta = -q,$$

equal to the positive charge at the point O. Finally it follows from the law of action and reaction that the total force on the conducting plane due to the attraction of q is the same as that which would be experienced by the image $-q$ at O', that is

$$F = -\frac{q^2}{d^2}. \tag{124-5}$$

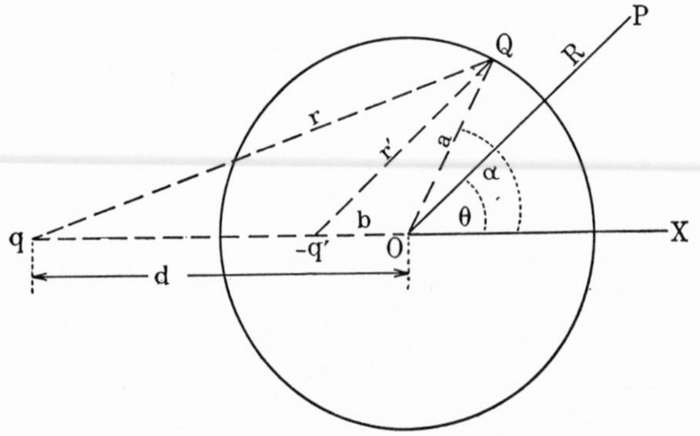

FIG. 123.

Next let us apply the method of electrical images to a point charge q (Fig. 123) and a conducting sphere of radius a. We wish to find the position and magnitude of an image $-q'$ such that the potential at any point Q on the surface of the sphere shall be zero. If the distances of q and $-q'$ from the center O of the sphere are denoted by d and b respectively, the potential at Q is

$$V = \frac{q}{r} - \frac{q'}{r'} = \frac{q}{\sqrt{d^2 + 2da\cos\alpha + a^2}} - \frac{q'}{\sqrt{a^2 + 2ab\cos\alpha + b^2}}.$$

If we make $b = a^2/d$

$$V = \frac{q - \frac{d}{a}q'}{\sqrt{d^2 + 2da\cos\alpha + a^2}},$$

and the potential vanishes for all values of α provided $q' = (a/d)q$.

The potential at any point P, then, due to q and the earthed sphere, is

$$V = \frac{q}{\sqrt{R^2 + 2Rd\cos\theta + d^2}} - \frac{\frac{a}{d}q}{\sqrt{R^2 + 2R\frac{a^2}{d}\cos\theta + \frac{a^4}{d^2}}}, \qquad (124\text{–}6)$$

and the charge per unit area on the surface of the sphere is

$$\sigma = -\frac{1}{4\pi}\frac{\partial V}{\partial R}, \quad R = a,$$

that is,

$$\sigma = -\frac{q}{4\pi a}\frac{d^2 - a^2}{(d^2 + 2da\cos\theta + a^2)^{3/2}}. \qquad (124\text{–}7)$$

The total charge on the sphere is equal to that of the image $-q'$ and, as in the previous case, the force between q and the sphere is the same as that between q and its image in the sphere.

Problem 124a. An earthed conducting sphere of radius a lies half way between two point charges q and $-q$ a distance $2d$ apart. Find the positions of the electrical images in the sphere and the potential at any point outside the sphere. Prove that if q and $-q$ are removed to a very great distance from the sphere the expression for the potential goes over into (123–3).

Ans. $$V = q\left\{\frac{1}{\sqrt{R^2 + 2Rd\cos\theta + d^2}} - \frac{1}{\sqrt{R^2 - 2Rd\cos\theta + d^2}}\right\}$$
$$-\frac{a}{d}q\left\{\frac{1}{\sqrt{R^2 + 2R\frac{a^2}{d}\cos\theta + \frac{a^4}{d^2}}} - \frac{1}{\sqrt{R^2 - 2R\frac{a^2}{d}\cos\theta + \frac{a^4}{d^2}}}\right\}.$$

Problem 124b. A homogeneous isotropic dielectric of permittivity κ extends from the YZ plane indefinitely to the left. A point charge q is placed on the X axis a distance a in front of the dielectric. Show that the field outside the dielectric is the same as that due to q and an image $-q(\kappa - 1)/(\kappa + 1)$ at a distance a behind the surface of the dielectric, and that the field inside the dielectric is the same as that of a charge $2q/(\kappa + 1)$ at the point actually occupied by q. Consider the case where $a = 0$.

125. Line Images. — Certain problems in which the potential is not a function of one of the rectangular coordinates can be solved by using line images in place of the point images of the last article. As an example we shall calculate the capacitance of a pair of infinitely long parallel conducting cylinders. For the moment suppose the cylinders to be filaments of infinitesimal cross-section. If they are separated by a distance d (Fig. 124) and have charges λ and $-\lambda$ per unit length, the potential at a point P is

$$V = -2\lambda \log r_1 + 2\lambda \log r_2 = 2\lambda \log \frac{r_2}{r_1} = \lambda \log \frac{r_2^2}{r_1^2} \qquad (125\text{–}1)$$

from the result of problem 110*a*, since it is clear from symmetry that the potential is zero midway between the two conductors.

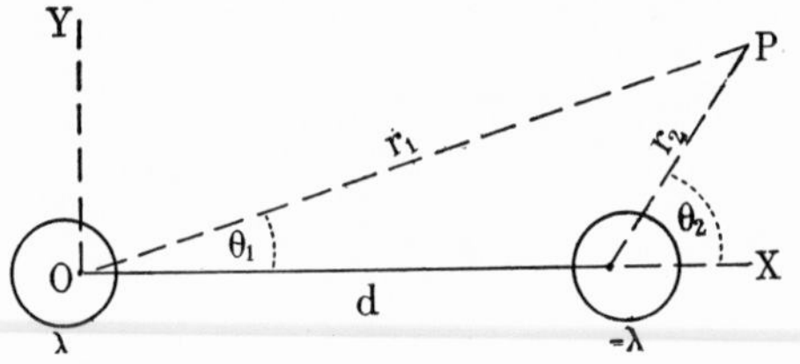

FIG. 124.

To get the equations of the equipotential curves in rectangular coordinates take the point O of intersection of the first filament with the XY plane as origin of the coordinates x_1, y_1. Then the equation of an equipotential curve is

$$\frac{r_2^2}{r_1^2} = \frac{r_1^2 - 2r_1 d \cos\theta_1 + d^2}{r_1^2} = m^2 \text{ (a constant)},$$

or

$$r_1^2 + 2r_1 \cos\theta_1 \frac{d}{m^2 - 1} = \frac{d^2}{m^2 - 1}.$$

Transforming to rectangular coordinates

$$\left(x_1 + \frac{d}{m^2 - 1}\right)^2 + y_1^2 = \frac{m^2 d^2}{(m^2 - 1)^2}. \qquad (125\text{–}2)$$

This is the equation of a circle of radius $\frac{md}{m^2 - 1}$ with center on the X axis a distance $-\frac{d}{m^2 - 1}$ from the origin. Therefore, as the equipotential curves are circles, we can take the one of radius a as the cross-section of a cylindrical conductor of finite dimensions, wiping out the portion of the field inside this circle. Replacing then each charged filament by a conducting cylinder of finite radius a whose periphery coincides with an equipotential circle, we find for the distance b between the axes of the two conductors

$$b = d + \frac{2d}{m^2 - 1} = \frac{m^2 + 1}{m^2 - 1} d.$$

Eliminating d between this equation and the equation

$$a = \frac{m}{m^2 - 1} d$$

for the radius of the equipotential circle coinciding with the periphery of the conducting cylinder, we get

$$m^2 - \frac{b}{a} m + 1 = 0,$$

of which the roots are

$$m = \frac{b \pm \sqrt{b^2 - 4a^2}}{2a}. \qquad (125\text{-}3)$$

Evidently the plus sign before the radical gives the value of m pertaining to the positively charged cylinder and the minus sign that pertaining to the negatively charged cylinder. Therefore the potential of the first is

$$V_1 = 2\lambda \log m_+ = 2\lambda \log \frac{b + \sqrt{b^2 - 4a^2}}{2a}$$

and that of the second

$$V_2 = 2\lambda \log m_- = 2\lambda \log \frac{b - \sqrt{b^2 - 4a^2}}{2a} = -V_1.$$

The difference of potential is

$$V_1 - V_2 = 2\lambda \log \frac{b + \sqrt{b^2 - 4a^2}}{b - \sqrt{b^2 - 4a^2}}, \qquad (125\text{-}4)$$

and the capacitance per unit length

$$C_1 = \frac{\lambda}{V_1 - V_2} = \frac{1}{2 \log \dfrac{b + \sqrt{b^2 - 4a^2}}{b - \sqrt{b^2 - 4a^2}}}. \tag{125–5}$$

If the cylinders are immersed in a dielectric of permittivity κ

$$C_1 = \frac{\kappa}{2 \log \dfrac{b + \sqrt{b^2 - 4a^2}}{b - \sqrt{b^2 - 4a^2}}}. \tag{125–6}$$

Problem 125a. A horizontal wire of negligible radius with a charge λ per unit length is suspended at a height h above the surface of a flat plain. Considering the surface of the earth to be a conductor, find the potential as a function of r and θ, where r is the distance from the wire and θ the angle with the vertical, and find the charge per unit area on the surface of the plain.

Ans. $V = \lambda \log \left(1 + 4\frac{h}{r}\cos\theta + 4\frac{h^2}{r^2}\right), \quad \sigma = -\frac{\lambda h}{\pi r^2}.$

126. Conjugate Functions. — If the potential is a function of x and y only the problem under consideration reduces to one in two dimensions. In solving such a problem the method of conjugate functions is often useful. Let z represent the complex quantity $x + iy$ where $i \equiv \sqrt{-1}$. Then any function $F(z)$ of z may be written

$$F(z) = F(x + iy) = g(x, y) + ih(x, y) \tag{126–1}$$

where the real functions $g(x, y)$ and $h(x, y)$ are known as *conjugate functions*. Now

$$\left. \begin{aligned} \frac{\partial F}{\partial x} &= \frac{dF}{dz}, \quad \frac{\partial^2 F}{\partial x^2} = \frac{d^2 F}{dz^2}, \\ \frac{\partial F}{\partial y} &= i\frac{dF}{dz}, \quad \frac{\partial^2 F}{\partial y^2} = -\frac{d^2 F}{dz^2}. \end{aligned} \right\} \tag{126–2}$$

Therefore

$$\frac{\partial^2 F}{\partial x^2} + \frac{\partial^2 F}{\partial y^2} = \frac{d^2 F}{dz^2} - \frac{d^2 F}{dz^2} = 0,$$

showing that $F(z)$ satisfies Laplace's equation. Consequently the real part $g(x, y)$ and the imaginary part $h(x, y)$ of *any* function $F(z)$ of the complex variable $x + iy$ are each solutions of Laplace's equation. Either of them represents the potential in a possible two-dimensional electrostatic field.

From (126–2), if we replace F by $g + ih$,

$$\frac{\partial g}{\partial y} + i\frac{\partial h}{\partial y} = \frac{\partial F}{\partial y} = i\frac{\partial F}{\partial x} = i\left(\frac{\partial g}{\partial x} + i\frac{\partial h}{\partial x}\right),$$

and separating real and imaginary parts

$$\frac{\partial g}{\partial y} = -\frac{\partial h}{\partial x}, \quad \frac{\partial h}{\partial y} = \frac{\partial g}{\partial x}. \qquad (126\text{–}3)$$

Consequently

$$(\nabla g)\cdot(\nabla h) = \frac{\partial g}{\partial x}\frac{\partial h}{\partial x} + \frac{\partial g}{\partial y}\frac{\partial h}{\partial y} = 0.$$

But ∇g is normal to the curve $g =$ const. and ∇h to the curve $h =$ const. Hence the two families of curves $g(x, y) =$ const. and $h(x, y) =$ const. intersect orthogonally. If one family represents traces on the XY plane of the equipotential surfaces in an electrostatic field the other represents lines of force.

Consider, for instance, the function

$$F(z) = \{A(x + iy)\}^{1/2} = g(x, y) + ih(x, y).$$

Squaring and separating real and imaginary parts,

$$Ax = g^2 - h^2, \quad Ay = 2gh.$$

If we take $h(x, y)$ for the potential function V, we get, on eliminating $g(x, y)$,

$$A^2y^2 = 4V^2(Ax + V^2). \qquad (126\text{–}4)$$

The equipotential surfaces are parabolic cylinders as illustrated in Fig. 125, the trace of the surface of zero potential being the portion of the X axis extending from the origin indefinitely to the right. Replacing this surface by a charged conducting plane, we have in (126–4) the specification of the field in the neighborhood of the edge of such a plane.

To get the charge per unit area differentiate (126–4) with respect to y. Then

$$\frac{\partial V}{\partial y} = \frac{A^2y}{4V(Ax + 2V^2)} = \frac{A\sqrt{Ax + V^2}}{2(Ax + 2V^2)}$$

on eliminating y by means of (126–4). Putting $V = 0$ is equivalent to making y zero, so

$$\sigma = -\frac{\kappa}{4\pi}\left(\frac{\partial V}{\partial y}\right)_{y=0} = -\frac{\kappa}{8\pi}\sqrt{\frac{A}{x}}. \qquad (126\text{–}5)$$

This gives the charge on one side of the plane only. The charge

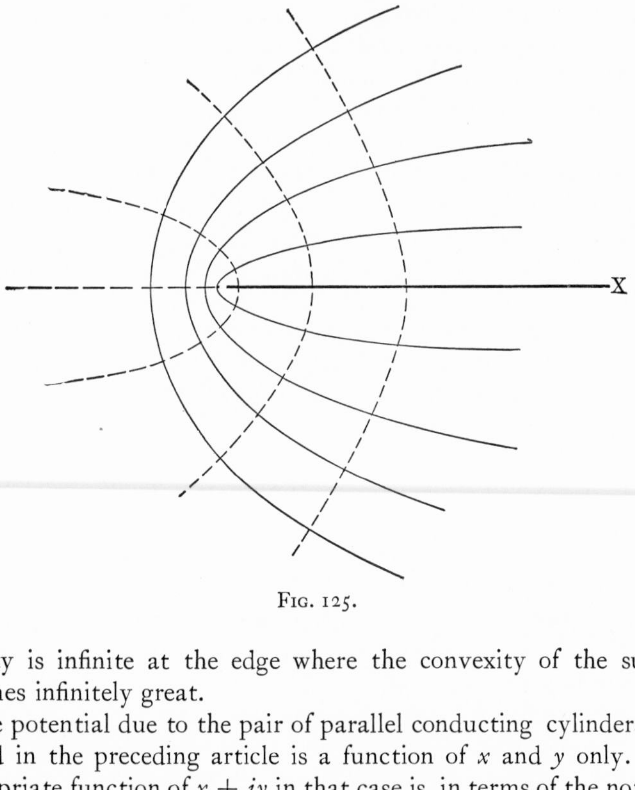

FIG. 125.

density is infinite at the edge where the convexity of the surface becomes infinitely great.

The potential due to the pair of parallel conducting cylinders discussed in the preceding article is a function of x and y only. The appropriate function of $x + iy$ in that case is, in terms of the notation of Fig. 124,

$$F(z) = \log\frac{x_2 + iy_2}{x_1 + iy_1} = \log\frac{r_2 e^{i\theta_2}}{r_1 e^{i\theta_1}} = \log\frac{r_2}{r_1} + i(\theta_2 - \theta_1).$$

Since the real part of the function represents the potential the equations of the lines of force are

$$\theta_2 - \theta_1 = \text{constant}. \qquad (126\text{–}6)$$

Problem 126a. Show that the imaginary part of $A(x + iy)^2$ represents the potential in the field of two plane conducting surfaces intersecting at right angles and find the charge density.

$$Ans. \quad \sigma = -\frac{\kappa A}{2\pi}x.$$

Problem 126b. Show that the lines of force represented by (126–6) are circles.

127. Magnetostatic Fields. — In magnetostatics we concern ourselves with magnetic poles at rest relative to the observer. Coulomb found that like poles repel and unlike poles attract with a force which varies inversely with the square of the distance between them. His experimental method was identical with that which he employed to find how the force between electric charges varies with the distance, the horizontal arm of the torsion balance being replaced by a bar magnet on which a torque is exerted by a pole of a second magnet which has been brought near to one pole of the suspended magnet.

If, now, we take as unit pole that pole, which, placed at a distance of one centimeter from a like equal pole *in vacuo*, repels it with a force of one dyne, the force between two poles m_1 and m_2 a distance r apart *in vacuo* is

$$F = \frac{m_1 m_2}{r^2}, \qquad (127\text{–}1)$$

a positive value of F indicating repulsion and a negative value attraction. No force exists between an electric charge and a magnetic pole both of which are at rest relative to the observer. The unit of pole defined above and the c.g.s. units of all quantities which are based upon equation (127–1) are known as *electromagnetic units* and designated by the abbreviation e.m.u.

As the law of force between magnetic poles is identical in form with that between electric charges, much of the theory developed in the earlier part of this chapter may be taken over bodily with nothing more than a change in the letters employed. Therefore without going into details we may summarize as follows:

The *magnetic intensity* or *field strength* **H** at a point in a magnetic field is the force that would be exerted on a unit positive pole at rest relative to the observer at the point in question. Therefore the force on a pole m is

$$\mathbf{F} = m\mathbf{H}. \qquad (127\text{–}2)$$

The electromagnetic unit of magnetic intensity is named the *oersted.*

The increase dV in magnetic potential is the work done against the magnetic intensity. Therefore

$$\mathbf{H} = -\nabla V. \tag{127–3}$$

Taking the potential to be zero at infinity, the magnetic potential due to a group of point poles m_1, m_2, m_3, etc., at distances r_1, r_2, r_3, etc., is

$$V = \sum \frac{m}{r}, \tag{127–4}$$

and that due to a continuous distribution of magnetism of pole strength ρ per unit volume is

$$V = \int_\tau \frac{\rho d\tau}{r}. \tag{127–5}$$

Defining the *magnetic flux* through an element of surface $d\mathbf{s}$ as the product of the component of the magnetic intensity normal to the surface by the area of the surface, Gauss' law for a magnetic field takes the integral form

$$\int_s \mathbf{H}\cdot d\mathbf{s} = 4\pi \int_\tau \rho d\tau, \tag{127–6}$$

or the differential form

$$\nabla \cdot \mathbf{H} = 4\pi\rho. \tag{127–7}$$

Furthermore we find by taking the curl of (127–3) that

$$\nabla \times \mathbf{H} = 0 \tag{127–8}$$

in a magnetostatic field. Equations (127–7) and (127–8) completely describe the field and are equivalent to Coulomb's law (127–1).

Lines of magnetic force are drawn in a magnetic field so as to have everywhere the direction of the magnetic intensity $\mathbf{H}$ and in such density that the number of bundles of M lines of force per unit cross-section, that is, the number of *tubes of force* per unit cross-section, is equal to the magnitude of the magnetic intensity. As in the electrical case, the magnetic flux through any surface is equal to the number of tubes of force passing through it, lines of force are continuous in regions containing no magnetic charges, and the number of tubes of force diverging from a pole m is equal to $4\pi m$.

Lines of force are directed perpendicular to equipotential surfaces from regions of higher potential toward those of lower potential.

From (127–7) and (127–3) we get Poisson's equation

$$\nabla \cdot \nabla V = -4\pi\rho \tag{127–9}$$

which reduces to Laplace's equation

$$\nabla \cdot \nabla V = 0 \tag{127–10}$$

in a region free from magnetic charges.

128. Magnetic Dipoles and Magnetic Shells. — The *magnetic dipole* or elementary magnet is the exact analog of the electric dipole discussed in article 112. If the two poles m and $-m$ are a distance l apart the *magnetic moment* $\mathbf{p}$ of the magnet is a vector directed along the line from $-m$ to m with the magnitude ml. By the same method as that employed in the electrical case we find for the potential at a distance r from a magnetic dipole large compared with its length

$$V = \frac{p}{r^2}\cos\theta = \frac{\mathbf{p}\cdot\mathbf{r}}{r^3}, \tag{128–1}$$

where θ is the angle between $\mathbf{r}$ and $\mathbf{p}$, and for the components of magnetic intensity in the directions of increasing r and increasing θ respectively

$$\left.\begin{aligned} H_r &= -\frac{\partial V}{\partial r} = \frac{2p}{r^3}\cos\theta, \\ H_\theta &= -\frac{\partial V}{r\partial\theta} = \frac{p}{r^3}\sin\theta. \end{aligned}\right\} \tag{128–2}$$

The energy of a magnetic dipole placed in an external field $\mathbf{H}$ so as to make an angle θ with the lines of force is

$$U = -\mathbf{p}\cdot\mathbf{H} = -pH\cos\theta \tag{128–3}$$

as in (112–3), the force it experiences is

$$\mathbf{F} = \mathbf{p}\cdot\nabla\mathbf{H} \tag{128–4}$$

from (112–4), and the torque about an origin from which the dipole is at a distance **r** is

$$\mathbf{L} = \mathbf{p} \times \mathbf{H} + \mathbf{r} \times \mathbf{F} \tag{128–5}$$

from (112–5), the first term representing the turning couple.

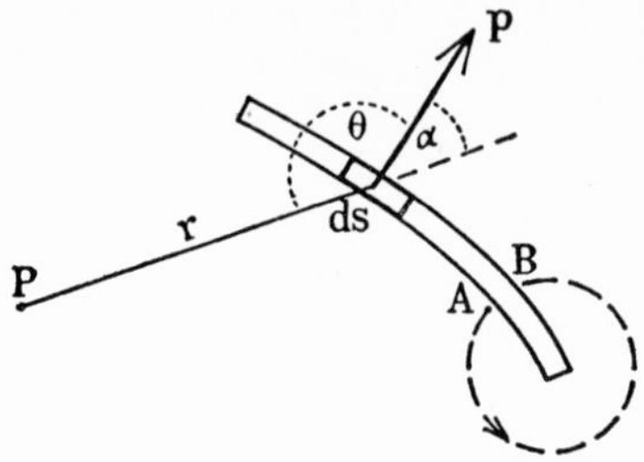

FIG. 126.

A *magnetic shell* is a thin sheet magnetized uniformly in a direction normal to its surface. The *strength* Φ of the shell is defined as the magnetic moment per unit area of its surface. Then the magnetic moment of a section of the shell of area ds (Fig. 126) is Φds and the potential at P due to it is

$$dV = \frac{\Phi ds}{r^2} \cos \theta = - \Phi \frac{ds \cos \alpha}{r^2}$$

from (128–1), since α is the supplement of the angle θ used previously. Therefore if $d\Omega$ is the solid angle subtended by ds at P,

$$dV = - \Phi d\Omega,$$

and the potential at P due to the entire shell is

$$V = - \int \Phi d\Omega. \tag{128–6}$$

Consider a shell of constant strength. Then

$$V = - \Phi\Omega, \tag{128–7}$$

where Ω is the solid angle subtended by the entire shell. So all magnetic shells of the same constant strength with coincident peripheries produce the same field at all exterior points irrespective of their shapes. Consider the work W done against the field in carrying a unit positive pole from a point A on the negative surface of the shell around the shell to an opposite point B on the positive side. We have

$$W = V_B - V_A = \Phi(\Omega_A - \Omega_B).$$

While Ω_A is positive, Ω_B, being the solid angle subtended at a point on the opposite side of the surface, is negative. But, as the thickness of the shell is negligible, the sum of the positive magnitudes of Ω_A and Ω_B is 4π. Hence

$$W = 4\pi\Phi. \tag{128–8}$$

Consider a magnetic shell of constant strength Φ placed in a magnetostatic field **H**. Taking the vector element of surface $d\mathbf{s}$ in the direction of the magnetic moment of the shell, we find for the energy of an element of the shell

$$dU = -\Phi\mathbf{H}\cdot d\mathbf{s}$$

from (128–3). Therefore the total energy of the shell is

$$U = -\Phi\int_s \mathbf{H}\cdot d\mathbf{s} = -\Phi N, \tag{128–9}$$

where N is the magnetic flux through the shell. As the flux through the shell depends only upon its periphery, all shells of the same strength with coincident peripheries have the same energy. To find the force on a rigid shell in a magnetic field suppose the shell to suffer a small displacement $d\xi$. If F is the component of the force on the shell in the direction of the displacement, the work done at the expense of the energy of the shell is $Fd\xi$. Therefore $Fd\xi = -dU = \Phi dN$, and

$$F = \Phi\frac{\partial N}{\partial\xi}. \tag{128–10}$$

Similarly the torque on the shell in the direction of the angular displacement $d\theta$ is

$$L = \Phi\frac{\partial N}{\partial\theta}. \tag{128–11}$$

We see from these expressions that the shell tends to move in such a direction as to increase the flux through it and that the force or torque on the shell depends only on its strength and its periphery.

Problem 128a. A magnetic dipole of moment p is placed at a distance r from a pole of strength m. Find the turning couple and the resultant force on it when its axis is (*a*) parallel to r, (*b*) perpendicular to r.

$$\textit{Ans.}\ (a)\ L = 0,\quad F_r = -2\frac{pm}{r^3},\quad (b)\ L = -\frac{pm}{r^2},\quad F_\theta = \frac{pm}{r^3}.$$

Problem 128b. A magnet M' is placed at a distant point on the extended axis of a magnet M with its axis perpendicular to that of M. Taking the center of either magnet as origin, show that the resultant torque on the one is equal and opposite to that on the other.

Problem 128c. Show that the magnetic intensity vanishes both inside and outside a closed magnetic shell of constant strength.

129. Measurement of H and p in Absolute Units. — In this article we shall describe a method of measuring both the strength H of a magnetic field and the magnetic moment p of a small bar magnet in absolute units.

For the moment suppose the field to be horizontal. Suspend the magnet by a torsionless fibre and set it in vibration in a horizontal plane. If θ is the angle between the axis of the magnet and the field the equation of motion is

$$I\frac{d^2\theta}{dt^2} = -\,pH\sin\theta$$

from (128–5), where I is the moment of inertia of the magnet. This is the differential equation (29–2) encountered in the theory of the simple pendulum. For small oscillations the period is

$$P = 2\pi\sqrt{\frac{I}{pH}},$$

or

$$pH = \frac{4\pi^2 I}{P^2}. \tag{129–1}$$

This equation gives the product pH in terms of easily measurable quantities. If the magnet is a cylindrical bar of radius a, length l and mass m, its moment of inertia is

$$I = m\left(\frac{a^2}{4}+\frac{l^2}{12}\right).$$

To find another relation involving p and H, fix the magnet in a horizontal position with its axis perpendicular to the field. At a distance r from the center of the magnet on the prolongation of its axis place a small compass needle free to turn in a horizontal plane. From (128–2) the compass needle is subject to a field $2p/r^3$ in the direction of the axis of the bar magnet as well as to the field H at right angles thereto. It will point in the direction of the resultant field, which makes an angle α with H given by

$$\tan \alpha = \frac{2p}{r^3 H}.$$

Therefore

$$\frac{p}{H} = \frac{1}{2} r^3 \tan \alpha \qquad (129\text{–}2)$$

gives the quotient of p and H in terms of easily measurable quantities. Eliminating p between this equation and (129–1) we find

$$H = \frac{2\pi}{P} \sqrt{\frac{2I}{r^3 \tan \alpha}}, \qquad (129\text{–}3)$$

and eliminating H

$$p = \frac{2\pi}{P} \sqrt{\frac{I r^3 \tan \alpha}{2}}. \qquad (129\text{–}4)$$

If the field is not horizontal this method of measurement gives only the horizontal component. But, as it is a simple matter to determine the dip of a field by means of a compass needle suspended at its center of mass and free to turn in a vertical plane, the total field strength is easily computed once the horizontal component is known.

Problem 129a. A cylindrical bar magnet of diameter 1 cm, length 10 cm and mass 100 gm vibrates 30 times a minute in a field H. When at a distance of 60 cm from its previous location with its axis at right angles to the field it deflects a compass needle 5° from the direction of H. Find the strength H of the field and the magnetic moment p of the bar magnet.

Ans. $H = 0.938$ e.m.u., $p = 8850$ e.m.u.

130. Magnetic Media. — With respect to their magnetic properties material substances are classified as ferromagnetic, paramagnetic or diamagnetic. When placed in a magnetic field those in the first two categories acquire a magnetic moment in the direction of the field, those in the last a magnetic moment opposite to the field. However, the magnetic moment acquired by the most strongly diamagnetic substances, such as bismuth, is very weak compared with that exhibited by many paramagnetic substances, which in turn are very weakly magnetic as compared with ferromagnetic substances such as iron, cobalt and nickel.

Although the law of force between magnetic poles has the same form as that between electric charges, magnets differ in one fundamental respect from electrified bodies. Every magnetized body is found to contain equal quantities of positive and negative magnetism. If a bar magnet is broken in two it becomes two magnets and there is no reason to believe that further division would not continue to produce the same effect until the molecules of the substance are reached. This fact, together with the possibility of magnetizing an iron bar by placing it in a magnetic field and tapping it with a hammer, the loss of magnetic properties at high temperatures, the phenomenon of saturation in ferromagnetic substances, and the like, has led to the molecular theory of magnetism.

On this theory each molecule or atom of a magnetic substance is assumed to be a magnetic dipole. In the case of a diamagnetic substance the magnetic dipoles are called into being by the impressed field, like the electric dipoles in a dielectric. In the case of a paramagnetic or ferromagnetic substance, on the other hand, the molecules are supposed to be permanent magnetic dipoles. When the body is unmagnetized the elementary magnets are oriented at random so that as many point in one direction as in any other. In this state the body as a whole shows no magnetic properties. When the body is placed in a magnetic field, the elementary magnets are swung around more or less into line with the field, and the body exhibits uncompensated poles at its ends. As the strength of the field is increased the elementary magnets turn more and more into line with the field until they are all parallel to it, after which no further increase in the strength of the impressed field produces any additional magnetization. Thus the phenomenon of saturation is simply accounted for.

Modern experiments indicate that the elementary magnets referred to here as molecules are really groups of molecules acting in unison. Individual groups, known as *domains*, may have volumes as great as $(10)^{-9}\text{cm}^3$.

We find the magnetic charge per unit volume in a magnetic medium precisely as in the case of a dielectric. If we define the *magnetization* **I** as the net magnetic moment per unit volume, it is only necessary to replace the electric polarization **P** in the formulae of article 112 by **I**. Thus we find for the magnetization charge per unit volume

$$\rho_I = -\nabla\cdot\mathbf{I}, \qquad (130\text{–}1)$$

and if we wish to express the pole-strength in the transition layer at the surface of a magnet separately from that in the body of the substance we have for the magnetization charge per unit area

$$\sigma_I = I_n, \qquad (130\text{–}2)$$

where I_n is the component of the magnetization inside the medium along the outward drawn normal to the surface.

Following the procedure of article 113 we find for Gauss' law in a region containing magnetic material

$$\int_s (\mathbf{H} + 4\pi\mathbf{I})\cdot d\mathbf{s} = 0,$$

since the magnetic case differs from the electrical analog in that no free magnetic charges exist in nature. So if we define the *magnetic induction* **B** by the relation

$$\mathbf{B} \equiv \mathbf{H} + 4\pi\mathbf{I}$$

Gauss' law takes the form

$$\int_s \mathbf{B}\cdot d\mathbf{s} = 0. \qquad (130\text{–}3)$$

The electromagnetic unit of magnetic induction is named the *gauss*. Since **B** and **H** have the same physical dimensions, the gauss and the oersted are identical.

We define the *flux of induction* through an element of surface $d\mathbf{s}$ as the product of the component of **B** normal to the surface by ds. It follows from (130–3) that the flux of induction through any closed surface vanishes. If we draw lines and tubes of induction defined in terms of **B** in exactly the same way that lines and tubes of force were defined in terms of **H**, we see from (130–3) that lines of induction, unlike lines of force, are everywhere continuous even when we pass out of a magnet through the pole on its end to the empty space beyond.

Following the procedure used several times previously we can express Gauss' law in the differential form

$$\nabla\cdot\mathbf{B} = 0, \qquad (130\text{–}4)$$

from which it follows that **B** is everywhere a solenoidal vector. Also we have in a magnetic medium, as well as in empty space, the equation

$$\nabla\times\mathbf{H} = 0, \qquad (130\text{–}5)$$

which expresses the fact that **H** is everywhere an irrotational vector. In addition to (130–4) and (130–5) we need a relation between **B** and **H** in order to describe the field in a permeable medium completely.

The boundary conditions at the surface of separation of two permeable media are found by the same method (art. 113) as in the case of dielectrics. They are

$$B_{2n} = B_{1n}, \tag{130-6}$$

$$V_2 = V_1. \tag{130-7}$$

The fields available in the laboratory are altogether too small to saturate a paramagnetic substance. Hence we may take over (116–2) from the theory of dielectrics composed of permanent dipoles, writing for the case of the homogeneous isotropic paramagnetic medium

$$\mathbf{I} = \frac{np_0^2}{3kT}\mathbf{H}_1, \tag{130-8}$$

where n is the number per unit volume of permanent magnetic dipoles of moment p_0 and $\mathbf{H}_1$ is the field due to external sources, the magnetization of the medium, and the attractions and repulsions of neighboring dipoles. This relation is known as *Curie's* law. Then

$$\mathbf{I} = \epsilon\mathbf{H} \tag{130-9}$$

just as in the electrostatic analog, the *magnetic susceptibility* ϵ being related to the ratio σ of I to H_1 by the same equation (115–6). As will be shown later, (130–9) also holds for a diamagnetic substance with a negative value of ϵ. Hence we have for either a paramagnetic or a diamagnetic homogeneous isotropic medium

$$\begin{aligned} \mathbf{B} &= (1 + 4\pi\epsilon)\mathbf{H} \\ &= \mu\mathbf{H}, \end{aligned} \tag{130-10}$$

where the dimensionless constant $\mu \equiv 1 + 4\pi\epsilon$ is called the *permeability* of the substance. It is the analog of the permittivity of a dielectric. It is well to note, however, that although the permittivity of no substance is less than unity, the permeability of a diamagnetic substance is slightly less. In the next chapter we shall develop a simple explanation of diamagnetism on Ampère's theory of magnetism. The dipole theory is unable to account for this phenomenon.

In the case of a ferromagnetic substance a relation of the form of (130–10) has little significance, since $\mathbf{B}$ is not only not proportional to $\mathbf{H}$, but is a function of the history of the specimen as well as of the field in which it lies.

Although an isolated magnetic point pole does not exist in nature, such a pole can be realized approximately by using one end of a very long needle-like permanent magnet. Suppose such a magnet to be immersed in a paramagnetic fluid. We wish to find the magnetic intensity at a distance r from the positive pole small compared with the length of the magnet. Let a be the cross-section of the needle, I the magnetization in the needle and B the magnetic induction in the fluid. Applying Gauss' law (130–3) to a spherical surface of radius r described about the positive pole we have $(4\pi r^2 - a)B$ for the flux of induction through the portion of the sphere not cut by the magnet and $a(H - 4\pi I)$ for the flux through the portion cut, the minus sign in front of I being due to the fact that the magnetization is along the inward drawn normal to the surface. If the needle is uniformly magnetized I is constant throughout it, the magnetic charge per unit area on the end is equal to I, and the strength m of the positive pole is Ia. Therefore Gauss' law gives

$$(4\pi r^2 - a)B + aH - 4\pi m = 0.$$

If the cross-section of the needle is very small we can neglect the terms containing the factor a and get

$$B = \frac{m}{r^2}.$$

Therefore, as $B = \mu H$,

$$H = \frac{m}{\mu r^2}, \qquad (130\text{–}11)$$

The stresses in a paramagnetic medium can be treated in a manner analogous to that used in the case of a dielectric in article 118. Corresponding to (118–14) for the force between two charges immersed in a fluid dielectric we find for the force between two poles m_1 and m_2 a distance r apart in a fluid of permeability μ the expression

$$F = \frac{m_1 m_2}{\mu r^2}. \qquad (130\text{–}12)$$

It follows from (130–11) that the potential due to a number of point poles immersed in a magnetic medium is

$$V = \sum \frac{m}{\mu r}. \qquad (130\text{–}13)$$

In the last three formulae the effect of the magnetization of the fluid is taken care of by the factor μ and therefore the poles m do not include the magnetic charges produced in the medium by its magnetization.

Problem 130a. A thin magnet of cross-section a and length l lies on the X axis with its nearer end at a distance b from the origin. The magnetization in the magnet is kx parallel to the X axis. Find the strength of the pole at each end, the volume density of magnetism in the interior of the magnet, and show that the total magnetic charge is zero. Also find the potential at the origin.

$$Ans.\ -kab,\quad ka(b+l),\quad -k,\quad -ka\log\left(1+\frac{l}{b}\right).$$

131. Kelvin's Specifications of B and H. — Kelvin has shown that **B** and **H** in a magnetic medium may each be interpreted as a force experienced by a unit pole placed in a cavity of appropriate shape. Consider, for instance, a block of iron (Fig. 127). From it we shall cut out a needlelike cavity AB parallel to the magnetization I. On the ends of the cavity appear poles of strength I and $-I$ per unit area, but if the cross-section of the cavity is small enough these poles are so weak as to produce no appreciable effect at a point P at the center of the cavity. Therefore the force on a unit positive pole placed at P is the magnetic intensity of the external field together with that due to the poles I_n per unit area on the surface of the body and $-\nabla\cdot\mathbf{I}$ per unit volume in its interior. Consequently this force is just the total magnetic intensity **H** existing at the point P in the block before the cavity was cut out.

If, on the other hand, we cut out a very thin pill-box shaped cavity CD the bases of which are perpendicular to the magnetization, the magnetic charges I and $-I$ per unit area on the bases of the cavity give rise to an appreciable force on a unit positive pole placed at its center Q. To calculate this force we observe that the surfaces of the pill-box constitute the magnetic analog of a parallel plate condenser. Therefore the force per unit pole is $4\pi\mathbf{I}$. In addition to this we have the force **H** due to the external field and the magnetic charges on the surface and in the interior of the block. Consequently the force on a unit positive pole placed at Q is the magnetic induction $\mathbf{B} = \mathbf{H} + 4\pi\mathbf{I}$ existing at Q before the cavity was cut out.

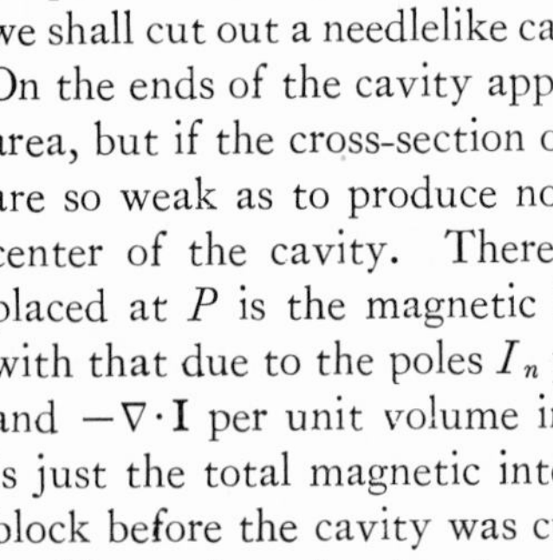

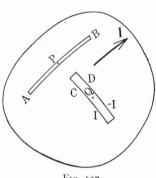

Fig. 127.

Consider an isolated uniformly magnetized bar magnet of length large compared with its diameter. The field at a point just outside the flat positive end of the magnet is determined by the magnetic charge on this end of the magnet alone since the negative pole is too far away to produce any appreciable effect. If the magnetization is I, the charge per unit area on the end of the magnet is also I, and since this flat uniformly charged surface is the magnetic analog of a uniformly charged plane the magnetic intensity H just outside the end of the magnet is $2\pi I$. Since this point is outside of the magnetic material, B is equal to H.

Now consider a point just inside the positive end of the magnet. As it is on the opposite side of the charged end surface, $H = -2\pi I$, and $B = H + 4\pi I = 2\pi I$, the same as outside. Finally take a point in the magnet midway between the two poles. Here H is negligibly small on account of the remoteness of the poles and therefore $B = H + 4\pi I = 4\pi I$. Thus the magnetic induction at the middle of the magnet is twice that at the ends and consequently half of the lines of induction passing through the central cross-section pass out of the magnet before reaching its end.

In the case of a permanent magnet such as that under discussion the permeability μ has little meaning. Thus the quotient of B by H just inside the end of the magnet is -1 and at the center $-\infty$.

132. Interaction of Two Uniformly Magnetized Spheres Immersed in a Paramagnetic Fluid. — Although (130–12) specifies correctly the force between two point poles immersed in a homogeneous isotropic paramagnetic fluid, it cannot be used to find the force or torque exerted by one extended magnet on another. To illustrate this fact, we shall calculate the field due to a permanent magnet M (Fig. 128) in the form of a uniformly magnetized sphere of radius a, and find the torque which it exerts on a second similar magnet M' of radius a' located on the extended axis of the first at a great distance R and oriented with its magnetic axis perpendicular to that of the first. This is the arrangement

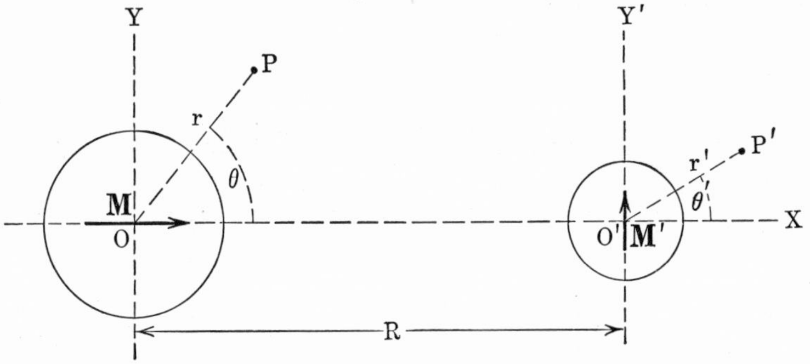

FIG. 128.

of magnets employed in the magnetometer (art. 129).

It is shown in the same manner as in the case of a dielectric (art.

114) that there can be no magnetization charge in the interior of a homogeneous isotropic paramagnetic or diamagnetic medium. Therefore it follows from (127–10) that the magnetic potential in the fluid in which the magnets M and M' are immersed is a solution of Laplace's equation. Furthermore, as the two magnets are uniformly magnetized, $\nabla \cdot \mathbf{I} = 0$ and consequently no magnetization charge is present in their interior. So here, too, the potential is a solution of Laplace's equation.

First we shall calculate the field of M in the absence of M'. Since $\mathbf{I}$ is parallel to the magnetic moment of M, its radial component is $I \cos \theta$. So only those potential functions which are linear in $\cos \theta$ will serve to satisfy the boundary conditions of the problem. Hence we need the two solutions (79–13) of Laplace's equation; the first, since it is finite at the origin, representing the potential inside the magnet, and the second, since it vanishes at infinity, representing the potential outside. Distinguishing the regions inside and outside M by the subscripts i and o, we have then

$$V_i = Ar \cos \theta, \quad V_o = C \frac{\cos \theta}{r^2}.$$

Remembering that $\mathbf{B} = \mathbf{H} + 4\pi \mathbf{I}$ inside the magnet and $\mathbf{B} = \mu \mathbf{H}$ outside, where $\mathbf{H} = -\nabla V$ in either region, the boundary conditions (130–6) and (130–7) at $r = a$ give

$$-A \cos \theta + 4\pi I \cos \theta = 2\mu \frac{C}{a^3} \cos \theta,$$

$$Aa \cos \theta = \frac{C}{a^2} \cos \theta,$$

from which we find that $C = 4\pi a^3 I/(2\mu + 1)$. So, as the magnetic moment p of the magnet is $(4/3)\pi a^3 I$, the potential in the paramagnetic fluid in which it is immersed is

$$V_o = \frac{p}{\gamma r^2} \cos \theta, \quad \gamma \equiv \frac{2\mu + 1}{3}. \qquad (132–1)$$

We see, then, that the field outside the magnet is diminished in the ratio $1/\gamma$ instead of in the ratio $1/\mu$ as might have been erroneously inferred by applying (130–11) to an extended distribution of magnetic charge. If μ is considerably greater than unity, γ differs very appreciably from μ.

The magnetic intensity due to M in the neighborhood of M' before the latter is placed in the medium can be considered, as a good approximation, to be constant and equal to that at the center of M', namely

$$H_o = -\left(\frac{\partial V_o}{\partial r}\right)_{\substack{r=R\\ \theta=o}} = \frac{2p}{\gamma R^3} = \left(\frac{\mu}{\gamma}\right)\frac{2p}{\mu R^3}. \tag{132–2}$$

Before considering the field due to M' we must consider how the otherwise constant field H_o is modified by the presence of the spherical cavity in which M' is placed. Taking a new origin O' at the center of this cavity, and designating the distance of a point P' in the fluid by r' and the angle which r' makes with the X axis by θ', we have for the potentials inside and outside the cavity

$$V'_{Ci} = A'r' \cos\theta', \quad V'_{Co} = -H_o r' \cos\theta' + C'\frac{\cos\theta'}{r'^2},$$

the first term in the expression for V'_{Co} being due to the fact that the field far from O' is the constant H_o. The boundary conditions for r' equal to the radius a' of the cavity are

$$-A'\cos\theta' = \mu\left\{H_o\cos\theta' + \frac{2C'}{a'^3}\cos\theta'\right\},$$

$$A'a'\cos\theta' = -H_o a'\cos\theta' + \frac{C'}{a'^2}\cos\theta'.$$

Solving for C' and substituting in the expression for V'_{Co} we find for the potential outside the cavity

$$V'_{Co} = -\left\{1 + \frac{\mu - 1}{2\mu + 1}\frac{a'^3}{r'^3}\right\}H_o r'\cos\theta'. \tag{132–3}$$

The potential in the surrounding medium due to the magnet M' is given by a formula analogous to (132–1), θ being replaced by the angle ϕ' which the radius vector r' makes with the magnetic moment p' of M'. It is

$$V'_{mo} = \frac{p'}{\gamma r'^2}\cos\phi'. \tag{132–4}$$

To compute the turning couple on M' we must calculate the shears on a spherical surface lying in the medium just outside the spherical magnet. The stress dyadic is identical in form with (118–10), the components of $\mathbf{E}$ being replaced by those of $\mathbf{H}$ and κ by μ.

As the only non-vanishing component of torque is that about the Z' axis, it will simplify the calculation to take a new set of spherical coordinates with O' as origin so that the polar axis is parallel to Z'. If α is the polar angle and β the azimuth, $\cos\theta' = \sin\alpha\cos\beta$ and $\cos\phi' = \sin\alpha\sin\beta$. Hence the total potential outside M', obtained by adding (132–3) and (132–4), is

$$V'_o = \frac{p'}{\gamma r'^2}\sin\alpha\sin\beta - \left\{1 + \frac{\mu - 1}{2\mu + 1}\frac{a'^3}{r'^3}\right\} H_o r' \sin\alpha\cos\beta. \qquad (132\text{–}5)$$

Replacing the unit vectors $\mathbf{i}$, $\mathbf{j}$, $\mathbf{k}$ in (118–10) by $\mathbf{r}_1$, $\boldsymbol{\alpha}_1$, $\boldsymbol{\beta}_1$ in the directions of increasing r', α, β respectively, κ by μ, E_x by H_r etc., the stress at any point on the surface of the spherical magnet M' is $\mathbf{r}_1\cdot\Psi$ from (47–10). Picking out the shear B_r in the direction of increasing β, which alone gives rise to a torque about Z', we find

$$\mathrm{B}_r = \frac{\mu}{4\pi}H_r H_\beta = \frac{\mu}{4\pi}\frac{\partial V_o'}{\partial r'}\frac{\partial V_o'}{r'\sin\alpha\partial\beta}, \quad r' = a'.$$

As the lever arm of this shear is $a'\sin\alpha$ we have for the turning couple about z'

$$L = \int_0^{2\pi}\int_0^{\pi} \mathrm{B}_r\,(a'\sin\alpha)\,a'^2\sin\alpha d\alpha d\beta$$

$$= -\frac{\mu}{\gamma}M'H_o$$

after a simple integration.

Finally, replacing H_o by (132–2) we find that the couple acting on M' is

$$L = -\left(\frac{\mu}{\gamma}\right)^2\frac{2pp'}{\mu R^3}, \quad \gamma \equiv \frac{2\mu + 1}{3}, \qquad (132\text{–}6)$$

instead of $-2pp'/\mu R^3$ as would be wrongly inferred if (130–12) were applied to the calculation of the torque. It should be noted that the factor μ/γ appears once in the calculation of the field due to M and again in the calculation of the torque exerted by this field on M'. Also attention must be drawn to the fact that γ is a geometrical coefficient, being a different function of μ for a spheroidal magnet than for a spherical magnet. The analogous problem in electrostatics leads to precisely similar results.

Problem 132a. Replacing the magnet M' of this article by a sphere with a uniform magnetic charge m', find the force exerted by M on m'.

$$\textit{Ans.}\quad \left(\frac{\mu}{\gamma}\right)\frac{2m'p}{\mu R^3}.$$

REFERENCES

PAGE AND ADAMS: *Principles of Electricity*, D. Van Nostrand Co., New York.

JEANS, J. H.: *Electricity and Magnetism*, Cambridge University Press, Cambridge.

LIVENS, G. H.: *The Theory of Electricity*, Cambridge University Press, Cambridge.

CHAPTER XI

ELECTRIC CURRENTS

133. Ampère's Law. — Although an electric charge at rest relative to the observer produces no effect on a magnetic pole, Oersted discovered in 1819 that a current of electricity in a wire deflects a compass needle so as to turn it into a position at right angles to the wire. The next year Ampère showed that electric currents exert forces on one another and gave the complete theory of the interaction between one electric current and another or between an electric current and a magnetic pole. Later Rowland showed that a convection current produced by the rapid motion of a charged body produces the same magnetic field as a conduction current in a wire.

The *current density* $\mathbf{j}$ at any point is a vector in the direction of the flow of positive electricity equal to the charge passing through a unit cross-section in a unit time. The total current i through any surface s is then the integral of $\mathbf{j}\cdot d\mathbf{s}$ over the given surface, that is,

$$i = \int_s \mathbf{j}\cdot d\mathbf{s}. \qquad (133\text{–}1)$$

Generally we deal with a current in a wire. If the current density is uniform throughout the cross-section s of the wire, as in the case of a direct or slowly alternating current, (133–1) reduces to $i = js$. Furthermore, in calculating the magnetic field at a distance from the wire large compared with its diameter, we can treat the current as if it were linear, that is, flowing along a path of negligible cross-section.

Consider a closed circuit ABC (Fig. 129) around which a current i is flowing in the sense of the arrow. Then *Ampère's law*, in the form in which we shall state it, gives for the magnetic intensity $d\mathbf{H}$ at P due to the current in the portion of the circuit of length $d\mathbf{l}$ at A

$$d\mathbf{H} = i\frac{d\mathbf{l}\times\mathbf{r}}{cr^3}, \qquad (133\text{–}2)$$

where $\mathbf{r}$ is the vector distance of P from A. In this formula i is measured in e.s.u., that is, the current i is the number of electrostatic units of charge passing a given cross-section of the circuit per second, and $d\mathbf{H}$ is measured in e.m.u. as in the last chapter. The constant c, which may be determined experimentally by a method to be described later, has the value $2.99790(10)^{10}$ cm/sec, which, for most purposes of computation, may be taken as $2.998(10)^{10}$ cm/sec or even $3(10)^{10}$ cm/sec with sufficient accuracy. The system of c.g.s. units which employs the e.s.u. of electric quantities (including current, electromotive force, capacitance, resistance, inductance) and the e.m.u. of magnetic quantities, is known as the *Gaussian system*. This system will be employed throughout this chapter.

The field $d\mathbf{H}$ at P is perpendicular to the plane of $d\mathbf{l}$ and $\mathbf{r}$ in the sense of advance of a right-handed screw rotated from the first to the second of these vectors. It is proportional in magnitude to $\sin\theta$ and inversely proportional to the square of the distance r. To find the total magnetic intensity at P due to the entire circuit we must integrate (133–2) around the circuit.

Evidently the lines of force produced by a current element of length dl are circles surrounding the element. Therefore the net magnetic flux out of any closed surface is zero. Since this statement is true for the field of every current element comprised in a current circuit, it holds for the resultant field produced by any arrangement of currents.

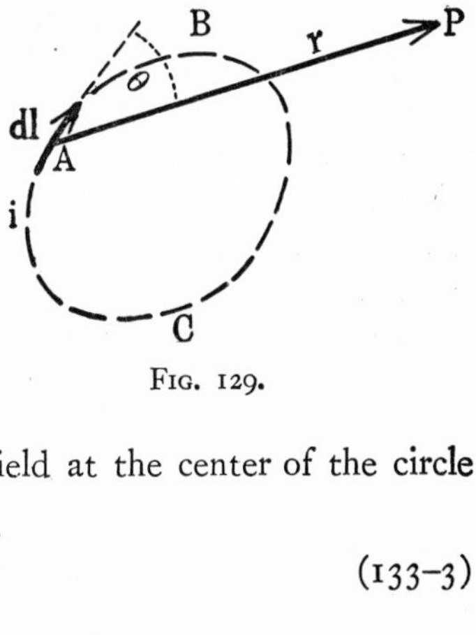

FIG. 129.

If a current i flows around a circular turn of wire of radius r we get from (133–2) for the magnetic field at the center of the circle

$$H = \frac{2\pi i}{cr} \tag{133–3}$$

in the direction of advance of a right-handed screw rotated in the plane of the circuit in the sense of the current.

Consider a pole m placed at P in Fig. 129. The force on it due to the current element at A is

$$m d\mathbf{H} = \frac{m}{r^2}\frac{i d\mathbf{l} \times \mathbf{r}}{cr}.$$

According to the law of action and reaction the pole m must exert an equal and opposite force on the current element at A. The field H at A due to the pole m is m/r^2 in the direction opposite to the radius vector $\mathbf{r}$. Therefore the force on the current element is

$$d\mathbf{F} = \frac{1}{c} i d\mathbf{l} \times \mathbf{H}. \qquad (133\text{–}4)$$

As there is no reference to the pole m in this equation we can take it as representing the force on a current element placed in any magnetic field, whatever its origin.

In terms of the current density $\mathbf{j}$ (133–4) becomes

$$d\mathbf{F} = \frac{1}{c} \mathbf{j} \times \mathbf{H}\, s dl,$$

where s is the cross-section of the current element. But sdl is the volume of the current element. Therefore the force per unit volume is

$$\mathbf{F} = \frac{1}{c} \mathbf{j} \times \mathbf{H}. \qquad (133\text{–}5)$$

It may be noted that the law of action and reaction, although valid for the interaction of a pole and a current element or of two complete current circuits, does not hold in general for the interaction of one current element with another. For, if we distinguish the two current elements under consideration by the subscripts 1 and 2, and designate the vector distance of the second from the first by $\mathbf{r}_{12}$, the magnetic field produced at the second by the first is

$$d\mathbf{H}_2 = \frac{i_1 d\mathbf{l}_1 \times \mathbf{r}_{12}}{cr^3}$$

where r is the scalar magnitude of $\mathbf{r}_{12}$, and the force on the second is

$$d^2\mathbf{F}_2 = \frac{i_1 i_2 d\mathbf{l}_2 \times (d\mathbf{l}_1 \times \mathbf{r}_{12})}{c^2 r^3}$$

from (133–4). Similarly the force exerted on the first by the magnetic field of the second is

$$d^2\mathbf{F}_1 = \frac{i_2 i_1 d\mathbf{l}_1 \times (d\mathbf{l}_2 \times \mathbf{r}_{21})}{c^2 r^3}$$

where $\mathbf{r}_{21} = -\mathbf{r}_{12}$. The vector sum of these two forces is

$$d^2\mathbf{F}_1 + d^2\mathbf{F}_2 = \frac{i_1 i_2 (d\mathbf{l}_2 \times d\mathbf{l}_1) \times \mathbf{r}_{12}}{c^2 r^3},$$

which vanishes only when the two current elements are parallel or both are perpendicular to $\mathbf{r}_{12}$. In the next chapter we shall see that the law of action and reaction and its corollary, the law of conservation of linear momentum, are valid only when we take into account the electromagnetic momentum of the field as well as that of the material particles involved.*

Let us calculate the magnetic intensity at a point P (Fig. 130) on the axis of a circular turn of wire of radius a at a distance x from

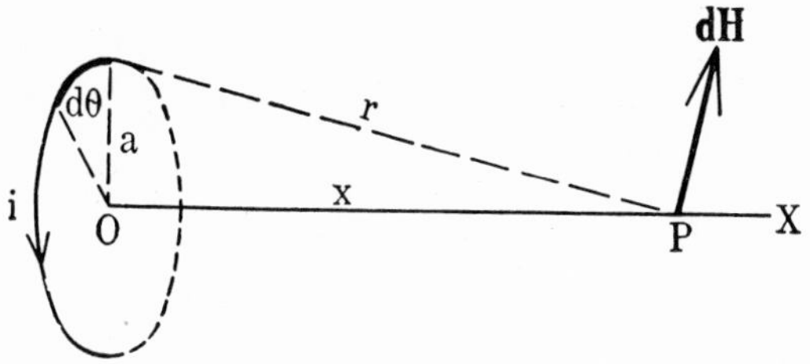

FIG. 130

its center. The field due to the current element subtended by the angle $d\theta$ is

$$|d\mathbf{H}| = \frac{ia\,d\theta}{cr^2}$$

from Ampère's law. From symmetry it is clear that the only component of the field which does not vanish on integration is that along the X axis. Therefore

$$H = H_x = \frac{1}{c}\int_0^{2\pi} \frac{ia}{r^2}\cdot\frac{a}{r}\,d\theta = \frac{2\pi i a^2}{cr^3} = \frac{2\pi i a^2}{c(a^2 + x^2)^{3/2}}. \qquad (133\text{-}6)$$

If the single turn of wire is replaced by a coil of N turns close together the field is N times as great.

Finally we shall compute the magnetic intensity at a point O

* For a detailed discussion see Page and Adams, *Am. Jour. Phys.* **13**, p. 141 (1945).

(Fig. 131) on the axis of a circular solenoid of radius a and length L containing N turns. A section of the solenoid of length dx contains $(N/L)dx$ turns and the field due to it is

$$dH = \frac{2\pi i a^2}{c(a^2 + x^2)^{3/2}} \frac{N}{L} dx$$

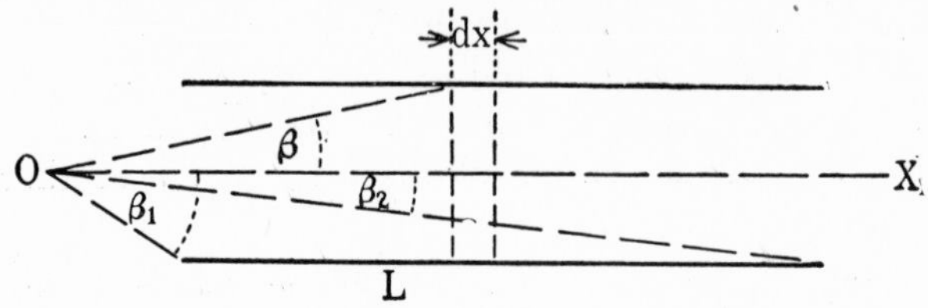

FIG. 131

parallel to the axis of the solenoid by (133–6). Put

$$x = a \cot \beta, \quad dx = -a \csc^2 \beta d\beta.$$

Then

$$\left. \begin{aligned} H &= -\frac{2\pi N}{cL} i \int_{\beta_1}^{\beta_2} \sin \beta d\beta \\ &= \frac{2\pi N}{cL} i(\cos \beta_2 - \cos \beta_1). \end{aligned} \right\} \qquad (133\text{–}7)$$

If the length of the solenoid is large compared with its radius $\cos \beta_1 = -1$, $\cos \beta_2 = 1$ at a point near the center, and if we put n for the number of turns per unit length.

$$H = \frac{4\pi n i}{c}. \qquad (133\text{–}8)$$

At the end of the solenoid $\cos \beta_1 = 0$, $\cos \beta_2 = 1$ and

$$H = \frac{2\pi n i}{c}. \qquad (133\text{–}9)$$

Therefore half the lines of force passing through the central section of the solenoid pass out through the sides before reaching the end. Consequently the H field of a long solenoid is identical with the B field of the uniformly magnetized bar magnet discussed in article 131.

Problem 133a. Check (133–2) as regards physical dimensions.

Problem 133b. Find the magnetic intensity at a distance R from (a) a finite straight current in terms of the angles β_1 and β_2 made by lines drawn to the ends of the current with the perpendicular to the current, (*b*) an infinitely long straight current.

Ans. (*a*) $\frac{i}{cR}(\sin\beta_2 - \sin\beta_1)$, (*b*) $2\frac{i}{cR}$.

Problem 133c. Find the field due to a rectangular circuit of dimensions $2l_1$ and $2l_2$ at a point P in the plane of the circuit on the perpendicular bisector of the side of length $2l_1$ at a distance R from the center of the rectangle. If R is very large compared to l_1 and l_2, to what does this expression reduce?

$$Ans.\ \frac{2i}{cl_1}\left\{\frac{\sqrt{(R-l_2)^2+l_1^2}}{R-l_2}-\frac{\sqrt{(R+l_2)^2+l_1^2}}{R+l_2}\right\},\quad \frac{i(2l_1)(2l_2)}{cR^3}.$$

Problem 133d. A conductor in the form of a long circular cylinder contains a cavity in the form of a parallel, but not co-axial, circular cylinder. If the current density **j** is constant throughout the conductor, show that the magnetic field in the cavity is uniform and equal to

$$\mathbf{H} = \frac{2\pi\mathbf{j}\times\mathbf{r}}{c},$$

where **r** is the vector distance of the axis of the cavity from that of the conductor.

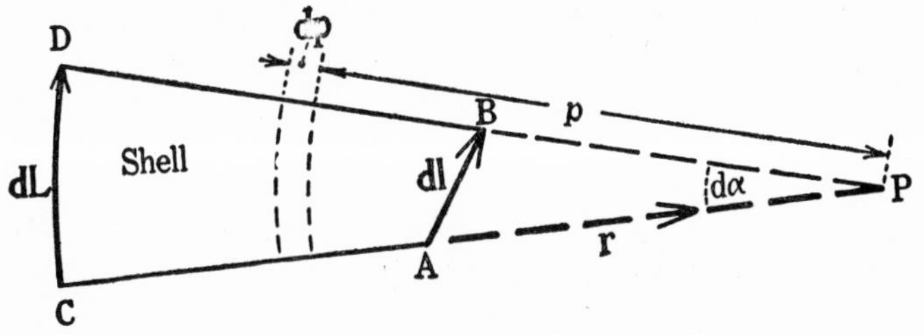

FIG. 132.

134. Magnetic Shell Equivalent to Current Circuit. — Consider a magnetic shell of constant strength Φ in the shape of the plane figure *ABDC* (Fig. 132) of infinitesimal width extending from *AB* to *CD*. Let the sides *DB* and *CA* subtend the angle $d\alpha$ at P and take the front surface of the shell as the positive side. We want to find the magnetic intensity at P due to the shell. The magnetic moment of the section of the shell included between the arc described about P of radius p and that of radius $p + dp$ is $\Phi dp\, pd\alpha$ directed outwards from the paper, and from (128–2) the field at P due to this element of the shell is

$$d^2H = \frac{\Phi dp\, pd\alpha}{p^3} = \Phi d\alpha\frac{dp}{p^2}$$

directed inward, as $\theta = 90°$ in the formulae (128–2). Integrating with respect to p from $PA = r$ to $PC = R$ the field at P due to the entire shell is

$$dH = \Phi d\alpha \int_r^R \frac{dp}{p^2} = \frac{\Phi d\alpha}{r} - \frac{\Phi d\alpha}{R}$$

$$= \frac{\Phi r^2 d\alpha}{r^3} - \frac{\Phi R^2 d\alpha}{R^3}.$$

Now $r^2 d\alpha$ is twice the area of the triangle ABP and therefore equal to the magnitude of the vector $d\mathbf{l} \times \mathbf{r}$ and, if $\mathbf{R}$ is the vector distance of P from C, $R^2 d\alpha$ is equal to the magnitude of the vector $d\mathbf{L} \times \mathbf{R}$. As both of these vectors have the direction of $d\mathbf{H}$, the magnetic intensity at the point P is given both in magnitude and in direction by the vector equation

$$d\mathbf{H} = \Phi \left\{ \frac{d\mathbf{l} \times \mathbf{r}}{r^3} - \frac{d\mathbf{L} \times \mathbf{R}}{R^3} \right\}.$$

Next let us consider a closed curve $ABCD$ (Fig. 133) of any shape and size. With any point P as vertex introduce a magnetic shell in

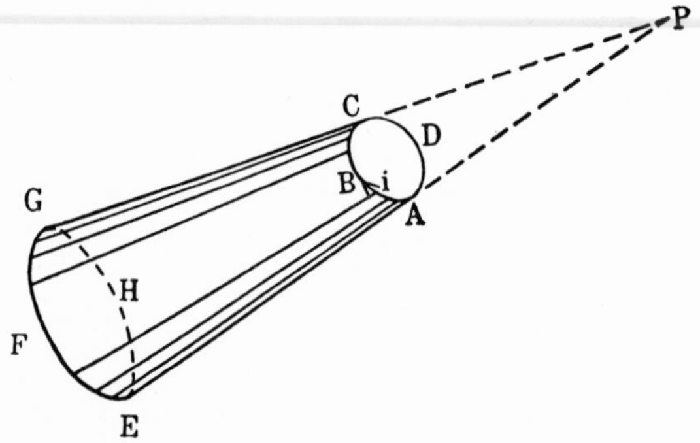

FIG. 133.

the form of a truncated cone extending from the closed curve $ABCD$ to the closed curve $EFGH$ at a distance R from P. Let this shell be closed over $EFGH$ by a shell of the same constant strength Φ in the form of a spherical cap of radius R about P as center, the side more remote from P being the positive side.

From the expression above the magnetic field $\mathbf{H}_1$ at P due to the conical part of the shell is

$$\mathbf{H}_1 = \Phi \oint_{ABCD} \frac{d\mathbf{l} \times \mathbf{r}}{r^3} - \Phi \oint_{EFGH} \frac{d\mathbf{L} \times \mathbf{R}}{R^3}$$

and, if $d\,\Omega$ is the solid angle subtended at P by an element of the spherical cap $EFGH$, the magnetic field $\mathbf{H}_2$ at P due to the cap is

$$\mathbf{H}_2 = -\int_{Cap} \frac{2\Phi R^2 d\Omega}{R^3} \left(\frac{\mathbf{R}}{R}\right)$$

from (128–2), since here $\theta = 180°$ in the formulae.

The total field at P produced by the shell of periphery $ABCD$ is then

$$\mathbf{H} = \mathbf{H}_1 + \mathbf{H}_2 = \Phi \oint_{ABCD} \frac{d\mathbf{l} \times \mathbf{r}}{r^3} + \frac{2\Phi}{R^3}\left\{-\oint_{EFGH} \frac{1}{2} d\mathbf{L} \times \mathbf{R} - \int_{Cap} R^2 d\Omega \left(\frac{\mathbf{R}}{R}\right)\right\}$$

$$= \Phi \oint_{ABCD} \frac{d\mathbf{l} \times \mathbf{r}}{r^3}. \qquad (134\text{–}1)$$

since the expression in the braces vanishes because it represents the vector area of the closed surface comprising the cone extending all the way from P to $EFGH$ and the cap closing the open end of this cone.

If, instead of the magnetic shell so far considered, we have a current i flowing around the curve $ABCD$ in the sense of the arrow, the magnetic field at P is

$$\mathbf{H} = \frac{i}{c} \oint_{ABCD} \frac{d\mathbf{l} \times \mathbf{r}}{r^3} \qquad (134\text{–}1.1)$$

from Ampère's law (133–2). Comparing with (134–1) we see that the field at P due to the shell is identical with that of the current provided $\Phi = i/c$. Now it was shown in article 128 that the fields produced at outside points by different magnetic shells of the same strength and the same periphery are the same. So the magnetic field of a current circuit is identical, at all points outside the shell, with that of any magnetic shell of strength i/c whose periphery coincides with the circuit and whose magnetization is in the sense of advance of a right-handed screw rotated in the sense in which the current is flowing. Such a shell is called an *equivalent magnetic shell.*

It was shown in article 128 that if we take a unit positive pole from a point A on the negative side of a magnetic shell around past the edge of the shell to an opposite point B on the positive side of the shell the work done against the field is $4\pi\Phi$. Therefore if we allow the unit pole to follow this path in the reverse sense from B to A an amount of work $4\pi\Phi$ is done by the field. If, then, we replace a circuit by its equivalent magnetic shell of strength $\Phi = i/c$, we find $4\pi i/c$ for the work done by the field when a unit positive pole is carried once completely around the wire carrying the current in the sense of rotation of a right-handed screw advancing in the direction of the current. But the work done by the field, called the *magnetomotive force* and designated by the abbreviation m.m.f., is

$$\oint \mathbf{H}\cdot d\mathbf{l},$$

where $d\mathbf{l}$ is a vector element of the closed curve around which the line integral is taken. Therefore we have the important result

$$\oint \mathbf{H}\cdot d\mathbf{l} = \frac{4\pi i}{c}, \tag{134-2}$$

to which we shall refer as the second form of Ampère's law. In this equation i represents the total current flowing through the surface s around the periphery of which the line integral on the left is evaluated. So if $\mathbf{j}$ is the current density (134–2) may be written

$$\oint \mathbf{H}\cdot d\mathbf{l} = \frac{4\pi}{c}\int_s \mathbf{j}\cdot d\mathbf{s}. \tag{134-3}$$

Applying Stokes' theorem to the left-hand member

$$\int_s \nabla\times\mathbf{H}\cdot d\mathbf{s} = \frac{4\pi}{c}\int_s \mathbf{j}\cdot d\mathbf{s}.$$

As this equation is true for any surface s we may make the surface infinitesimal getting

$$\nabla\times\mathbf{H}\cdot d\mathbf{s} = \frac{4\pi}{c}\,\mathbf{j}\cdot d\mathbf{s}.$$

Now if we take $d\mathbf{s}$ parallel successively to the X, Y and Z axes we find that each rectangular component of the vector $\nabla\times\mathbf{H}$ is equal to the corresponding rectangular component of the vector $4\pi\mathbf{j}/c$. Therefore

$$\nabla \times \mathbf{H} = \frac{4\pi}{c}\mathbf{j}. \qquad (134\text{–}4)$$

This is the differential form of Ampère's law corresponding to the integral form (134–3). For many purposes it is much more convenient than the latter.

If the magnetic field under consideration is due solely to currents, the flux of **H** through any closed surface vanishes, and the differential form of Gauss' law becomes

$$\nabla \cdot \mathbf{H} = 0. \qquad (134\text{–}5)$$

As equations (134–4) and (134–5) specify both the curl and the divergence of **H**, they describe completely the magnetic field due to a given distribution of currents. They should be contrasted with (127–7) and (127–8) which describe the magnetostatic field produced by an assigned distribution of magnetic charge.

The second form of Ampère's law provides us with a simple means of calculating the field produced by a current circuit in cases where symmetry enables us to draw a closed curve around the current coincident with a line of force such that H has the same magnitude at all points of the curve. Consider, for instance, a long straight wire of circular cross-section. Let a be the radius of the wire and i the current. To find the magnetic intensity at a distance r from the axis of the wire apply (134–2) to a circular path of radius r in a plane perpendicular to the wire with center on its axis. We have

$$2\pi r H = \frac{4\pi i'}{c},$$

where i' is the current passing through the circle of radius r. If $r \geq a$, i' is the total current i and

$$H = \frac{2i}{cr} \qquad (134\text{–}6)$$

at any point outside the wire. If $r < a$

$$i' = \frac{r^2}{a^2}i,$$

provided the current density in the wire is constant, as in the case of an unvarying current. Therefore

$$H = \frac{2i}{ca^2} r \qquad (134\text{–}7)$$

at a point inside the wire. If we plot H against r we get the identical curve shown in Fig. 80 for the velocity of the fluid particles in a rectilinear vortex of radius a plotted against the distance r from the axis of the vortex.

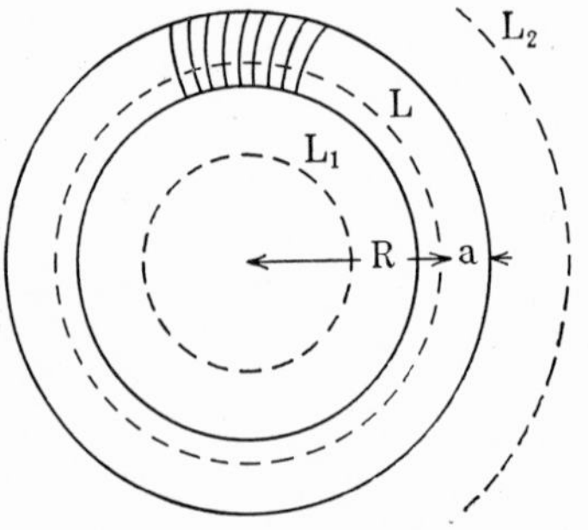

FIG. 134.

Again consider a toroidal solenoid (Fig. 134) of mean radius R and cross-sectional radius a. Apply (134–2) to the circular path represented by the broken line L. Then if N is the number of turns of wire and i the current

$$HL = \frac{4\pi Ni}{c}$$

as the current is circumscribed N times. Hence

$$H = \frac{4\pi Ni}{cL}. \qquad (134\text{–}8)$$

If R is very large compared with a, the lengths L of all circular paths lying inside the toroid in planes perpendicular to its axis and with centers on the axis are practically the same. Therefore the field is nearly uniform throughout the cross-section of the solenoid and equal to the field

$$H = \frac{4\pi ni}{c} \qquad (134\text{–}9)$$

at a point on the axis of a long straight solenoid far from the ends, n being the number of turns per unit length. As a short section of the toroidal solenoid becomes nearly straight if R is made very great compared with a we conclude that the field is also uniform over a cross-section of a straight solenoid far removed from the ends.

If we apply Ampère's law to the circular path L_1 we find

$$HL_1 = 0$$

as no current is circumscribed, and therefore H vanishes. Similarly for the path L_2

$$HL_2 = 0$$

since the current passes inward through the area bounded by L_2 as often as outward. Therefore we conclude that the magnetic field is confined entirely to the inside of the toroid and vanishes everywhere outside.

Problem 134a. Find the force per unit length between two long straight parallel wires a distance d apart (*a*) when the currents are parallel, (*b*) when the currents are opposite.

Ans. $\dfrac{2i_1i_2}{c^2d}$.

Problem 134b. By taking the divergence of the expression (133–2) for Ampère's law, confirm (134–5).

135. Ampère's Theory of Magnetism. — Since the field produced by a current circuit is of the same nature as that due to a magnet at all exterior points, Ampère was led to suggest that the molecule of a magnetic substance owes its magnetic properties to the presence of currents flowing without resistance in closed circuits in its interior. To-day these intra-molecular currents are attributed to rings of negative electrons revolving about the positive nucleus of the atom, or possibly to the rotation of electrons about their diameters as axes. Ampère's theory of magnetism enables us to dispense with the concept of a magnetic pole as a physical entity, and to ascribe all magnetic phenomena to the presence of electric currents. The new point of view, however, necessitates a revision of our previous definition of magnetic induction.

Consider a medium composed of molecules or atoms in each of which a current i_0 is flowing around a small circular circuit of cross-section A. The exterior magnetic field of each atom is that of a plane magnetic shell of strength i_0/c and area A whose periphery coincides with the circuit, the positive normal to the shell being that along which a right-handed screw advances when rotated in the sense of the current. We can therefore define the magnetic moment $\mathbf{p}$ of the circuit as the moment of the equivalent magnetic shell. Then $\mathbf{p}$ has the magnitude i_0A/c and the direction of the positive normal to the shell.

Now consider a surface s bounded by a closed curve l, which lies wholly or partly inside the magnetic material. We wish to calculate the total current i_{I} passing through the surface s due to the Ampèrian currents circulating in the atoms of the medium. Only those Ampèrian circuits which cut the surface s contribute to the current i_{I}. Let B and C (Fig. 135) be the points of intersection

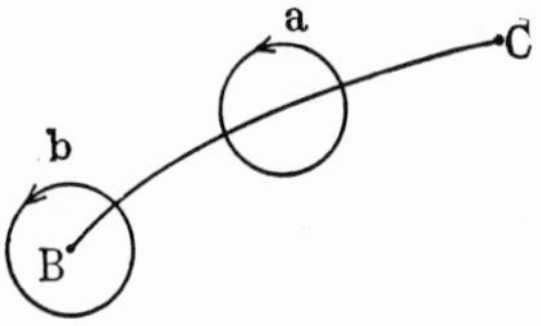

FIG 135.

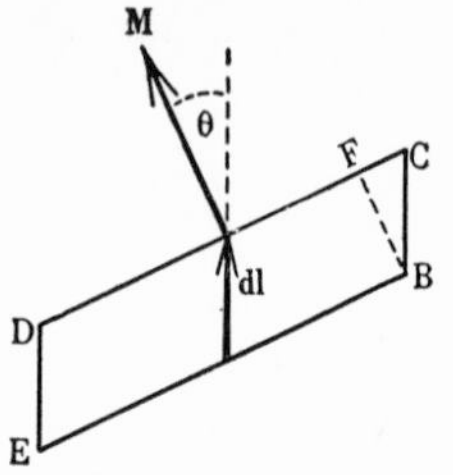

FIG. 136

of the curve l with the plane of the paper, the line BC being the trace of the surface s. An Ampèrian circuit such as a, which cuts s on both sides of the circuit, gives rise to equal currents flowing through s in each sense and therefore contributes nothing to i_{I}. Only a circuit like b, which surrounds the curve l and therefore cuts s on one side only, contributes to the net current i_{I} through the surface. Moreover, if the Ampèrian currents threaded by the curve l at B are oriented so that as many of them have magnetic axes pointing in any one direction as in the opposite direction, then as many give rise to currents passing down through the surface s to the right of B as up, and the net contribution to the current through the surface is zero. It is only when more circuits are oriented with their magnetic axes in one direction along l than in the opposite that they make a finite contribution to the current through s.

Consider a small element $d\mathbf{l}$ (Fig. 136) of the curve l. Directing attention to those Ampèrian circuits whose magnetic moments $\mathbf{p}$ make angles between θ and $\theta + d\theta$ with $d\mathbf{l}$, it is clear that all circuits whose centers lie in the slanting cylinder $BCDE$ of altitude $BF = dl \cos\theta$ and circular cross-section DC equal to the cross-section A of an Ampèrian circuit are threaded by the line $d\mathbf{l}$ and therefore contribute to the current i_{I} through the surface s. If dn is the number of atoms per unit volume whose magnetic axes are oriented in this manner, the total contribution $d^2 i_{\mathrm{I}}$ to i_{I} made by these is

$$d^2 i_{\mathrm{I}} = i_0 (A dl \cos\theta) dn = c p dn dl \cos\theta,$$

since i_0A/c is the magnetic moment p of a single atom.

Now $pdn\cos\theta$ is the sum of the components in the direction $d\mathbf{l}$ of the magnetic moments of the dn atoms. Denoting by $d\mathbf{I}$ the resultant magnetic moment due to these dn atoms in a unit volume,

$$d^2 i_{\mathrm{I}} = c\,d\mathbf{I}\cdot d\mathbf{l}.$$

Summing up over all directions

$$di_{\mathrm{I}} = c\mathbf{I}\cdot d\mathbf{l},$$

where $\mathbf{I}$ is the resultant magnetic moment of all the n atoms in a unit volume, or the magnetization. Integrating around the closed curve l we find for the total current passing through the surface s due to the Ampèrian circuits

$$i_{\mathrm{I}} = c\oint \mathbf{I}\cdot d\mathbf{l}. \qquad (135\text{–}1)$$

Designate by i the sum of all the other currents, such as conduction currents in wires, passing through the surface s. Then if we denote the total magnetic field strength by $\mathbf{H}_i$ the second form of Ampère's law (134–2) becomes

$$\oint \mathbf{H}_i\cdot d\mathbf{l} = \frac{4\pi i}{c} + 4\pi\oint \mathbf{I}\cdot d\mathbf{l}$$

or, if we express i in terms of the current density $\mathbf{j}$ of the conduction or convection currents passing through the surface s,

$$\oint (\mathbf{H}_i - 4\pi\mathbf{I})\cdot d\mathbf{l} = \frac{4\pi}{c}\int_s \mathbf{j}\cdot d\mathbf{s}. \qquad (135\text{–}2)$$

The form of the left-hand member of this equation suggests the convenience of defining a new vector function

$$\mathbf{H}_m \equiv \mathbf{H}_i - 4\pi\mathbf{I}.$$

Putting this in (135–2) and passing to the differential form of the equation by means of Stokes' theorem in precisely the same manner that we went from (134–3) to (134–4), we get

$$\nabla\times\mathbf{H}_m = \frac{4\pi}{c}\mathbf{j}. \qquad (135\text{–}3)$$

While the current density in (134–4) represents that due to all currents, including the Ampèrian currents in a permeable medium, the current density in (135–3) is that due to conduction and convection currents alone, the term due to the Ampèrian currents having been transposed to and included in the left-hand member of the equation. Finally if we take the divergence of the relation defining $\mathbf{H}_m$ we find

$$\nabla \cdot \mathbf{H}_m = -4\pi \nabla \cdot \mathbf{I}, \qquad (135\text{–}4)$$

since $\nabla \cdot \mathbf{H}_i = 0$ by (134–5).

These two equations, (135–3) and (135–4), completely describe the field $\mathbf{H}_m$ in terms of any assigned distribution of current density $\mathbf{j}$ due to conduction or convection currents and any specified distribution of magnetization $\mathbf{I}$ in the permeable media present. In order to discover the physical significance of $\mathbf{H}_m$ let us consider a region where magnetic substances alone are present without the added complication of conduction or convection currents. Then $\mathbf{j} = 0$ in (135–3), and comparison of (135–3) and (135–4) with (127–8) and (127–7) respectively shows that $\mathbf{H}_m$ represents the field that would be produced by a fictitious charge density $-\nabla \cdot \mathbf{I}$. This, however, is just the charge density (130–1) found to actually exist in a magnetized medium on the dipole theory. Hence the field $\mathbf{H}_m$ of Ampère's theory of magnetism is identical with the field $\mathbf{H}$ of the dipole theory. It is the magnetic field that would exist if each Ampèrian circuit were replaced by its equivalent magnetic shell.

Furthermore, as $\mathbf{H}_i = \mathbf{H}_m + 4\pi\mathbf{I}$ in consequence of the relation defining $\mathbf{H}_m$, the field $\mathbf{H}_i$ of Ampère's theory is the counterpart of the magnetic induction $\mathbf{B}$ of the dipole theory. Like $\mathbf{B}$ of that theory the field $\mathbf{H}_i$ of Ampère's theory is everywhere solenoidal from (134–5) and the $\mathbf{H}_i$ tubes are everywhere continuous.

Henceforth we shall discard the dipole theory of magnetism and formulate our equations on the basis of Ampère's theory. In deference to convention, however, we shall replace $\mathbf{H}_i$ by $\mathbf{B}$ and $\mathbf{H}_m$ by $\mathbf{H}$ in the fundamental relations $\nabla \cdot \mathbf{H}_i = 0$, $\nabla \times \mathbf{H}_m = 4\pi\mathbf{j}/c$ and $\mathbf{H}_i = \mathbf{H}_m + 4\pi\mathbf{I}$, writing

$$\left.\begin{array}{ll} \nabla \cdot \mathbf{B} = 0, \quad (a) & \nabla \times \mathbf{H} = \dfrac{4\pi}{c}\mathbf{j}, \quad (b) \\ \multicolumn{2}{c}{\mathbf{B} = \mathbf{H} + 4\pi\mathbf{I}. \quad (c)} \end{array}\right\} \qquad (135\text{–}5)$$

It must be remembered, however, that from the point of view of Ampère's theory of magnetism, which is universally accepted to-day, $\mathbf{B}$ inside a magnetic substance is the average resultant magnetic intensity, and **H** inside a magnetic material is not the magnetic intensity actually existing at all, but a fictitious field equal to the true magnetic intensity due to all outside sources, such as currents in wires, plus the magnetic intensity that would be produced by the fictitious magnetic charge $-\nabla \cdot \mathbf{I}$ per unit volume. Outside magnetic media **B** and **H** are the same and either represents the true magnetic intensity.

Problem 135a. Show by direct calculation that the mean magnetic intensity averaged over an atomic volume $1/n$ due to an Ampèrian current i_0 exceeds that due to an equivalent magnetic shell by $4\pi n\mathbf{p} = 4\pi\mathbf{I}$. Hence show that $\mathbf{H}_m$ is the magnetic intensity that would exist in a magnetic medium if each Ampèrian circuit were replaced by an equivalent magnetic shell. (*Hint.* — A plane magnetic shell of uniform strength is the magnetic analog of a parallel plate condenser in electrostatics.)

136. Galvanometers. We shall describe three types of galvanometer of which the first is an absolute instrument.

I. *Tangent Galvanometer.* — This instrument consists of a circular coil of radius a containing N turns of wire placed vertically with its plane parallel to the horizontal control field H, which may be the horizontal component of the earth's field. At its center is pivoted a short compass needle free to turn in a horizontal plane. When a current i passes through the coil a field

$$H' = \frac{2\pi i N}{ca}$$

is produced at its center perpendicular to its plane by (133–3). The compass needle comes to rest with its magnetic axis parallel to the resultant field. Therefore it is deflected by the current through an angle γ given by

$$\tan\gamma = \frac{H'}{H} = \frac{2\pi i N}{caH}.$$

Solving for i we have

$$i = \frac{caH}{2\pi N}\tan\gamma. \tag{136–1}$$

As the control field H can be measured in absolute units by the method described in article 129, the current can be determined in absolute units from this equation.

II. *D'Arsonval Galvanometer.* — The tangent galvanometer is easily disturbed by stray fields due to neighboring circuits. This defect is avoided in the d'Arsonval galvanometer which consists of a rectangular coil $ABCD$ (Fig. 137) suspended by a torsion fibre T so as to hang vertically between the poles of a permanent horseshoe magnet with its plane parallel to the lines of force. Let us assume the field H due to the magnet to be uniform over the region occupied by the coil. Then when a current i passes through the coil in the sense of the arrows the side AD is urged forward with a force $NilH/c$ from (133–4), where l is the length AD and N the number of turns, and BC is urged backward with the same force. If h is the length AB the torque due to this couple is

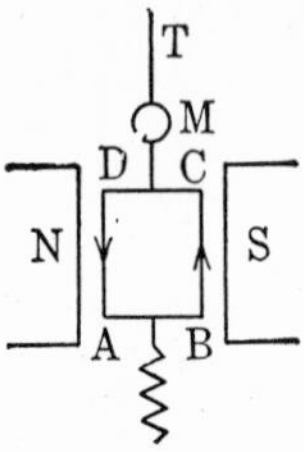

FIG. 137.

$$L = \frac{NilhH}{c} = pH,$$

since $Nilh/c$ is the magnetic moment p of the coil. So if the angle γ through which the coil is deflected is small,

$$NilhH = k\gamma,$$

and

$$i = \frac{k}{NlhH}\gamma.$$

The sensitivity is

$$\frac{d\gamma}{di} = \frac{NlhH}{k}.$$

For high sensitivity the number of turns should be large, the field H strong, and the suspension very fine to make k small. To read deflections a mirror M is attached to the coil. A fixed telescope to which a horizontal scale is fastened is placed a meter or so in front of the galvanometer and focused on the image of the scale in the mirror. As the mirror turns, the image of the scale revolves twice as rapidly.

This type of galvanometer, as generally constructed, is not absolute and must be calibrated by comparison with an absolute instrument. Its sensitivity may be made great enough to measure currents of $(10)^{-11}$ ampere. As the field H is large, stray fields produce relatively unimportant disturbances.

III. *Einthoven String Galvanometer.* — This galvanometer consists of a silvered quartz fibre AB (Fig. 138) under tension in the space between the poles of a strong magnet. When a current passes through the fibre, in the direction indicated by the arrow, the fibre is deflected into the paper according to equation (133–4). The deflection is observed through a hole in one of the pole pieces by means of a microscope. On account of the lightness of the fibre it is very quick to respond and air damping makes it nearly dead beat. Currents of $(10)^{-12}$ ampere can be detected with this type of instrument.

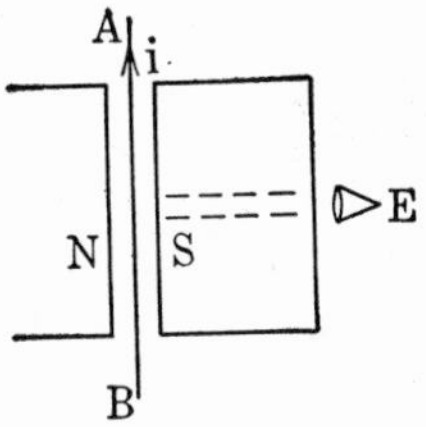

FIG. 138.

137. Magnetic Field Due to a Circular Current. — In the theory of the tangent galvanometer given in the last article the force exerted by the current on the poles of the compass needle was taken to be that due to the field at the center of the coil. While this is nearly the case if the length of the needle is very small compared with the radius of the coil, a more accurate formula can be deduced if we find the field strength at the points where the poles of the compass needle are actually located.

Let O (Fig. 139) be the center of a circular turn of wire of radius a lying in a plane perpendicular to the X axis, the current i emerging from the plane of the paper at A and entering it at B. To find the field at a point Q on the axis of the circuit we can replace the current by a magnetic shell of strength i/c in the form of a spherical cap ACB described about Q as center. The area S of this cap is

$$S = \int_0^\alpha 2\pi b^2 \sin\phi d\phi = 2\pi b^2(1 - \cos\alpha),$$

where b is the radius of the sphere and ϕ the angle which the radius vector makes with the negative X axis. The solid angle subtended by the cap at Q is

$$\Omega = -\frac{S}{b^2} = -2\pi(1 - \cos\alpha) = -2\pi\left\{1 - \frac{x}{\sqrt{a^2 + x^2}}\right\},$$

where x is the abscissa of Q referred to the center O of the circuit as origin. This solid angle is negative because we have taken the current in such a sense as to make positive the side of the surface S facing Q.

Therefore the potential at Q due to the magnetic shell is

$$V = -\frac{i}{c}\Omega = \frac{2\pi i}{c}\left\{1 - \frac{x}{\sqrt{a^2 + x^2}}\right\} \qquad (137\text{–}1)$$

from (128–7). As we are interested in the field at a distance from the center of the circuit small compared with its radius we need consider

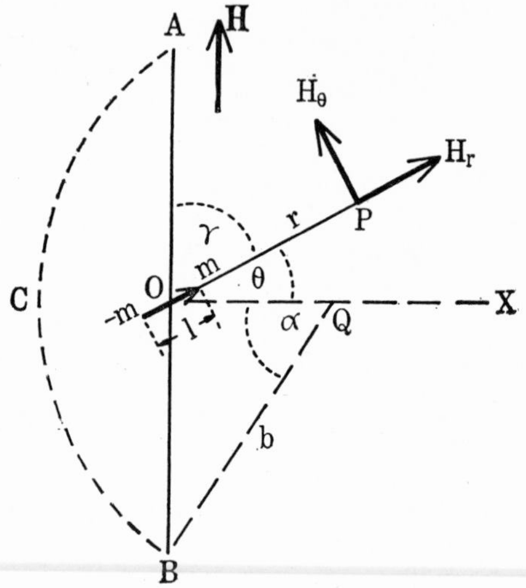

FIG. 139.

only those points Q for which $x < a$. Expanding (137–1) by the binomial theorem, we get

$$V = \frac{2\pi i}{c}\left\{1 - \frac{x}{a} + \frac{1}{2}\frac{x^3}{a^3} \cdots\right\}. \qquad (137\text{–}2)$$

As shown in article 127, the potential in a magnetostatic field must satisfy Laplace's equation in any region free from magnetic poles. Therefore to find the potential at a point P off the X axis at a distance r from O small compared with a we have to write down a series consisting of a sum of solutions of Laplace's equation which reduces to the boundary condition (137–2) for points on the axis. From symmetry it is clear that the potential at P is a function of r and θ only. Evidently the desired series is

$$V = \frac{2\pi i}{c}\left\{1 - \frac{r}{a}\cos\theta + \frac{1}{4}\frac{r^3}{a^3}(5\cos^3\theta - 3\cos\theta)\ldots\right\} \qquad (137\text{–}3)$$

built up out of a constant, the first of the two solutions (79–14), and the first of (79–16). For since $r = x$ when $\theta = 0$, this series goes over into (137–2) for points on the axis. Differentiating we get for the components of the magnetic intensity at P in the directions of increasing r and increasing θ respectively

$$H_r = -\frac{\partial V}{\partial r} = \frac{2\pi i}{ca}\left\{\cos\theta - \frac{3}{4}\frac{r^2}{a^2}(5\cos^3\theta - 3\cos\theta)\ldots\right\}, \qquad (137\text{–}4)$$

$$H_\theta = -\frac{\partial V}{r\partial\theta} = \frac{2\pi i}{ca}\left\{-\sin\theta + \frac{3}{4}\frac{r^2}{a^2}(5\cos^2\theta - 1)\sin\theta\ldots\right\}. \qquad (137\text{–}5)$$

These are the components of the field due to a magnetic shell of strength i/c and periphery coincident with the circuit. On account of the equivalence of circuit and shell they also describe the field produced by the current circuit.

Suppose, now, that AB represents the coil of a tangent galvanometer. For simplicity we shall consider it to consist of a single turn of wire. If we denote the deflection of the compass needle pivoted at O from the plane of the coil by γ, it is clear from the figure that γ is the complement of θ. The torque on the compass needle due to the current is produced by the component H_θ of the field. If l is the length of the needle and m the strength of its positive pole, the torque tending to increase γ is

$$-mlH_\theta = \frac{2\pi ip}{ca}\cos\gamma\left\{1 + \frac{3}{16}\frac{l^2}{a^2}(1 - 5\sin^2\gamma)\ldots\right\} \qquad (137\text{–}6)$$

from (137–5), since $ml = p$ and $r = l/2$. Acting against this torque is the torque $pH\sin\gamma$ due to the control field H parallel to the plane of the coil. So for equilibrium

$$pH\sin\gamma = \frac{2\pi ip}{ca}\cos\gamma\left\{1 + \frac{3}{16}\frac{l^2}{a^2}(1 - 5\sin^2\gamma)\ldots\right\},$$

and the current is given in terms of the deflection of the needle by

$$i = \frac{caH}{2\pi}\tan\gamma\left\{1 - \frac{3}{16}\frac{l^2}{a^2}(1 - 5\sin^2\gamma)\ldots\right\}. \qquad (137\text{–}7)$$

If the coil of the galvanometer contains N turns, N appears as a factor in the numerator of (137–6) and therefore in the denominator of (137–7). If 5 $\sin^2 \gamma = 1$, that is, $\gamma = 26.6°$, the correction term in (137–7) vanishes.

Problem 137a. Find the magnetic intensity at a distance from the center of a circular current greater than the radius of the circuit.

$$\textit{Ans. } H_r = \frac{2\pi i}{ca}\left\{\frac{a^3}{r^3}\cos\theta - \frac{3}{4}\frac{a^5}{r^5}(5\cos^3\theta - 3\cos\theta)\ldots\right\},$$

$$H_\theta = \frac{2\pi i}{ca}\left\{\frac{1}{2}\frac{a^3}{r^3}\sin\theta - \frac{9}{16}\frac{a^5}{r^5}(5\cos^2\theta - 1)\sin\theta\ldots\right\}.$$

138. Motion of Ions in Uniform Electric and Magnetic Fields. — We shall now consider the motion of a charged particle or ion of mass m and charge e subject to the simultaneous action of an electric and a magnetic field. From the definition of electric intensity it follows that the force on the ion due to the electric field is $e\mathbf{E}$. If the ion is at rest in the observer's inertial system it is subject to no force in consequence of the magnetic field, but if it has a velocity $\mathbf{v}$ it constitutes a current element and is subject to the force per unit volume specified by (133–5). If ρ is the charge per unit volume in the small region τ occupied by the particle, the current density $\mathbf{j}$ in this region is $\rho\mathbf{v}$. Hence the total force on the ion is obtained by integrating $\rho\mathbf{v} \times \mathbf{H}d\tau/c$ over the volume τ. Now, if the particle is rigid, as we shall suppose, $\mathbf{v}$ is constant over τ, and as the particle is small, $\mathbf{H}$ does not vary appreciably in this region. Therefore the total force exerted on it by the magnetic field is $e\mathbf{v} \times \mathbf{H}/c$. If the ion is moving through a magnetic medium as is the case when an electric current consisting of a stream of electrons passes through a magnet, we must replace $\mathbf{H}$ in this expression by $\mathbf{B}$, for we have seen (art. 135) that the true magnetic intensity inside a magnetic substance composed of Ampèrian currents is not $\mathbf{H}$ but $\mathbf{B}$. Hence, adding the magnetic force to the electric force we have, in the most general case, for the total electromagnetic force on the ion

$$\mathbf{F} = e\left(\mathbf{E} + \frac{1}{c}\mathbf{v} \times \mathbf{B}\right), \tag{138–1}$$

In our present discussion, however, we shall suppose the ion under consideration to be moving through empty space. Then $\mathbf{B} = \mathbf{H}$ and, equating the force to the product of mass by acceleration, the equation of motion of the ion is seen to be

$$m\mathbf{f} = e(\mathbf{E} + \frac{1}{c}\mathbf{v} \times \mathbf{H}). \qquad (138\text{–}2)$$

(a) *Uniform Electric Field.* In this case the force is the constant $e\mathbf{E}$. Consequently the orbits are parabolas as shown in article 23.

(b) *Uniform Magnetic Field.* At first we shall confine our attention to motion in a plane perpendicular to **H**. The force $e\mathbf{v} \times \mathbf{H}/c$ lies in this plane at right angles to the path and has the magnitude evH/c. Consequently the particle describes a circle with constant speed. If ω is its angular velocity about the center of this circle, the centripetal acceleration is $v\omega$ from (19–14), and substitution in (138–2) shows that the magnitude of the angular velocity is eH/mc. As the acceleration is in the direction of $e\mathbf{v} \times \mathbf{H}$, however, $\boldsymbol{\omega}$ has the opposite sense to **H**. Hence, in vector form,

$$\boldsymbol{\omega} = -\frac{e}{mc}\mathbf{H}. \qquad (138\text{–}3)$$

Thus a positive ion describes a circular orbit about the lines of force of the magnetic field in the opposite sense to the rotation of a right-handed screw advancing along the lines of force, and a negative ion in the same sense. Especially noteworthy is the fact that the angular velocity of an ion is independent of its linear speed. The radius ρ of the circular orbit, on the other hand, is v/ω, that is,

$$\rho = \left|\frac{mcv}{eH}\right|, \qquad (138\text{–}4)$$

which is proportional to the speed.

If the initial velocity of the ion is not at right angles to **H**, the component of its velocity parallel to the lines of forces remains constant, since the magnetic force $e\mathbf{v} \times \mathbf{H}/c$ has no component in this direction. The projection of the motion on a plane at right angles to **H**, however, remains that described by (138–3) and (138–4), provided we understand by v in the latter equation the component of the velocity perpendicular to **H**. The orbit, consequently, is a helix.

(c) *Combined Uniform Electric and Magnetic Fields.* First we shall suppose that the two fields are perpendicular, **E** being parallel to the Y axis and **H** to the Z axis, and that the initial velocity of the ion lies in the XY plane. Expressing the acceleration **f** as the time derivative of the velocity **v**, (138–2) may be written

$$\frac{d\mathbf{v}}{dt} = \frac{e}{m}\left(\mathbf{E} + \frac{1}{c}\mathbf{v} \times \mathbf{H}\right). \tag{138–5}$$

Now consider a second set of axes $X'Y'Z'$ in uniform motion relative to the axes XYZ of the observer's inertial system with velocity $\mathbf{u} \equiv c\mathbf{E} \times \mathbf{H}/H^2$ in the X direction. If $\mathbf{v}'$ denotes the velocity of the ion relative to the moving axes, $\mathbf{v} = \mathbf{v}' + \mathbf{u}$ and $\dfrac{d\mathbf{v}}{dt} = \dfrac{d\mathbf{v}'}{dt}$. Substituting in (138–5) we find for the equation of motion relative to the moving axes

$$\begin{aligned}\frac{d\mathbf{v}'}{dt} &= \frac{e}{m}\left\{\mathbf{E} + \frac{1}{c}(\mathbf{v}' + \mathbf{u}) \times \mathbf{H}\right\} \\ &= \frac{e}{m}\left\{\mathbf{E} + \frac{(\mathbf{E} \times \mathbf{H}) \times \mathbf{H}}{H^2} + \frac{1}{c}\mathbf{v}' \times \mathbf{H}\right\} \\ &= \frac{e}{mc}\mathbf{v}' \times \mathbf{H}. \end{aligned} \tag{138–6}$$

But this is just the equation of motion of an ion moving in a uniform magnetic field **H** alone. By transferring our observations to the moving inertial system we have eliminated the electric field. This example illustrates the fact that the resolution of an electromagnetic field into electric and magnetic parts depends upon the state of motion of the observer. A field which is in part electric and in part magnetic relative to observers in one inertial system, may be entirely electric or entirely magnetic relative to observers in another. Nevertheless, the fundamental equations of electromagnetism, which we are in the process of developing, are valid relative to *any* inertial system.

We have discussed the motion described by (138–6) and know that the orbit of the ion relative to the moving axes $X'Y'Z'$ is a circle described about the lines of magnetic force with angular velocity (138–3), and of radius

$$\rho' = \left|\frac{mcv'}{eH}\right|. \tag{138–7}$$

Its path relative to XYZ, therefore, is a cycloid generated by a rolling circle of radius

$$a = \frac{u}{\omega} = \left|\frac{mcu}{eH}\right| = \left|\frac{mc^2E}{eH^2}\right|. \qquad (138\text{–}8)$$

According as ρ' is greater than, equal to, or less than a, this cycloid is curtate, common, or prolate as illustrated by the three paths (a), (b), (c) in Fig. 140 for a positive ion. The paths for a negative ion are obtained by rotating those shown in the figure through the angle π about the horizontal axis. It should be noted that the drift velocity $u = cE/H$ of the ion in the direction at right angles to the fields is independent of the charge, mass or initial velocity of the ion and is in the same sense for both positive and negative ions.

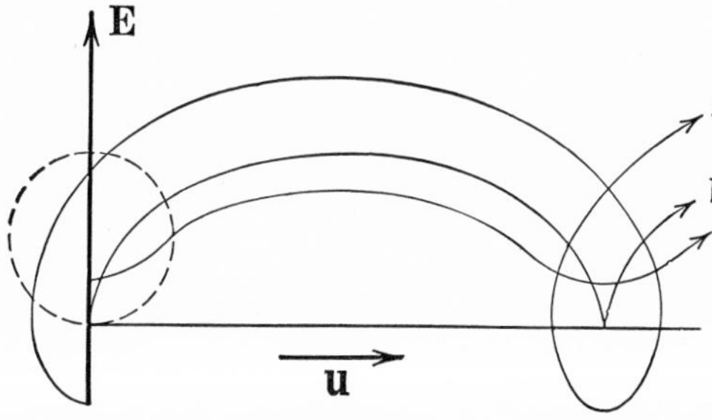

FIG. 140.

If **E** and **H** are not perpendicular and the initial velocity **v** of the ion does not lie in the XY plane, the projection of the motion on a plane perpendicular to **H** is identical with that just described, provided that we understand by E and v' in the formulae obtained the components at right angles to **H** of the electric intensity and of the velocity relative to $X'Y'Z'$. The motion along the lines of magnetic force is uniformly accelerated, the force in this direction being that due to the component of **E** parallel to **H**.

It is evident from (138–2) that the ratio of the charge to the mass of an ion of known velocity can be determined by measuring the deflection it suffers in any combination of known uniform electric and magnetic fields. In one method a stream of ions is projected at right angles to crossed electric and magnetic fields so adjusted that no deflection occurs. Then $\mathbf{f} = 0$ in (138–2) and $v = cE/H$. Now the electric field is suppressed and a stream of ions produced in the same manner and therefore having the same velocity is projected at right angles to the lines of force of a known magnetic field. As v is known and the radius ρ of curvature can be calculated from the observed deflection, the ratio e/m is obtained at once from (138–4). Methods of this type, first employed successfully by J. J. Thomson, give for the ratio of charge to mass of the electron

$$\frac{e}{m} = -\ 5.274(10)^{17}\ \text{e.s.u./gm.}$$

Combining this with the value for the charge of the electron (art. 81) we find for the mass of the electron

$$m = 9.11(10)^{-28}\ \text{gm.}$$

Problem 138a. Show how the cycloidal path of an ion in crossed electric and magnetic fields approaches a straight line as the charge e approaches zero.

Problem 138b. Electrons emerge from one plate of a parallel plate condenser with negligible initial velocities under the influence of ultra-violet light. If the condenser is in a uniform magnetic field H parallel to the plates, find the relation between H, the potential V of the condenser, and the distance d between the plates so that the electrons just fail to reach the farther plate.

Ans. $V = \dfrac{e}{2mc^2} d^2H^2.$

Problem 138c. The magnetron consists of a heated filament of radius a surrounded by a coaxial conducting tube of radius b placed in a uniform magnetic field H parallel the axis. Find the relation between H and the potential difference V between the electrodes so that the electrons emitted by the heated filament with negligible initial velocities just fail to reach the outer electrode.

Ans. $V = \dfrac{eN^2}{8\pi^2 mc^2 b^2}$, where $N = \pi(b^2 - a^2)H$ is the flux of H through a cross-section between the two cylinders.

Problem 138d. Find the drift velocity u of ions moving in crossed gravitational (g) and magnetic fields. Do ions of both signs drift in the same sense as in crossed electric and magnetic fields?

Ans. $\mathbf{u} = \dfrac{mc}{e} \dfrac{\mathbf{g} \times \mathbf{H}}{H^2}.$

Problem 138e. Find the integrated equations of motion of an ion moving in crossed electric and magnetic fields, **E** being parallel to the Y axis and **H** to the Z axis, and the initial velocity being $\mathbf{v}_0$.

$$Ans.\ x = \frac{mc}{e}\left\{\frac{v_{0y}}{H}\left(1 - \cos\frac{eH}{mc}t\right) + \left(\frac{v_{0x}}{H} - \frac{cE}{H^2}\right)\sin\frac{eH}{mc}t\right\} + \frac{E}{H}ct,$$

$$y = \frac{mc}{e}\left\{-\left(\frac{v_{0x}}{H} - \frac{cE}{H^2}\right)\left(1 - \cos\frac{eH}{mc}t\right) + \frac{v_{0y}}{H}\sin\frac{eH}{mc}t\right\},$$

$$z = v_0 t.$$

139. Electron Theory of Metallic Conduction. — On the electron theory of matter the passage of an electric current along a wire is ascribed to the drift of free electrons under the influence of the applied field. As the charge on the electron is negative, the free electrons actually move in the direction opposite to that conventionally chosen for the current. Similarly the conduction of heat by a metal is attributed to the transport of energy from the hotter to the cooler portions of the metal by free electrons. In this way we explain the experimental fact that good conductors of electricity are also good conductors of heat. We shall develop a simple form of the electron theory of electrical and thermal conductivity.

I. *Electrical Conductivity.* — The first step in computing the electrical conductivity is to find the drift velocity of the free electrons in an electric field E. We shall neglect the Maxwellian distribution of electronic velocities and attribute to all free electrons the same speed u of thermal agitation, which we shall take to be large compared with the superposed drift velocity produced by the field. Furthermore, on account of the small dimensions of the electron, we shall assume that collisions between electrons occur so infrequently as to be negligible in number compared with collisions of electrons with atoms.

If, then, e is the charge of the electron and m its mass the acceleration given it by a field E is

$$f = \frac{eE}{m}.$$

As the average time between successive collisions is the quotient of the mean free path λ by the velocity u of thermal agitation, the drift velocity acquired in the course of a single free path is

$$v = f\frac{\lambda}{u} = \frac{e\lambda}{mu}E$$

in the direction of the field. As the drift velocity is zero at the beginning of the free path, the mean drift velocity $\bar{v}$ is half of this. If, then, n is the number of free electrons per unit volume, the charge passing through a unit cross-section in a unit time or the current density is

$$j = ne\bar{v} = \frac{1}{2}\frac{ne^2\lambda}{mu}E. \qquad (139\text{–}1)$$

The *conductivity* σ is defined as the ratio of the current density to the electric intensity. Therefore

$$\sigma = \frac{1}{2}\frac{ne^2\lambda}{mu}. \qquad (139\text{–}2)$$

As u varies with the square root of T, the conductivity should vary inversely with the square root of the absolute temperature, provided the other quantities appearing in this equation are constants. In pure metals it is actually more nearly proportional to the inverse first power of T.

The *resistivity* ρ is the reciprocal of the conductivity. If A is the cross-section of a wire carrying a current i

$$i = jA = \sigma AE = \frac{AE}{\rho}. \qquad (139\text{–}3)$$

The *electromotive force* $\mathcal{E}$ along a specified curve l from a point P to a point Q is defined as the work done on a unit positive charge transported from P to Q along the given path. If $\mathbf{E}$ is the force per unit charge the electromotive force is equal to the line integral

$$\mathcal{E} = \int_P^Q \mathbf{E}\cdot d\mathbf{l} \qquad (139\text{–}4)$$

evaluated along the curve l. In the case of an electromotive force due to an electromagnetic field, $\mathbf{E}$ represents the electric intensity, for the force due to the magnetic field, being at right angles to the velocity of the transported charge, does no work. In a cell, however, we may have forces separating the positive and negative ions which are not immediately recognizable as electromagnetic in character. The electromotive force due to these chemical forces is still defined by (139–4), provided $\mathbf{E}$ represents the chemical force per unit charge. Electromotive force, designated by the abbreviation e.m.f., is the electric analog of magnetomotive force defined in article 134.

If **E** is expressible as the gradient of a scalar potential function, as in an electrostatic field, the electromotive force from P to Q is equal to the potential drop. Consequently in this case the electromotive force is independent of the path followed from P to Q and vanishes for a closed curve, in accord with (15–2). If, however, the force per unit charge is not derivable from a scalar potential, $\mathcal{E}$ depends upon the path and does not necessarily vanish when taken around a closed loop. Such a case exists whenever an electric current flows around a closed circuit, whether the source of electromotive force is a cell or a dynamo. As in the case of a magnetomotive force, an electromotive force may exist along an open or closed curve l no matter whether a conducting wire coincides with l or not. When a field is the resultant of several fields due to different sources it is often convenient to consider the total electromotive force along the specified curve as the sum of the electromotive forces due to the individual fields.

The resultant e.m.f. along a conducting wire of length l in which a current i is flowing is

$$\mathcal{E} = \int \mathbf{E} \cdot d\mathbf{l} = i\frac{\rho l}{A} \qquad (139\text{–}5)$$

from (139–3). The constant ratio of the e.m.f. to the current is called the *resistance* R of the wire. We have then

$$R = \rho\frac{l}{A}, \qquad (139\text{–}6)$$

showing that the resistance is directly proportional to the length and inversely proportional to the cross-section of the wire. In terms of the resistance (139–5) becomes

$$\mathcal{E} = iR, \qquad (139\text{–}7)$$

which is *Ohm's law.*

A source of electromotive force, such as a battery or a dynamo, has the ability to separate positive from negative electricity, the work $\mathcal{E}_A$ per unit charge which it is capable of performing being independent of the magnitude of the current flowing. On open circuit such a source builds up opposite charges on the two terminals until the potential drop $\mathcal{E}_V$ due to their electrostatic field is just equal and opposite to $\mathcal{E}_A$, when the separation of charge ceases, since an amount of work greater than $\mathcal{E}_A$ would be required to produce any further separation. In the equilibrium state, then, the resultant electromotive force $\mathcal{E}_A + \mathcal{E}_V$ through the source is zero.

If the terminals of the source are connected externally through a number of resistances $R_1, R_2 \ldots R_n$ so that a current flows, the relation $\mathcal{E}_A + \mathcal{E}_V = 0$ still holds if the source itself has no resistance, for then the resultant force per unit charge in the source must vanish at every instant. If the source has a resistance R_A, however, (139–7) requires that the resultant electromotive force should equal iR_A, whence

$$\mathcal{E}_A + \mathcal{E}_V = iR_A.$$

Now the potential drop $\mathcal{E}'_V$ in the external portion of the circuit must be

$$\mathcal{E}'_V = iR_1 + iR_2 \ldots + iR_n$$

by (139–7). Adding these two equations

$$\mathcal{E}_A = i(R_A + R_1 + R_2 \ldots + R_n), \qquad (139\text{–}8)$$

since $\mathcal{E}_V + \mathcal{E}'_V$, which represents the potential drop around the entire circuit due to the charges on the circuit, must vanish. This is Ohm's law for a closed circuit containing a source of electromotive force. Since the total electromotive force $\mathcal{E}_A + \mathcal{E}_V + \mathcal{E}'_V$ around the entire circuit is equal to $\mathcal{E}_A$, the latter is generally referred to as the electromotive force of the circuit even though it may be localized in a small portion thereof. It is customary to call $\mathcal{E}_A$ the *applied electromotive force*. Ohm's law holds very accurately for moderate currents in metallic conductors, although Bridgman has found slight deviations from it at very high current densities.

II. *Thermal Conductivity.* — We shall calculate the heat Q which passes through a unit area perpendicular to the X axis in a unit time in a metal in which there is a temperature gradient in the X direction. From (104–2) we have for the number of electrons, originating in a volume element $d\tau$, which pass through a unit area at the origin in unit time

$$\frac{dN}{dt} = \frac{\Gamma n}{4\pi r^2} e^{-r/\lambda} \cos\theta d\tau,$$

where θ is the angle between the radius vector and the X axis and Γ is the collision frequency. Each of these electrons has a kinetic energy determined by the temperature of the volume element in which it had its last collision. In accord with the equipartition theorem this energy is

$$\frac{3}{2}k\left\{T+\frac{\partial T}{\partial x}r\cos\theta\right\}.$$

Replacing $d\tau$ by $2\pi r^2 \sin\theta\, d\theta\, dr$ and multiplying the last two expressions together, we get for the flow of heat in the positive X direction

$$Q = -\frac{3}{4}nk\Gamma\int_0^\infty\int_0^\pi e^{-r/\lambda}\left(T+\frac{\partial T}{\partial x}r\cos\theta\right)\cos\theta\sin\theta\, d\theta\, dr$$

$$= -\frac{1}{2}nk\Gamma\lambda^2\frac{\partial T}{\partial x}.$$

As $\Gamma\lambda$ is equal to the mean velocity u of thermal agitation,

$$Q = -\tfrac{1}{2}nk\lambda u\frac{\partial T}{\partial x}. \qquad (139\text{–}9)$$

Therefore the coefficient of thermal conductivity is

$$K = \tfrac{1}{2}nk\lambda u. \qquad (139\text{–}10)$$

The expressions for the coefficients of electrical and thermal conductivity found above contain too many unknown quantities to be compared with experimental values. If, however, we take the ratio of the thermal to the electrical conductivity we get

$$\frac{K}{\sigma} = \frac{kmu^2}{e^2}.$$

Now mu^2 is twice the mean kinetic energy of an electron and is equal to $3kT$ by the principle of equipartition of energy. Consequently

$$\frac{K}{\sigma} = 3\left(\frac{k}{e}\right)^2 T. \qquad (139\text{–}11)$$

This is known as the *law of Wiedemann and Franz*. According to it the ratio of the conductivities of all metals should be the same at the same temperature. As k and e are accurately known, it can be checked by experiment. For

$$e = -4.80(10)^{-10} \text{ e.s.u.}$$

$$k = 1.38(10)^{-16} \text{ erg}/1^\circ \text{ C.},$$

and we have the theoretical value

$$\frac{K}{\sigma} = 0.68(10)^{-10} \text{ e.s.u.}$$

for the ratio of the conductivities at a temperature of 273° absolute. Furthermore the temperature coefficient of the ratio, that is, the increase in the ratio per unit rise in temperature divided by the value of the ratio at 0° C., is 1/273° C. = $3.66(10)^{-3}$/1° C. In the following table are given some experimental values obtained by Jäger and Diesselhorst:

Metal	K/σ at 0° C.	Temp. Coef.
Copper	0.747 $(10)^{-10}$ e.s.u.	3.95 $(10)^{-3}$
Silver	0.763	3.77
Gold	0.789	3.75
Zinc	0.748	3.85
Lead	0.796	4.07
Tin	0.818	3.4

The agreement of theory with experiment is seen to be fairly satisfactory. Unfortunately a more careful calculation of the ratio of the conductivities, taking Maxwell's law of distribution of velocities into account, leads to a formula with a somewhat different numerical coefficient which shows worse agreement with the experimental values. However it is interesting to note that the quantum theory of electronic conduction gives the formula of the simple theory developed here.

140. Steady Currents. — Ohm's law (139–8) suffices for the solution of problems involving a steady current in a single circuit. For a current network the following laws, due to Kirchhoff, are needed:

I. *The algebraic sum of all the currents flowing toward a junction of three or more branches is zero.* For if this were not the case there would be an accumulation of charge at the junction.

II. *The algebraic sum of the products of current by resistance of the branches of any closed circuit in a network is equal to the electromotive force.* This follows at once from Ohm's law.

Consider a circuit of length l in which λ is the charge per unit length of the free electrons which constitute the current. Then the force per unit length on the free electrons is $\lambda\mathbf{E}$ and if $\bar{\mathbf{v}}$ is the drift velocity of the electrons the rate at which work is done is $\lambda\mathbf{E}\cdot\bar{\mathbf{v}}$. In a length dl, then, work is done at the rate $\lambda\mathbf{E}\cdot\bar{\mathbf{v}}dl = \lambda\bar{v}\mathbf{E}\cdot d\mathbf{l}$ since $\bar{\mathbf{v}}$ and $d\mathbf{l}$ have the same direction. But $\lambda\bar{v}$ is the current i. So, integrating around the entire circuit, the power is

$$P = i\oint \mathbf{E}\cdot d\mathbf{l} = i\mathcal{E}. \tag{140–1}$$

If the current is steady the work done by the electromotive force in a time t is

$$W = i\mathcal{E}t. \tag{140–2}$$

Since we have described a method of measuring a magnetic field H in absolute units in article 129, we can use the formula (136–1), or the more accurate formula (137–7), to determine the value of the constant c from the deflection γ of a tangent galvanometer provided that we develop an independent method of measuring the current i in absolute units. Then, from (136–1),

$$c = \frac{2\pi Ni}{aH\tan\gamma}. \tag{140–3}$$

Such a method of measuring i is provided by the circuit of Fig. 140.1, where the prong T of a tuning fork vibrating ν times a second makes contact alternately with A and B, charging the condenser of known capacitance C from the battery of known electromotive force $\mathcal{E}$ through the galvanometer G when in contact with A, and discharging it when in contact with B. Then the current through the galvanometer is

$$i = \nu C\mathcal{E}. \tag{140–4}$$

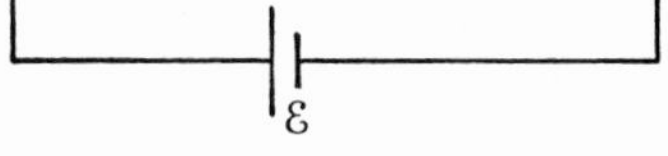

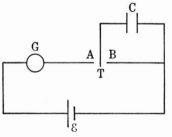

FIG. 140.1.

As many of the c.g.s. units are of inconvenient magnitude, the electrical engineer uses a set of practical or m.k.s. units based upon the meter, kilogram and second as fundamental units. In the following table are listed a few of the more important m.k.s. units and their equivalents in the c.g.s. Gaussian units that we are employing. The last of these will be defined in a later article. The figure 3 in the table should be more accurately 2.998.

Quantity	Practical m.k.s. Unit	Equivalent in c.g.s. Units
Force................	Newton	$(10)^5$ dyne
Energy..............	Joule	$(10)^7$ erg
Power...............	Watt	$(10)^7$ erg/sec
Charge..............	Coulomb	$3\ (10)^9$ e.s.u.
Current..............	Ampere	$3\ (10)^9$ e.s.u.
Potential or e.m.f......	Volt	$\frac{1}{3}\ (10)^{-2}$ e.s.u.
Resistance...........	Ohm	$\frac{1}{9}\ (10)^{-11}$ e.s.u.
Capacitance..........	Farad	$9\ (10)^{11}$ e.s.u.
Inductance...........	Henry	$\frac{1}{9}\ (10)^{-11}$ e.s.u.

Problem 140a. Two cells of electromotive forces 6 and 10 volts and resistances 0.5 and 1 ohm respectively are connected in parallel with a resistance of 12 ohms. Find the current through each branch of the circuit and the potential difference between the two junctions. *Ans.* −2.27 amp, 2.86 amp, 0.59 amp, 7.14 volts.

Problem 140b. A galvanometer of 150 ohms resistance is deflected one scale division by a current of 0.00013 amp. With what resistance should it be connected and how in order to convert it (*a*) into an ammeter reading directly in amperes, (*b*) into a voltmeter reading in volts? *Ans.* (*a*) 0.01953 ohms in parallel, (*b*) 7542 ohms in series.

Problem 140c. A Wheatstone's bridge is slightly out of balance. Find the current through the galvanometer. Find the sensitivity of the bridge at balance, that is, the change in the current through the galvanometer per unit change in the unknown resistance.

141. Faraday's Law. — In 1831 Faraday in England and Henry in America discovered independently the phenomenon of current induction. The discovery is generally attributed to Faraday since he was the first to publish his results. *Faraday's law* states that whenever the flux of induction N through a closed curve fixed in the observer's inertial system changes, an electromotive force is induced equal to the time rate of decrease of flux divided by c, that is,

$$\mathcal{E} = -\frac{1}{c}\frac{dN}{dt}. \qquad (141\text{–}1)$$

In this equation the positive direction of the flux through the circuit is related to the positive sense of the electromotive force by the same convention as that adopted in article 3 to relate the positive normal of a surface to the positive sense of describing its periphery. Since $\mathcal{E}$ is the line integral of the electric intensity around the specified closed curve l, and N is the surface integral of the magnetic induction over any surface s bounded by the given curve, (141–1) may be written

$$\oint \mathbf{E} \cdot d\mathbf{l} = -\frac{1}{c} \int_s \frac{\partial \mathbf{B}}{\partial t} \cdot d\mathbf{s}, \qquad (141\text{–}2)$$

where the integrand on the right is written as a partial derivative since **B** may be a function of the coordinates as well as of the time. Following precisely the same procedure as that employed to pass from (134–3) to (134–4) in the case of Ampère's law, we get for the differential form of Faraday's law,

$$\nabla \times \mathbf{E} = -\frac{1}{c}\frac{\partial \mathbf{B}}{\partial t}, \qquad (141\text{–}3)$$

corresponding to the integral form (141–2). It is important to note that Faraday's law, like Ampère's law, applies to any closed curve whether or not a conducting wire coincides with it. Of course, only when a conducting circuit is present does the electromotive force give rise to a current.

Faraday's law requires that a changing magnetic flux in the observer's inertial system shall always be accompanied by an electric field whose curl is given by (141–3). As its curl does not vanish **E** cannot be expressed as the gradient of a scalar potential function. Hence we cannot employ the concepts of equipotential surfaces or of potential drop in this case, the e.m.f. between two points depending upon the path followed as well as upon the location of the termini.

In addition to the electromotive force induced in a fixed circuit by changing magnetic flux, it is found that an electromotive force is induced in a conducting wire moving with velocity **v** relative to the observer whenever a magnetic field **H** is present. This e.m.f. is called a *motional electromotive force*, and its value can be obtained from (133–5). For if ρ is the charge per unit volume of the free electrons in the wire, the motion gives rise to a convection current of current density $\mathbf{j} = \rho\mathbf{v}$ and the force on a unit volume of the wire due to the action of the magnetic field is

$$\mathbf{F} = \frac{1}{c}\mathbf{j} \times \mathbf{H} = \frac{1}{c}\rho\mathbf{v} \times \mathbf{H}.$$

Therefore the force per unit charge is

$$\mathbf{E} = \frac{\mathbf{F}}{\rho} = \frac{1}{c}\mathbf{v} \times \mathbf{H},$$

and, if $d\mathbf{l}$ is a vector element of length of the wire, the electromotive force around the circuit is

$$\oint \mathbf{E}\cdot d\mathbf{l} = \frac{1}{c}\oint \mathbf{v} \times \mathbf{H}\cdot d\mathbf{l} = -\frac{1}{c}\oint \mathbf{H}\cdot\mathbf{v} \times d\mathbf{l}. \qquad (141\text{-}4)$$

Now $\mathbf{v} \times d\mathbf{l}$ is the time rate of increase of vector area caused by the displacement of the element $d\mathbf{l}$ of the periphery of the circuit, and the right-hand member of the equation is the time rate of decrease of flux due to change in vector area of the circuit divided by c. Consequently the e.m.f. around a circuit is equal to the time rate of decrease of flux divided by c, whether the latter is due to changing $\mathbf{B}$ as in (141–2) or to motion of the circuit relative to the observer as in (141–4). It must be noted, however, that the electric field implied in a motional electromotive force exists only in the inertial system of the moving conductor, and not in that of the observer. Here we have another illustration of the fact noted in article 138 that the resolution of an electromagnetic field into electric and magnetic parts depends upon the choice of the inertial system to which it is referred. Although the stationary observer may be aware of a magnetic field alone, an electric field as well as a magnetic field exists in the inertial system of the moving wire. The magnitude of the induced e.m.f. depends upon the velocity of the conductor relative to the observer's inertial system, not upon a supposed velocity relative to the magnetic field.

On Ampère's theory of magnetism $\mathbf{B}$ represents the total mean magnetic intensity inside a magnetic substance. So if we have a current moving through a magnetic medium we should replace $\mathbf{H}$ by $\mathbf{B}$ in (141–4) and write

$$\oint \mathbf{E}\cdot d\mathbf{l} = -\frac{1}{c}\int_s \mathbf{B}\cdot\frac{\partial}{\partial t}d\mathbf{s} \qquad (141\text{-}5)$$

where we have expressed the time rate of decrease of flux due to the change in area of the circuit by a surface integral over the surface s bounded by the circuit instead of by a line integral as in (141–4).

If both the area of the circuit and $\mathbf{B}$ change with the time the total electromotive force is the sum of (141–5) and (141–2), that is,

$$\oint \mathbf{E}\cdot d\mathbf{l} = -\frac{1}{c}\frac{d}{dt}\int_s \mathbf{B}\cdot d\mathbf{s}. \qquad (141\text{-}6)$$

As this is identical in form with (141–1), we may extend the validity of the latter equation to the case of a circuit moving through a varying magnetic field. This more general relation is known as *Neumann's law*.

Problem 141a. A symmetrically magnetized cylindrical magnet is rotating with constant angular velocity about its axis of symmetry. A straight wire at right angles to and in the plane of the axis of the magnet is arranged so that it can be rotated about the same axis. Is there an e.m.f. along the wire (*a*) when it is at rest, (*b*) when it is rotating with the magnet? Explain why.

Problem 141b. A magnet of moment p with its axis perpendicular to the wall of a room is moved away with velocity v. Discuss the electric field in the plane of the wall when the magnet is at a distance h.

Ans. $E = \frac{3pahv}{c(h^2 + a^2)^{5/2}}$, where a is the radius of the circular line of force.

Problem 141c. The symmetric magnetic flux through a circular circuit containing a condenser is changing uniformly with the time. If d is the distance between the plates, l the circumference of the circle, and $\mathcal{E}$ the e.m.f. around the entire circle, show that the potential difference ΔV between the plates is $(1 - d/l)\mathcal{E}$. If $\kappa = 1$, what is total E between the plates and the charge density on each?

Ans. $\frac{\mathcal{E}}{d}$, $\frac{\Delta V}{4\pi d}$.

142. Diamagnetism. — We are now prepared to offer an explanation of diamagnetism. Assuming that the Ampèrian currents in a magnetic medium are due to rings of electrons revolving in circles about the nucleus of an atom under a central force F, the equation of motion of a single electron is

$$m\omega_0^2 r_0 = F_0, \qquad (142\text{–}1)$$

where ω_0 is the angular velocity of revolution, r_0 the radius of the circular path and F_0 the force at distance r_0 from the nucleus.

If, now, a magnetic field $\mathbf{H}_1$ is applied in a direction at right angles to the plane of such a circular orbit in the sense of the vector ω_0, it gives rise to a centrifugal force evH_1/c which changes the angular velocity from ω_0 to ω. As $v = r\omega$, where r is the radius of the orbit after the magnetic field has been established, the equation of motion now is

$$m\omega^2 r = F - \frac{e\omega r}{c} H_1, \qquad (142\text{–}2)$$

where F is the force at distance r from the nucleus.

From (142–1) and (142–2) we get

$$\omega^2 r^4 - \omega_0{}^2 r_0{}^4 = \frac{r^3F - r_0{}^3F_0}{m} - \frac{e\omega r^4}{mc} H_1,$$

or, factoring the left-hand member,

$$\omega r^2 - \omega_0 r_0{}^2 = \frac{r^3F - r_0{}^3F_0}{m(\omega r^2 + \omega_0 r_0{}^2)} - \frac{er^2}{2mc} H_1 \qquad (142\text{–}3)$$

where, in the small term involving H_1, we have replaced $\omega r^2 + \omega_0 r_0{}^2$ by $2\omega r^2$.

To find how the radius of the orbit changes during the growth of the magnetic field, we make use of Faraday's law. As the electromotive force around the circular path is $2\pi rE$, the force on the electron tangent to the path is

$$eE = -\frac{e}{2\pi cr}\frac{dN}{dt}.$$

Equating this to the product of the mass by the transverse component of the acceleration (19–6) we have

$$\frac{m}{r}\frac{d}{dt}\left(r^2\frac{d\theta}{dt}\right) = -\frac{e}{2\pi cr}\frac{dN}{dt},$$

which gives on integration

$$\omega r^2 - \omega_0 r_0{}^2 = -\frac{e}{2\pi mc}N = -\frac{er^2}{2mc}H_1 \qquad (142\text{–}4)$$

since $\frac{d\theta}{dt}$ is the angular velocity ω and $N = \pi r^2 H_1$.

Comparing (142–4) with (142–3) we find that

$$r^3F - r_0{}^3F_0 = 0.$$

Consequently, if F is an inverse square force, or anything except an inverse cube force, $r = r_0$ and

$$\Delta\omega \equiv \omega - \omega_0 = -\frac{eH_1}{2mc}. \qquad (142\text{–}5)$$

If there are N electrons in the ring under consideration, the equivalent current is $Ne\omega/2\pi$ and hence the magnetic moment of the ring is $p = Ner^2\omega/(2c)$. The change in magnetic moment, therefore, is proportional to that in ω, or

$$\Delta p = \frac{p}{\omega}\Delta\omega = -\frac{peH_1}{2mc\omega}. \qquad (142\text{–}6)$$

This equation shows that a field applied in the direction of the magnetic moment of an Ampèrian circuit diminishes its moment, whereas one applied in the opposite direction increases the moment. The net effect, if the Ampèrian circuits are oriented at random, is to produce a magnetization opposite to the applied magnetic field. Although the theory indicates that all magnetic substances should exhibit diamagnetism, this effect is masked in paramagnetic and ferromagnetic media by the much more intense effect due to the alignment of the elementary magnets by the magnetic field.

In diamagnetic media the atom or molecule is supposed to contain a number of rigidly connected Ampèrian circuits so oriented with respect to one another that the resultant magnetic moment in the normal state is zero. An applied magnetic field, then, induces a magnetic moment opposite to itself without giving rise to a turning couple. If $\mathbf{H}_1$ makes an angle θ with the magnetic moment $\mathbf{p}$ of an individual ring, it is clear that the only component of $\mathbf{H}_1$ effective in changing the magnetic moment of the ring is that parallel to $\mathbf{p}$, and consequently (142–6) must be replaced by

$$\Delta p = -\frac{peH_1}{2mc\omega}\cos\theta. \qquad (142\text{–}7)$$

Hence, if there are n such rings per unit volume oriented at random, the number dn making angles between θ and $\theta + d\theta$ with H_1 is $\frac{1}{2}n \sin\theta\, d\,\theta$ and the magnetization is

$$I = \int \Delta p \cos\theta dn = -\frac{nep}{6mc\omega}H_1$$

$$= -\frac{nNe^2r^2}{12mc^2}H_1. \qquad (142\text{–}8)$$

Although H_1 is analogous to E_1 of article 115, the diamagnetic effect is so small that we need not distinguish between H_1 and H, and may take the coefficient of H_1 in (142–8) as representing the susceptibility. From its observed value we may estimate the number of electrons in the outer atom. The results are in fair accord with expectations.

The phenomenon of diamagnetism constitutes strong evidence for Ampère's theory of magnetism, for it is difficult to see how this effect could be explained on the dipole theory. As already noted, it has no counterpart in the polarization of dielectrics.

143. Energy of a Number of Current Circuits. — Consider n circuits fixed relative to the observer. The flux of induction through any one of these circuits is due partly to the current in the circuit itself and partly to the neighboring currents. Since H is proportional to the current producing the flux according to Ampère's law, the same is true of N provided the permeability of the medium in which the circuits are located is constant, and therefore we can write

$$N_1 = cL_1 i_1 + cM_{12} i_2 \ldots + cM_{1n} i_n \qquad (143\text{-}1)$$

for the flux through circuit 1 due to a current i_1 in this circuit and currents $i_2 \ldots i_n$ in the neighboring circuits. The coefficient L_1 is known as the *coefficient of self-induction* or the *self-inductance* of the circuit and the *M's* as *coefficients of mutual induction* or *mutual inductances*. If the currents change, the electromotive force induced in circuit 1 is

$$\mathcal{E}_1 = -L_1 \frac{di_1}{dt} - M_{12} \frac{di_2}{dt} \ldots - M_{1n} \frac{di_n}{dt}. \qquad (143\text{-}2)$$

From this equation we may define the coefficient of self-induction L_1 as the electromotive force in circuit 1 produced by a unit time rate of decrease of the current in this circuit, the coefficient of mutual induction M_{12} as the electromotive force in circuit 1 produced by a unit time rate of decrease of the current in circuit 2, and so forth. The practical unit of self or mutual inductance is called the *henry*.

The work done in a time dt against the induced electromotive forces in the n circuits is

$$dU = -i_1 \mathcal{E}_1 dt - i_2 \mathcal{E}_2 dt \ldots - i_n \mathcal{E}_n dt. \qquad (143\text{-}3)$$

Let us denote the final values of the currents by $I_1, I_2 \ldots I_n$ and let us build up the currents in such a way that at any instant every current is the same ratio of its final value. Then $i_1 = xI_1$, $i_2 = xI_2, \ldots i_n = xI_n$ where x increases from 0 to 1. Putting (143–2) and similar expressions for the electromotive forces in the other circuits into (143–3), we find for the total work done in establishing the currents

$$\left.\begin{aligned} U = \{&L_1I_1^2 + M_{12}I_1I_2 \ldots + M_{1n}I_1I_n \\ &+ M_{21}I_2I_1 + L_2I_2^2 \ldots + M_{2n}I_2I_n \\ &\cdot\quad\cdot\quad\cdot\quad\cdot\quad\cdot\quad\cdot\quad\cdot\quad\cdot\quad\cdot\quad\cdot \\ &+ M_{n1}I_nI_1 + M_{n2}I_nI_2 \ldots + L_nI_n^2\}\int_0^1 x\,dx \\ = \tfrac{1}{2}\{&L_1I_1^2 + M_{12}I_1I_2 \ldots + M_{1n}I_1I_n \\ &+ M_{21}I_2I_1 + L_2I_2^2 \ldots + M_{2n}I_2I_n \\ &\cdot\quad\cdot\quad\cdot\quad\cdot\quad\cdot\quad\cdot\quad\cdot\quad\cdot\quad\cdot\quad\cdot \\ &+ M_{n1}I_nI_1 + M_{n2}I_nI_2 \ldots + L_nI_n^2\}. \end{aligned}\right\} \quad (143\text{–}4)$$

Now if we vary I_1 keeping all the other currents constant,

$$\frac{\partial U}{\partial I_1}dI_1 = \{L_1I_1 + \tfrac{1}{2}(M_{12} + M_{21})I_2 \ldots + \tfrac{1}{2}(M_{1n} + M_{n1})I_n\}\,dI_1. \quad (143\text{–}5)$$

But when I_1 alone is changed

$$\mathcal{E}_1 = -L_1\frac{dI_1}{dt}, \quad \mathcal{E}_2 = -M_{21}\frac{dI_1}{dt}, \ldots \mathcal{E}_n = -M_{n1}\frac{dI_1}{dt},$$

and the work done against the induced electromotive forces is

$$\begin{aligned} \frac{\partial U}{\partial I_1}dI_1 &= \left\{L_1I_1\frac{dI_1}{dt} + M_{21}I_2\frac{dI_1}{dt} \ldots + M_{n1}I_n\frac{dI_1}{dt}\right\}dt \\ &= \{L_1I_1 + M_{21}I_2 \ldots + M_{n1}I_n\}\,dI_1. \end{aligned}$$

Therefore, as $I_1, I_2 \ldots I_n$ are arbitrary, we see by comparing this expression with (143–5) that

$$M_{21} = M_{12}, \quad M_{31} = M_{13}, \ldots M_{n1} = M_{1n},$$

and in general

$$M_{ji} = M_{ij}. \quad (143\text{–}6)$$

In calculating the energy (143–4) of the group of circuits we have omitted the work done by the currents in overcoming resistance since this work is dissipated in heat and is not stored up as energy of the system.

Problem 143a. A circuit consists of two coaxial cylindrical shells of radii a and b and common length l connected by flat end plates. Find the self-inductance and the energy of the circuit. Take $b > a$.

$$Ans.\ L = \frac{2\mu l}{c^2}\log\frac{b}{a},\quad U = \frac{\mu i^2 l}{c^2}\log\frac{b}{a}.$$

Problem 143b. Find the self-inductance of a toroidal solenoid of mean radius b and cross-sectional radius a containing N turns of wire.

$$Ans.\ \frac{4\pi\mu N^2 b}{c^2}\left[1 - \sqrt{1 - \frac{a^2}{b^2}}\right].$$

Problem 143c. On the toroidal solenoid of the last problem is wound a secondary of m turns. Find the mutual inductance.

$$Ans.\ \frac{4\pi\mu N m b}{c^2}\left[1 - \sqrt{1 - \frac{a^2}{b^2}}\right].$$

144. Forces and Torques on Rigid Circuits. — For simplicity we shall confine ourselves to a pair of circuits and calculate the force or torque on one due to the other. If one circuit is fixed and the other suffers a small displacement $d\xi$ the work done by the electromagnetic forces is $Fd\xi$, where F is the component of the force exerted by the one circuit on the other in the direction of the displacement.

As each circuit is rigid the relative motion of the two circuits changes the mutual inductance M but not the self-inductances L_1 and L_2. Therefore the induced electromotive force in circuit 1 is

$$\mathcal{E}_1 = -L_1\frac{dI_1}{dt} - M\frac{dI_2}{dt} - I_2\frac{dM}{dt}$$

and the rate at which work is done by it is

$$I_1\mathcal{E}_1 = -L_1I_1\frac{dI_1}{dt} - MI_1\frac{dI_2}{dt} - I_1I_2\frac{dM}{dt}.$$

Similarly the rate at which work is done by the electromotive force in circuit 2 is

$$I_2\mathcal{E}_2 = -L_2I_2\frac{dI_2}{dt} - MI_2\frac{dI_1}{dt} - I_1I_2\frac{dM}{dt}.$$

So the total work done per unit time at the expense of the energy of the circuits is

$$\frac{dW}{dt} = F\frac{d\xi}{dt} - L_1I_1\frac{dI_1}{dt} - MI_1\frac{dI_2}{dt} - MI_2\frac{dI_1}{dt} - L_2I_2\frac{dI_2}{dt} - 2I_1I_2\frac{dM}{dt}.$$

This must equal the rate of decrease of energy. The energy of the pair of circuits is

$$U = \tfrac{1}{2}L_1I_1^2 + MI_1I_2 + \tfrac{1}{2}L_2I_2^2,$$

and the rate of decrease of energy is

$$-\frac{dU}{dt} = -L_1I_1\frac{dI_1}{dt} - MI_1\frac{dI_2}{dt} - MI_2\frac{dI_1}{dt} - L_2I_2\frac{dI_2}{dt} - I_1I_2\frac{dM}{dt}.$$

Equating this to the expression above for the rate at which work is done we find

$$F\frac{d\xi}{dt} - I_1I_2\frac{dM}{dt} = 0,$$

or

$$F = I_1I_2\frac{\partial M}{\partial \xi}. \qquad (144\text{–}1)$$

Similarly, if we are concerned with a torque instead of a force, the component L of the torque in the direction of the angular displacement $d\theta$ is

$$L = I_1I_2\frac{\partial M}{\partial \theta}. \qquad (144\text{–}2)$$

From these equations it is clear that the force and torque on the circuit are in such directions as to increase M. Therefore a circuit tends to move in such a direction as to increase the flux of induction through it. Its equilibrium position is that for which the flux is a maximum subject to whatever mechanical constraints may be imposed.

Now suppose that we supply an external electromotive force to each circuit sufficient to keep the current constant while the displacement is taking place. The necessary electromotive force for circuit 1 is

$$\mathcal{E}_1 = I_2\frac{dM}{dt}$$

since the currents do not change, and the rate at which work is done by this electromotive force is

$$I_1\mathcal{E}_1 = I_1I_2\frac{dM}{dt}.$$

As work is done at an equal rate on the second circuit, the rate at which energy must be supplied from outside in order to keep the currents constant during the displacement is

$$2I_1I_2\frac{dM}{dt},$$

which is twice the rate at which work is done by the magnetic forces. Therefore the energy of the circuits increases at the same rate as that at which work is done. This is known as *Kelvin's law*.

In the preceding discussion we have treated the circuits as if they had no resistance, since we are not interested in the energy dissipated in the form of heat. If we prefer to consider circuits with finite resistances we can introduce an external electromotive force into each circuit just sufficient to maintain the current against resistance without affecting any of the preceding reasoning.

As the flux N through circuit 1 due to circuit 2 is cI_2M we can write (144–1) and (144–2) for the force or torque on circuit 1 in the forms

$$F = \frac{I_1}{c}\left(\frac{\partial N}{\partial \xi}\right)_{I_2}, \tag{144–3}$$

$$L = \frac{I_1}{c}\left(\frac{\partial N}{\partial \theta}\right)_{I_2}, \tag{144–4}$$

the subscript indicating that I_2 remains constant and therefore the flux N is that of a magnetostatic field.

Since the force or torque on circuit 1 is produced by the magnetic field in its neighborhood, it makes no difference whether the flux N is produced by a second circuit as we have supposed or by a magnet. Comparing (144–3) and (144–4) with (128–10) and (128–11) respectively we see that the force or torque on a current circuit is equal to that on a magnetic shell of constant strength equal to the current divided by c, whose periphery coincides with the circuit. So we have established the equivalence of a magnetic shell and a current circuit both as regards the field produced and the force or torque experienced.

Problem 144a. Two parallel circular turns of wire of radii a and b are a distance x apart. If a is large compared with b find the mutual inductance and if they carry currents i_a and i_b respectively find the force between them.

$$\textit{Ans.}\ M = \frac{2\pi^2a^2b^2}{c^2(a^2+x^2)^{3/2}},\quad F = -\frac{6\pi^2a^2b^2i_ai_b}{c^2(a^2+x^2)^{5/2}}x.$$

Problem 144b. The normal to a plane coil of N turns of area A makes an angle θ with the lines of force of a field H. Find the torque on the coil when a current i passes through it.

$$Ans.\ L = -\frac{NiAH}{c}\sin\theta.$$

145. Growth and Decay of Currents. — Let us consider the growth of current in a circuit of resistance R and self-inductance L to which a constant electromotive force $\mathcal{E}$ is applied. From Ohm's law

$$Ri = \mathcal{E} - L\frac{di}{dt},$$

since in addition to the applied electromotive force $\mathcal{E}$ we have the electromotive force $-L\frac{di}{dt}$ due to self-induction. Arranging terms we get

$$\frac{di}{i - \frac{\mathcal{E}}{R}} = -\frac{R}{L}dt$$

of which the integral is

$$i - \frac{\mathcal{E}}{R} = ae^{-(R/L)t}.$$

We shall determine the constant of integration a by taking $t = 0$ when $i = 0$. Then

$$i = \frac{\mathcal{E}}{R}\left\{1 - e^{-(R/L)t}\right\}. \qquad (145\text{–}1)$$

The current approaches the steady value $\mathcal{E}/R$ asymptotically, reaching $\left(1 - \frac{1}{e}\right)$th of its final value, that is $0.632\ \mathcal{E}/R$, in the time L/R. Therefore the current grows the more rapidly the smaller L/R. This quantity is known as the *time constant* of the circuit.

If we remove the applied electromotive force when a current i_0 is flowing in a circuit of resistance R and self-inductance L, the equation of decay of the current is

$$Ri = -L\frac{di}{dt}$$

of which the integral is

$$i = i_0e^{-(R/L)t} \qquad (145\text{–}2)$$

provided we determine the constant of integration by making $t = 0$ when $i = i_0$. The current decays to $1/e$th of its original value, that is $0.368 i_0$, in the time L/R and therefore decays the more rapidly the smaller the time constant.

Problem 145a. A circuit contains a ring solenoid of 20 cm radius and 5 cm² cross-section containing 10,000 turns. It incloses iron of permeability 1000 and has a resistance of 10 ohms. Find the time for the current in it to build up to 0.632 of its final value, or to decay to 0.368 of its original value.

Ans. 5 sec.

Problem 145b. In the circuit described by (145–1), show that, if the initial rate of increase of the current were maintained, the current would reach its final value in a time equal to the time constant L/R.

Problem 145c. Show that if a steady e.m.f. is introduced into a circuit containing a resistance R and a capacitance C in series, but no self-inductance, the charge on the condenser grows according to a formula analogous to (145–1) with a time constant RC.

Problem 145d. Find the growth of current in a circuit containing self-inductance but no resistance.

Ans. $i = \frac{\mathcal{E}}{L} t.$

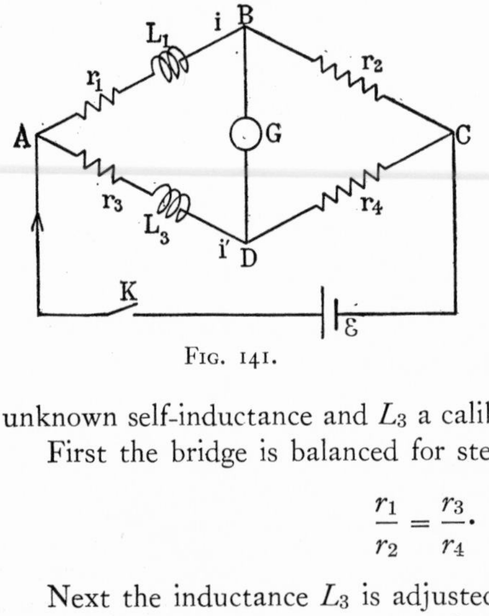

Fig. 141.

146. Comparison of Self-Inductances and Capacitances. — In two arms of the bridge illustrated in Fig. 141 are placed the non-inductive resistances r_2 and r_4 and in the other two arms coils of resistances r_1 and r_3 and self-inductances L_1 and L_3 respectively. Of the latter L_1 is an unknown self-inductance and L_3 a calibrated variable inductance.

First the bridge is balanced for steady currents. Therefore

$$\frac{r_1}{r_2} = \frac{r_3}{r_4}. \tag{146–1}$$

Next the inductance L_3 is adjusted without changing the resistance r_3 until the galvanometer G shows no deflection just after the key K is depressed. Then

$$V_A - V_B = r_1 i + L_1 \frac{di}{dt} = V_A - V_D = r_3 i' + L_3 \frac{di'}{dt},$$

$$V_B - V_C = r_2 i = V_D - V_C = r_4 i'.$$

Consequently

$$\frac{r_1}{r_2} + \frac{L_1}{r_2}\frac{\frac{di}{dt}}{i} = \frac{r_3}{r_4} + \frac{L_3}{r_4}\frac{\frac{di'}{dt}}{i'},$$

and in view of (146–1)

$$\frac{L_1}{r_2}\frac{\frac{di}{dt}}{i} = \frac{L_3}{r_4}\frac{\frac{di'}{dt}}{i'}.$$

But $r_2 i = r_4 i'$. Therefore

$$L_1 \frac{di}{dt} = L_3 \frac{di'}{dt}$$

and integrating

$$L_1 i = L_3 i'.$$

Hence

$$\frac{L_1}{L_3} = \frac{r_2}{r_4} = \frac{r_1}{r_3}. \tag{146–2}$$

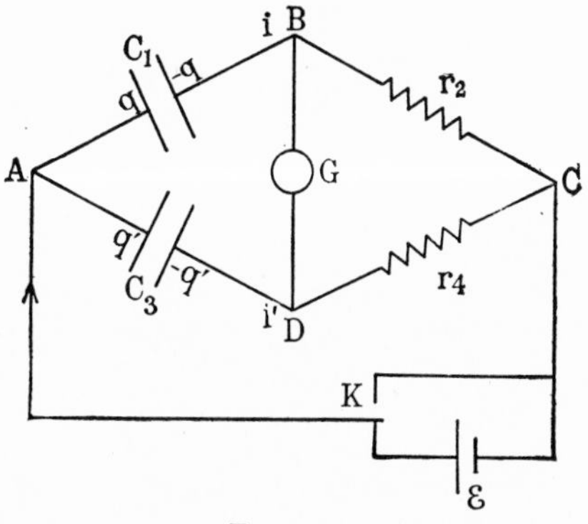

FIG. 142.

To compare capacitances we use the bridge shown in Fig. 142 where r_2 and r_4 are non-inductive resistances, C_1 is an unknown capacitance and C_3 a known capacitance. Either the known capacitance or one of the resistances is varied until the galvanometer G shows no deflection when the key K is depressed. Then

$$V_A - V_B = \frac{q}{C_1} = V_A - V_D = \frac{q'}{C_3},$$

$$V_B - V_C = ir_2 = V_D - V_C = i'r_4.$$

Differentiating the first with respect to the time

$$\frac{i}{C_1} = \frac{i'}{C_3},$$

and dividing by the second

$$C_1 r_2 = C_3 r_4.$$

Therefore

$$\frac{C_1}{C_3} = \frac{r_4}{r_2}. \qquad (146\text{–}3)$$

Note that this ratio is the inverse of that for inductances given in (146–2).

147. Ballistic Galvanometer. — It is often necessary to measure the quantity of electricity passing through a circuit due to a momentary current. For instance, when a condenser of capacitance C charged to a potential V is short circuited by a wire connecting its two plates a charge $q = CV$ passes through the circuit. Again, if the flux through a coil in a circuit of resistance R is changed from N_1 to N_2 an electromotive force $\mathcal{E}$ is induced equal to

$$\mathcal{E} = -\frac{1}{c}\frac{dN}{dt},$$

and this gives rise to a current

$$i = \frac{\mathcal{E}}{R} = -\frac{1}{cR}\frac{dN}{dt}.$$

The total quantity of electricity passing through the circuit is

$$q = \int i dt = -\frac{1}{cR}\int_{N_1}^{N_2} dN = \frac{N_1 - N_2}{cR}. \qquad (147\text{–}1)$$

A ballistic galvanometer is one designed to measure the quantity of electricity passing through a circuit due to a momentary current. It is usually an instrument of the d'Arsonval type discussed in article 136 the coil of which has a period of oscillation long compared with the duration of the current and very little damping.

On account of the long period of the coil the torque on it due to the current lasts only for a very small fraction of the swing. As this torque is proportional to the current we can write

$$I\frac{d^2\theta}{dt^2} = ki = k\frac{dq}{dt},$$

where I is the moment of inertia of the coil and θ its deflection. We have omitted the torque of restitution due to the torsion of the suspension since it is proportional to the deflection which remains practically zero throughout this portion of the motion. Integrating the above equation we get

$$\frac{d\theta}{dt} = \frac{k}{I} q \tag{147-2}$$

for the angular velocity imparted to the coil by the momentary current. The remainder of the swing of the galvanometer proceeds according to the equation of motion

$$\frac{d^2\theta}{dt^2} + 2l\frac{d\theta}{dt} + \kappa^2\theta = 0$$

of a damped simple harmonic oscillator subject to no impressed torque which was discussed in article 27. The solution (27–2) is

$$\theta = \alpha e^{-lt} \cos (\omega_0 t - \beta), \quad \omega_0 \equiv \sqrt{\kappa^2 - l^2},$$

where we have replaced x by θ and A by the angular amplitude α.

To determine the constants of integration α and β we have θ equals zero and the angular velocity equals kq/I when t is zero. From the first

$$\beta = \pi/2$$

and

$$\theta = \alpha e^{-lt} \sin \omega_0 t,$$

from which

$$\frac{d\theta}{dt} = \alpha e^{-lt} (- l \sin \omega_0 t + \omega_0 \cos \omega_0 t).$$

Therefore the second condition gives

$$\alpha = \frac{k}{I\omega_0} q.$$

The successive throws $\alpha_1, \alpha_2, \alpha_3 \ldots$ in alternate directions, which occur at the times $t_1, t_1 + \pi/\omega_0, t_1 + 2\pi/\omega_0 \ldots$ for which $\frac{d\theta}{dt}$ vanishes, are diminished progressively by damping. As $\tan \omega_0 t_1 = \omega_0/l$,

$$\alpha_1 = \frac{\alpha e^{-lt_1}}{\sqrt{1 + \dfrac{l^2}{\omega_0{}^2}}},$$

and hence

$$q = \left[\frac{I\omega_0}{k} e^{lt_1} \sqrt{1 + \frac{l^2}{\omega_0{}^2}}\right] \alpha_1, \quad t_1 \equiv \frac{1}{\omega_0} \tan^{-1} \frac{\omega_0}{l}. \qquad (147\text{–}3)$$

As all the quantities contained within the brackets are constants of the galvanometer, the charge passing through the instrument is proportional to the throw. The angular frequency $\omega_0 = 2\pi/P$ is easily determined by measuring the period P of the oscillations, and the damping constant l may be obtained from the logarithmic decrement

$$\delta \equiv 2 \log \frac{\alpha_1}{\alpha_2} = 2 \log \frac{\alpha_2}{\alpha_3} = \ldots = lP$$

as in (27–4), the factor 2 appearing since we are counting throws in both directions. However the ratio I/k is not so readily determined.

The galvanometer may be calibrated by passing through it a charge from a condenser of known capacitance charged to a known difference of potential, or by changing the flux through a coil connected to it by a known amount. In the latter case the resistance of the circuit must be known and the circuit broken immediately after the charge has passed through the galvanometer to avoid electromagnetic damping produced by the induced currents set up in the galvanometer coil by its oscillation in the control field.

The galvanometer can also be calibrated by observing the deflection θ_s produced by a known steady current i_s. For ki_s is the torque due to the current and $-I\kappa^2\theta_s$ the torque of restitution. Therefore

$$k = I\kappa^2 \left(\frac{\theta_s}{i_s}\right).$$

From (27–4)

$$\kappa^2 = \frac{4\pi^2 + \delta^2}{P^2},$$

and hence

$$\frac{I}{k} = \frac{P^2}{4\pi^2 + \delta^2} \left(\frac{i_s}{\theta_s}\right),$$

which gives the ratio I/k in terms of measurable quantities.

Consequently (147–3) becomes, if we replace ω_0 by $2\pi/P$ and l by δ/P,

$$q = \left[\frac{P}{2\pi}\frac{e^{lt_1}}{\sqrt{1+\frac{\delta^2}{4\pi^2}}}\left(\frac{i_s}{\theta_s}\right)\right]\alpha_1. \tag{147–4}$$

If the damping is small and hence l and δ are nearly zero, we can write to a sufficient approximation

$$q = \left[\frac{P}{2\pi}\left(\frac{i_s}{\theta_s}\right)\right]\alpha_1. \tag{147–5}$$

One use of the ballistic galvanometer is in finding the B–H curve of a magnetic material, such as iron. Consider a toroidal solenoid of iron of circumferential length L and cross-section A wound with a primary of N_p turns of wire outside of which is a secondary of N_s turns connected to a ballistic galvanometer. The primary is connected through an ammeter and a variable resistance to a battery. When a current i flows through the primary a magnetic intensity

$$H = \frac{4\pi N_p i}{cL} = \frac{4\pi n i}{c}$$

is set up inside the iron, where n is the number of turns per unit length in the primary. When the current in the primary is increased by Δi the field increases by $\Delta H = 4\pi n\Delta i/c$ and if B is the magnetic induction in the iron the flux of induction through the secondary increases by $N_s A\Delta B$. Therefore a quantity of electricity

$$q = \frac{N_1 - N_2}{cR} = -\frac{N_s A\Delta B}{cR}$$

passes through the ballistic galvanometer. From this equation ΔB can be determined. Starting with the iron core in the unmagnetized state represented by O in (Fig. 143) and increasing i step by step the curve Oa is found. On decreasing the current to zero and then increasing it in the opposite direction we get the curve abc and continuation of the process give cda. The lagging of B behind H is known as *hysteresis*.

The back electromotive force in the primary as the current varies is

$$\mathcal{E} = -\frac{1}{c} N_p A \frac{dB}{dt},$$

and the work done on the iron core in a time dt is

$$dW = -i\mathcal{E}\,dt = \frac{1}{c} iN_p AdB = \frac{HL}{4\pi} AdB = \frac{V}{4\pi} HdB,$$

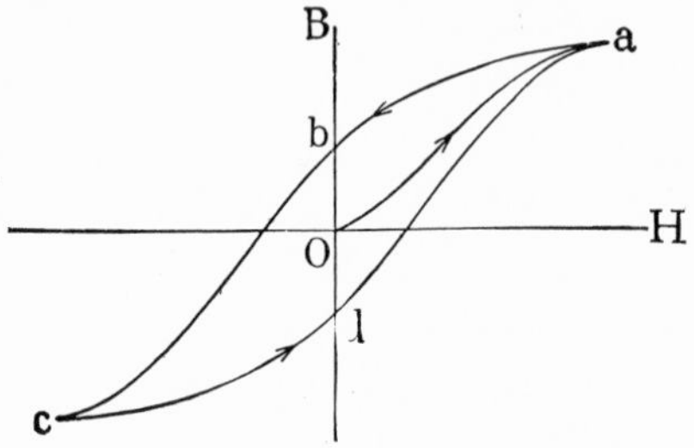

FIG. 143.

where V is the volume LA of the core. So the work w per unit volume per cycle is

$$w = \frac{1}{4\pi} \oint HdB, \qquad (147\text{–}6)$$

which is $1/(4\pi)$ times the area of the hysteresis loop *abcda*. Putting

$$B = H + 4\pi I,$$

$$w = \oint HdI, \qquad (147\text{–}7)$$

since $\oint HdH = 0$. In iron the energy dissipated in heat per cycle in orienting the molecular magnets is of the order of $(10)^5$ erg/cm³.

In a homogeneous isotropic paramagnetic or diamagnetic medium in which the relation $B = \mu H$ holds (147–6) vanishes. If, however, instead of integrating around a complete loop, we find the work done in increasing the field from 0 to H, we obtain for the energy per unit volume of the magnetic substance

$$u = \frac{\mu}{4\pi} \int_0^H HdH = \frac{\mu}{8\pi} H^2. \qquad (147\text{–}8)$$

Problem 147a. A secondary coil of N turns is wound around the middle of a long solenoid of n turns per unit length and cross-section A. Find the mutual inductance. The secondary is connected to a ballistic galvanometer, the resistance of the circuit being R. Find the quantity of electricity passing through the secondary when the current i in the primary is reversed. If $\alpha_1 = 10$ scale divisions, $i = 10$ amp, $R = 100$ ohms, $N = 1000$ turns, $n = 100$ turns/cm, $A = 20$ cm^2, $\mu = 100$, find the calibration constant of the galvanometer in coulombs per scale division.

Ans. $M = \frac{4\pi\mu NnA}{c^2}$, $q = \frac{8\pi\mu NnAi}{cR}$, 0.0503 coulomb/scale div.

Problem 147b. The coil of a ballistic galvanometer has a period of 10 sec for free oscillations, and throws $\alpha_1 = 12$, $\alpha_2 = 10$, etc. A steady current of $(10)^{-4}$ amp produces a deflection of 10 scale divisions. Find the capacitance of a condenser which, when charged to 100 volts and then discharged through the galvanometer, produces a first throw of 8 scale divisions.

Ans. 1.39 microfarad.

148. Alternating Currents. — Consider a circuit (Fig. 144) containing a resistance R, a self-inductance L and a condenser of capacitance C connected in series with an applied simple harmonic electromotive force

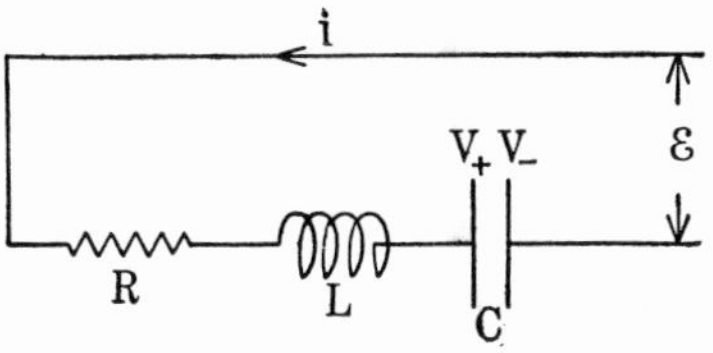

FIG. 144.

$$\mathcal{E} = \mathcal{E}_0 \sin \omega t.$$

If we denote the potentials of the positive and negative plates of the condenser by V_+ and V_- respectively, we have in addition to the applied electromotive force,

Electromotive force due to self-induction

$$= -L\frac{di}{dt},$$

Electromotive force due to condenser

$$= -(V_+ - V_-) = -\frac{q}{C} = -\frac{1}{C}\int_0^t idt,$$

where the last is negative because the electromotive force in the circuit due to the condenser is in the direction opposite to the current when q is positive. Therefore Ohm's law takes the form

$$Ri = \mathcal{E}_0 \sin \omega t - L\frac{di}{dt} - \frac{1}{C}\int_0^t idt. \qquad (148\text{–}1)$$

A more detailed analysis of the electromotive forces appearing in the various portions of the circuit is instructive. If the source of electromotive force $\mathcal{E}$ and the self-inductance L are without resistance the electric intensity in each of these portions of the circuit must vanish at every instant. This is accomplished by a separation of charge which gives rise to an electromotive force equal and opposite to $\mathcal{E}$ in the first instance and to $-L\frac{di}{dt}$ in the second. Denoting the electromotive forces due to separation of charge in the source and in the self-inductance by $\mathcal{E}_1$ and $\mathcal{E}_2$ respectively, we have then

$$\mathcal{E} + \mathcal{E}_1 = 0,$$

$$-L\frac{di}{dt} + \mathcal{E}_2 = 0.$$

Similarly there must be an electromotive force $\mathcal{E}_3$ across the resistance due to separation of charge such that

$$\mathcal{E}_3 = Ri,$$

in order to satisfy Ohm's law (139–7), and finally the charge on the condenser gives rise to the electromotive force

$$\mathcal{E}_4 = \frac{q}{C}$$

between the plates.

Adding these four equations we have

$$\mathcal{E} - L\frac{di}{dt} + \mathcal{E}_1 + \mathcal{E}_2 + \mathcal{E}_3 + \mathcal{E}_4 = Ri + \frac{q}{C}.$$

Now $\mathcal{E}_1 + \mathcal{E}_2 + \mathcal{E}_3 + \mathcal{E}_4$ is the electromotive force around a closed circuit due to the charges accumulated on the circuit. As the field of these charges is expressible as the gradient of a scalar potential, this electromotive force must vanish, as noted in article 139. Hence we are left with (148–1).

Differentiating (148–1) with respect to the time and rearranging terms

$$\frac{d^2i}{dt^2} + \frac{R}{L}\frac{di}{dt} + \frac{1}{LC}i = \frac{\omega}{L}\mathcal{E}_0 \cos \omega t. \qquad (148\text{–}2)$$

This is the equation (27–6) of a damped simple harmonic oscillator subject to a simple harmonic impressed force where

$$2l = \frac{R}{L}, \quad \kappa^2 = \frac{1}{LC}, \quad a = \frac{\omega}{L}\mathcal{E}_0.$$

The self-inductance corresponds to the mass of the oscillator and the capacitance to the coefficient in the force of restitution. The solution (27–9) for the steady state existing after the transients have been damped out is

$$i = \frac{\mathcal{E}_0}{\sqrt{R^2 + \left(\omega L - \frac{1}{\omega C}\right)^2}} \cos(\omega t - \phi), \quad \tan\phi \equiv -\frac{R}{\omega L - \frac{1}{\omega C}},$$

or, if we put $\phi \equiv \delta + \pi/2$,

$$i = \frac{\mathcal{E}_0}{\sqrt{R^2 + \left(\omega L - \frac{1}{\omega C}\right)^2}} \sin(\omega t - \delta), \quad \tan\delta \equiv \frac{\omega L - \frac{1}{\omega C}}{R}. \tag{148–3}$$

At low frequencies C holds the current down, at high frequencies L. The expression

$$\sqrt{R^2 + \left(\omega L - \frac{1}{\omega C}\right)^2} \tag{148–4}$$

is called the *impedance* of the circuit for the frequency ω and takes the place of the resistance in the case of a constant electromotive force. If $\omega L > 1/(\omega C)$, $\delta > 0$ and the current lags behind the impressed electromotive force, whereas if $\omega L < 1/(\omega C)$, $\delta < 0$ and the current is ahead of the electromotive force. If $\omega L = 1/(\omega C)$ the current is in phase with the impressed electromotive force and the impedance is a minimum. By analogy with the simple harmonic oscillator this is said to be the case of *resonance*. The frequency for resonance is

$$\omega = \frac{1}{\sqrt{LC}}. \tag{148–5}$$

The power delivered to the circuit is

$$P = i\mathcal{E} = \frac{\mathcal{E}_0^2}{\sqrt{R^2 + \left(\omega L - \frac{1}{\omega C}\right)^2}} \sin\omega t \sin(\omega t - \delta),$$

and the mean power, averaged over a period $2\pi/\omega$, is

$$\bar{P} = \frac{\omega}{2\pi}\int_0^{2\pi/\omega} i\mathcal{E}\,dt$$

$$= \frac{\omega}{2\pi}\frac{\mathcal{E}_0^2}{\sqrt{R^2+\left(\omega L - \frac{1}{\omega C}\right)^2}}\left\{\cos\delta\int_0^{2\pi/\omega}\sin^2\omega t dt - \sin\delta\int_0^{2\pi/\omega}\sin\omega t\cos\omega t dt\right\}$$

$$= \frac{1}{2}\frac{\mathcal{E}_0^2}{\sqrt{R^2+\left(\omega L - \frac{1}{\omega C}\right)^2}}\cos\delta. \tag{148-6}$$

The *effective electromotive force* $\mathcal{E}_e$ is defined by

$$\mathcal{E}_e = \sqrt{\text{average } \mathcal{E}^2} = \frac{1}{\sqrt{2}}\mathcal{E}_0, \tag{148-7}$$

and the *effective current* i_e by

$$i_e = \sqrt{\text{average } i^2} = \frac{1}{\sqrt{2}}\frac{\mathcal{E}_0}{\sqrt{R^2+\left(\omega L - \frac{1}{\omega C}\right)^2}}. \tag{148-8}$$

Hence

$$i_e = \frac{\mathcal{E}_e}{\sqrt{R^2+\left(\omega L - \frac{1}{\omega C}\right)^2}} \tag{148-9}$$

and

$$\bar{P} = i_e\mathcal{E}_e\cos\delta. \tag{148-10}$$

The quantity $\cos\delta$ is called the *power factor*. At resonance it is unity and the maximum of power is delivered to the circuit. A coil of large self-inductance and small resistance in a circuit makes δ approach $\pi/2$ and cuts down the current by increasing the impedance without wasting power in the development of heat as a rheostat does in a direct current circuit. Such a coil is called a *choke coil.*

Problem 148a. A circuit has an alternating electromotive force of 100 cos ωt volts, a resistance of 2 ohms, a self-inductance of 0.001 henry, and a condenser of capacitance 1000 microfarads, all connected in series. Find the effective current if (*a*) $\omega = 0$ i.e. steady electromotive force, (*b*) $\omega = 10/\text{sec}$, (*c*) $\omega = 100/\text{sec}$, (*d*) resonance, (*e*) $\omega = 10{,}000/\text{sec}$, (*f*) $\omega = 100{,}000/\text{sec}$, and plot the effective current against the logarithm of the frequency.

Ans. (*a*) 0, (*b*) 0.707 amp, (*c*) 6.93 amp, (*d*) 35.3 amp, (*e*) 6.93 amp, (*f*) 0.707 amp.

Problem 148b. A voltmeter is connected across the self-inductance L in Fig. 144. Does it measure $-L\frac{di}{dt}$ or $+L\frac{di}{dt}$?

Problem 148c. An inductance L and capacitance C in parallel are connected in series with a resistance R and an applied simple harmonic e.m.f. $\mathcal{E} = \mathcal{E}_0 \sin \omega t$. Show that the impedance of the circuit is infinite when the relation (148–5) is satisfied.

149. Discharging Condenser. — Consider a condenser of capacitance C (Fig. 145) in series with an inductance L and a spark gap R. When the condenser has been charged up to a sufficiently high potential, it discharges across the gap. We shall consider the oscillations which occur after the dielectric between the terminals of the gap breaks down. As there is no impressed electromotive force the equation of the circuit is

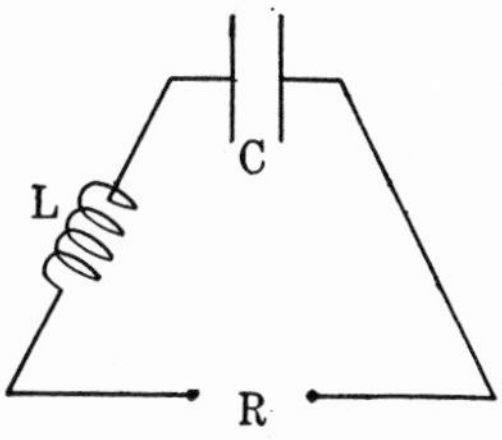

FIG. 145.

$$\frac{d^2i}{dt^2} + \frac{R}{L}\frac{di}{dt} + \frac{1}{LC}i = 0, \qquad (149\text{–}1)$$

where the resistance R of the circuit is mostly the resistance of the gap. This is the equation (27–1) of a damped simple harmonic oscillator subject to no impressed force, l and κ having the same values as in the last article. Referring to article 27 we see that the motion is periodic provided

$$\frac{1}{LC} > \frac{R^2}{4L^2}.$$

The solution (27–2) of the differential equation for the periodic case is

$$i = Ae^{-(R/2L)t}\cos(\omega_0 t - \beta), \quad \omega_0 \equiv \sqrt{\frac{1}{LC} - \frac{R^2}{4L^2}}. \qquad (149\text{–}2)$$

To determine the constants of integration we shall take $i = 0$ when $t = 0$ and denote the initial potential difference of the condenser by $-\mathcal{E}_0$. Then $\beta = \pi/2$ and

$$i = Ae^{-(R/2L)t}\sin\omega_0 t.$$

At the time $t = 0$ the equation

$$-L\left(\frac{di}{dt}\right)_{t=0} - \frac{q}{C} = 0$$

must be satisfied, since the term Ri vanishes as $i = 0$. Therefore

$$-LA\omega_0 + \mathcal{E}_0 = 0,$$

and hence

$$i = \frac{\mathcal{E}_0}{\omega_0 L}e^{-(R/2L)t}\sin\omega_0 t,\quad \omega_0 \equiv \sqrt{\frac{1}{LC} - \frac{R^2}{4L^2}}. \qquad (149\text{–}3)$$

This is a damped oscillation differing from that illustrated in Fig. 33 only in that the curve starts at the origin. If $1/(LC)$ is large compared with $R^2/(4L^2)$, as is generally the case, the period is given to a sufficient degree of approximation by

$$P = \frac{2\pi}{\omega_0} = 2\pi\sqrt{LC}. \qquad (149\text{–}4)$$

The oscillator originally used by Hertz to produce electromagnetic waves in his famous experiments of 1888 consisted of two metal plates A and B (Fig. 146) connected by short wires to a spark gap R. The plates form a condenser, the self-inductance of the circuit being that of the wires connecting the plates to the spark gap. Effectively we have the same circuit as that illustrated diagrammatically in Fig. 145. Hertz showed that the electromagnetic waves radiated by the oscillator have all the properties of light waves, thereby confirming the electromagnetic theory of light proposed by Maxwell which will be considered in the next chapter.

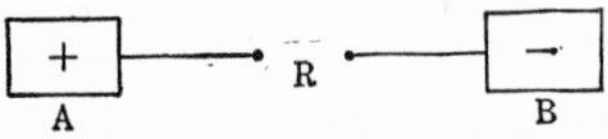

FIG. 146.

150. Complex Variables in Alternating Current Theory. — To represent graphically the complex quantity

$$z = x + iy \qquad (150\text{–}1)$$

where x and y are real and $i \equiv \sqrt{-1}$, we plot x as abscissa and y as ordinate, as shown in Fig. 147. Therefore z locates a point P in the XY plane whose abscissa is the real part of the complex quantity and whose ordinate is the imaginary part. The complex quantity z may be considered to represent the vector OP in the XY plane.

Transforming to polar coordinates ρ and θ

$$z = \rho(\cos\theta + i\sin\theta) = \rho e^{i\theta}, \tag{150-2}$$

where ρ is known as the *modulus* and θ as the *argument* of the complex quantity.

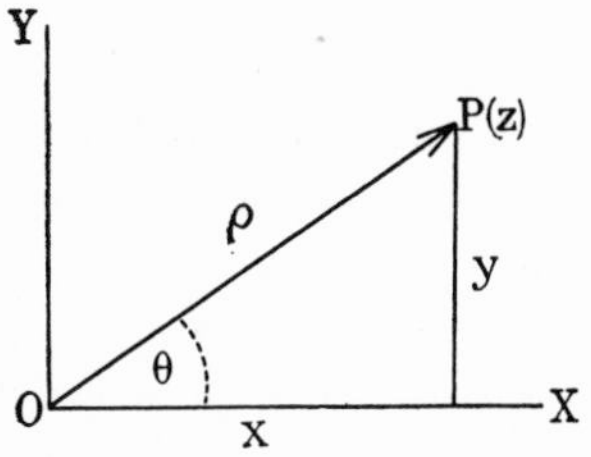

FIG. 147.

Let

$$z = x + iy = \rho e^{i\theta}$$

and

$$z' = x' + iy' = \rho' e^{i\theta'}$$

be two complex quantities. Then

$$z + z' = x + x' + i(y + y'). \tag{150-3}$$

So complex quantities add just as vectors do.

If we multiply two complex quantities,

$$zz' = \rho\rho' e^{i(\theta+\theta')}. \tag{150-4}$$

The modulus of the product is the product of the moduli of the factors and the argument of the product the sum of the arguments of the factors. In particular if $z'' = e^{i\theta''}$,

$$zz'' = \rho e^{i(\theta+\theta'')}. \tag{150-5}$$

So multiplication by $e^{i\theta''}$ merely rotates z through the angle θ'' without changing the value of its modulus.

Consider the differential equation

$$a_1 \frac{d^2u}{dt^2} + a_2 \frac{du}{dt} + a_3 u = b(t) + ic(t), \tag{150-6}$$

where a_1, a_2, a_3 are real constants and $b(t)$ and $c(t)$ are real functions of the real variable t. Let a solution be

$$u = x(t) + iy(t). \tag{150-7}$$

Then

$$a_1 \frac{d^2x}{dt^2} + ia_1 \frac{d^2y}{dt^2} + a_2 \frac{dx}{dt} + ia_2 \frac{dy}{dt} + a_3 x + ia_3 y = b(t) + ic(t).$$

Separating real and imaginary parts it follows that

$$a_1 \frac{d^2x}{dt^2} + a_2 \frac{dx}{dt} + a_3 x = b(t), \tag{150–8}$$

$$a_1 \frac{d^2y}{dt^2} + a_2 \frac{dy}{dt} + a_3 y = c(t). \tag{150–9}$$

So if u is a solution of (150–6) the real part of u is a solution of (150–8) and the imaginary part a solution of (150–9). As the equation of a circuit subject to an impressed simple harmonic electromotive force is of the type (150–8), we can use complex variables advantageously in discussing such circuits. Let us take the real part of

$$\mathcal{E} = \mathcal{E}_0 e^{i\omega t}$$

for the impressed electromotive force, where the constant $\mathcal{E}_0$ is not necessarily real. We may write

$$\mathcal{E}_0 = \mathcal{E}'_0 e^{i\phi}$$

where $\mathcal{E}'_0$ is real, and the impressed electromotive force is then

$$\text{Real Part of } \{\mathcal{E}'_0 e^{i(\omega t+\phi)}\} = \mathcal{E}'_0 \cos(\omega t + \phi). \tag{150–10}$$

Now if we write the equation (148–1) in the form

$$L\frac{dI}{dt} + RI + \frac{1}{C}\int I\,dt = \mathcal{E}_0 e^{i\omega t}, \tag{150–11}$$

where the current has been denoted by I so as to avoid confusion with $i \equiv \sqrt{-1}$; the real part of the solution is the current corresponding to the electromotive force (150–10). To solve this equation try

$$I = I_0 e^{i\omega t}$$

where I_0 is not necessarily real. Substituting in the differential equation we find that it is satisfied provided

$$I_0\left\{R + i\left(\omega L - \frac{1}{\omega C}\right)\right\} = \mathcal{E}_0,$$

or

$$\mathcal{E}_0 = \sqrt{R^2 + \left(\omega L - \frac{1}{\omega C}\right)^2}\, I_0 e^{i\delta}, \tag{150–12}$$

$$I_0 = \frac{\mathcal{E}_0}{\sqrt{R^2 + \left(\omega L - \frac{1}{\omega C}\right)^2}} e^{-i\delta}, \qquad (150\text{–}13)$$

where

$$\tan \delta \equiv \frac{\omega L - \frac{1}{\omega C}}{R}.$$

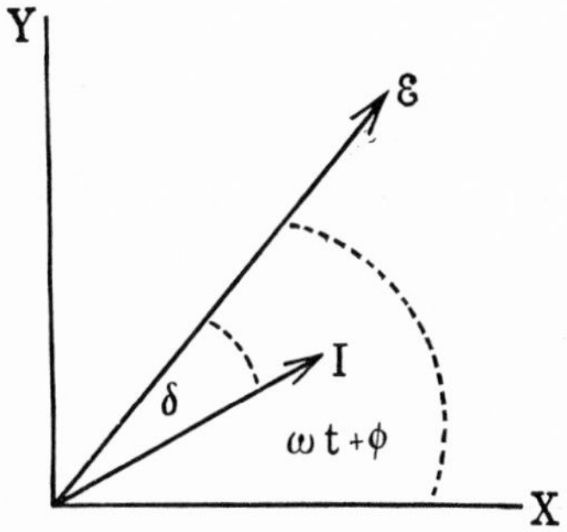

FIG. 148.

Therefore $\mathcal{E}$ and I represent vectors rotating in the XY plane with angular velocity ω (Fig. 148), the latter lagging behind the former by the angle δ. The actual electromotive force and current at any instant are represented by the projections of these vectors on the X axis.

If we put

$$Z = R + i\left(\omega L - \frac{1}{\omega C}\right) = \sqrt{R^2 + \left(\omega L - \frac{1}{\omega C}\right)^2} e^{i\delta},$$

$$A = \frac{1}{R + i\left(\omega L - \frac{1}{\omega C}\right)} = \frac{1}{\sqrt{R^2 + \left(\omega L - \frac{1}{\omega C}\right)^2}} e^{-i\delta}$$

the complex quantities Z and A are known as *impedance* and *admittance* respectively. The imaginary part of the impedance, that is,

$$\omega L - \frac{1}{\omega C}$$

is known as the *reactance* of the circuit. From (150–12) and (150–13) it follows that

$$\mathcal{E} = ZI, \qquad I = A\mathcal{E}. \qquad (150\text{–}14)$$

Consider two portions of a circuit of impedances Z_1 and Z_2 connected in series. The electromotive forces are respectively

$$\mathcal{E}_1 = Z_1 I, \qquad \mathcal{E}_2 = Z_2 I,$$

as the current is the same in the two. Therefore the total electromotive force is

$$\mathcal{E} = \mathcal{E}_1 + \mathcal{E}_2 = (Z_1 + Z_2)I. \qquad (150\text{–}15)$$

On the other hand, if the two portions of a circuit are connected in parallel with the applied electromotive force $\mathcal{E}$,

$$I_1 = A_1\mathcal{E}, \qquad I_2 = A_2\mathcal{E},$$

where A_1 and A_2 are the admittances. Hence the total current is

$$I = I_1 + I_2 = (A_1 + A_2)\mathcal{E}. \tag{150–16}$$

Problem 150a. A resistance of 1 ohm, a self-inductance of 3 millihenrys and a capacitance of 2 millifarads are connected in series with an alternating electromotive force $\mathcal{E}$. If the effective value of $\mathcal{E}$ is 10 volts and the circuit 60 cycle/sec, find the effective e.m.f. across the resistance, the self-inductance and the capacitance. Draw the complex e.m.f. diagram and check your answers geometrically. *Ans.* 9.81 volts, 11.10 volts, 13.02 volts.

Problem 150b. Two coils are connected in parallel with an effective electromotive force of 10 volts at 60 cycle/sec. The first has a resistance of 1 ohm and a self-inductance of 1 millihenry, the second a resistance of 1 ohm and a self-inductance of 3 millihenrys. Find the effective current in each and the total effective current. Check answers geometrically.
Ans. 9.36 amp, 6.62 amp, 15.52 amp.

151. Absolute Standards. — If we have available absolute standards of two of the three quantities, electromotive force, current, resistance, we can measure the third in absolute units by the aid of Ohm's law. The last two are the most convenient to use for the purpose of preparing absolute standards.

I. *Absolute Standard of Current.* — The tangent galvanometer described in article 136 is an absolute instrument for measuring currents. A better instrument is Kelvin's *ampere balance.* This consists of a horizontal coil of radius b suspended from one arm of a beam balance half way between two parallel fixed coils of radius a. The current i to be measured passes through all three coils, the fixed coils being connected so that the current traverses them in opposite senses. If $2x$ is the distance between the fixed coils and b is small compared with a, it follows from the result of problem 144a that the force on the movable coil is

$$F = \frac{12\pi^2 a^2 b^2 i^2}{c^2 (a_2 + x^2)^{5/2}}\, x \tag{151–1}$$

for one turn in each coil. As this force can be balanced by a weight placed in the pan on the opposite arm of the balance, the current i can be measured in absolute electromagnetic units. Placing a silver voltameter in series with the ampere balance it is found that one ampere deposits 0.001118 gm of silver on the cathode per second.

II. *Absolute Standard of Resistance.* — Consider a coil AB (Fig. 149) rotating with angular velocity ω about the vertical diameter chosen as Z axis in a uniform horizontal field H, such as the horizontal component of the earth's field. At the center of the coil is placed a short compass needle free to turn in the horizontal plane of the paper.

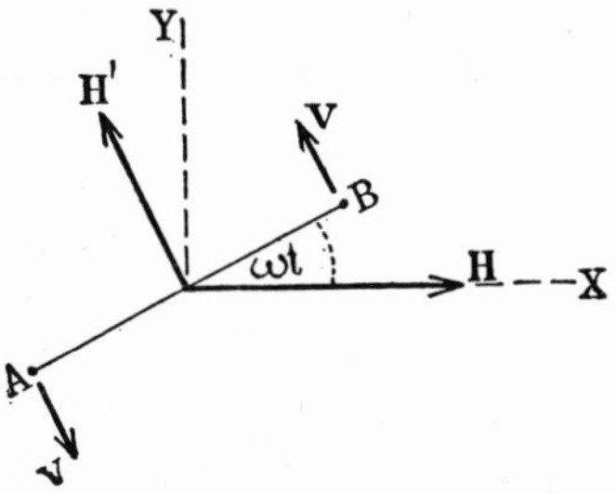

FIG. 149.

For simplicity we shall consider the coil to consist of a single turn of wire of radius a. Taking the positive normal to the circuit in the direction of $\mathbf{H}'$ the electromotive force $\mathcal{E}$ due to the changing flux is

$$\mathcal{E} = -\frac{1}{c}\frac{dN}{dt} = \frac{\pi a^2 \omega}{c} H \cos \omega t$$

and the current

$$i = \frac{\pi a^2 \omega H}{c\sqrt{R^2 + \omega^2 L^2}} \cos (\omega t - \delta), \quad \tan \delta \equiv \frac{\omega L}{R},$$

where R is the resistance and L the self-inductance of the coil. The field H' at the center of the coil due to this current is

$$H' = \frac{2\pi i}{ca} = \frac{2\pi^2 a \omega H}{c^2\sqrt{R^2 + \omega^2 L^2}} \cos (\omega t - \delta).$$

The mean values of the components of H' along X and Y are then

$$H'_x = -\frac{2\pi^2 a \omega H}{c^2\sqrt{R^2 + \omega^2 L^2}} \overline{\cos (\omega t - \delta) \sin \omega t} = -\frac{\pi^2 a \omega H}{c^2\sqrt{R^2 + \omega^2 L^2}} \sin \delta,$$

$$H'_y = \frac{2\pi^2 a \omega H}{c^2\sqrt{R^2 + \omega^2 L^2}} \overline{\cos (\omega t - \delta) \cos \omega t} = \frac{\pi^2 a \omega H}{c^2\sqrt{R^2 + \omega^2 L^2}} \cos \delta.$$

Therefore the resultant field at the center of the coil has the component

$$H + H'_x = H\left\{1 - \frac{\pi^2 a \omega}{c^2\sqrt{R^2 + \omega^2 L^2}} \sin \delta\right\}$$

along the X axis, and

$$H'_y = H\left\{\frac{\pi^2 a\omega}{c^2\sqrt{R^2 + \omega^2 L^2}} \cos\delta\right\}$$

along the Y axis. Consequently the compass needle is deflected from the direction of the field H by an angle α given by

$$\tan\alpha = \frac{H'_y}{H + H'_x} = \frac{\pi^2 a\omega R}{c^2R^2 + c^2\omega^2L^2 - \pi^2 a\omega^2 L}$$

if we put in the values of $\sin\delta$ and $\cos\delta$ in terms of R and ωL. If the reactance of the circuit is made small compared with its resistance we can neglect the terms containing ωL and get

$$R = \frac{1}{c^2}\pi^2 a\omega \cot\alpha, \qquad (151\text{–}2)$$

which determines the resistance in terms of easily measurable quantities. Once the value of a resistance is known in absolute units the value of any other resistance may be determined by the aid of Wheatstone's bridge. In this way the ohm is found to be the resistance of a column of mercury 106.162 cm long and 1 mm^2 in cross-section at 0° C.

III. *Absolute Standard of Electromotive Force.* — Having a standard ohm and an absolute instrument for measuring current, the electromotive force of a constant cell can be determined in absolute units from Ohm's law, since an electromotive force of one volt produces a current of one ampere in a circuit of one ohm resistance. Electromotive forces can be compared with one another by means of the *potentiometer* illustrated in Fig. 150, where B represents a battery and AC a wire of uniform resistance along which the contact S may be slid. First a standard cell of electromotive force $\mathcal{E}$ and then a cell of unknown electromotive force $\mathcal{E}'$ is placed at D and in each case the position of the contact S is so adjusted that the galvanometer G shows no deflection. If l and l' are the lengths AS in the two cases, it follows from Ohm's law that

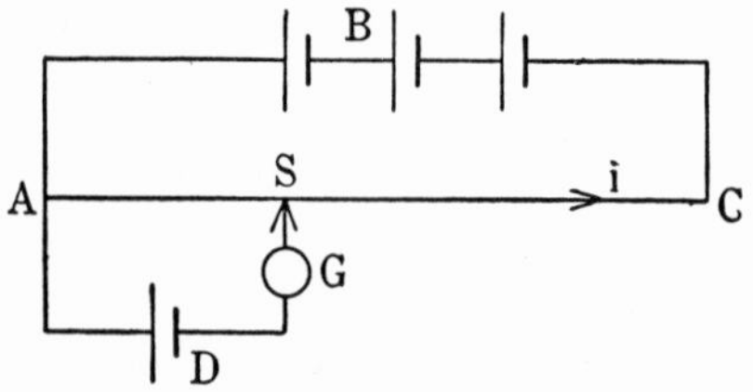

Fig. 150

$$\mathcal{E} = irl,$$
$$\mathcal{E}' = irl',$$

where r is the resistance of a unit length of the slide wire. Therefore

$$\frac{\mathcal{E}'}{\mathcal{E}} = \frac{l'}{l}. \tag{151–3}$$

IV. *Absolute Standard of Inductance.* — The self-inductance of circuits of certain simple geometrical forms can be calculated from their dimensions, as in problems 143*a* and 143*b*. Using such as standards the self-inductance of any other circuit may be determined by the bridge method of article 146.

V. *Absolute Standard of Capacitance.* — The capacitances of condensers of simple geometrical forms can be calculated from their dimensions, as in problem 119*a*. Once a standard capacitance has been determined, the capacitance of any other condenser may be measured by the comparison method of article 146.

Problem 151a. The absolute value of a resistance R may be determined by connecting it in parallel with a rotating disk (Faraday disk) of area A placed at the center of a long solenoid of n turns/cm with its axis parallel to that of the solenoid, the current entering the disk along its axis and leaving through a brush in contact with its periphery. The divided circuit, consisting of R and the disk, is in series with the solenoid and a constant e.m.f., and the disk is rotated with a frequency ν sufficient to make the current through it vanish. Prove that $R = 4\pi n\nu A/c^2$.

152. Systems of Units. — Indicating by the subscript g that a quantity is measured in the Gaussian units which we have been using, the fundamental equations of electromagnetism as developed so far take the form

$$\nabla\cdot\mathbf{D}_g = 4\pi\rho_g, \quad (a_g) \qquad \nabla\cdot\mathbf{B}_g = 0, \quad (b_g)$$

$$\nabla\times\mathbf{E}_g = -\frac{1}{c}\frac{\partial\mathbf{B}_g}{\partial t}, \quad (c_g) \qquad \nabla\times\mathbf{H}_g = \frac{4\pi}{c}\mathbf{j}_g, \quad (d_g)$$

$$\mathbf{D}_g = \mathbf{E}_g + 4\pi\mathbf{P}_g = (\kappa\mathbf{E}_g), \quad (e_g) \quad \mathbf{B}_g = \mathbf{H}_g + 4\pi\mathbf{I}_g = (\mu\mathbf{H}_g), \quad (f_g)$$

$$\mathbf{F} = \rho_g\left\{\mathbf{E}_g + \frac{1}{c}\mathbf{v}\times\mathbf{B}_g\right\}, \quad (g_g)$$

in these units. Here (a_g) and (b_g) are Gauss' laws (113–3) and (135–5*a*), (c_g) is Faraday's law (141–3), (d_g) is Ampère's law (135–5*b*), (g_g) is the force per unit volume obtained from (138–1), and the expressions in parentheses apply only in the case of homogeneous isotropic dielectric or paramagnetic media.

Although magnetic poles do not appear in these equations, since we are basing them on Ampère's theory of magnetism, it is convenient to introduce a fictitious pole-strength m in addition to the electric charge q in order to facilitate conversion to other systems of units. Then, to convert to any other system of c.g.s. units, indicated by accents, we may put $q_g = \alpha q'$, $m_g = \beta m'$, $\mathbf{D}_g = \gamma \mathbf{D}'$, $\mathbf{B}_g = \delta \mathbf{B}'$, where the constants α, β, γ, δ may be dimensional. As we wish to preserve unaltered the definitions

$$\mathbf{F} = q_g \mathbf{E}_g = q' \mathbf{E}', \tag{152–1}$$

$$\mathbf{F} = m_g \mathbf{H}_g = m' \mathbf{H}', \tag{152–2}$$

$$t = \frac{q_g}{i_g} = \frac{q'}{i'}, \tag{152–3}$$

we have $\mathbf{E}_g = \mathbf{E}'/\alpha$, $\mathbf{H}_g = \mathbf{H}'/\beta$, $\mathbf{j}_g = \alpha \mathbf{j}'$. Moreover, as $P \propto q$, and $I \propto m$, $\mathbf{P}_g = \alpha \mathbf{P}'$ and $\mathbf{I}_g = \beta \mathbf{I}'$. Therefore the fundamental equations become

$$\nabla \cdot \mathbf{D}' = 4\pi \left(\frac{\alpha}{\gamma}\right) \rho', \quad (a') \qquad \nabla \cdot \mathbf{B}' = 0, \quad (b')$$

$$\nabla \times \mathbf{E}' = -\frac{\alpha\delta}{c} \frac{\partial \mathbf{B}'}{\partial t}, \quad (c') \qquad \nabla \times \mathbf{H}' = \frac{4\pi\alpha\beta}{c} \mathbf{j}', \quad (d')$$

$$\mathbf{D}' = \frac{1}{\alpha\gamma} \mathbf{E}' + 4\pi \left(\frac{\alpha}{\gamma}\right) \mathbf{P}' = \left(\frac{\kappa}{\alpha\gamma} \mathbf{E}'\right), \quad (e')$$

$$\mathbf{B}' = \frac{1}{\beta\delta} \mathbf{H}' + 4\pi \left(\frac{\beta}{\delta}\right) \mathbf{I}' = \left(\frac{\mu}{\beta\delta} \mathbf{H}'\right), \quad (f')$$

$$\mathbf{F} = \rho' \left\{ \mathbf{E}' + \frac{\alpha\delta}{c} \mathbf{v} \times \mathbf{B}' \right\}. \quad (g')$$

The constants κ and μ, being pure ratios, are the same in all units.

The complete electromagnetic system, still used although much less than formerly, is obtained by making $\alpha = \gamma = c$, $\beta = \delta = 1$.

The most important system for theoretical work, because it is the simplest, is the Heaviside-Lorentz system, in which $\alpha = \beta = 1/\sqrt{4\pi}$ and $\gamma = \delta = \sqrt{4\pi}$. Quantities measured in these units, designated h.l.u., will be indicated by the subscript l. In Heaviside-Lorentz units the fundamental equations become

$$\nabla\cdot\mathbf{D}_l = \rho_l, \quad (a_l) \qquad \nabla\cdot\mathbf{B}_l = 0, \quad (b_l)$$

$$\nabla\times\mathbf{E}_l = -\frac{1}{c}\frac{\partial\mathbf{B}_l}{\partial t}, \quad (c_l) \qquad \nabla\times\mathbf{H}_l = \frac{1}{c}\,\mathbf{j}_l, \quad (d_l)$$

$$\mathbf{D}_l = \mathbf{E}_l + \mathbf{P}_l = (\kappa\mathbf{E}_l), \quad (e_l) \qquad \mathbf{B}_l = \mathbf{H}_l + \mathbf{I}_l = (\mu\mathbf{H}_l), \quad (f_l)$$

$$\mathbf{F} = \rho_l\left\{\mathbf{E}_l + \frac{1}{c}\mathbf{v}\times\mathbf{B}_l\right\}, \quad (g_l)$$

in which the 4π's, which appear when Gaussian units are used, have been eliminated. The force between two point charges at rest is

$$F = \frac{q_l q'_l}{4\pi r^2} \tag{152–4}$$

in h.l.u. Therefore the unit charge is that which repels a like equal charge at a distance of 1 cm in vacuo with a force of $1/(4\pi)$ dyne.

Since the practical units now used by the electrical engineer are based on the meter, kilogram and second as fundamental units, the unit of force, called the *newton*, is $(10)^5$ dynes. If, now, we distinguish electric and magnetic quantities measured in m.k.s. units by double accents, (152–1) and (152–2) must be replaced by

$$q_g\mathbf{E}_g = (10)^5\,\frac{\text{gm}\ \text{cm}}{\text{kg}\ \ \text{m}}\,q''\mathbf{E}'', \tag{152–5}$$

$$m_g\mathbf{H}_g = (10)^5\,\frac{\text{gm}\ \text{cm}}{\text{kg}\ \ \text{m}}\,m''\mathbf{H}''. \tag{152–6}$$

As, however, the units of many electromagnetic quantities, when expressed in terms of the units of length, mass and time, involve awkward fractional indices, we shall confine our transformation relations to equations between numerics, writing the relations above in the form

$$q_g\mathbf{E}_g = (10)^5 q''\mathbf{E}'', \tag{152–7}$$

$$m_g\mathbf{H}_g = (10)^5 m''\mathbf{H}''. \tag{152–8}$$

Let us now put $q_g = (10)^{9/2}\alpha q''$, $m_g = (10)^{9/2}\beta m''$, $\mathbf{D}_g = (10)^{1/2}\gamma\mathbf{D}''$, $\mathbf{B}_g = (10)^{1/2}\delta\mathbf{B}''$. As polarization has the dimensions of charge per unit area, $\mathbf{P}_g = (10)^{1/2}\alpha\mathbf{P}''$ and similarly $\mathbf{I}_g = (10)^{1/2}\beta\mathbf{I}''$. Also, as $i_g = (10)^{9/2}\alpha i''$, it follows that $\mathbf{j}_g = (10)^{1/2}\alpha\mathbf{j}''$. Finally, if we designate geometrical and dynamical quantities measured in m.k.s. units by the subscript p, $\mathbf{F} = (10)^{-1}\,\mathbf{F}_p$, $\nabla = (10)^{-2}\nabla_p$ and $c = (10)^2 c_p$. Then the fundamental equations become

$$\nabla_p \cdot \mathbf{D}'' = 4\pi \left(\frac{\alpha}{\gamma}\right) \rho'', \quad (a'') \qquad \nabla_p \cdot \mathbf{B}'' = 0, \quad (b'')$$

$$\nabla_p \times \mathbf{E}'' = -\frac{\alpha\delta}{c_p}\frac{\partial \mathbf{B}''}{\partial t}, \quad (c'') \qquad \nabla_p \times \mathbf{H}'' = \frac{4\pi\alpha\beta}{c_p}\mathbf{j}'', \quad (d'')$$

$$\mathbf{D}'' = \frac{1}{\alpha\gamma}\mathbf{E}'' + 4\pi\left(\frac{\alpha}{\gamma}\right)\mathbf{P}'' = \left(\frac{\kappa}{\alpha\gamma}\mathbf{E}''\right), \quad (e'')$$

$$\mathbf{B}'' = \frac{1}{\beta\delta}\mathbf{H}'' + 4\pi\left(\frac{\beta}{\delta}\right)\mathbf{I}'' = \left(\frac{\mu}{\beta\delta}\mathbf{H}''\right), \quad (f'')$$

$$\mathbf{F}_p = \rho''\left\{\mathbf{E}'' + \frac{\alpha\delta}{c_p}\mathbf{v}_p \times \mathbf{B}''\right\}. \quad (g'')$$

It should be noted that these equations are identical in form with (a') to (g').

In any m.k.s. system the joule is the unit of energy and the watt the unit of power. In order to retain the remaining six internationally recognized practical units, the coulomb, ampere, volt, ohm, farad, henry, all that is necessary is to make α equal to $3(10)^{9/2}$, or, more accurately, to $2.998(10)^{9/2}$, as is evident at once from the table in article 140 and such relations as $U = qV$, $\mathcal{E} = Ri$, $C = q/V$, $U = \frac{1}{2}Li^2$. This leaves the three constants β, γ, δ arbitrary. If we made $\beta = \alpha$ and $\delta = \gamma$, the equations would retain the symmetrical form of the Gaussian or the Heaviside-Lorentz system, and one parameter, γ, would still be arbitrary. However, the International Electrotechnical Commission at a plenary session in June 1935 decided to sacrifice the advantages of symmetry in favor of making the coefficients of the right-hand members of (c'') and (d'') equal to unity. This fixes the values of β and δ as well as α, and, even though γ is still arbitrary, a symmetrical set of units is no longer possible. Finally, γ is selected so as to make the coefficient of $\mathbf{P}''$ in (e'') equal to unity, like that of $\mathbf{I}''$ in (f'').

This gives the four constants at our disposal the magnitudes:

$$\left.\begin{aligned} \alpha &= 2.998(10)^{9/2}, & \beta &= \frac{c_p}{4\pi\alpha} = 0.7958(10)^{5/2}, \\ \gamma &= 4\pi\alpha = 3.767(10)^{11/2}, & \delta &= \frac{c_p}{\alpha} = (10)^{7/2}. \end{aligned}\right\} \quad (152\text{–}9)$$

This system is the accepted *practical system* today. Indicating practical units throughout by the subscript p and putting

$$\kappa_0 \equiv \frac{1}{\alpha\gamma} = \frac{1}{4\pi\alpha^2} = 8.854(10)^{-12}, \qquad (152\text{–}10)$$

$$\mu_0 \equiv \frac{1}{\beta\delta} = \frac{4\pi\alpha^2}{c_p{}^2} = 1.257(10)^{-6}, \qquad (152\text{–}11)$$

the fundamental equations in these units take the form

$$\nabla_p \cdot \mathbf{D}_p = \rho_p, \quad (a_p) \qquad \nabla_p \cdot \mathbf{B}_p = 0, \quad (b_p)$$

$$\nabla_p \times \mathbf{E}_p = -\frac{\partial \mathbf{B}_p}{\partial t}, \quad (c_p) \qquad \nabla_p \times \mathbf{H}_p = \mathbf{j}_p, \quad (d_p)$$

$$\mathbf{D}_p = \kappa_0 \mathbf{E}_p + \mathbf{P}_p = (\kappa\kappa_0 \mathbf{E}_p), \quad (e_p)$$

$$\mathbf{B}_p = \mu_0 \mathbf{H}_p + \mathbf{I}_p = (\mu\mu_0 \mathbf{H}_p), \quad (f_p)$$

$$\mathbf{F}_p = \rho_p\{\mathbf{E}_p + \mathbf{v}_p \times \mathbf{B}_p\}. \quad (g_p)$$

Although α may be given arbitrary physical dimensions, it is evident that $1/\sqrt{\kappa_0\mu_0} = c_p$ has the dimensions of a velocity

Since the fundamental equations (a'') to (g'') in m.k.s. units are identical in form with the equations (a') to (g') in c.g.s. units, it is evident that either these equations or any equation derived from them can be written in terms of α, β, γ, δ in such a manner that by giving these constants appropriate values the equation can be formulated in *any* c.g.s. or *any* m.k.s. system. To obtain the equation in c.g.s. Gaussian units, for instance, all four constants must be given the value unity, in c.g.s. electromagnetic units, $\alpha = \gamma = c$, $\beta = \delta = 1$, in m.k.s. practical units the constants must have the values specified in (152–9), and so forth. For example, Coulomb's law of force becomes

$$F = \frac{\alpha^2 qq'}{r^2}$$

in *any* c.g.s. or m.k.s. units. Putting $\alpha^2 = 1/(4\pi\kappa_0)$ this gives, in practical units,

$$F_p = \frac{q_p q'_p}{4\pi\kappa_0 r_p{}^2} = 8.988(10)^9 \frac{q_p q'_p}{r_p{}^2}.$$

Problem 152a. The capacitance of a parallel plate condenser consisting of two plates of area A a distance d apart is $\kappa A/(4\pi d)$ in Gaussian units. Find the capacitance in e.m.u., in h.l.u. and in practical units.

Ans. $\dfrac{\kappa A}{4\pi c^2 d}, \quad \dfrac{\kappa A}{d}, \quad \dfrac{\kappa\kappa_0 A}{d}.$

Problem 152b. The charge passing through a circuit when the magnetic flux changes from N_1 to N_2 is $(N_1 - N_2)/(cR)$ in Gaussian units. What is it in e.m.u., h.l.u and in practical units?

Ans. $\dfrac{N_1 - N_2}{R}, \quad \dfrac{N_1 - N_2}{cR}, \quad \dfrac{N_1 - N_2}{R}.$

Problem 152c. Show that in any system of units, whether c.g.s. or m.k.s., the magnetic field of a long solenoid with n turns per unit length is

$$H = \frac{4\pi\alpha\beta n i}{c}.$$

153. Electromagnetic Waves Along Wires. — A steady current distributes itself uniformly throughout the cross-section of the conductor in which it is flowing. In the case of an alternating current, however, the current density is greatest at the surface of the conductor and least at its center, and in the case of very rapid oscillations the current is almost entirely confined to the surface. The reason for this concentration of current at the surface is easily seen from the result of problem 143*a*. The self-inductance of the circuit described there is greater the smaller the radius a of the inner cylindrical shell and becomes indefinitely great as a approaches zero. If now we replace the inner shell by a solid cylinder we can consider this cylinder as built up of shells of successively increasing radius. The portions of the current flowing in the inner shells have a greater self-inductance and hence a greater impedance to overcome than those flowing in the outer shells. As the current tends to follow the path of least impedance, the current density is greatest at the surface of the cylinder. Moreover, as the self-inductance enters into the expression for the impedance (148–4) in the term ωL, the effect is greater the greater the frequency ω of the circuit. In the case of the very rapid oscillations to be considered in the present article we can consider the current to be confined entirely to the surface of the conductor which carries it.

Consider two very long parallel wires (Fig. 152) of negligible resistance connected at one end to the two sides of a Hertzian oscillator H such as was depicted in Fig. 146. Consider a small length dx of the pair of wires. At the instant considered we shall suppose that this section of the upper wire is positively charged and that the current is directed away from the oscillator, while the corresponding section of the lower wire is negatively charged and the current is directed toward the oscillator. The capacitance of the pair of wires, which was calculated in article 125, may be represented diagrammatically by placing fictitious condensers at regular intervals between the two wires, as shown by broken lines in the figure. We wish to write down the equation of the infinitesimal circuit $ABCD$. Let q_1 be the charge per unit length on the upper wire, C_1 the capacitance per unit length and L_1 the self-inductance per unit length of the pair. Then at A the difference of potential between the two wires is

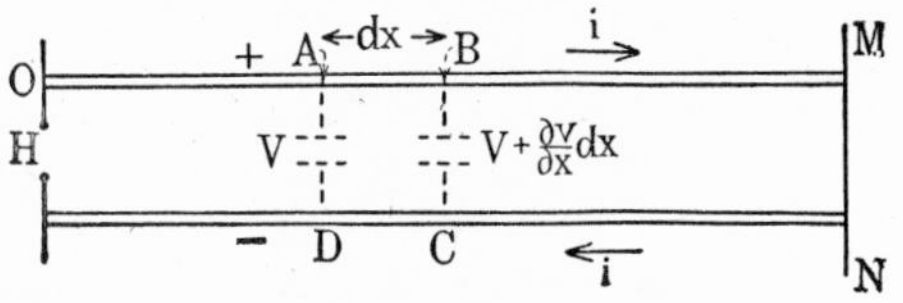

FIG. 152.

$$V = \frac{q_1}{C_1},$$

and at B

$$V + \frac{\partial V}{\partial x} dx = \frac{q_1}{C_1} + \frac{1}{C_1}\frac{\partial q_1}{\partial x} dx.$$

Consequently the electromotive force around the circuit $ABCD$ due to capacitance is

$$-\frac{\partial V}{\partial x} dx = -\frac{1}{C_1}\frac{\partial q_1}{\partial x} dx.$$

From Faraday's law the electromotive force due to self-induction is

$$-L_1 \frac{\partial i}{\partial t} dx.$$

As the resistance of the circuit has been assumed to be negligible the total electromotive force must vanish. Hence the equation of the circuit is

$$L_1 \frac{\partial i}{\partial t} + \frac{1}{C_1}\frac{\partial q_1}{\partial x} = 0. \qquad (153\text{-}1)$$

Now the time rate of increase of the charge on the length *AB* is equal to the excess of the current flowing into this section of the wire at *A* over that flowing out at *B*. So we have the equation of continuity

$$\frac{\partial q_1}{\partial t}\,dx = i - \left(i + \frac{\partial i}{\partial x}\,dx\right) = -\frac{\partial i}{\partial x}\,dx,$$

or

$$\frac{\partial q_1}{\partial t} = -\frac{\partial i}{\partial x}. \qquad (153\text{–}2)$$

Differentiating (153–1) with respect to x and (153–2) with respect to t and eliminating i we get

$$\frac{\partial^2 q_1}{\partial t^2} = \frac{1}{L_1C_1}\frac{\partial^2 q_1}{\partial x^2}. \qquad (153\text{–}3)$$

This is the equation of a wave traveling with velocity

$$v = \frac{1}{\sqrt{L_1C_1}} \qquad (153\text{–}4)$$

along the wires. If the wave is simple harmonic

$$q_1 = q_{10}\cos\frac{2\pi}{\lambda}(x - vt). \qquad (153\text{–}5)$$

At the oscillator $x = 0$ and

$$q_1 = q_{10}\cos 2\pi\frac{v}{\lambda}t = q_{10}\cos 2\pi\nu t,$$

where ν is the frequency of the oscillator. Therefore the wave length is

$$\lambda = \frac{v}{\nu} = \frac{1}{\nu\sqrt{L_1C_1}}. \qquad (153\text{–}6)$$

The potential difference between the wires is

$$V = \frac{q_1}{C_1} = \frac{q_{10}}{C_1}\cos\frac{2\pi}{\lambda}(x - vt). \qquad (153\text{–}7)$$

To find the current we have from (153–2)

$$\frac{\partial i}{\partial x} = -\frac{\partial q_1}{\partial t} = -\frac{2\pi v}{\lambda}q_{10}\sin\frac{2\pi}{\lambda}(x - vt),$$

whence

$$i = vq_{10} \cos \frac{2\pi}{\lambda}(x - vt). \tag{153–8}$$

Comparing (153–5), (153–7), and (153–8) we see that q_1, V and i are in phase.

If the wires are terminated at $x = s$ by a perfectly conducting plate MN, the waves progressing out from the oscillator will be reflected and standing waves will be formed. In this case the difference of potential between the wires must vanish at every instant at the plate. As the reflected wave is a function of $x + vt$, the total potential difference at any point due to both outgoing and returning waves is

$$V = \frac{q_{10}}{C_1} \cos \frac{2\pi}{\lambda}(x - vt) + A \cos \frac{2\pi}{\lambda}(x + vt + l)$$

$$= \left[\frac{q_{10}}{C_1} \cos \frac{2\pi}{\lambda} x + A \cos \frac{2\pi}{\lambda}(x + l)\right] \cos \frac{2\pi}{\lambda} vt$$

$$+ \left[\frac{q_{10}}{C_1} \sin \frac{2\pi}{\lambda} x - A \sin \frac{2\pi}{\lambda}(x + l)\right] \sin \frac{2\pi}{\lambda} vt.$$

The amplitude A and the phase l of the reflected wave are determined by equating to zero the coefficients of the trigonometrical functions of t for $x = s$. This gives $A = q_{10}/C_1$ and $l = \lambda/2 - 2s$. Hence at any point

$$V = \frac{q_{10}}{C_1}\left\{\left[\cos \frac{2\pi}{\lambda} x - \cos \frac{2\pi}{\lambda}(2s - x)\right] \cos \frac{2\pi}{\lambda} vt\right.$$

$$\left. + \left[\sin \frac{2\pi}{\lambda} x - \sin \frac{2\pi}{\lambda}(2s - x)\right] \sin \frac{2\pi}{\lambda} vt\right\}$$

$$= 2\frac{q_{10}}{C_1} \sin \frac{2\pi}{\lambda}(x - s) \sin \frac{2\pi}{\lambda}(vt - s). \tag{153–9}$$

Therefore

$$q_1 = C_1 V = 2q_{10} \sin \frac{2\pi}{\lambda}(x - s) \sin \frac{2\pi}{\lambda}(vt - s), \tag{153–10}$$

and from (153–2)

$$i = 2vq_{10} \cos \frac{2\pi}{\lambda}(x - s) \cos \frac{2\pi}{\lambda}(vt - s). \tag{153–11}$$

So q_1 and V are in phase, but i is out of phase with them by a quarter wave length and a quarter period. The nodes in V may be located by connecting the two wires by a sliding wire containing a short spark gap, moving the latter back and forth until positions are found at which sparking ceases. Once the positions of the nodes have been found the wave length is known and if the frequency of the oscillator is determined by the aid of a revolving mirror the velocity of propagation can be computed. In this way Hertz found that the velocity of electromagnetic waves along wires is nearly equal to the velocity of light *in vacuo*.

We can, however, calculate the velocity of propagation from the capacitance and the self-inductance per unit length by (153–4). The former was computed for an electrostatic field in article 125; we shall calculate the latter now for steady currents. Although we cannot altogether justify the use of these static expressions in the case of varying fields which we are considering here, nevertheless they must be very nearly correct if the distance between the wires is small compared with the wave length. Actually we arrive at the correct result, as the rigorous solution of the problem given in the next chapter will show.

We shall make use of the notation of article 125 and refer to Fig. 124. Just as the electric field between the two wires is the same as if all the charge were located on the image filaments, we should expect the magnetic field to be the same as if the currents were concentrated on these two filaments. Then, if $\mathbf{k}$ is a unit vector parallel to the Z axis, the magnetic intensity at P obtained from (134–6) is

$$\mathbf{H} = \frac{2i}{cr_1^2}\mathbf{k} \times \mathbf{r}_1 - \frac{2i}{cr_2^2}\mathbf{k} \times \mathbf{r}_2 = \frac{2i}{c}\mathbf{k} \times \left(\frac{\mathbf{r}_1}{r_1^2} - \frac{\mathbf{r}_2}{r_2^2}\right). \qquad (153\text{–}12)$$

The electric intensity at P, however, if we replace λ of article 125 by q_1 to accord with our present notation, is

$$\mathbf{E} = \frac{2q_1}{r_1^2}\mathbf{r}_1 - \frac{2q_1}{r_2^2}\mathbf{r}_2 = 2q_1\left(\frac{\mathbf{r}_1}{r_1^2} - \frac{\mathbf{r}_2}{r_2^2}\right). \qquad (153\text{–}13)$$

Comparing these two equations we see that $\mathbf{H}$ is everywhere perpendicular to $\mathbf{E}$ and therefore the lines of magnetic force coincide with the circular traces of the equipotential surfaces found in article 125. As the current is confined to the surface of the conductor, none of these circular lines of force can enter the conductor, for, if they did, the line integral of $\mathbf{H}$ around a circular path lying in a plane perpendicular to the axis of the wire and wholly within the conductor would not vanish as demanded by Ampère's law (134–2). Therefore the trace of the surface of the wire must coincide with one of these circular lines of force in order to give (153–12) for the magnetic field outside the wire. But, as these same circles represent the traces of the equipotential surfaces of the electric field, the trace of the surface of the wire must coincide with one of them in order to give (153–13) for the electric field outside. Consequently (153–12) specifies the magnetic field and (153–13) the electric field at all points outside a given pair of parallel wires of circular cross-section, both fields vanishing inside the conductors.

To calculate the magnetic flux per unit length of the wire system we may integrate along any strip of unit width extending from the surface of one wire to that of the other. Convenience suggests a strip whose trace coincides with the X axis. Then for the field H_1 due to the current in the left-hand wire of Fig. 124 the flux is

$$N_1 = \int H_1 dr_1 = \frac{2i}{c}\int \frac{dr_1}{r_1} = \frac{2i}{c} \log m_+$$

since the ratio of r_1 at the surface of the right-hand wire to r_1 at the surface of the left-hand wire is equal to the ratio m_+ of r_2 to r_1 at the surface of the latter wire. Similarly the flux due to the opposite current in the right-hand wire is

$$N_2 = -\frac{2i}{c} \log m_-.$$

Therefore the total flux through a strip of unit width stretching across from the surface of the first wire to that of the second is

$$N = N_1 + N_2 = \frac{2i}{c} \log \frac{m_+}{m_-} = \frac{2i}{c} \log \frac{b + \sqrt{b^2 - 4a^2}}{b - \sqrt{b^2 - 4a^2}},$$

and the self-inductance per unit length is

$$L_1 = \frac{2}{c^2} \log \frac{b + \sqrt{b^2 - 4a^2}}{b - \sqrt{b^2 - 4a^2}}. \qquad (153\text{–}14)$$

If the wires are immersed in a medium of permeability μ (153–14) requires the additional factor μ and

$$L_1 = \frac{2\mu}{c^2} \log \frac{b + \sqrt{b^2 - 4a^2}}{b - \sqrt{b^2 - 4a^2}}. \qquad (153\text{–}15)$$

In article 125 the capacitance per unit length was found to be

$$C_1 = \frac{\kappa}{2 \log \dfrac{b + \sqrt{b^2 - 4a^2}}{b - \sqrt{b^2 - 4a^2}}}. \tag{153-16}$$

Therefore the velocity of propagation of electromagnetic waves along a parallel wire system of negligible resistance is

$$v = \frac{1}{\sqrt{L_1 C_1}} = \frac{c}{\sqrt{\kappa\mu}} \tag{153-17}$$

from (153–4). As c is identical with the measured value of the velocity of light in vacuo to within the experimental error, it is impossible to doubt that light waves are merely electromagnetic waves of very short wave length. In the next chapter we shall see that electromagnetic waves have many other characteristics in common with light.

Problem 153a. Show that if the parallel wires considered in article 153 have resistance R_1 per unit length the velocity of propagation of electromagnetic waves of wave length λ along the wires is slowed down to

$$v = \frac{1}{\sqrt{L_1 C_1 + \dfrac{\lambda^2}{16\pi^2} R_1^2 C_1^2}}.$$

Problem 153b. A submarine cable consists of a cylindrical wire surrounded by a concentric cylindrical conducting shell. Neglecting resistance, show from the results of problems 119*a* and 143*a* that the velocity of propagation of electromagnetic waves along the cable is

$$v = \frac{c}{\sqrt{\kappa\mu}}.$$

REFERENCES

Page and Adams: *Principles of Electricity*, D. Van Nostrand Co., New York.

Starling, S. G.: *Electricity and Magnetism*, Longmans, Green & Co., London.

Jeans, J. H.: *Electricity and Magnetism*, Cambridge University Press, Cambridge.

Carson, J. R.: *Electric Circuit Theory and the Operational Calculus*, McGraw-Hill Book Co., New York

CHAPTER XII

ELECTROMAGNETIC THEORY

154. Electromagnetic Equations. — In this chapter we shall use symmetrical Heaviside-Lorentz units throughout. The fundamental equations of electromagnetism, as formulated in the last two chapters to express in analytical form the experimental discoveries of Coulomb, Ampère and Faraday, are represented in these units by (a_l)–(g_l) of article 152. Equations (a_l)–(d_l) inclusive are known as the *field equations*, for, with the aid of constitutive relations such as $\mathbf{D} = \kappa\mathbf{E}$ and $\mathbf{B} = \mu\mathbf{H}$, they determine the electric and magnetic fields produced by any assigned distribution of charge density ρ and current density $\mathbf{j}$. Finally the *force equation* (g_l) specifies the force per unit volume experienced by charge of density ρ moving with velocity $\mathbf{v}$ through a specified electromagnetic field.

Maxwell's great contribution to electromagnetic theory consisted in showing that these equations are not consistent with the equation of continuity and in amending Ampère's law so as to secure such consistency. Without this change in Ampère's law there could have been no electromagnetic theory of light.

The equation of continuity in electromagnetism asserts that the time rate of increase of charge in any region is equal to the excess of the charge flowing in per unit time over that flowing out. It is equivalent to the statement that electricity is uncreatable and indestructible. It is deduced in exactly the same way as the corresponding equation (63–1) in hydrodynamics, and is identical with this equation, namely

$$\frac{\partial \rho}{\partial t} + \nabla\cdot(\rho\mathbf{v}) = 0, \qquad (154\text{–}1)$$

provided we interpret ρ as the charge per unit volume instead of the mass of fluid per unit volume.

Now if we differentiate (a_l) with respect to the time we get

$$\frac{\partial \rho}{\partial t} = \nabla\cdot\dot{\mathbf{D}},$$

where the dot over the letter indicates the *partial* derivative with respect to the time. This is the conventional notation in electromagnetic theory, and should be carefully distinguished from that used in dynamics where the dot indicates the *total* derivative with respect to the time.

But if we replace $\mathbf{j}$ by its equivalent $\rho\mathbf{v}$ in Ampère's law (d_1) and take the divergence of both sides of the equation we find

$$\nabla \cdot (\rho\mathbf{v}) = 0$$

since $\nabla \cdot \nabla \times \mathbf{H}$ vanishes identically. Therefore the equation of continuity is not satisfied in general in fields which are not static. What we should have in place of the last equation is

$$\nabla \cdot (\rho\mathbf{v}) = - \nabla \cdot \dot{\mathbf{D}}$$

in order to satisfy (154–1). Therefore we must replace (d_1) of article 152 by

$$\nabla \times \mathbf{H} = \frac{1}{c} (\dot{\mathbf{D}} + \rho\mathbf{v}). \qquad (154\text{–}2)$$

This is Maxwell's revision of Ampère's law. Maxwell called $\dot{\mathbf{D}}$ the *displacement current*. It follows from the definition of $\mathbf{P}$ in article 112 that the part of $\dot{\mathbf{D}}$ involved in the time rate of change of polarization represents the current due to the oscillations of the bound electrons in a dielectric. In the case of a steady current $\mathbf{D}$ is constant and (154–2) reduces to the original form of Ampère's law.

Consider a region in which no currents are present other than displacement currents. Then $\rho\mathbf{v} = 0$ and if we integrate (154–2) over an arbitrary surface σ

$$\int_\sigma \nabla \times \mathbf{H} \cdot d\boldsymbol{\sigma} = \frac{1}{c} \int_\sigma \dot{\mathbf{D}} \cdot d\boldsymbol{\sigma}.$$

Applying Stokes' theorem to the left-hand member

$$\oint \mathbf{H} \cdot d\boldsymbol{\lambda} = \frac{1}{c} \int_\sigma \dot{\mathbf{D}} \cdot d\boldsymbol{\sigma},$$

where the line integral is taken around the periphery of the surface σ. This equation states that the work done in taking a unit positive pole around any circuit is proportional to the time rate of change of flux of displacement through the circuit, just as Faraday's law states that the work done in taking a unit positive charge around a circuit is proportional to the time rate of change of flux of induction through the circuit. Why then is this equation not as susceptible to direct experimental verification as Faraday's law? The reason is that there exists in nature no conductor of magnetism and therefore no sensitive method of detecting a magnetomotive force. Were it not that metals are excellent conductors of electricity Faraday would never have been able to detect so simply the electromotive force induced in a circuit by a varying flux of induction.

Collecting results, then, we have the electromagnetic equations

$$\nabla \cdot \mathbf{D} = \rho, \qquad (a) \qquad\qquad \nabla \cdot \mathbf{B} = 0, \qquad (b)$$

$$\nabla \times \mathbf{E} = -\frac{1}{c}\dot{\mathbf{B}}, \quad (c) \qquad \nabla \times \mathbf{H} = \frac{1}{c}(\dot{\mathbf{D}} + \rho\mathbf{v}), \qquad (d)$$

$$\mathbf{D} = \mathbf{E} + \mathbf{P} = (\kappa\mathbf{E}), \quad (e) \qquad \mathbf{B} = \mathbf{H} + \mathbf{I} = (\mu\mathbf{H}), \quad (f)$$

$$\mathbf{F} = \rho\left(\mathbf{E} + \frac{1}{c}\mathbf{v} \times \mathbf{B}\right), \quad (g)$$

in Heaviside-Lorentz units. These are the fundamental equations on which all our further theoretical developments will be based.

155. Energy Equation. — If we take the scalar product of (c) by $\mathbf{H}$, of (d) by $\mathbf{E}$, and subtract the second equation from the first, we get, on replacing $\mathbf{D}$ by $\kappa\mathbf{E}$ and $\mathbf{B}$ by $\mu\mathbf{H}$,

$$\frac{\partial}{\partial t}\left\{\tfrac{1}{2}(\kappa E^2 + \mu H^2)\right\} + c\{\mathbf{H}\cdot\nabla \times \mathbf{E} - \mathbf{E}\cdot\nabla \times \mathbf{H}\} + \rho\mathbf{E}\cdot\mathbf{v} = 0.$$

Now

$$\mathbf{H}\cdot\nabla \times \mathbf{E} - \mathbf{E}\cdot\nabla \times \mathbf{H} = \nabla\cdot(\mathbf{E} \times \mathbf{H}),$$

and therefore

$$\frac{\partial}{\partial t}\left\{\tfrac{1}{2}(\kappa E^2 + \mu H^2)\right\} + c\nabla\cdot(\mathbf{E} \times \mathbf{H}) + \rho\mathbf{E}\cdot\mathbf{v} = 0. \qquad (155\text{–}1)$$

Forming the volume integral of this expression over any arbitrary region τ, the integral of the second term can be transformed by Gauss' theorem into a surface integral over the surface σ bounding τ, so that

$$\frac{d}{dt}\int_\tau \tfrac{1}{2}(\kappa E^2 + \mu H^2)d\tau + c\int_\sigma \mathbf{E} \times \mathbf{H}\cdot d\boldsymbol{\sigma} + \int_\tau \rho\mathbf{E}\cdot\mathbf{v}d\tau = 0. \qquad (155\text{–}2)$$

As the force on a moving charge due to the magnetic field through which it is passing is always perpendicular to its velocity, no work is done by the magnetic intensity. So the third term of (155–2 measures the rate at which work is done by the electromagneti forces on the charges in the volume τ.

Consider a region τ at all points on the boundary of which **E** an **H** vanish. Then the surface integral in (155–2) drops out. Th law of conservation of energy requires that the rate at which th electromagnetic energy in this region increases plus the rate at whic the field does work on the charges inside it shall vanish. Therefore as the last term in (155–2) represents the rate at which work is don on the charges inside τ by the field, the first term must represent th rate of increase of electromagnetic energy inside the region. Con sequently we may attribute to each unit volume the energy

$$u = \tfrac{1}{2}(\kappa E^2 + \mu H^2), \qquad (155\text{–}3$$

which we may separate into the electric energy $\frac{1}{2}\kappa E^2$ and the magneti energy $\frac{1}{2}\mu H^2$ per unit volume.

Let us now consider a region τ on the boundary of which **E** and **H** do not vanish. As the field does not vanish over the surface there exists the possibility of a flow of electromagnetic energy throug this surface. In this case the law of conservation of energy reads the rate at which the electromagnetic energy within the region increases, plus the rate at which energy flows out through the bound ing surface σ, plus the rate at which work is done on the charge within the region, is equal to zero. Therefore, in view of the inter pretation already given to the first and third terms of (155–2), i follows that the second term represents the rate at which energ flows out through the surface σ. Consequently we may interpre the vector

$$\mathbf{s} = c(\mathbf{E} \times \mathbf{H}) \qquad (155\text{–}4$$

as the flow of energy per unit cross-section per unit time. This vecto is known as the *Poynting flux*. It is directed at right angles to th plane of **E** and **H** in the sense of advance of a right-handed screw rotated from **E** to **H** through the smaller angle between them. I exists only where both electric and magnetic fields are present an the lines of force of the two fields are not parallel.

Problem 155a. Calculate the energy of a spherical conductor of radius a charged with a quantity of electricity Q by the method of the last article an show that the result agrees with (119–2).

Problem 155b. Calculate the energy of the circuit of problem 143*a* by the method of the last article and show that the result agrees with that previously obtained.

Problem 155c. A straight wire of resistance R carries a current i. Compute the Poynting flux through the surface and show that it accounts for the production of heat at the rate Ri^2.

156. Electromagnetic Waves. — In a homogeneous isotropic medium in which there is no charge or current the field equations (*a*), (*b*), (*c*), (*d*) take the form

$$\nabla \cdot \mathbf{E} = 0, \quad (a') \qquad \nabla \cdot \mathbf{H} = 0, \quad (b')$$

$$\nabla \times \mathbf{E} = -\frac{\mu}{c}\dot{\mathbf{H}}, \quad (c') \qquad \nabla \times \mathbf{H} = \frac{\kappa}{c}\dot{\mathbf{E}}. \quad (d')$$

To eliminate **H** between (c') and (d') take the curl of (c'),

$$\nabla \times \nabla \times \mathbf{E} = -\frac{\mu}{c}\nabla \times \dot{\mathbf{H}}$$

and the time derivative of (d')

$$\nabla \times \dot{\mathbf{H}} = \frac{\kappa}{c}\ddot{\mathbf{E}}.$$

Then

$$\nabla \times \nabla \times \mathbf{E} = -\frac{\kappa\mu}{c^2}\ddot{\mathbf{E}}. \qquad (156\text{–}1)$$

But

$$\nabla \times \nabla \times \mathbf{E} = \nabla\nabla \cdot \mathbf{E} - \nabla \cdot \nabla\mathbf{E} = -\nabla \cdot \nabla\mathbf{E}$$

on account of (a'). Therefore (156–1) becomes

$$\nabla \cdot \nabla\mathbf{E} = \frac{\kappa\mu}{c^2}\ddot{\mathbf{E}}, \qquad (156\text{–}2)$$

and similarly we find

$$\nabla \cdot \nabla\mathbf{H} = \frac{\kappa\mu}{c^2}\ddot{\mathbf{H}}. \qquad (156\text{–}3)$$

These are the equations of a wave progressing with the phase velocity

$$v = \frac{c}{\sqrt{\kappa\mu}}. \qquad (156\text{–}4)$$

If the term on the right-hand side of (d') which Maxwell introduced into Ampère's law had been absent, the wave equations

(156–2) and (156–3) would not have been obtained by elimination of **H** and **E** respectively from Faraday's and Ampère's laws, and the electromagnetic theory of light could never have been proposed. As it is, equation (156–4) shows that electromagnetic waves in empty space, where κ and μ are unity, travel with a velocity c which is identical with the measured value of the velocity of light *in vacuo*, whereas in material media the velocity is modified by the properties of the substance through which the waves are passing. The inference that light waves are electromagnetic in character is inescapable. Further investigation of the properties of electromagnetic waves confirms this hypothesis. For instance, they exhibit the phenomenon of polarization characteristic of light. Furthermore the coefficients of reflection and refraction of electromagnetic waves are given by the same formulae which have been established empirically by Fresnel for light waves. The electromagnetic theory of the double refraction by crystals accords exactly with the observed phenomena in the case of light, both the normal and anomalous dispersion of light by dielectrics finds a satisfactory explanation on the electromagnetic theory, and the electromagnetic theory of metallic reflection yields values of the conductivity obtained from measurements of the reflecting power for infra-red radiation in good agreement with the conductivity of the metal for steady currents. While most of these developments of the theory must be omitted here on account of lack of space, we shall have occasion to go a little further into the details of some of the more important of them.

The index of refraction n of a material medium is defined as the ratio of the velocity of light *in vacuo* to that in the medium. Therefore

$$n = \frac{c}{v} = \sqrt{\kappa\mu}. \tag{156–5}$$

As will be shown later in the case of κ, the permittivity and the permeability are functions of the frequency in an oscillating field. In fact μ is always unity for frequencies as great as those of light. Hence

$$n = \sqrt{\kappa}. \tag{156–6}$$

If we measure the index of refraction for infra-red waves of a wave length greater than that corresponding to the last absorption band of the substance we should find agreement between the square of the index of refraction and the permittivity measured in steady fields. This agreement is shown by the following table:

Substance	κ for Steady Fields	n^2 for Infra-red Radiation
Air	1.000586	1.000585
H_2	1.000264	1.000277
CO_2	1.000984	1.000909
CO	1.000694	1.000670

Let us now consider a plane wave advancing in the X direction. Then **E** and **H** are functions of x and t only and the wave equations (156–2) and (156–3) reduce to

$$\frac{\partial^2 \mathbf{E}}{\partial x^2} = \frac{1}{v^2}\frac{\partial^2 \mathbf{E}}{\partial t^2},$$

$$\frac{\partial^2 \mathbf{H}}{\partial x^2} = \frac{1}{v^2}\frac{\partial^2 \mathbf{H}}{\partial t^2},$$

of which the solutions are

$$\left.\begin{aligned} E_x &= f(x - vt), & H_x &= i(x - vt), \\ E_y &= g(x - vt), & H_y &= j(x - vt), \\ E_z &= h(x - vt), & H_z &= k(x - vt). \end{aligned}\right\} \quad (156\text{–}7)$$

But (a') and (b') give

$$\frac{\partial E_x}{\partial x} = 0, \qquad \frac{\partial H_x}{\partial x} = 0,$$

since E_y and H_y are not functions of y, and E_z and H_z are not functions of z. Therefore E_x and H_x are constants. Since we are interested only in the variable field constituting the wave and not in superposed static fields we shall put E_x and H_x equal to zero. Hence we conclude that plane electromagnetic waves are transverse. In this respect they have the characteristics of light waves.

If we substitute (156–7) in the Y and Z components of equation (c') we find

$$-\frac{\partial E_z}{\partial x} = -h' = -\frac{\mu}{c}\dot{H}_y = \frac{\mu v}{c} j', \quad j = -\sqrt{\frac{\kappa}{\mu}}\, h;$$

$$\frac{\partial E_y}{\partial x} = g' = -\frac{\mu}{c}\dot{H}_z = \frac{\mu v}{c}k', \quad k = \sqrt{\frac{\kappa}{\mu}}\,g;$$

where we have used primes to indicate differentiation of a function with respect to its argument. So (156–7) becomes

$$\left.\begin{aligned} E_x &= 0, & H_x &= 0, \\ E_y &= g(x - vt), & H_y &= -\sqrt{\frac{\kappa}{\mu}}\,h(x - vt), \\ E_z &= h(x - vt), & H_z &= \sqrt{\frac{\kappa}{\mu}}\,g(x - vt). \end{aligned}\right\} \quad (156\text{–}8)$$

Now

$$\mathbf{E}\cdot\mathbf{H} = E_yH_y + E_zH_z = -\sqrt{\frac{\kappa}{\mu}}\,gh + \sqrt{\frac{\kappa}{\mu}}\,gh = 0.$$

Hence **E** and **H** are perpendicular. The Poynting flux

$$\mathbf{s} = c\mathbf{E}\times\mathbf{H} = \mathbf{i}c(E_yH_z - E_zH_y) = \mathbf{i}v\kappa(g^2 + h^2) \quad (156\text{–}9)$$

has the direction of propagation. So **E** and **H** are perpendicular in such a sense that a right-handed screw, rotated from the first of these vectors to the second, advances in the direction of propagation. If, for instance, **E** is directed along the Y axis, then **H** is directed along the Z axis in the case of a wave advancing in the positive X direction and along the $-Z$ axis in the case of a wave advancing in the negative X direction. Furthermore it appears from (156–8) that **E** and **H** are in phase. In empty space, $\kappa = \mu = 1$ and **E** and **H** have the same magnitude.

The electromagnetic energy per unit volume is

$$u = \tfrac{1}{2}(\kappa E^2 + \mu H^2) = \kappa(g^2 + h^2), \quad (156\text{–}10)$$

of which half is associated with the electric field and half with the magnetic field. Hence

$$s = v\mu, \quad (156\text{–}11)$$

and all the energy of the wave progresses with the phase velocity v.

Problem 156a. Two sets of plane electromagnetic waves

$$E'_y = A\cos\frac{2\pi}{\lambda}(x - ct) \quad \text{and} \quad E''_y = A\cos\frac{2\pi}{\lambda}(x + ct)$$

are traveling through empty space. Find the resultant **E** and **H**, the mean energy density, mean flux of energy, and the positions of the nodes and loops.

$$Ans.\ E_y = 2A\cos\frac{2\pi}{\lambda}x\cos\frac{2\pi c}{\lambda}t,\quad H_z = 2A\sin\frac{2\pi}{\lambda}x\sin\frac{2\pi c}{\lambda}t,$$

$$\bar{u} = \bar{u}' + \bar{u}'',\quad \bar{s} = 0.$$

156.1. Waves Guided by Perfect Conductors. — In article 153 the electromagnetic wave traveling along a pair of parallel perfectly conducting wires was discussed by circuit theory methods. Let us now examine this and other examples of guided waves as boundary value problems in the solution of the electromagnetic field equations (a') to (d') of article 156. As the conductors guiding the waves will be assumed to be perfect conductors without resistance, the electric intensity **E** must vanish everywhere inside a conductor. Consequently the tangential component of **E** just outside the surface of a conductor must be zero, since it was shown in article 113 that this component is continuous across the surface. This is the only boundary condition which has to be satisfied at the surface of a perfect conductor.

The electric intensity in the region outside the conducting guides must satisfy the wave equation (156–2) as well as the solenoidal condition $\nabla\cdot\mathbf{E} = 0$ given in (a'). The general method which we shall follow in obtaining solenoidal solutions of the vector wave equation consists in finding first a solution Φ of the scalar wave equation

$$\nabla\cdot\nabla\Phi = \frac{1}{v^2}\frac{\partial^2\Phi}{\partial t^2},\qquad v \equiv \frac{c}{\sqrt{\kappa\mu}},\qquad (156.1\text{–}1)$$

with the same velocity of propagation v, and then obtaining a solution of the vector wave equation by multiplying Φ by one of the unit vectors **i**, **j**, or **k**. Choosing **i**, for instance, we have the solution $\mathbf{V} = \mathbf{i}\Phi$. If this vector function happens to be solenoidal, it represents the electric intensity or the magnetic intensity in a possible electromagnetic wave. If it is not solenoidal, we can build from it a solenoidal solution of the vector wave equation by taking its curl, for the divergence of the curl is identically zero. To show that $\nabla\times\mathbf{V}$ is a solution of the wave equation if **V** is, we note that

$$\nabla\cdot\nabla(\nabla\times\mathbf{V}) = \nabla\times(\nabla\cdot\nabla\mathbf{V}) = \nabla\times\left(\frac{1}{v^2}\frac{\partial^2\mathbf{V}}{\partial t^2}\right) = \frac{1}{v^2}\frac{\partial^2}{\partial t^2}(\nabla\times\mathbf{V}).$$

Thus, if $\mathbf{V} = \mathbf{i}\Phi$, where Φ satisfies (156.1–1), $\nabla \times \mathbf{V}$ and $\nabla \times \nabla \times \mathbf{V}$ are solenoidal solutions of the vector wave equation and represent either **E** or **H** in a possible electromagnetic wave.

We shall confine ourselves to simple harmonic waves of angular frequency ω. Then Φ may be specified as the real part of

$$\Phi = \Psi(x, y, z)e^{-i\omega t}, \qquad (156.1\text{–}2)$$

where, in wave theory, it is more convenient to take the time factor with the negative exponent $-i\omega t$ rather than with the positive exponent $i\omega t$ used in circuit theory. Then,

$$\mathbf{V} = \mathbf{i}\Psi(x, y, z)e^{-i\omega t}$$

and, if we take $\nabla \times \mathbf{V}$ for the electric intensity, we have from (c') of article 156

$$\mathbf{E} = \nabla \times \mathbf{V}, \qquad \mathbf{H} = -\frac{ic}{\mu\omega}\nabla \times \nabla \times \mathbf{V}, \qquad (156.1\text{–}3)$$

whereas, if we take $\nabla \times \nabla \times \mathbf{V}$ for the electric intensity, (d') gives

$$\mathbf{E} = \nabla \times \nabla \times \mathbf{V}, \qquad \mathbf{H} = -\frac{i\kappa\omega}{c}\nabla \times \mathbf{V}. \qquad (156.1\text{–}4)$$

I. *Parallel Cylindrical Conductors.*—If the guides consist of cylindrical conductors parallel to the X axis, such as two parallel wires of the same radius a a distance b apart, or a coaxial cable consisting of a cylindrical conductor of radius a inside another of larger radius b, the simplest function representing a wave traveling in the X direction is

$$\Phi = f(y, z)e^{i(\sigma x - \omega t)} \qquad (156.1\text{–}5)$$

where $\sigma \equiv \omega/v$. Substituting this in (156.1–1) we find that the wave equation reduces to the two-dimensional Laplace's equation

$$\frac{\partial^2 f}{\partial y^2} + \frac{\partial^2 f}{\partial z^2} = 0. \qquad (156.1\text{–}6)$$

We have seen in article 126 that either the real or the imaginary part of any function $F(y + iz)$ of the complex variable $y + iz$ satisfies this equation. So, if $F(y + iz) = g(y, z) + ih(y, z)$, both g and

h are solutions of (156.1–6). Therefore we have two solutions of (156.1–5), namely,

$$\Phi_1 = g(y, z)e^{i(\sigma x-\omega t)}, \quad \Phi_2 = h(y, z)e^{i(\sigma x-\omega t)} \qquad (156.1\text{–}7)$$

Putting $\mathbf{V}_1 = \mathbf{i}\Phi_1$ and $\mathbf{V}_2 = \mathbf{i}\Phi_2$, we may take for the electric intensity either $\nabla \times \mathbf{V}_1$ or $\nabla \times \mathbf{V}_2$. The first gives

$$\mathbf{E} = \left\{ \mathbf{j}\frac{\partial g}{\partial z} - \mathbf{k}\frac{\partial g}{\partial y} \right\} e^{i(\sigma x-\omega t)}. \qquad (156.1\text{–}8)$$

But, corresponding to (126–3), we have

$$\frac{\partial g}{\partial z} = -\frac{\partial h}{\partial y}, \quad \frac{\partial g}{\partial y} = \frac{\partial h}{\partial z}, \qquad (156.1\text{–}9)$$

which enables us to write

$$\mathbf{E} = -\left\{ \mathbf{j}\frac{\partial h}{\partial y} + \mathbf{k}\frac{\partial h}{\partial z} \right\} e^{i(\sigma x-\omega t)} = -\nabla h(y, z)e^{i(\sigma x-\omega t)}. \qquad (156.1\text{–}10)$$

To get $\mathbf{H}$ from (156.1–3) we take the curl of (156.1–8). Using (156.1–6) we find

$$\mathbf{H} = \sqrt{\frac{\kappa}{\mu}}\left\{ \mathbf{j}\frac{\partial g}{\partial y} + \mathbf{k}\frac{\partial g}{\partial z} \right\} e^{i(\sigma x-\omega t)} = \sqrt{\frac{\kappa}{\mu}}\nabla g(y, z)e^{i(\sigma x-\omega t)}. \qquad (156.1\text{–}11)$$

Similarly, if we take $\nabla \times \mathbf{V}_2$ for $\mathbf{E}$, we get

$$\mathbf{E} = \left\{ \mathbf{j}\frac{\partial g}{\partial y} + \mathbf{k}\frac{\partial g}{\partial z} \right\} e^{i(\sigma x-\omega t)} = \nabla g(y, z)e^{i(\sigma x-\omega t)}, \qquad (156.1\text{–}12)$$

$$\mathbf{H} = \sqrt{\frac{\kappa}{\mu}}\left\{ \mathbf{j}\frac{\partial h}{\partial y} + \mathbf{k}\frac{\partial h}{\partial z} \right\} e^{i(\sigma x-\omega t)} = \sqrt{\frac{\kappa}{\mu}}\nabla h(y, z)e^{i(\sigma x-\omega t)}. \qquad (156.1\text{–}13)$$

Since $\nabla g \cdot \nabla h = 0$, the lines of electric force intersect the lines of magnetic force orthogonally. The equations of the former are $g(y, z) = \text{const.}$ and of the latter $h(y, z) = \text{const.}$ for the field specified by (156.1–10) and (156.1–11) and *vice versa* for that given by (156.1–12) and (156.1–13).

The appropriate function for the parallel wire system discussed in article 153 is

$$F(y + iz) = \log\frac{y + iz + l}{y + iz - l} = g(y, z) + ih(y, z)$$

multiplied by an arbitrary constant coefficient, from which we find that

$$g(y, z) = \tfrac{1}{2} \log \frac{(y + l)^2 + z^2}{(y - l)^2 + z^2}, \qquad (156.1\text{–}14)$$

$$h(y, z) = -\tan^{-1} \frac{2lz}{y^2 + z^2 - l^2}. \qquad (156.1\text{–}15)$$

If we define **E** by (156.1–12) the lines of electric force are the family of circles

$$y^2 + (z + l \cot h)^2 = l^2 \csc^2 h, \quad 0 \leq h < \pi, \quad (156.1\text{–}16)$$

shown by broken lines in Fig. 152.1, and the lines of magnetic force by the second family of circles

$$(y - l \coth g)^2 + z^2 = l^2 \operatorname{csch}^2 g, \quad -\infty < g < \infty, \quad (156.1\text{–}17)$$

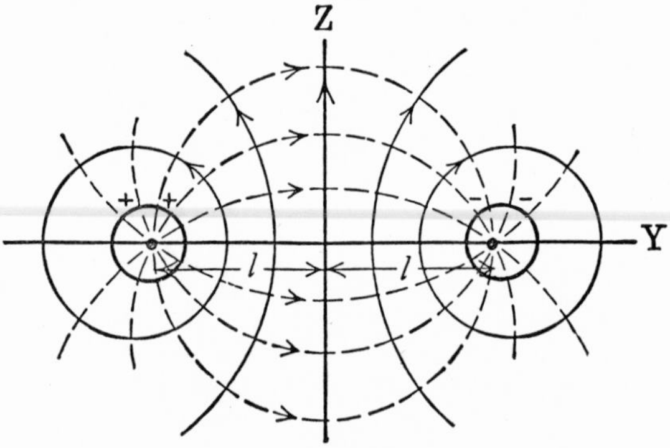

FIG. 152.1.

shown by solid lines. The boundary conditions are satisfied by taking any pair of the solid circles for the traces of the conducting wires. If the two wires have the same radius a the distance between their axes is $b = 2\sqrt{l^2 + a^2}$ from (156.1–17). The electric and the magnetic intensities are given by (156.1–12) and (156.1–13).

II. *Parallel Conducting Planes.* — Consider electromagnetic waves traveling in the X direction in a homogeneous isotropic medium of permittivity κ and permeability μ filling the space between two perfectly conducting planes $y = 0$ and $y = a$. If Φ is not a function f z the scalar wave equation becomes

$$\frac{\partial^2\Phi}{\partial x^2}+\frac{\partial^2\Phi}{\partial y^2}=\frac{1}{v^2}\frac{\partial^2\Phi}{\partial t^2}, \qquad v\equiv\frac{c}{\sqrt{\kappa\mu}}. \tag{156.1–18}$$

Ve are interested in a wave of the form $\Phi = Y(y)e^{i(lx-\omega t)}$. Sub- ituting in (156.1–18) we find that Y must satisfy the equation

$$\frac{d^2Y}{dy^2}+m^2Y=0, \qquad l^2+m^2\equiv\frac{\omega^2}{v^2}. \tag{156.1–19}$$

If $m = 0$, Y may be a constant, and $\mathbf{j}\Phi$ and $\mathbf{k}\Phi$ are both solenoidal lutions of the vector wave equation. Therefore both

$$\mathbf{E} = \mathbf{j}Ae^{i(\sigma x-\omega t)} = \mathbf{j}A\cos(\sigma x-\omega t)$$

nd

$$\mathbf{E} = \mathbf{k}Ae^{i(\sigma x-\omega t)} = \mathbf{k}A\cos(\sigma x-\omega t),$$

here $\sigma \equiv \omega/v$, represent possible electromagnetic waves. How- ver, only the first of these satisfies the boundary condition that $\mathbf{E}$ the surface must be normal to the surface. It represents an dinary plane wave advancing with normal phase velocity v.

If, now, $m \neq 0$, the solution of (156.1–19) is a constant multiply- g $\cos(my-\delta)$, and

$$\Phi = A\cos(my-\delta)e^{i(lx-\omega t)}, \tag{156.1–20}$$

hich represents a wave traveling in the X direction with phase elocity

$$\frac{\omega}{l}=\frac{v}{\sqrt{1-\dfrac{m^2v^2}{\omega^2}}} \tag{156.1–21}$$

eater than v. Putting $\mathbf{V} = \mathbf{i}\Phi$ we get from (156.1–3)

$$\begin{aligned}\mathbf{E} &= \mathbf{k}Am\sin(my-\delta)e^{i(lx-\omega t)}\\ &= \mathbf{k}Am\sin(my-\delta)\cos(lx-\omega t),\end{aligned} \tag{156.1–22}$$

and from (156.1–4)

$$\mathbf{E} = Am\{\mathbf{i}m \cos (my - \delta) - \mathbf{j}il \sin (my - \delta)\}e^{i(lx-\omega t)}$$

$$= Am\{\mathbf{i}m \cos (my - \delta) \cos (lx - \omega t) + \mathbf{j}l \sin (my - \delta) \sin (lx - \omega t)\}. \quad (156.1\text{–}23$$

The first of these satisfies the boundary conditions at $y = 0$ an $y = a$ provided $\delta = 0$ and $m = k\pi/a$, where k is an integer greate than zero, and the second does likewise provided $\delta = \pi/2$ an $m = k\pi/a$. From (156.1–20) it follows that the minimum frequenc $\nu_{\min}$ for which these waves can exist is given by the smallest value c ω for which ω/l is real, when m has its smallest value π/a. Hence

$$\nu_{\min} = \frac{\omega_{\min}}{2\pi} = \frac{c}{2a\sqrt{\kappa\mu}}. \quad (156.1\text{–}24$$

The physical significance of the abnormal phase velocity indicate by (156.1–21) and the minimum frequency specified by (156.1–24)i revealed at once if we write (156.1–22) with $\delta = 0$ in the form

$$\mathbf{E}=\mathbf{k}\tfrac{1}{2}Am \sin (lx+my-\omega t)-\mathbf{k}\tfrac{1}{2}Am \sin (lx-my-\omega t), \quad (156.1\text{–}25$$

which shows that the wave motion is due to the superposition of tw trains of ordinary plane waves. Similarly (156.1–23) with $\delta = \pi/$ may be written in the form

$$\mathbf{E} = \tfrac{1}{2}Am\{(\mathbf{i}m - \mathbf{j}l) \sin (lx + my - \omega t) - (\mathbf{i}m + \mathbf{j}l) \sin (lx - my - \omega t)\}. \quad (156.1\text{–}26$$

In order to analyze these plane waves further, it will be co venient to introduce the *wave slowness* **S**, a vector in the directio of propagation with a magnitude equal to the reciprocal of the phas velocity. Then the argument of the trigonometrical function repre senting a simple harmonic plane wave advancing in the X directio is $\omega\,(Sx - t) = \omega(\mathbf{S}\cdot\mathbf{r} - t)$ where $\mathbf{r} = \mathbf{i}x + \mathbf{j}y + \mathbf{k}z$. In the latte form the argument is independent of the orientation of the axes en ployed. Comparing with (156.1–25) and (156.1–26), we see that for the first wave in each $\omega S_x = l$, $\omega S_y = m$, whence $S = \sqrt{l^2 + m^2}/\omega = 1/v$. Therefore the wave is traveling with normal phase velocity v at an angle α with the X axis whose tangent is m/l.

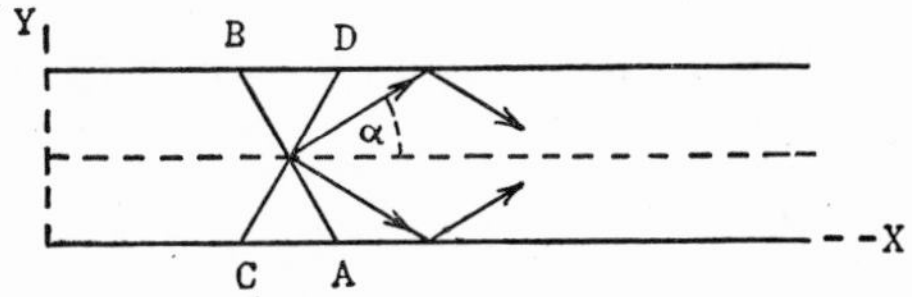

FIG. 152.2.

Similarly the second wave in each expression is traveling with normal phase velocity v at an angle $-\alpha$ with the X axis. These two waves are shown in Fig. 152.2, AB being a wave front of the first and CD one of the second. On reflection at the upper conductor a wave front of the first becomes a wave front of the second train of waves, and *vice versa* on reflection at the lower conductor. Since the phase velocity (156.1–21) of the composite wave is the reciprocal of the projection in the X direction of the wave slowness $\mathbf{S}$ of either component wave, it is greater than v, and becomes infinite when $\alpha = 90°$. The waves described by (156.1–25) differ from those described by (156.1–26) only in that the former are polarized with the electric vector perpendicular to the XY plane whereas the latter are polarized with the electric vector in this plane in a direction normal to $\mathbf{S}$.

The minimum frequency occurs when $\alpha = 90°$. Then the conducting planes are at the nodes of a set of standing waves propagated in the Y direction between the two planes, the distance between the planes being a half wave length.

III. *Rectangular Wave Guide.* — Here we are concerned with the waves propagated inside a tube of rectangular cross-section bounded by the conducting planes $z = 0$, $z = b$ in addition to the conducting planes $y = 0$, $y = a$. We are interested in solutions of the complete wave equation

$$\frac{\partial^2 \Phi}{\partial x^2} + \frac{\partial^2 \Phi}{\partial y^2} + \frac{\partial^2 \Phi}{\partial z^2} = \frac{1}{v^2}\frac{\partial^2 \Phi}{\partial t^2} \qquad (156.1\text{–}27)$$

of the form $\Phi = Y(y)Z(z)e^{i(lx-\omega t)}$. These solutions are similar to those found in the case just discussed, each wave being resolvable into four ordinary plane waves advancing with normal phase velocity v. The minimum frequency for this case is

$$\nu_{\min} = \frac{c}{2\sqrt{\kappa\mu}}\frac{\sqrt{a^2 + b^2}}{ab}. \qquad (156.1\text{–}28)$$

Problem 156.1a. Find the magnetic flux through a strip of unit width extending from the one to the other of the parallel wires discussed in (I), and compare the result with (153–14).

Problem 156.1b. Derive the expression (156.1–28) for the minimum frequency for propagation in a rectangular wave guide.

Problem 156.1c. Plane electromagnetic waves are incident normally on the surface of a perfect conductor. Show that reflection takes place with 180° change in phase and without loss of intensity, indicating that a perfect conductor is a perfect reflector of electromagnetic waves.

157. Radiation Pressure. — The quantities ρ and $\rho\mathbf{v}$ may be eliminated from the force equation (*g*) of article 154 by means of the field equations (*a*), (*b*), (*c*), (*d*). We shall suppose that the moving charges are immersed in a homogeneous medium for which the relations $\mathbf{D} = \kappa\mathbf{E}$ and $\mathbf{B} = \mu\mathbf{H}$ are valid. Making use of (*a*) to eliminate ρ from (*g*), and (*d*) to eliminate $\rho\mathbf{v}$, we get

$$\mathbf{F} = \rho\mathbf{E} + \frac{\mu}{c}\rho\mathbf{v} \times \mathbf{H}$$

$$= \kappa\nabla\cdot\mathbf{E}\mathbf{E} + \mu(\nabla \times \mathbf{H}) \times \mathbf{H} - \frac{\kappa\mu}{c}\dot{\mathbf{E}} \times \mathbf{H}. \qquad (157\text{–}1)$$

Multiplying (*b*) by $\mathbf{H}$ we have

$$0 = \mu\nabla\cdot\mathbf{H}\mathbf{H},$$

and taking the vector product of (*c*) by $\kappa\mathbf{E}$

$$0 = \kappa(\nabla \times \mathbf{E}) \times \mathbf{E} + \frac{\kappa\mu}{c}\dot{\mathbf{H}} \times \mathbf{E}.$$

Adding these three equations

$$\mathbf{F} = -\frac{\kappa\mu}{c}\frac{\partial}{\partial t}(\mathbf{E}\times\mathbf{H}) + \kappa\nabla\cdot\mathbf{E}\mathbf{E} + \kappa(\nabla\times\mathbf{E})\times\mathbf{E} + \mu\nabla\cdot\mathbf{H}\mathbf{H} + \mu(\nabla\times\mathbf{H})\times\mathbf{H}.$$

Integrating this expression over any region τ we find for the total force on all the charges and currents within this region,

$$\mathbf{K} = \int_\tau \mathbf{F}d\tau$$

$$= -\frac{\kappa\mu}{c}\frac{d}{dt}\int_\tau (\mathbf{E} \times \mathbf{H})d\tau$$

$$+\kappa\int_\tau\{\nabla\cdot\mathbf{EE}+(\nabla\times\mathbf{E})\times\mathbf{E}\}d\tau$$

$$+\mu\int_\tau\{\nabla\cdot\mathbf{HH}+(\nabla\times\mathbf{H})\times\mathbf{H}\}d\tau. \qquad (157\text{–}2)$$

For the moment put

$$\mathbf{J}\equiv\int_\tau\{\nabla\cdot\mathbf{EE}+(\nabla\times\mathbf{E})\times\mathbf{E}\}d\tau$$

$$=\int_\tau\{\nabla\cdot\mathbf{EE}+\mathbf{E}\cdot\nabla\mathbf{E}-\tfrac{1}{2}\nabla(\mathbf{E}\cdot\mathbf{E})\}d\tau$$

$$=\int_\tau\{\nabla\cdot(\mathbf{EE})-\tfrac{1}{2}\nabla(\mathbf{E}\cdot\mathbf{E})\}d\tau.$$

By (118–6)

$$\int_\tau\nabla\cdot(\mathbf{EE})d\tau=\int_\sigma\mathbf{EE}\cdot d\boldsymbol{\sigma},$$

and by (118–2)

$$\int_\tau\nabla(\mathbf{E}\cdot\mathbf{E})d\tau=\int_\sigma\mathbf{E}\cdot\mathbf{E}d\boldsymbol{\sigma},$$

where σ is the surface bounding the volume τ. Hence

$$\mathbf{J}=\int_\sigma\mathbf{EE}\cdot d\boldsymbol{\sigma}-\tfrac{1}{2}\int_\sigma\mathbf{E}\cdot\mathbf{E}d\boldsymbol{\sigma}$$

and similarly for the terms involving **H** in the third integral on the right of (157–2). Therefore the force on the matter in the region τ is expressed in terms of the fields **E** and **H** alone by

$$\mathbf{K}=-\frac{\kappa\mu}{c^2}\frac{d}{dt}\int_\tau\mathbf{s}d\tau+\int_\sigma(\kappa\mathbf{EE}+\mu\mathbf{HH})\cdot d\boldsymbol{\sigma}-\tfrac{1}{2}\int_\sigma(\kappa E^2+\mu H^2)d\boldsymbol{\sigma}, \qquad (157\text{–}3)$$

where we have expressed the integrand in the volume integral in terms of the Poynting flux **s** by means of (155–4).

Since the last two terms in the expression for the force **K** appear as surface integrals, they can be interpreted as arising from stresses acting on the surface σ bounding τ. To find the components of stress on a surface normal to the X axis we must evaluate the inte grands of the two surface integrals with $d\sigma = \mathbf{i}$, obtaining

$$X_x = \kappa(E_x^2 - \tfrac{1}{2}E^2) + \mu(H_x^2 - \tfrac{1}{2}H^2), \qquad Y_x = \kappa E_x E_y + \mu H_x H$$

$$Z_x = \kappa E_x E_z + \mu H_x H_z,$$

and similarly to find the components of stress on surfaces normal t the Y or Z axes. Thus we are led to the stress dyadic

$$\left.\begin{aligned}
\Psi = \mathbf{ii}&\left\{\frac{\kappa}{2}(E_x^2 - E_y^2 - E_z^2) + \frac{\mu}{2}(H_x^2 - H_y^2 - H_z^2)\right\}\\
&+ \mathbf{ij}\{\kappa E_x E_y + \mu H_x H_y\} + \mathbf{ik}\{\kappa E_x E_z + \mu H_x H_z\}\\
&+ \mathbf{ji}\{\kappa E_y E_x + \mu H_y H_x\}\\
&+ \mathbf{jj}\left\{\frac{\kappa}{2}(E_y^2 - E_z^2 - E_x^2) + \frac{\mu}{2}(H_y^2 - H_z^2 - H_x^2)\right\}\\
&\qquad\qquad + \mathbf{jk}\{\kappa E_y E_z + \mu H_y H_z\}\\
&+ \mathbf{ki}\{\kappa E_z E_x + \mu H_z H_x\} + \mathbf{kj}\{\kappa E_z E_y + \mu H_z H_y\}\\
&+ \mathbf{kk}\left\{\frac{\kappa}{2}(E_z^2 - E_x^2 - E_y^2) + \frac{\mu}{2}(H_z^2 - H_x^2 - H_y^2)\right\},
\end{aligned}\right\} \quad (157\text{–}4$$

from which the stress on any surface can be found by (47–10). Thi expression should be compared with (118–10), to which it reduce when $\mathbf{H} = 0$ and $\mathbf{E}$ is expressed in e.s.u.

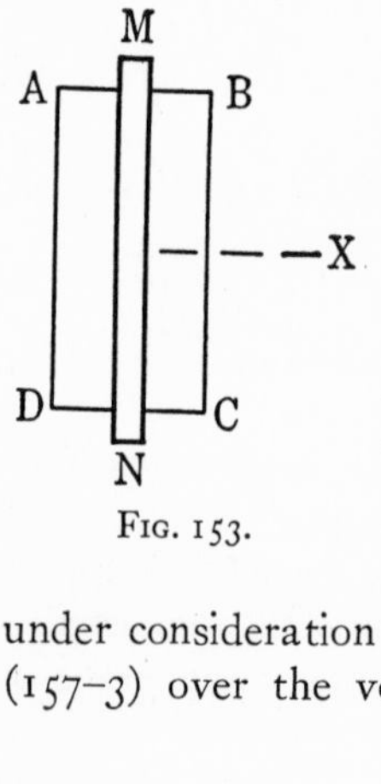

Fig. 153.

We shall apply (157–3) to the calculation o the stress exerted on a rigidly supported slab o matter MN (Fig. 153) by radiation inciden on its right-hand face. It will be assumed tha the region surrounding the slab is empty spac ($\kappa = \mu = 1$) and that the slab absorbs or reflect all the radiation striking it, none being trans- mitted. Describe a pill-box shaped surfac around a unit area of the slab, with its fla faces BC and AD parallel to the surface of the slab. The force $\mathbf{K}$ on the unit area of the slab under consideration is obtained by evaluating the volume integral in (157–3) over the volume of the pill-box and the surface integrals epresenting the stresses over its surface. If the intensity of the ncident radiation is maintained constant, the mean Poynting flux loes not vary with the time, and, since the mean force is what we are nterested in, the volume integral drops out. As there is no field to he left of the slab, the surface integrals need be evaluated only over he face BC of the pill-box and over the cylindrical surface of which AB and DC are the traces. Now the field at points on BC is that due to he radiation, while the field at points on the cylindrical surface is hat responsible for the forces exerted by the remainder of the slab n the unit area under consideration. Hence the surface integrals ver BC represent the force due to the radiation field, while the ntegrals over the cylindrical surface represent the equal reaction xerted by the rest of the rigidly supported slab on the unit area nside the pill-box. Therefore the components of the stress exerted y the radiation on the slab, found from the last two terms of 157–3), are

$$\left.\begin{aligned} X_x &= \tfrac{1}{2}(E_x^2 - E_y^2 - E_z^2) + \tfrac{1}{2}(H_x^2 - H_y^2 - H_z^2), \\ Y_x &= E_xE_y + H_xH_y, \\ Z_x &= E_xE_z + H_xH_z. \end{aligned}\right\} \qquad (157\text{–}5)$$

Suppose that the radiation consists of plane waves incident ormally on MN. As E_x and H_x vanish there are no tangential tresses. The normal stress is a pressure

$$p = - X_x = \tfrac{1}{2}(E^2 + H^2) = u, \qquad (157\text{–}6)$$

vhere u is the energy density of the radiation field. If u_1 is the nergy density of the incident radiation and ρ the reflecting power,

$$u = u_1 + \rho u_1$$

nd

$$p = u_1(1 + \rho). \qquad (157\text{–}7)$$

The pressure is greatest on a perfect reflector and least on a erfect absorber.

Next consider a box with perfectly reflecting walls containing adiation moving equally in all directions. The mean values of the omponents of **E** and **H** are zero, but the mean value of the square f each component of **E** or **H** is equal to one-third the mean value of he square of total **E** or total **H** respectively. Therefore the tangential stresses on the walls of the box vanish and the normal stress is the pressure

$$p = -X_x = \tfrac{1}{6}(E^2 + H^2) = \tfrac{1}{3}u, \tag{157–8}$$

where u is the mean energy density of the radiation.

Problem 157a. The earth receives 20 large calories of energy per square meter per minute from the sun. Calculate the maximum electric intensity and magnetic intensity in sunlight. Assuming that all the light is absorbed compute the mean pressure at normal incidence. *Ans.* E = 10.2 volt/cm, H = 0.0341 oersted, p = 4.6(10)$^{-5}$ dyne/cm^2.

158. Electromagnetic Momentum. — We shall confine our attention in this article to electromagnetic fields in empty space, making $\kappa = \mu = 1$. Then (157–3) may be written

$$\mathbf{K} + \frac{1}{c^2}\frac{d}{dt}\int_\tau \mathbf{s}\,d\tau = \int_\sigma (\mathbf{EE} + \mathbf{HH})\cdot d\boldsymbol{\sigma} - \frac{1}{2}\int_\sigma (E^2 + H^2)d\boldsymbol{\sigma}. \tag{158–1}$$

Suppose now that the closed surface σ is infinitely remote. If **E** and **H** fall off with the inverse square of the distance r, the surface integrals fall off with $1/r^2$ and therefore go to zero as r goes to infinity. Hence (158–1) reduces to

$$\mathbf{K} + \frac{1}{c^2}\frac{d}{dt}\int_\tau \mathbf{s}\,d\tau = 0, \tag{158–2}$$

where the volume integral is taken over all space. Now **K** represents the resultant of all the forces exerted by the electromagnetic field on charges and currents. If, then, we wish to retain the law of action and reaction and its corollary, the law of conservation of linear momentum, we must interpret

$$\frac{1}{c^2}\frac{d}{dt}\int_\tau \mathbf{s}\,d\tau$$

as a force exerted by matter on the electromagnetic field. The fact that this force appears as a time derivative allows us to interpret

$$\mathbf{G} \equiv \frac{1}{c^2}\int_\tau \mathbf{s}\,d\tau \tag{158–3}$$

as the momentum of the field and

$$\mathbf{g} \equiv \frac{1}{c^2}\mathbf{s} = \frac{1}{c}\mathbf{E} \times \mathbf{H} \tag{158–4}$$

as the momentum per unit volume. To distinguish this momentum from that of material bodies, it is called *electromagnetic momentum.*

If the surface σ over which the surface integrals are evaluated is not infinitely remote, equation (158–1) states that the vector sum of the forces on the charges and the currents inside the surface σ, plus the time rate of increase of electromagnetic momentum of the portion of the field inside the surface, is equal to the force exerted by the stresses acting over the surface σ.

Now it is clear that the reason why the forces between two current elements, calculated in article 133, fail to balance is that the change in electromagnetic momentum of the field has not been taken into account.

As an example of the utility of the concept of electromagnetic momentum, consider plane electromagnetic waves incident on a perfectly reflecting surface MN (Fig. 153) at an angle θ with the normal represented by the X axis. If u_1 is the energy density of the incident radiation, the Poynting flux in the incident beam is

$$s_1 = cu_1 \tag{158–5}$$

by (156–11). So the momentum of the radiation striking a unit area of the reflecting surface in a unit time is

$$G_1 = \frac{1}{c^2} s_1 c \cos\theta = u_1 \cos\theta.$$

This momentum is transferred from the incident to the reflected beam by the process of reflection. Therefore the vector change in the momentum of the radiation per unit time is

$$\frac{dG_1}{dt} = 2G_1 \cos\theta = 2u_1 \cos^2\theta$$

in the X direction. This represents the force exerted on the radiation field by a unit area of the slab MN. The stress on the slab is equal and opposite, consisting of the pressure

$$p = 2u_1 \cos^2\theta. \tag{158–6}$$

If the radiation is incident normally, $\cos\theta$ is unity and this expression agrees with (157–7) for the case where $\rho = 1$.

In the case of radiation incident equally at all angles on the right-hand side of the slab, we must write

$$dp = 2du_1 \cos^2\theta$$

where

$$du_1 = \tfrac{1}{2}u \sin\theta d\theta.$$

Then

$$p = 2\int_0^{\pi/2} du_1 \cos^2\theta = u\int_0^{\pi/2} \cos^2\theta \sin\theta d\theta = \tfrac{1}{3}u, \qquad (158\text{–}7)$$

agreeing with (157–8).

Equation (158–6) is sometimes more conveniently written in terms of the intensity I of the radiation, that is, the energy striking the reflecting surface per unit area per unit time. As

$$I = u_1 c \cos\theta$$

we have

$$p = 2\frac{I}{c}\cos\theta. \qquad (158\text{–}8)$$

From (158–4) and (158–5) it follows that

$$g = \frac{u}{c}$$

in a beam of plane waves of energy density u, or for the whole train of waves

$$G = \frac{U}{c}. \qquad (158\text{–}9)$$

On the quantum theory each train of waves is considered to be a distinct entity known as a *photon* with an energy U which is related to its frequency ν by the formula

$$U = h\nu, \qquad (158\text{–}10)$$

where h is Planck's constant referred to in article 99. Therefore the momentum of a photon is

$$G = \frac{h\nu}{c}. \qquad (158\text{–}11)$$

Problem 158a. The frequency of the yellow sodium line is $5(10)^{14}$ per sec. Find the energy and momentum of a photon of this frequency and compare with those of a hydrogen molecule at 0° C.

Ans. $3.3(10)^{-12}$ erg, $1.1(10)^{-22}$ gm cm/sec.

Problem 158b. Considering a sheet of electrons emitted simultaneously from the condenser plate of Prob. 138*b*, show that the momentum of the electrons at the top of their cycloidal path is just equal to the decrease in electromagnetic momentum caused by the weakening of the electric field between the sheet of particles and the plate from which they came.

159. Field of a Point Charge Moving with Constant Velocity. — We wish to find the electric and magnetic intensities at a distance r from a point charge e moving with constant velocity $\mathbf{v}$ relative to the observer. We shall assume that the charge is moving through empty space so that $\kappa = \mu = 1$. Then the electric intensity at all points outside the charge must satisfy the equation (156–2), that is,

$$\frac{\partial^2 \mathbf{E}}{\partial x^2} + \frac{\partial^2 \mathbf{E}}{\partial y^2} + \frac{\partial^2 \mathbf{E}}{\partial z^2} = \frac{1}{c^2}\frac{\partial^2 \mathbf{E}}{\partial t^2}, \tag{159–1}$$

as well as the solenoidal condition

$$\frac{\partial E_x}{\partial x} + \frac{\partial E_y}{\partial y} + \frac{\partial E_z}{\partial z} = 0 \tag{159–2}$$

obtained from (*a*). If the charge is located at the origin at the instant considered, the boundary conditions of the problem are: (1) the electric flux through any small surface surrounding the origin, or the number of tubes of electric force diverging from the origin, must equal e, (2) the electric intensity must vanish at infinity.

Take the X axis in the direction of motion. As its field moves with the charge the electric intensity at the point $x + v\,dt, y, z$ at the time $t + dt$ must be the same as that at x, y, z at the time t, that is,

$$\mathbf{E}(x + v\,dt, y, z, t + dt) = \mathbf{E}(x, y, z, t)$$

or

$$\mathbf{E}(x, y, z, t) + \frac{\partial \mathbf{E}}{\partial x} v\,dt + \frac{\partial \mathbf{E}}{\partial t} dt = \mathbf{E}(x, y, z, t).$$

Consequently

$$\frac{\partial \mathbf{E}}{\partial t} = -v\frac{\partial \mathbf{E}}{\partial x},$$

and

$$\frac{\partial^2 \mathbf{E}}{\partial t^2} = \frac{\partial}{\partial t}\left(\frac{\partial \mathbf{E}}{\partial t}\right) = -v\frac{\partial}{\partial x}\left(-v\frac{\partial \mathbf{E}}{\partial x}\right) = v^2\frac{\partial^2 \mathbf{E}}{\partial x^2}.$$

Therefore if we put β for the ratio of v to c (159–1) becomes

$$(1-\beta^2)\frac{\partial^2 \mathbf{E}}{\partial x^2}+\frac{\partial^2 \mathbf{E}}{\partial y^2}+\frac{\partial^2 \mathbf{E}}{\partial z^2}=0.$$

If we transform to a new set of coordinates x_0, y, z where

$$x_0=\frac{x}{\sqrt{1-\beta^2}} \tag{159–3}$$

we get

$$\frac{\partial^2 \mathbf{E}}{\partial x_0{}^2}+\frac{\partial^2 \mathbf{E}}{\partial y^2}+\frac{\partial^2 \mathbf{E}}{\partial z^2}=0. \tag{159–4}$$

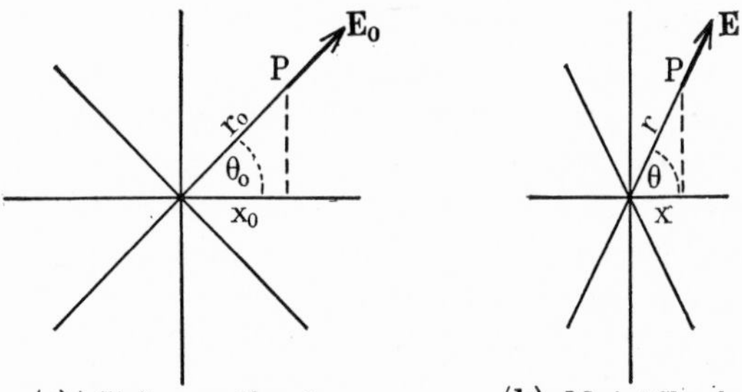

FIG. 155.

Therefore each component of $\mathbf{E}$ satisfies Laplace's equation in the x_0, y, z space.

The transformation (159–3) tells us that the x, y, z space is obtained from the x_0, y, z space by contracting dimensions in the X direction in the ratio $\sqrt{1-\beta^2}:1$. We shall prove now that if the uniformly diverging lines of force (Fig. 155*a*) of the electrostatic field

$$E_0=\frac{e}{4\pi r_0{}^2},\quad r_0\equiv\sqrt{x_0{}^2+y^2+z^2}, \tag{159–5}$$

of a point charge e permanently at rest at the origin of the x_0, y, z space are distorted by compressing the whole figure longitudinally in the ratio $\sqrt{1-\beta^2}:1$ so as to pass over to the x, y, z space of Fig. 155*b*, the electric field $\mathbf{E}$ so obtained is that of a point charge e located at the origin and moving in the X direction with constant velocity $\mathbf{v}$.

In the first place, if V is the potential of the electrostatic field of Fig. 155*a*, we have $\nabla \cdot \nabla V = 0$ everywhere except at the origin, the operator ∇ being expressed in the coordinates x_0, y, z. Hence, as $\mathbf{E}_0 = -\nabla V$, it follows that $\nabla \cdot \nabla \mathbf{E}_0 = 0$. But the distortion necessary to pass from the field of Fig. 155*a* to that of Fig. 155*b* is one for which the ratio of any rectangular component of **E** to the same rectangular component of $\mathbf{E}_0$ at the corresponding point is a constant independent of the position of this point. Actually, since the component of **E** in any direction is equal to the number of tubes of force per unit area through an elementary surface with normal in that direction, $E_x = E_{0x}$, $E_y = E_{0y}/\sqrt{1 - \beta^2}$ and $E_z = E_{0z}/\sqrt{1 - \beta^2}$. Hence, as the components of $\mathbf{E}_0$ satisfy Laplace's equation in the x_0, y, z space, the components of **E** do also. Consequently the condition expressed by (159–4) is fulfilled.

Second, as the lines of force of the field **E** of Fig. 155*b* are continuous outside the origin, the divergence equation (159–2) is satisfied. Finally the boundary conditions are satisfied, for as many lines of force diverge from the origin of Fig. 155*b* as from that of Fig. 155*a*, and **E** vanishes at infinity since $\mathbf{E}_0$ does.

Therefore, as **E** satisfies (159–4) and (159–2) and the necessary boundary conditions, it represents the electric intensity of a point charge e moving in the X direction with velocity $v = \beta c$. Evidently it has the direction of the radius vector, so all that remains is to find its magnitude. If $r \equiv \sqrt{x^2 + y^2 + z^2}$, comparison of the two diagrams in Fig. 155 gives

$$r_0 \cos\theta_0 = \frac{r\cos\theta}{\sqrt{1-\beta^2}}, \qquad r_0 \sin\theta_0 = r\sin\theta,$$

whence

$$r_0^2 = r^2\,\frac{1 - \beta^2\sin^2\theta}{1-\beta^2},$$

$$\tan\theta_0 = \sqrt{1-\beta^2}\,\tan\theta,$$

$$\sin\theta_0 = \frac{\sqrt{1-\beta^2}\,\sin\theta}{\sqrt{1-\beta^2\sin^2\theta}}, \qquad \cos\theta_0 = \frac{\cos\theta}{\sqrt{1-\beta^2\sin^2\theta}},$$

$$d\theta_0 = \frac{\sqrt{1-\beta^2}}{1-\beta^2\sin^2\theta}\,d\theta.$$

The electric flux dN through annular rings about the horizonta axis subtended by corresponding angles $d\theta_0$ and $d\theta$ in the two figure is the same since the second diagram has been obtained from the firs by a distortion which involves no change in the number of lines o force emanating from the charge. Therefore

$$dN = E 2\pi r^2 \sin \theta d\theta = E_0 2\pi r_0{}^2 \sin \theta_0 d\theta_0.$$

Substituting the values of r_0, $\sin \theta_0$ and $d\theta_0$ in terms of r, sin and $d\theta$,

$$E = \frac{E_0}{\sqrt{1 - \beta^2 \sin^2 \theta}}, \qquad (159\text{–}6$$

and using (159–5)

$$E = \frac{e(1 - \beta^2)}{4\pi r^2 (1 - \beta^2 \sin^2 \theta)^{3/2}} \qquad (159\text{–}7$$

in the direction of the radius vector. Denoting the components of parallel and normal to the velocity by the subscripts p and n respectively,

$$\left.\begin{aligned} E_p &= \frac{E_0 \cos \theta}{\sqrt{1 - \beta^2 \sin^2 \theta}} = E_0 \cos \theta_0 = E_{0p}, \\ E_n &= \frac{E_0 \sin \theta}{\sqrt{1 - \beta^2 \sin^2 \theta}} = \frac{E_0 \sin \theta_0}{\sqrt{1 - \beta^2}} = \frac{E_{0n}}{\sqrt{1 - \beta^2}}. \end{aligned}\right\} \qquad (159\text{–}8$$

Since the moving charge constitutes a current in the X direction it is clear that the lines of magnetic force must be circles in plane perpendicular to the direction of motion with centers on a straigh line through the charge parallel to its velocity. The magnitude o the magnetic intensity may be determined from either Faraday' law (*c*) or the Ampère-Maxwell law (*d*). We shall determine i from the latter as the necessary analysis is somewhat simpler.

Let A and B (Fig. 156) be the points of intersection of a circula line of magnetic force with a plane through the X axis. Describ a spherical cap with e as center whose periphery coincides with thi line of force. We shall integrate the Ampère-Maxwell equation (*d* over the surface σ of the spherical cap. As $\rho\mathbf{v} = 0$,

$$\int_\sigma \nabla \times \mathbf{H} \cdot d\sigma = \frac{1}{c} \int_\sigma \frac{\partial \mathbf{E}}{\partial t} \cdot d\sigma.$$

But

$$\int_\sigma \nabla \times \mathbf{H} \cdot d\boldsymbol{\sigma} = \oint \mathbf{H} \cdot d\boldsymbol{\lambda} = H 2\pi r \sin\theta$$

by Stokes' theorem, where $d\boldsymbol{\lambda}$ is a vector element of the circular periphery of the cap. Also we may write

$$\frac{1}{c}\int_\sigma \frac{\partial \mathbf{E}}{\partial t} \cdot d\boldsymbol{\sigma} = \frac{1}{c}\frac{d}{dt}\int_\sigma \mathbf{E} \cdot d\boldsymbol{\sigma}$$

if we keep the periphery of the cap fixed. Therefore as **E** is perpendicular to the surface of the cap and its magnitude is a function of r and θ only,

$$2\pi r H \sin\theta = \frac{1}{c}\frac{d}{dt}\int_0^\theta E 2\pi r^2 \sin\theta d\theta.$$

On account of the motion of the charge the electric flux through the cap AB at the time $t + dt$ is the same as that through the cap CD or FG at the time t, where $CA = v\,dt$. Therefore we may replace the time rate of increase of flux through the cap AB of fixed periphery by the corresponding space rate of increase of flux through an expanding cap. As

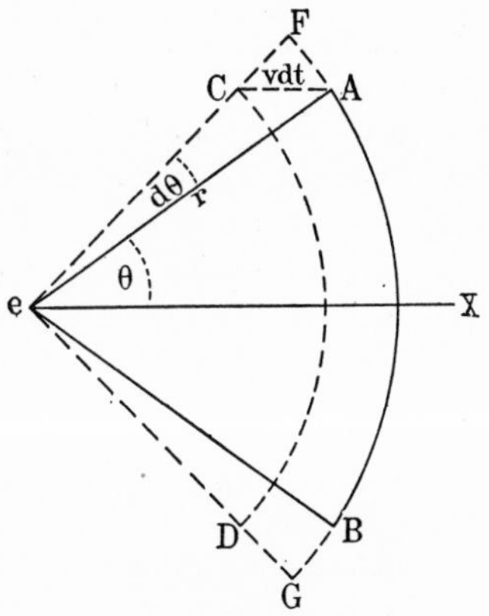

FIG. 156.

$$r d\theta = v\,dt \sin\theta$$

from the figure, we have

$$\frac{d}{dt} = \frac{v \sin\theta}{r}\frac{d}{d\theta}$$

and

$$2\pi r H \sin\theta = \frac{\beta \sin\theta}{r}\frac{d}{d\theta}\int_0^\theta 2\pi r^2 E \sin\theta d\theta$$

$$= \frac{\beta \sin\theta}{r} 2\pi r^2 E \sin\theta.$$

Therefore

$$H = E\beta \sin\theta$$

$$= \frac{e(1 - \beta^2)\beta \sin\theta}{4\pi r^2 (1 - \beta^2 \sin^2\theta)^{3/2}} \qquad (159\text{–}9)$$

or

$$H = \beta E_n = \frac{\beta E_{0n}}{\sqrt{1 - \beta^2}}. \qquad (159\text{–}10)$$

It is clear from (159–3) that the shrinkage in the X dimensions of the electric field becomes greater and greater as the velocity of light is approached, and (159–7) and (159–9) show that when $\beta = 1$ both the electric and magnetic fields are confined to a plane through the charge perpendicular to its direction of motion.

Problem 159a. Show that the first form (133–2) of Ampère's law follows from (159–9) when $\beta^2 \ll 1$.

Problem 159b. Find the magnetic field due to an infinitely long straight current from (159–9) without neglect of terms in β^2 and show that the result agrees exactly with (134–6).

160. The Principle of Relativity. — In the last article we found that when a point charge is set into motion relative to the observer the dimensions of its electric field in the direction of motion suffer a contraction which increases with the velocity until the entire field is compressed into the equatorial plane when the velocity of light is attained. We wish to know whether a like contraction occurs in material bodies in motion relative to the observer.

The *principle of relativity*, enunciated by Einstein in 1905, asserts that the laws of physics are the same when determined relative to one inertial system as when determined relative to any other. Insofar as the laws of dynamics are concerned, Einstein's pronouncement contained nothing new, for we have already shown in article 20 that the laws of motion are the same when referred to a secondary inertial system as when referred to the primary inertial system. Insofar as electromagnetic and optical phenomena are concerned, however, it had been supposed that the primary inertial system occupied a unique position, in the case of the first on account of the appearance of velocities in the electromagnetic equations and in the case of the second on account of the fundamental significance of the velocity of light. If, now, we accept Einstein's principle, the speed of light is the same constant, independent of position, direction or time, whether measured in one inertial system or another. Obviously, if this is the case, the so-called *Galilean transformations* or relations between measurements of distances and intervals of time in different inertial systems, which have been tacitly assumed heretofore, require radical modification.

Let S and S' be two inertial systems. In the first we shall fix a set of rectangular axes XYZ and in the second a parallel set $X'Y'Z'$, the two sets being so oriented that the velocity $\mathbf{v}$ of S' relative to S is in the positive X direction. Denote time and coordinates as measured in S by t, x, y, z and as measured in S' by t', x', y', z' and determine the zero of time by taking $t = t' = 0$ at the origins of the two systems when they are passing each other.

For such a pair of inertial systems the Galilean transformations used in article 20 are

$$\left.\begin{aligned} t' &= t, \\ x' &= x - vt, \\ y' &= y, \\ z' &= z. \end{aligned}\right\} \qquad (160\text{–}1)$$

These transformations do not make the speed of a light wave the same when measured in S' as when measured in S. Therefore we have to look for another set of transformations in order to satisfy the requirements of the principle of relativity.

If the speed of light has the same constant value c in systems S and S' the equation of a spherical wave-front diverging from the origin in system S is

$$x^2 + y^2 + z^2 - c^2t^2 = 0, \qquad (160\text{–}2)$$

and the equation of the same wave-front referred to system S' is

$$x'^2 + y'^2 + z'^2 - c^2t'^2 = 0. \qquad (160\text{–}3)$$

It is clear from symmetry that $y' = y$ and $z' = z$. Also x' and t' must be linear functions of x and t if the transformation is to be the same in all regions of space and at all epochs of time. Therefore we may put $x' = k(x - at)$ and $t' = l(t - bx)$ where k, l, a, b are constants. Now consider a point fixed in S' so that $dx' = 0$. Then $dx - adt = 0$ or $a = dx/dt = v$. So the first of these linear relations can be replaced by $x' = k(x - vt)$. Then, substituting in (160–3),

$$k^2(x^2 - 2vxt + v^2t^2) + y^2 + z^2 - c^2l^2(t^2 - 2bxt + b^2x^2) = 0,$$

or

$$x^2(k^2 - c^2l^2b^2) - 2xt(k^2v - c^2l^2b) - c^2t^2\left(l^2 - k^2\frac{v^2}{c^2}\right) + y^2 + z^2 = 0.$$

This equation must be identical with (160–2). Comparing we see that

$$k^2 - c^2l^2b^2 = 1, \quad k^2v - c^2l^2b = 0, \quad l^2 - k^2\frac{v^2}{c^2} = 1.$$

Solving for k, l, b, we find

$$k = l = \frac{1}{\sqrt{1 - \frac{v^2}{c^2}}}, \qquad b = \frac{v}{c^2}.$$

Consequently if we put

$$\beta \equiv \frac{v}{c}, \qquad k \equiv \frac{1}{\sqrt{1 - \beta^2}},$$

we have the *Lorentz transformations* of the relativity theory

$$\left.\begin{aligned} t' &= k\left(t - \frac{\beta}{c}x\right), & t &= k\left(t' + \frac{\beta}{c}x'\right), \\ x' &= k(x - vt), & x &= k(x' + vt'), \\ y' &= y, & y &= y', \\ z' &= z, & z &= z', \end{aligned}\right\} \quad (160\text{–}4)$$

where the transformations in the second column have been obtained from those in the first by solving for t, x, y, z. We shall consider two remarkable effects which these transformations imply.

I. *Contraction in Length of a Moving Body.* — Consider a rod, such as a meter stick, at rest in system S' with its axis parallel to the X' axis. Designating its two ends by the subscripts a and b,

$$x_b' = k(x_b - vt),$$

$$x_a' = k(x_a - vt),$$

provided the coordinates x_a and x_b of its two ends in S are determined at the same time t. Subtracting

$$x_b - x_a = \sqrt{1 - \beta^2}(x_b' - x_a'). \qquad (160\text{–}5)$$

Therefore the measured length of the rod as determined in system

S is less than that as determined in system S' in the ratio $\sqrt{1-\beta^2} : 1$. According to the relativity principle the dimensions in the direction of motion of material objects moving relative to the observer suffer the same contraction as that which we found in the last article for a moving electric field. The effect under discussion is reciprocal, that is to say, if a meter rod is at rest in system S with its axis parallel to the X axis, its length as measured in system S' is less than a meter in the ratio $\sqrt{1-\beta^2} : 1$. It must be emphasized that the contraction occurs in the *measured length*, and is indeed a result of the method of measurement which has been employed. The measured length is, however, the only length we can speak about; the term *real length* is utterly without meaning.

II. *Slowing Down of a Moving Clock.* – Consider a clock at rest in S'. Let t_a' and t_b' be two times indicated by the clock. Then

$$t_b = k\left(t_b' + \frac{\beta}{c}x'\right),$$

$$t_a = k\left(t_a' + \frac{\beta}{c}x'\right),$$

as the coordinates of the clock relative to the axes fixed in S' do not change with the time. Subtracting

$$t_b - t_a = \frac{1}{\sqrt{1-\beta^2}}(t_b' - t_a'). \qquad (160\text{–}6)$$

Therefore the interval of time which has elapsed in S is greater than that which has elapsed in S'. Observers in S conclude, then, that the moving clock is running slow. Again the effect is reciprocal. If a clock is at rest in S observers in S' find that it runs slow as compared with clocks at rest in their system.

Next we shall find relations between the components V_x, V_y, V_z of the velocity of a moving point as measured in S, and the components, V_x', V_y', V_z' of the velocity of the same moving point as measured in S'. Differentiating the transformations in the first column of (160–4) we have

$$dt' = k\left(dt - \frac{\beta}{c}dx\right),$$

$$dx' = k(dx - v\,dt),$$

$$dy' = dy,$$

$$dz' = dz.$$

Therefore

$$\left.\begin{aligned}
V_x' &= \frac{dx'}{dt'} = \frac{dx - vdt}{dt - \frac{\beta}{c}dx} = \frac{V_x - v}{1 - \beta\frac{V_x}{c}}, & V_x &= \frac{V_x' + v}{1 + \beta\frac{V_x'}{c}}, \\
V_y' &= \frac{dy'}{dt'} = \frac{dy}{k\left(dt - \frac{\beta}{c}dx\right)} = \frac{V_y}{k\left(1 - \beta\frac{V_x}{c}\right)}, & V_y &= \frac{V_y'}{k\left(1 + \beta\frac{V_x'}{c}\right)}, \\
V_z' &= \frac{dz'}{dt'} = \frac{dz}{k\left(dt - \frac{\beta}{c}dx\right)} = \frac{V_z}{k\left(1 - \beta\frac{V_x}{c}\right)}, & V_z &= \frac{V_z'}{k\left(1 + \beta\frac{V_x'}{c}\right)},
\end{aligned}\right\} \quad (160\text{–}7)$$

where the relations in the second column have been obtained from those in the first by solving for V_x, V_y, V_z.

Consider a body which has a velocity V' relative to S' in the direction of the X axis. Its velocity as measured in S is

$$V = \frac{V' + v}{1 + \beta\frac{V'}{c}},$$

or

$$\frac{V}{c} = \frac{\frac{V'}{c} + \frac{v}{c}}{1 + \frac{v}{c}\frac{V'}{c}} = 1 - \frac{\left(1 - \frac{v}{c}\right)\left(1 - \frac{V'}{c}\right)}{1 + \frac{v}{c}\frac{V'}{c}}.$$

If v and V' are less than c, then V/c is always less than unity and V is less than c. For instance, if $v = 0.9c$ and $V' = 0.9c$, $V = 0.994c$ instead of $1.8c$ as on the Galilean transformations.

If we put $l \equiv ict$ where $i \equiv \sqrt{-1}$ the Lorentz transformations become

$$\left.\begin{aligned} l' &= k(l - i\beta x), \\ x' &= k(x + i\beta l), \\ y' &= y, \\ z' &= z. \end{aligned}\right\} \qquad (160\text{–}8)$$

If we make the further substitution

$$\sin\alpha = -\,i\beta k = -\frac{i\beta}{\sqrt{1-\beta^2}}, \quad \cos\alpha = k = \frac{1}{\sqrt{1-\beta^2}},$$

which satisfies the necessary condition

$$\sin^2\alpha + \cos^2\alpha = 1,$$

the Lorentz transformations take the form

$$\left.\begin{aligned} l' &= l\cos\alpha + x\sin\alpha, \\ x' &= x\cos\alpha - l\sin\alpha, \\ y' &= y, \\ z' &= z. \end{aligned}\right\} \qquad (160\text{–}9)$$

These are the transformations necessary to pass from one set of four-dimensional rectangular axes $LXYZ$ to another set $L'X'Y'Z'$ which is obtained from the first by a rotation through the angle $-\alpha$ in the XL plane. Now we may represent graphically the history of a moving point by plotting in a four-dimensional $LXYZ$ space points indicating its coordinates x, y, z at every instant l of time. The locus of these points, represented by the curve OP in Fig. 157, is known as the *world line* of the point. In view of the relations (160–9), then, the four-dimensional coordinates l', x', y', z' referred to the axes $L'X'Y'Z'$ of any point P on the world line represent the time and space coordinates as measured in system S' corresponding to the time and space coordinates as measured in system S which are represented by the four-dimensional coordinates l, x, y, z of P referred to the axes $LXYZ$. The world line in this four-dimensional representative space is the same no matter in what inertial system kinematical measurements are made. The Lorentz transformations enabling us to pass from measurements made in one inertial system to those in another correspond to a rotation of the axes through an imaginary angle determined by the relative velocity of the two systems.

The theory of which we have developed a small part is known as the *special theory of relativity* in that it is restricted to inertial systems moving with constant velocities relative to one another. In the *general theory of relativity*, in which the principle is extended so as to apply to systems accelerated relative to one another, Einstein employs a curved $LXYZ$ space. This theory forms the basis for a theory of gravitation which has superseded Newton's and which has accounted for a long-standing anomaly in the precession of Mercury's perihelion and has predicted the bending of a ray of light in the gravitational field of a massive body such as the sun.

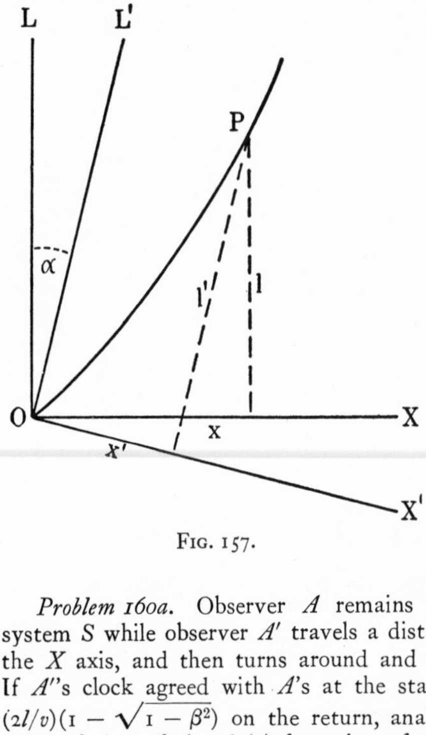

FIG. 157.

Problem 160a. Observer A remains permanently at rest in inertial system S while observer A' travels a distance l from A with speed v along the X axis, and then turns around and returns to A at the same speed. If A''s clock agreed with A's at the start, show that it will be slow by $(2l/v)(1 - \sqrt{1 - \beta^2})$ on the return, analyzing the problem (1) from the point of view of A and (2) from that of A'. (*Hint.*—When A' reverses his motion the other clocks in his inertial system are thrown out of synchronism with his own clock and must be reset.)

161. Electromagnetic Mass of the Electron. — Considerations of symmetry suggest that the electron may be a uniformly charged spherical shell relative to an observer with respect to whom it is momentarily at rest. When in motion relative to the observer the relativity theory requires that it should contract in the direction of motion in the same ratio $\sqrt{1 - \beta^2} : 1$ as that in which its electric field contracts. Thus it becomes an oblate spheroid with the short axis in the direction of motion.

The electromagnetic momentum of the electron's field may be calculated from the expression (158–3),

$$\mathbf{G} = \frac{1}{c^2}\int \mathbf{s}\,d\tau,$$

where the volume integral is extended over all space outside the electron, the region inside being omitted as there is no field in the interior of the electron. If the electron is moving in the X direction with velocity $\mathbf{v}$ it is clear from symmetry that $G_y = G_z = 0$, and from the definition (155–4) of $\mathbf{s}$,

$$G_x = \frac{1}{c}\int (E_y H_z - E_z H_y)\,d\tau. \qquad (161\text{–}1)$$

Designating by the subscript $_0$ the electric intensity in the corresponding electrostatic system of article 159, that is, in the inertial system in which the electron is at rest, we have from (159–8)

$$E_y = \frac{E_{0y}}{\sqrt{1 - \beta^2}}, \qquad E_z = \frac{E_{0z}}{\sqrt{1 - \beta^2}}.$$

As regards the magnetic intensity we can write (159–10) in the vector form

$$\mathbf{H} = \frac{\mathbf{v} \times \mathbf{E}_0}{c\sqrt{1 - \beta^2}}$$

since $\mathbf{H}$ is perpendicular to the plane of the current element $e\mathbf{v}$ and the radius vector parallel to $\mathbf{E}_0$ in the sense of advance of a right-handed screw rotated from $\mathbf{v}$ to $\mathbf{E}_0$ by Ampère's law. This gives us

$$H_y = -\frac{\beta E_{0z}}{\sqrt{1 - \beta^2}}, \qquad H_z = \frac{\beta E_{0y}}{\sqrt{1 - \beta^2}}.$$

Finally, on account of the similar contraction of the electron and its field,

$$d\tau = \sqrt{1 - \beta^2}\,d\tau_0.$$

Therefore (161–1) becomes

$$G_x = \frac{\beta}{c\sqrt{1 - \beta^2}}\int (E_{0y}^2 + E_{0z}^2)\,d\tau_0, \qquad (161\text{–}2)$$

where the volume integral is to be extended from the surface of the spherical electron of radius a in the corresponding electrostatic system to infinity. From the symmetry of the electrostatic field $\mathbf{E}_0$,

$$\int E_{0x}{}^2 d\tau_0 = \int E_{0y}{}^2 d\tau_0 = \int E_{0z}{}^2 d\tau_0 = \tfrac{1}{3}\int E_0{}^2 d\tau_0$$

$$= \frac{e^2}{48\pi^2}\int_a^\infty \frac{1}{r^4} 4\pi r^2 dr = \frac{e^2}{12\pi a}.$$

Therefore

$$\mathbf{G} = \frac{e^2}{6\pi a c^2} \frac{\mathbf{v}}{\sqrt{1 - \frac{v^2}{c^2}}}. \tag{161-3}$$

Suppose now that the velocity of the electron is slowly changed. Since the alteration in its field occasioned by the change in velocity takes place with the speed of light, we conclude that the field near to the electron is at every instant very closely that appropriate to a uniformly moving electron having the same velocity as the actual accelerated electron. But the field near to the electron contributes by far the greater part to the integral expressing the electromagnetic momentum. Hence to a high degree of approximation the electromagnetic momentum of a slowly accelerated electron is at every instant the same as that of an electron moving uniformly with the same velocity.

If, then, $\mathbf{f}$ is the acceleration of the electron, the force exerted by it on its field is

$$\mathbf{K} = \frac{d\mathbf{G}}{dt} = \frac{e^2}{6\pi a c^2}\left\{\frac{\mathbf{f}}{\sqrt{1-\beta^2}} + \frac{\frac{\mathbf{f}\cdot\mathbf{v}}{c^2}\mathbf{v}}{(1-\beta^2)^{3/2}}\right\}. \tag{161-4}$$

The component of the force parallel to the velocity is

$$K_l = \frac{e^2}{6\pi a c^2(1-\beta^2)^{3/2}} f_l, \tag{161-5}$$

and that perpendicular

$$K_t = \frac{e^2}{6\pi a c^2\sqrt{1-\beta^2}} f_t, \tag{161-6}$$

where f_l is the component of acceleration parallel to the velocity and f_t that at right angles.

The law of action and reaction requires that the electron's field shall exert an equal and opposite force on the electron. So the components of the force exerted on the electron by its field are proportional to the components of acceleration f_l and f_t and opposite in direction to these accelerations. Here we have a purely electromagnetic explanation of the kinetic reaction of the electron or of any other elementary charged particle similarly constituted. Insofar as gross matter is composed of charged particles, we have deduced the second law of motion from electromagnetic theory.

Since mass is the ratio of the applied force to the acceleration produced, we see from (161–5) and (161–6) that the mass of an electron varies with its velocity and in a different way according as the applied force is parallel or perpendicular to the direction of motion. If we denote by m_0 the *rest mass* effective when the velocity relative to the observer is zero, by m_l the *longitudinal mass* which comes into play when the applied force is parallel to the direction of motion, and by m_t the *transverse mass* involved when the force is perpendicular to the velocity, we have

$$m_0 = \frac{e^2}{6\pi a c^2} = \frac{2e_s^{\,2}}{3ac^2}, \tag{161–7}$$

where e_s is the charge of the electron in e.s.u.,

$$m_l = \frac{m_0}{(1 - \beta^2)^{3/2}}, \tag{161–8}$$

$$m_t = \frac{m_0}{\sqrt{1 - \beta^2}}, \tag{161–9}$$

and the electromagnetic momentum of the electron is

$$\mathbf{G} = m_t \mathbf{v}. \tag{161–10}$$

For any velocity greater than zero the longitudinal mass is larger than the transverse mass and therefore the acceleration does not in general have the same direction as the applied force. Since both masses become infinite as the velocity of the electron approaches the velocity of light, no finite force can give an electron a velocity as great as that of light. This theoretical deduction is well borne out by the fact that beta rays (electrons) emitted from the nuclei of radioactive atoms have velocities nearly as great as that of light but never surpassing this theoretical limit.

The experiments of Bucherer and of Neumann on the deflections suffered by fast moving beta rays subject to forces at right angles to the direction of motion have shown that the mass varies with the velocity as predicted by (161–9). This indicates that the mass of the electron, and by inference that of every elementary particle, is entirely electromagnetic. Such a particle is to be imagined, therefore, not as matter charged with electricity, but as disembodied electricity itself. Even the neutron, with no net electric charge, has a magnetic moment and is therefore in all probability a composite of equal and opposite electric charges. As electrons, protons and neutrons are the bricks out of which all atoms are built, we infer that matter is electricity and nothing more.

The manner in which the field of an accelerated electron exerts a force on it in a direction opposite to its acceleration sufficient to balance the applied force is shown in Fig. 158. From the symmetry

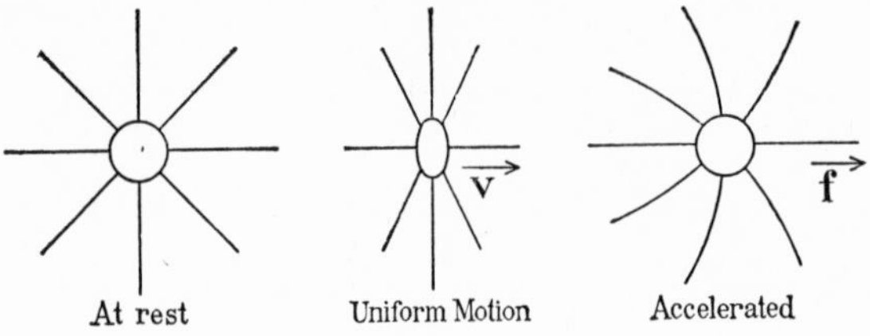

FIG. 158.

of the first two diagrams it is clear that the resultant force exerted by its field on an electron at rest or in uniform motion vanishes, whereas the curvature of the lines of force illustrated in the third diagram indicates that the force on an accelerated electron is in the direction opposite to its acceleration. The force on an electron due to its own field may be computed directly without introducing the concept of electromagnetic momentum. The calculation is more laborious than that employed above, although it has the advantage of leading to higher order terms in the kinetic reaction in addition to the mass reaction obtained by the present treatment. These higher order terms are absent from the equations above because we have limited ourselves to the quasi-stationary state of very slowly changing motion.

Consider an electron which, starting from rest, acquires a velocity $\mathbf{v}$ under the action of a very small force $\mathbf{K}$ acting for a very long time. As the motion is quasi-stationary (161–4) may be taken for the equation of motion. The kinetic energy acquired, measured in the usual way, is

$$T = \int_0^t \mathbf{K}\cdot\mathbf{v}dt = \int_0^t m_l \frac{dv}{dt} vdt,$$

as

$$f_l = \frac{dv}{dt}.$$

Therefore

$$T=m_0\int_0^v \frac{v\,dv}{\left(1-\frac{v^2}{c^2}\right)^{3/2}} = m_0c^2\left\{\frac{1}{\sqrt{1-\beta^2}}-1\right\} = (m_t-m_0)c^2. \quad (161\text{–}11)$$

If v is small compared with c we get approximately the expression

$$T = m_0c^2\left\{1+\frac{1}{2}\frac{v^2}{c^2}+\ldots-1\right\} = \tfrac{1}{2}m_0v^2$$

of the classical dynamics.

Now all energy measurements consist in the determination of the excess or defect of the energy of the state under consideration over that of some standard state. If, instead of following the usual convention of taking the state of zero kinetic energy as that in which the electron is at rest relative to the observer, we choose the standard state so that the electron has the large energy m_0c^2 when at rest, we may write

$$T = m_tc^2 \quad (161\text{–}12)$$

in place of (161–11). This simpler formula gives the same result as the previous expression in any calculation of change of energy. From it we draw the important conclusion that the kinetic energy of an electron is proportional to its transverse mass, the energy and the mass increasing or decreasing in the same ratio when the velocity changes.

In the relativity dynamics developed in this article the three laws of Newton are still valid when referred to any inertial system, provided (*a*) we replace the Galilean space and time transformations (160–1) by the Lorentz transformations (160–4), (*b*) we replace the constant mass of the older dynamics by the variable mass of the relativity theory, (*c*) we include the momenta of radiation and the reactions due to it in applying the second and third laws of motion.

By means of (161–7) the radius of any elementary charged particle can be calculated from its rest mass, found by the methods described in article 138. The formula shows that the radius is inversely proportional to the mass. Hence the proton, if it is an elementary particle, must have a radius only 1/1836 of that of the electron, since its mass is 1836 times as great. In the following table are given values of charge, mass and radius of electron and proton. While the numerical coefficient of the expression (161–7) and hence the calculated value of the radius depends upon the particular assumption we have made regarding the distribution of charge in the particle, the order of magnitude of the radius is the same whatever assumption may be made

	Charge	Rest Mass m_0	Radius a
Electron	$-4.803\,(10)^{-10}$ e.s.u.	$9.11\,(10)^{-28}$ gm	$1.88\,(10)^{-13}$ cm
Proton	$4.803\,(10)^{-10}$ e.s.u.	$1.67\,(10)^{-24}$ gm	$1.02\,(10)^{-16}$ cm

The radius of the atom is of the order of $(10)^{-8}$ cm, that is, about 100,000 times the radius of the electron. So the portion of the volume of an atom like carbon, which contains twelve electrons in the outer atom, that is actually filled by matter, is to the total volume of the atom as 1 is to 100,000,000,000,000. Nearly all the space apparently filled by matter is actually empty.

Problem 161a. Calculate the mean charge per unit volume of the electron, the electric intensity at the surface of the electron and at a distance from the center of the electron equal to the radius $(10)^{-8}$ cm of the atom.

Ans. $5.7(10)^{18}$ coulomb/cm^3, $4.0(10)^{18}$ volt/cm, $1.4(10)^{9}$ volt/cm.

Problem 161b. Calculate the work necessary to increase the velocity of an electron from 0 to $0.95c$ both from the rigorous formula (161–11) and from the approximate formula $\frac{1}{2}m_0v^2$ and note the discrepancy. Compute the work necessary to increase its velocity from $0.95c$ to $0.99c$ and compare with the previous result. *Ans.* $1.78(10)^{-6}$ erg, $3.66(10)^{-7}$ erg, $3.15(10)^{-6}$ erg.

161.1. Acceleration of Charged Particles. — Various methods may be employed to accelerate charged particles so as to obtain high energies. We shall describe two which are of interest as applications of the theory which has been developed.

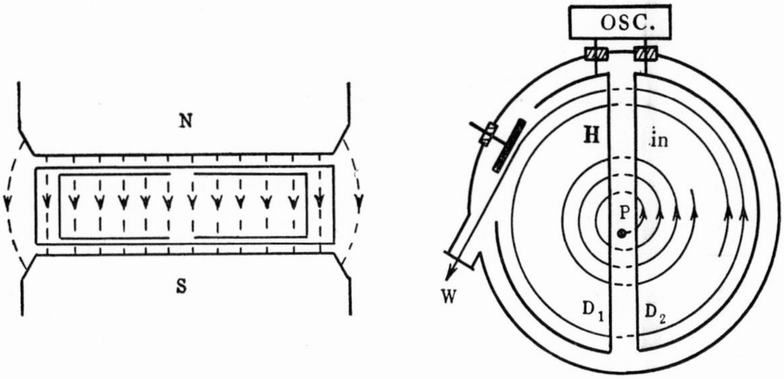

FIG. 158.1

I. *The Cyclotron.* — This device, first constructed by E. O. Lawrence in 1932, consists of a metal pill-box cut into two semi-circular *dees* D_1 and D_2 (Fig. 158.1) which are placed between the poles N, S of a strong magnet designed to produce a very uniform field $\mathbf{H}$ throughout the region occupied by the dees. The latter are connected to a high-frequency electric oscillator which gives rise to an alternating electric field of frequency ν between the dees. Ions are produced in the gap between the dees near the center, where they are accelerated by the electric field so as to enter one of the dees. Here, protected from the electric field by the shielding effect of the metal dee, their paths are curved by the magnetic field so as to bring them back to the gap between the dees when the electric field is reversed. There they get an added increment in velocity before entering the other dee. Continuing in this fashion in ever widening semicircles, they emerge finally at W under the influence of an auxiliary deflecting electric field.

The operation of the cyclotron depends upon formula (138–3), which shows that, if we neglect the variation of mass with velocity, the time of describing a semicircle in a uniform magnetic field is independent of the velocity of the ion. On the other hand the radius of the path increases linearly with the speed, as indicated by (138–4).

In the following table are given, for the electron, the proton and the deuteron, the ratios of m_t to m_0 and of v to c for various energies $(m_t - m_0)c^2$ measured in million electron-volts (Mev). The *electron-volt* is the energy acquired by a particle with the electronic charge $4.803(10)^{-10}$ e.s.u. in falling through a potential drop of one volt and is equal to $1.60(10)^{-12}$ erg. It is seen that the mass of the proton or of the deuteron remains nearly constant up to fairly high energies, but that the mass of the electron has increased by a large amount even at energies as low as 1 Mev. So the cyclotron is unsuited for the production of high energy electrons, and requires modification even for the production of very high energy protons or deuterons.

Energy	Electron		Proton		Deuteron	
$(m_t - m_0)c^2$	m_t/m_0	v/c	m_t/m_0	v/c	m_t/m_0	v/c
1 *Mev*	2.95	0.941	1.001	0.05	1.000	0.03
10 *Mev*	20.5	0.999	1.011	0.15	1.005	0.10
100 *Mev*	196	1.000	1.106	0.43	1.053	0.31

To take account of the variation of mass with velocity we must replace the mass m in (138–3) by the transverse mass m_t. But, as $T = m_t c^2$, we can write the revised equation in the form

$$\boldsymbol{\omega} = -\frac{ec}{T}\mathbf{H}, \qquad (161.1\text{–}1)$$

which shows that the angular velocity decreases as the energy increases. Hence an ion, which is revolving in phase with the oscillating electric field at low energy, will begin to lag behind it as the energy rises, and will finally cross the gap between the dees when the field is decelerating instead of accelerating. This will diminish its energy, thereby increasing its angular velocity. Therefore the energy of the ion will oscillate about the value given by (161.1–1) with $\omega/2\pi$ equal to the frequency ν of the alternating electric field.

To obtain a higher energy either ν must be decreased or **H** increased. The first of these methods is used in the synchro-cyclotron and the second in the synchrotron.

II. *The Betatron.* — This instrument, developed by D. W. Kerst in 1941, is used to produce electron beams of energies so great that m_t is many times the rest mass m_0. It consists of a large electromagnet (Fig. 158.2) the pole pieces of which are so shaped that the magnetic

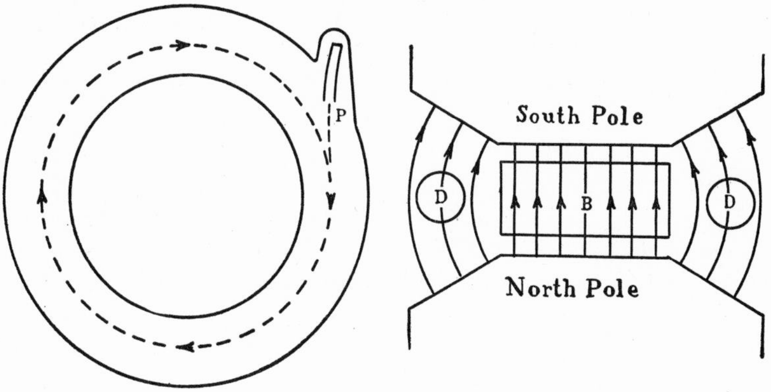

FIG. 158.2.

field is stronger near the center than at the edges. Between the pole pieces is placed an evacuated toroidal chamber *DD* known as a *doughnut.* The magnet is actuated by an alternating current so as to produce a sinusoidally varying magnetic field. This in turn gives rise, in accord with Faraday's law, to an electric field the lines of force of which are circles such as shown by the broken line in the longitudinal section of the doughnut in the left part of the figure. This electric field accelerates electrons injected at *P*, while the central force due to the accompanying magnetic field holds them to a circle of radius r_0 known as the *equilibrium path.*

If r is the distance from the axis, the magnetic flux through the area bounded by the equilibrium path is

$$N_0 = \int_0^{r_0} H\, 2\pi r\, dr,$$

and the varying electric field along this path is given by Faraday's law

$$2\pi r_0 E_0 = -\frac{1}{c}\frac{dN_0}{dt}. \qquad (161.1\text{–}2)$$

Since the longitudinal acceleration f_l tangent to the path is equal to the time rate of increase of speed, (161–5) may be written in the form

$$K_l = \frac{d}{dt}\left(\frac{m_0 v}{\sqrt{1-\beta^2}}\right) = \frac{d}{dt}(m_t v). \qquad (161.1\text{–}3)$$

Hence the motion along the path is specified by

$$\frac{d}{dt}(m_t v) = -\frac{e}{2\pi r_0 c}\frac{dN_0}{dt} \qquad (161.1\text{–}4)$$

whereas the motion at right angles is given by

$$m_t \frac{v^2}{r_0} = \frac{1}{c} evH_0 \qquad (161.1\text{–}5)$$

in terms of the magnetic intensity H_0 at the path.

Integrating (161.1–4) subject to the condition that $v = 0$ when $N_0 = 0$,

$$m_t v = -\frac{eN_0}{2\pi r_0 c}, \qquad (161.1\text{–}6)$$

whereas (161.1–5) gives

$$m_t v = \frac{er_0 H_0}{c}. \qquad (161.1\text{–}7)$$

Consequently $N_0 = -2\pi r_0^2 H_0$, which is twice the flux which would exist if the magnetic field were uniform. Therefore the magnetic field must be more intense at the axis of the magnet than along the equilibrium path. This is accomplished in part by a suitable shaping of the pole pieces and in part by the insertion of a soft iron block in the center of the gap.

The nonuniform character of the magnetic field has the important effect of bringing the electron beam back to the equilibrium path whenever it strays from it. If the deviation is from the median plane, the curvature of the lines of force is such as to give rise to a component of force directed toward this plane. On the other hand, if the deviation is in the median plane focusing can be secured by designing the magnet so that in the neighborhood of the equilibrium path H is proportional to a power of $1/r$ between 0 and 1. For then it follows from (161.1–5) that if r increases the centrifugal reaction decreases less rapidly than the central force, whereas if r decreases the centrifugal reaction increases more rapidly than the central force.

After a quarter period of the exciting current, the electron beam is forced by an auxiliary field to leave the equilibrium path and strike a target, producing X-rays.

Problem 161.1a. A cyclotron employing deuterons of mass $3.34(10)^{-24}$ gm has a magnetic field of 16,000 oersteds and a radius of 75 cm. Find the required frequency ν of the oscillating electric field, and the velocity and the energy of the emergent beam. If the potential difference between the dees is 50,000 volts, find the number of revolutions made by the ions.

Ans. $12.2(10)^6$/sec, $5.75(10)^9$cm/sec, 34.5 Mev, 690 rev.

Problem 161.1b. The radius of the equilibrium path in a betatron is 18.8 cm and the frequency of the current exciting the magnet is 180 cycle/sec. What is the maximum magnetic intensity H_0 at the equilibrium path necessary to give electron energies of 20 Mev? Approximately how far do the electrons travel in acquiring this energy? How many revolutions do they make?

Ans. $3.56(10)^4$ oersted, 417 kilometers, $3.5(10)^5$ rev.

162. The Compton Effect. — Consider the impact of a photon on a free electron originally at rest. If **G** is the initial and **G′** the final momentum of the photon (Fig. 159) and $\mathbf{G}_e$ the momentum of the electron after the collision, the law of conservation of momentum requires that

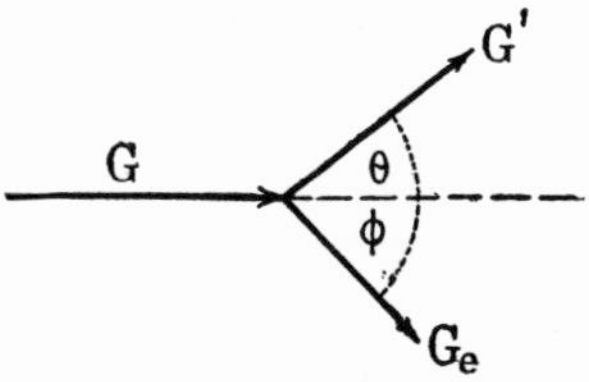

FIG. 159.

$$G = G' \cos \theta + G_e \cos \phi,$$

$$0 = G' \sin \theta - G_e \sin \phi.$$

Denoting by ν the frequency of the radiation before the collision

and by ν' that after, and by v the velocity acquired by the electron as a result of the impact, we have from (158–11) and (161–10)

$$\frac{h\nu}{c} = \frac{h\nu'}{c}\cos\theta + \frac{m_0 v}{\sqrt{1-\beta^2}}\cos\phi, \tag{162–1}$$

$$0 = \frac{h\nu'}{c}\sin\theta - \frac{m_0 v}{\sqrt{1-\beta^2}}\sin\phi. \tag{162–2}$$

Furthermore the principle of conservation of energy requires that

$$h\nu = h\nu' + m_0 c^2\left\{\frac{1}{\sqrt{1-\beta^2}} - 1\right\} \tag{162–3}$$

since there is no dissipation of energy during the collision. Eliminating ϕ between (162–1) and (162–2)

$$\frac{h^2}{m_0 c^2}(\nu^2 - 2\nu\nu'\cos\theta + \nu'^2) = m_0 c^2\left\{\frac{1}{1-\beta^2} - 1\right\}.$$

Solving (162–3) for the reciprocal of $1 - \beta^2$

$$h(\nu - \nu')\left\{2 + \frac{h}{m_0 c^2}(\nu - \nu')\right\} = m_0 c^2\left\{\frac{1}{1-\beta^2} - 1\right\},$$

and eliminating β between the last two equations

$$\frac{c}{\nu'} - \frac{c}{\nu} = \frac{h}{m_0 c}(1 - \cos\theta). \tag{162–4}$$

Written in terms of wave lengths (162–4) becomes

$$\lambda' - \lambda = \frac{h}{m_0 c}(1 - \cos\theta). \tag{162–5}$$

Wave lengths are usually measured in Ångström units, where $1\text{Å} = (10)^{-8}$ cm. The length $h/(m_0 c)$ has the numerical value 0.0243Å. Therefore the wave length of a photon scattered by impact with a free electron should be increased by $0.0243\text{Å}(1 - \cos\theta)$. As the change in wave length is small it is inappreciable in the visible region of the spectrum but it is large enough to be measured in the X-ray region. The effect was discovered by A. H. Compton, who has verified the formula (162–5) for the X-rays scattered by elements of low atomic number.

163. Dispersion. — In article 156 we found that the index of refraction of a dielectric such as glass is proportional to the square root of its permittivity κ. We also remarked that κ is a function of the frequency of the radiation passing through the dielectric. We shall now investigate the form of this function.

We shall assume that the bound electrons in the atoms of a dielectric are held to their positions of equilibrium by simple harmonic forces of restitution. In addition we shall suppose that each electron is subject to a damping force proportional to its velocity. The impressed force on each electron is $e\mathbf{E}_1$, where $\mathbf{E}_1$ is the electric field applied from outside plus that due to the surrounding polarized atoms. The force due to the magnetic field in the wave is negligible on account of the factor v/c in the second term of the force equation (*g*) of article 154. If, then, the radiation traveling through the medium consists of electromagnetic waves of angular frequency ω we can represent $\mathbf{E}_1$ by the complex quantity $\mathbf{A}e^{-i\omega t}$, where $\mathbf{A}$ is a constant. The equation of motion of a bound electron is then

$$\frac{d^2\mathbf{r}}{dt^2} + 2l\frac{d\mathbf{r}}{dt} + k_0{}^2\mathbf{r} = \frac{e}{m}\mathbf{A}e^{-i\omega t} \tag{163-1}$$

where $\mathbf{r}$ is the displacement of the electron from its equilibrium position.

We are interested in the particular solution representing the steady state existing after the transients have died down. Try

$$\mathbf{r} = \mathbf{a}e^{-i\omega t}.$$

Substituting in the differential equation we get

$$\mathbf{a}\{(k_0{}^2 - \omega^2) - 2i\omega l\} = \frac{e}{m}\mathbf{A},$$

from which it follows that the desired solution is

$$\mathbf{r} = \frac{\dfrac{e}{m}\mathbf{A}}{(k_0{}^2 - \omega^2) - 2i\omega l}e^{-i\omega t}. \tag{163-2}$$

Therefore the electric moment per unit volume or polarization of the medium is

$$\mathbf{P} = Ne\mathbf{r} = \frac{1}{(k_0{}^2 - \omega^2) - 2i\omega l}\frac{Ne^2}{m}\mathbf{E}_1, \tag{163-3}$$

where N is the number of bound electrons per unit volume and we have restored $\mathbf{E}_1$ for $\mathbf{A}e^{-i\omega t}$. The ratio σ of $\mathbf{P}$ to $\mathbf{E}_1$ in Heaviside-Lorentz units is 4π times the ratio of these quantities expressed in electrostatic units in (115–6), as appears at once from the conversion table on page 370. Therefore equation (115–6) becomes

$$\kappa = \frac{1 + \frac{2}{3}\sigma}{1 - \frac{1}{3}\sigma} = 1 + \frac{\sigma}{1 - \frac{1}{3}\sigma}$$

when σ is expressed in Heaviside-Lorentz units. Substituting the value of σ from (163–3) and putting

$$k^2 \equiv k_0{}^2 - \frac{Ne^2}{3m}$$

we have

$$\kappa = 1 + \frac{1}{(k^2 - \omega^2) - 2i\omega l}\frac{Ne^2}{m}$$

$$= 1 + \frac{(k^2 - \omega^2)\dfrac{Ne^2}{m}}{(k^2 - \omega^2)^2 + 4\omega^2 l^2} + i\frac{2\omega l\dfrac{Ne^2}{m}}{(k^2 - \omega^2)^2 + 4\omega^2 l^2}. \qquad (163\text{–}4)$$

As the permittivity is complex the same is true of the index of refraction or the phase velocity v. To find the meaning of a complex phase velocity consider a plane wave advancing in the X direction. As shown in article 156 the electric intensity satisfies the equation

$$\frac{\partial^2 \mathbf{E}}{\partial x^2} = S^2 \frac{\partial^2 \mathbf{E}}{\partial t^2},$$

where the wave slowness S has been put for the reciprocal of the wave velocity v. The solution of this equation representing a simple harmonic wave of frequency ω is given by the real part of

$$\mathbf{E} = \mathbf{A}e^{i\omega(Sx - t)}.$$

Now if S is complex we can put

$$S = S' + iS''$$

where S' and S'' are real. Therefore $\mathbf{E}$ is the real part of

$$\mathbf{E} = \mathbf{A}e^{-\omega S'' x} e^{i\omega(S'x - t)},$$

hat is,

$$\mathbf{E} = \mathbf{A}e^{-\omega S''x} \cos \omega(S'x - t).$$

We see then that the imaginary part of the wave slowness repre-ents a damping in the amplitude of the wave as it progresses into he medium, and the real part the reciprocal of the actual velocity f propagation. As the index of refraction n is complex let us put

$$n \equiv \nu(1 + i\chi)$$

vhere ν and χ are real. Then

$$\nu + i\nu\chi = cS = cS' + icS'',$$

nd

$$\nu = cS'$$

s the ratio of the velocity of light *in vacuo* to the actual velocity of ropagation in the medium. It is then the real part of the index of efraction which we wish to compute. If we denote the real and maginary parts of the permittivity by κ' and κ'' respectively,

$$\nu^2(1 - \chi^2) = \kappa',$$

$$2\nu^2\chi = \kappa'',$$

s $n^2 = \kappa$. Eliminating χ we find

$$\nu^4 - \nu^2\kappa' - \frac{\kappa''^2}{4} = 0,$$

r

$$\nu^2 = \tfrac{1}{2}\{\kappa' + \sqrt{\kappa'^2 + \kappa''^2}\} \qquad (163\text{–}5)$$

vhere we have taken the positive sign in front of the radical since $^2 = \kappa'$ when $\kappa'' = 0$.

From (163–4) we have

$$\kappa' = 1 + \frac{(k^2 - \omega^2)\dfrac{Ne^2}{m}}{(k^2 - \omega^2)^2 + 4\omega^2 l^2},$$

$$\kappa'' = \frac{2\omega l\dfrac{Ne^2}{m}}{(k^2 - \omega^2)^2 + 4\omega^2 l^2}.$$

We shall assume that the damping of the bound electrons i small. Therefore we can neglect κ'' as compared with κ' in thos regions of the spectrum in which ω is not nearly equal to the effectiv natural frequency k. In these regions

$$\nu^2 = \kappa' = 1 + \frac{\frac{Ne^2}{m}}{k^2 - \omega^2} \tag{163-6}$$

if we neglect the small term $4\omega^2 l^2$ in the denominator. For $\omega < k$ ν^2 is greater than unity and for $\omega > k$ less than unity. In eithe case the index of refraction increases with increasing frequency of th radiation.

In the region where ω is nearly equal to k the term $(k^2 - \omega^2)^2$ i the denominators of κ' and κ'' becomes very small and we canno neglect $4\omega^2 l^2$ as compared with it. Moreover κ'' and hence χ become large and the radiation is strongly absorbed. For this reason thi region is known as an *absorption band*. At the center of an absorp tion band $\omega = k$, κ' becomes unity and

$$\nu^2 = \tfrac{1}{2}\{1 + \sqrt{1 + \kappa''^2}\} \tag{163-7}$$

which is always greater than one.

The curve obtained by plotting ν^2 against ω^2 is shown in Fig. 16c The region AB is that of normal dispersion represented approxi

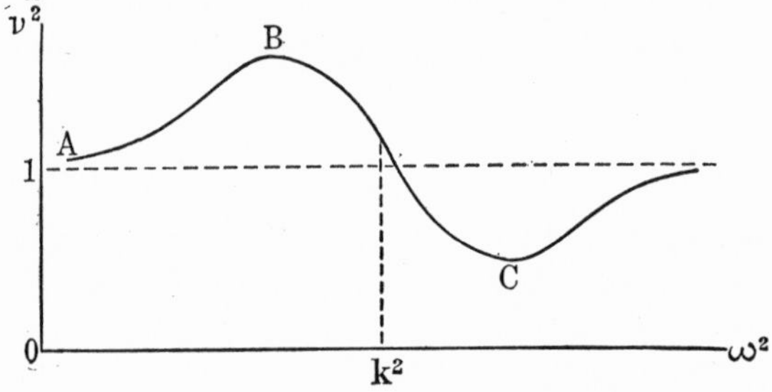

FIG. 160.

mately by equation (163–6) while the region of anomalous dispersio occurring in the neighborhood of an absorption band is shown by BC In this region the index of refraction decreases with increasin frequency, reaching a value less than unity at C. The phase velocit at C, therefore, is greater than the velocity of light *in vacuo*. This is not inconsistent with the relativity principle, however, for, as Sommerfeld has shown, the phase velocity of an infinite train of simple harmonic waves is not at all the same thing as the velocity with which a light signal can be transmitted. The signal velocity, even in a dielectric in the region of anomalous dispersion, is never greater than the velocity of light *in vacuo*.

We have assumed that all the bound electrons in the atoms of the dielectric under consideration are held to their equilibrium positions by forces of restitution of the same magnitude. It is more reasonable to suppose that inner electrons are more firmly bound than those near the periphery of the atom. Then instead of the single absorption band illustrated in Fig. 160 we would have a series of bands scattered through the spectrum. For instance glass, which is very transparent in the visible region, absorbs ultra-violet light strongly and has another absorption band in the infra-red.

164. Radiation from an Oscillating Electric Dipole. — In empty space the electric intensity must satisfy the wave equation

$$\nabla \cdot \nabla \mathbf{E} = \frac{1}{c^2} \ddot{\mathbf{E}} \qquad (164\text{–}1)$$

and the solenoidal condition

$$\nabla \cdot \mathbf{E} = 0. \qquad (164\text{–}2)$$

To find a solenoidal solution of (164–1) which represents the field of an oscillating electric dipole we follow the method developed in article 156.1. First we seek a solution of the scalar wave equation

$$\nabla \cdot \nabla \Phi = \frac{1}{c^2} \ddot{\Phi} \qquad (164\text{–}3)$$

representing a spherical wave diverging from the point at which the dipole is located, which we shall take as origin. The simplest such wave is that for which Φ is a function of the radius vector r and the time t only. Then (164–3) becomes

$$\frac{\partial^2 \Phi}{\partial r^2} + \frac{2}{r} \frac{\partial \Phi}{\partial r} = \frac{1}{c^2} \frac{\partial^2 \Phi}{\partial t^2}$$

from (79–5), or

$$\frac{\partial^2}{\partial r^2} (r\Phi) = \frac{1}{c^2} \frac{\partial^2}{\partial t^2} (r\Phi),$$

of which a solution is

$$\Phi = \frac{B}{r} \cos \frac{2\pi}{\lambda} (r - ct). \tag{164-4}$$

Consequently a solenoidal solution of the vector wave equation is

$$\mathbf{E} = \nabla \times \nabla \times (\mathbf{k}\Phi) = \nabla\nabla\cdot(\mathbf{k}\Phi) - \nabla\cdot\nabla(\mathbf{k}\Phi)$$

$$= \nabla \frac{\partial \Phi}{\partial z} - \mathbf{k}\nabla\cdot\nabla\Phi$$

$$= \nabla \frac{\partial \Phi}{\partial z} - \mathbf{k} \frac{1}{c^2} \frac{\partial^2 \Phi}{\partial t^2} \tag{164-5}$$

by (164–3). Taking the Z axis for polar axis and expressing ∇ in the form (11–11) we have

$$\mathbf{E} = \mathbf{r}_1 \left\{ \frac{\partial^2 \Phi}{\partial r \partial z} - \frac{1}{c^2} \frac{\partial^2 \Phi}{\partial t^2} \cos \theta \right\} + \boldsymbol{\theta}_1 \left\{ \frac{\partial^2 \Phi}{r \partial \theta \partial z} + \frac{1}{c^2} \frac{\partial^2 \Phi}{\partial t^2} \sin \theta \right\}.$$

Now

$$\frac{\partial \Phi}{\partial z} = \frac{\partial \Phi}{\partial r} \frac{\partial r}{\partial z} = \frac{\partial \Phi}{\partial r} \cos \theta$$

$$= B \cos \theta \left\{ -\frac{1}{r^2} \cos \frac{2\pi}{\lambda} (r - ct) - \frac{2\pi}{\lambda r} \sin \frac{2\pi}{\lambda} (r - ct) \right\},$$

$$\frac{1}{c^2} \frac{\partial^2 \Phi}{\partial t^2} = -\frac{4\pi^2 B}{\lambda^2 r} \cos \frac{2\pi}{\lambda} (r - ct).$$

Therefore the components of $\mathbf{E}$ in the directions of increasing r, θ and ϕ respectively are

$$\left.\begin{aligned} E_r &= B \cos \theta \left\{ \frac{2}{r^3} \cos \frac{2\pi}{\lambda} (r - ct) + \frac{4\pi}{\lambda r^2} \sin \frac{2\pi}{\lambda} (r - ct) \right\}, \\ E_\theta &= B \sin \theta \left\{ \left(\frac{1}{r^3} - \frac{4\pi^2}{\lambda^2 r} \right) \cos \frac{2\pi}{\lambda} (r - ct) + \frac{2\pi}{\lambda r^2} \sin \frac{2\pi}{\lambda} (r - ct) \right\}, \\ E_\phi &= 0. \end{aligned}\right\} \tag{164-6}$$

At a distance from the origin small compared with the wave length of the emitted radiation, the terms in $1/r^3$ predominate over those in

$1/(\lambda r^2)$ and $1/(\lambda^2 r)$, and $\cos(2\pi/\lambda)(r - ct)$ may be replaced by $\cos(2\pi c/\lambda)t$. Hence

$$\left.\begin{aligned} E_r &= \frac{2B}{r^3}\cos\theta\cos\frac{2\pi c}{\lambda}t, \\ E_\theta &= \frac{B}{r^3}\sin\theta\cos\frac{2\pi c}{\lambda}t, \end{aligned}\right\} \qquad (164\text{–}7)$$

in the vicinity of the origin. The field due to an electric dipole of constant moment p is given in electrostatic units by (112–2). Converting to Heaviside-Lorentz units we find

$$E_r = \frac{2p}{4\pi r^3}\cos\theta,$$

$$E_\theta = \frac{p}{4\pi r^3}\sin\theta.$$

Comparing we see that (164–7) represents the field of a dipole with electric moment

$$p = 4\pi B\cos\frac{2\pi c}{\lambda}t, \qquad (164\text{–}8)$$

and therefore the complete field (164–6) is that produced by an oscillating electric dipole of frequency c/λ. If the dipole is supposed to consist of a proton at rest at the origin and an electron of charge e executing simple harmonic vibrations of amplitude A along the Z axis it is clear that

$$B = \frac{eA}{4\pi} \qquad (164\text{–}9)$$

and the displacement of the electron at any instant is

$$z = A\cos\frac{2\pi c}{\lambda}t. \qquad (164\text{–}10)$$

At a great distance from the origin the terms in $1/(\lambda^2 r)$ predominate over the other terms in (164–6). Hence the electric intensity in the radiation field is

$$\left.\begin{aligned} E_r &= 0, \\ E_\theta &= -\frac{\pi e A}{\lambda^2 r}\sin\theta\cos\frac{2\pi}{\lambda}(r - ct), \\ E_\phi &= 0, \end{aligned}\right\} \qquad (164\text{–}11)$$

provided we eliminate B by means of (164–9). The wave, therefore, is transverse, and the amplitude of the electric vector is inversely proportional to the square of the wave length λ and to the first power of r. As it is also proportional to $\sin\theta$, the most intense radiation is emitted in the equatorial plane and there is no emission along the polar axis. The wave is plane polarized with the electric vector in the plane determined by the radius vector and the line along which the oscillation takes place.

Now the acceleration f_0 of the electron at the time $t_0 = t - r/c$ at which the radiation was emitted is

$$f_0 = \left[\frac{d^2z}{dt^2}\right]_{t=t_0} = -\frac{4\pi^2c^2}{\lambda^2} A \cos\frac{2\pi}{\lambda}(r - ct) \qquad (164\text{–}12)$$

from (164–10). Therefore the elecric intensity E_θ at a great distance from the origin may be written

$$E_\theta = \frac{ef_0 \sin\theta}{4\pi rc^2}, \qquad (164\text{–}13)$$

showing that the electric vector in the wave is proportional to the component in the direction perpendicular to the radius vector of the acceleration of the electron at the time the radiation was emitted. This result is quite general, as is indicated by the fact that the expression for the electric intensity contains no reference to any particular type of motion.

At a great distance from the source any small portion of the wave front is approximately plane and therefore the wave is similar in character to the plane wave discussed in article 156. So the components of magnetic intensity in the radiation field are

$$\left.\begin{aligned} H_r &= 0, \\ H_\theta &= 0, \\ H_\phi &= -\frac{\pi eA}{\lambda^2 r}\sin\theta\cos\frac{2\pi}{\lambda}(r - ct). \end{aligned}\right\} \qquad (164\text{–}14)$$

The Poynting flux is directed along the radius vector and is equal to

$$\begin{aligned} s &= cE_\theta H_\phi \\ &= \frac{\pi^2e^2A^2c}{\lambda^4r^2}\sin^2\theta\cos^2\frac{2\pi}{\lambda}(r - ct). \end{aligned}$$

Therefore the total energy passing through a sphere of radius r in a unit time is

$$\frac{dR}{dt} = \int_0^{2\pi}\int_0^{\pi} sr^2 \sin\theta d\theta d\phi$$

$$= \frac{8\pi^3 e^2 A^2 c}{3\lambda^4} \cos^2 \frac{2\pi}{\lambda}(r - ct)$$

$$= \frac{e^2 f_0^2}{6\pi c^3} \qquad (164\text{–}15)$$

by virtue of (164–12). This represents the rate at which energy was radiated by the electron at the time $t - r/c$. This expression, which is quite general, shows that on classical electromagnetic theory an electron which is accelerated must radiate energy.

Since **H**, as well as **E**, is a solenoidal solution of the wave equation, the expressions contained in (164–6) represent equally well the components of the magnetic field of an oscillating magnetic dipole, such as is approximated by a small circuit in which an oscillatory current is flowing.

Problem 164a. If i_0 is the amplitude and ω the angular frequency of the oscillatory current in a small circuit of area A, write expressions for **E** and **H** at a great distance from the circuit.

Problem 164b. For visible light of frequency $(10)^{15}$ per sec find (*a*) how long it would take an atom to emit one photon, (*b*) the length of the photon, (*c*) the number of waves which it contains. *Ans.* $1.48(10)^{-8}$ sec, 450 cm, $1.5(10)^7$ waves.

165. The Zeeman Effect. — It was shown in the last article that an accelerated electron acts as a source of electromagnetic radiation in which the electric intensity is proportional to the acceleration of the charged particle. Therefore a group of atoms containing vibrating electrons emits radiation of frequencies equal to the dynamical frequencies of oscillation. Suppose now that a group of electronic oscillators of normal angular frequency ω_0 are placed in a steady magnetic field **H**. We desire to investigate the change in frequency of the oscillators and therefore of the radiation emitted due to the presence of the magnetic field.

The equation of motion of an electron in the electric field **E** due to the rest of the atom and the constant magnetic field **H** impressed from outside is

$$m\mathbf{f}_0 = e\left\{\mathbf{E} + \frac{1}{c}\mathbf{v}_0 \times \mathbf{H}\right\} \qquad (165\text{–}1)$$

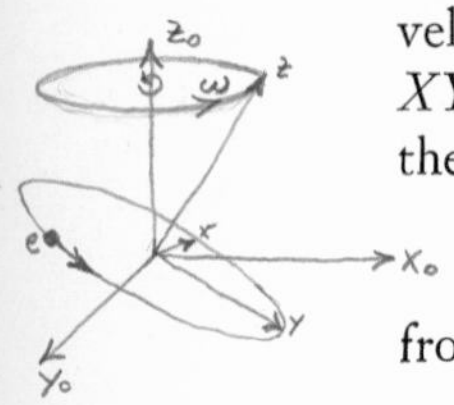

referred to axes $X_0Y_0Z_0$ fixed in an inertial system. If $\mathbf{v}$ is the velocity and $\mathbf{f}$ the acceleration of the electron relative to a set of axes XYZ rotating with constant angular velocity $\boldsymbol{\omega}$ about an axis through the common origin of the two sets of coordinate axes, then

$$\mathbf{v}_0 = \boldsymbol{\omega} \times \mathbf{r} + \mathbf{v}$$

from (31–8), and

$$\mathbf{f}_0 = \boldsymbol{\omega} \times (\boldsymbol{\omega} \times \mathbf{r}) + 2\boldsymbol{\omega} \times \mathbf{v} + \mathbf{f}$$

from (32–6). Therefore (165–1) may be written

$$m\boldsymbol{\omega} \times (\boldsymbol{\omega} \times \mathbf{r}) + 2m\boldsymbol{\omega} \times \mathbf{v} + m\mathbf{f} = e\left\{\mathbf{E} + \frac{1}{c}(\boldsymbol{\omega} \times \mathbf{r}) \times \mathbf{H} + \frac{1}{c}\mathbf{v} \times \mathbf{H}\right\}$$

or

$$m\mathbf{f} = e\mathbf{E} + 2m\mathbf{v} \times \left\{\boldsymbol{\omega} + \frac{e}{2mc}\mathbf{H}\right\} + m(\boldsymbol{\omega} \times \mathbf{r}) \times \left\{\boldsymbol{\omega} + \frac{e}{mc}\mathbf{H}\right\}.$$

If, now, we make

$$\boldsymbol{\omega} = -\frac{e}{2mc}\mathbf{H} \tag{165–2}$$

we have

$$\begin{aligned} m\mathbf{f} &= e\mathbf{E} - m\left\{\left(\frac{e}{2mc}\mathbf{H}\right) \times \mathbf{r}\right\} \times \left(\frac{e}{2mc}\mathbf{H}\right) \\ &= e\mathbf{E} \end{aligned} \tag{165–3}$$

to a sufficient degree of approximation, since even for the strongest fields available in the laboratory, the frequency $(e/2mc)H$ is so small compared with the normal angular frequency ω_0 that its square is negligible. But (165–3) is just the equation of motion which would exist relative to fixed axes in the absence of the magnetic field. Therefore in the magnetic field the electrons execute relative to axes rotating with the angular velocity (165–2) about the lines of force the same motions which they execute relative to fixed axes in the absence of the field. This is known as *Larmor's theorem*.

Suppose that the magnetic field is parallel to the X_0 axis (Fig. 161) and consider an electron which is executing simple harmonic oscillations of angular frequency ω_0 and amplitude A along the line OP. On account of the action of the field the path OP revolves around the X_0 axis with the angular velocity ω specified by (165–2).

The simple harmonic vibration under consideration may be resolved into three vibrations along the axes $X_0Y_0Z_0$ as follows:

$$x_0 = A \cos \omega_0 t \cos \theta,$$

$$y_0 = A \cos \omega_0 t \sin \theta \cos \omega t = \tfrac{1}{2}A \sin \theta \{\cos (\omega_0 - \omega)t + \cos (\omega_0 + \omega)t\},$$

$$z_0 = A \cos \omega_0 t \sin \theta \sin \omega t = \tfrac{1}{2}A \sin \theta \{- \sin (\omega_0 - \omega)t + \sin (\omega_0 + \omega)t\}.$$

Now

$$y_1 = \tfrac{1}{2}A \sin \theta \cos (\omega_0 - \omega)t,$$

$$z_1 = - \tfrac{1}{2}A \sin \theta \sin (\omega_0 - \omega)t,$$

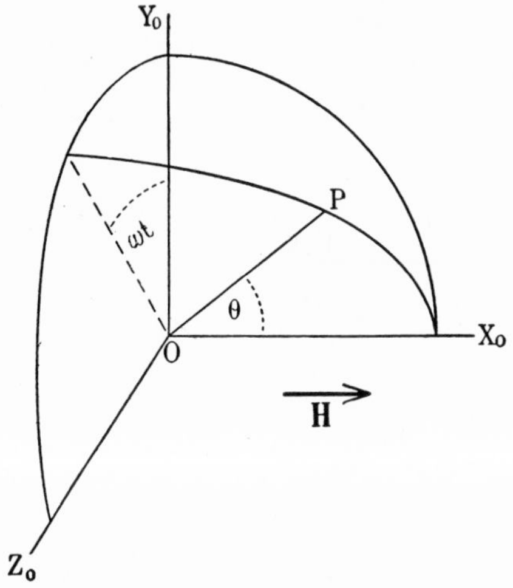

FIG. 161.

represents a circular vibration in the Y_0Z_0 plane of angular frequency $\omega_0 - \omega$ in the clockwise sense, and

$$y_2 = \tfrac{1}{2}A \sin \theta \cos (\omega_0 + \omega)t,$$

$$z_2 = \tfrac{1}{2}A \sin \theta \sin (\omega_0 + \omega)t,$$

a circular vibration of frequency $\omega_0 + \omega$ in the counter-clockwise sense. Putting in the value of ω given in (165–2) we find that we have resolved the original vibration into a linear vibration along the X_0 axis of frequency ν_0 equal to the normal frequency of the oscillator and two circular vibrations in the Y_0Z_0 plane of frequencies

$$\nu_1 = \nu_0 + \frac{e}{4\pi mc} H \qquad (165\text{–}4)$$

and

$$\nu_2 = \nu_0 - \frac{e}{4\pi mc} H \qquad (165\text{-}5)$$

respectively. While radiation is emitted in all directions as a result of the circular vibrations, we saw in the last article that a linear oscillator emits no radiation along its axis. Therefore no radiation of frequency ν_0 proceeds in the direction of the magnetic field.

The radiating atoms at the origin may be viewed from a point on the X_0 axis or from one in the Y_0Z_0 plane. The first method of viewing the radiation is known as *longitudinal observation*, the second as *transverse observation*. Let us consider longitudinal observation first. As the oscillations along the X_0 axis emit no radiation in this direction, the only lines observed in the spectroscope are circularly (c) polarized lines of frequencies ν_1 and ν_2. For transverse observation, on the other hand, three lines appear of frequencies ν_1, ν_0 and ν_2. These constitute the *normal Lorentz triplet*. The first and last are due to the projection perpendicular to the field of the circular vibrations in the Y_0Z_0 plane. Therefore, as shown in the previous article, they are plane polarized with the electric vector perpendicular to the magnetic field. Such lines are said to exhibit s(*senkrecht*) polarization. On the other hand the middle line is due to a linear

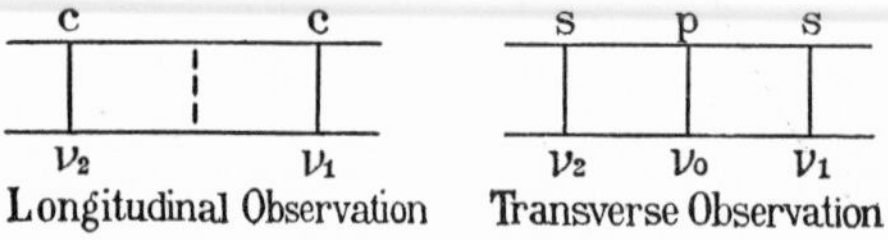

FIG. 162.

vibration parallel to the field. Hence it is plane polarized with the electric vector parallel to the lines of magnetic force, that is, the line is p(*parallel*) polarized. The spectra for both types of observation are indicated in the diagram in Fig. 162.

From the observed separation

$$\Delta\nu = \frac{e}{4\pi mc} H \qquad (165\text{-}6)$$

of the lines in the normal Lorentz triplet the ratio e/m may be calculated. This was one of the earliest methods of measuring this important constant.

Unfortunately the normal Lorentz triplet is observed only in the simplest spectra. The anomalous Zeeman pattern more frequently found consists of a greater number of lines with a different spacing. It is explained on quantum theory by the assumption that the electron has a spin.

166. Emission and Absorption by a Linear Oscillator. — The interaction between radiation and matter constitutes one of the most important of physical problems. So far we have studied some details of this interaction in our discussion of the characteristics of the electromagnetic waves emitted by an individual oscillating dipole. In this article and in the next we shall treat the problem from a statistical point of view, concerning ourselves with the mean emission and the mean absorption of energy by a large number of oscillators. Only through the agency of matter can energy be transferred from a group of electromagnetic waves of one frequency to a group of another frequency. If the matter present absorbs more rapidly than it emits radiation of a given frequency, it will gain energy from the radiation field, and vice versa. In this way it can transfer energy from radiation of one frequency to that of another.

The mean rate of radiation of a linear oscillator, obtained from (164–15) by giving the square of the cosine function its mean value one-half, is

$$\frac{dR}{dt} = \frac{\omega_0{}^4 e^2 A^2}{12\pi c^3} \tag{166–1}$$

in terms of the angular frequency $\omega_0 = 2\pi c/\lambda$. But the energy of the oscillator is

$$U = \tfrac{1}{2} m \omega_0{}^2 A^2 \tag{166–2}$$

from (26–6). So, in terms of the frequency $\nu_0 = \omega_0/2\pi$ of oscillation,

$$\frac{dR}{dt} = \frac{2\pi\nu_0{}^2}{3c^3}\frac{e^2}{m}U. \tag{166–3}$$

The mean rate of absorption of energy of a damped linear oscillator subject to a simple harmonic impressed force $ma \cos \omega t$ is

$$\frac{dU}{dt} = \frac{ma^2\omega^2 l}{(\kappa^2 - \omega^2)^2 + 4\omega^2 l^2} \tag{166-4}$$

from (27–17). If a linear electric oscillator free to vibrate in the Z direction is absorbing energy from a simple harmonic electromagnetic wave of angular frequency ω which is passing over it, the impressed force is

$$eE_z = eE_{0z} \cos \omega t$$

and the constant a has the value

$$a = \frac{eE_{0z}}{m}.$$

So (166–4) becomes

$$\frac{dU}{dt} = \frac{\frac{e^2}{m}\,\omega^2 l E_{0z}{}^2}{(\kappa^2 - \omega^2)^2 + 4\omega^2 l^2}. \tag{166-5}$$

Let $u_\nu d\nu$ be the energy of the radiation of frequencies between ν and $\nu + d\nu$ per unit volume. Then

$$u_\nu d\nu = \tfrac{1}{2}(\overline{E^2} + \overline{H^2}) = \overline{E^2} = 3\overline{E_z{}^2} = \tfrac{3}{2}E_{0z}{}^2$$

if equal amounts of energy are traveling in all directions. Consequently

$$\frac{dU}{dt} = \frac{\frac{2}{3}\frac{e^2}{m}\,\omega^2 l}{(\kappa^2 - \omega^2)^2 + 4\omega^2 l^2}\, u_\nu d\nu. \tag{166-6}$$

If the damping of the oscillator is small the rate of absorption is negligible except when the angular frequency ω of the radiation passing over the oscillator is nearly equal to its natural frequency $\omega_0 = \kappa$. Hence to get the total rate of absorption from waves of all frequencies passing over the oscillator we need integrate (166–6) only from $\kappa - \epsilon$ to $\kappa + \epsilon$, where ϵ is a quantity very small compared with κ but very large compared with l. So, putting $d\nu = d\omega/(2\pi)$ and $u_{\nu 0}$ for the value of u_ν in the neighborhood of the frequency $\kappa/(2\pi)$, we have

$$\text{Total}\,\frac{dU}{dt} = \frac{1}{3\pi}\frac{e^2}{m}\,u_{\nu 0}\int_{\kappa-\epsilon}^{\kappa+\epsilon}\frac{l\omega^2 d\omega}{(\kappa^2 - \omega^2)^2 + 4\omega^2 l^2}.$$

We may put κ for ω everywhere in the integrand except in the factor $\kappa - \omega$ in the denominator. Therefore

$$\frac{l\omega^2 d\omega}{(\kappa^2 - \omega^2)^2 + 4\omega^2 l^2} = \frac{l\kappa^2 d\omega}{4\kappa^2(\kappa - \omega)^2 + 4\kappa^2 l^2} = \frac{1}{4l}\frac{d\omega}{1 + \left(\frac{\kappa - \omega}{l}\right)^2}.$$

As the integrand has an appreciable value only in the range between $\kappa - \epsilon$ and $\kappa + \epsilon$ we make a negligible error if we replace $(\omega - \kappa)/l$ by x and integrate from $-\infty$ to ∞. Hence

$$\int_{\kappa-\epsilon}^{\kappa+\epsilon}\frac{l\omega^2 d\omega}{(\kappa^2 - \omega^2)^2 + 4\omega^2 l^2} = \frac{1}{4}\int_{-\infty}^{\infty}\frac{dx}{1 + x^2} = \frac{1}{4}\left|\tan^{-1}x\right|_{-\infty}^{\infty} = \frac{\pi}{4},$$

and the total mean rate of absorption is

$$\frac{dU}{dt} = \frac{1}{12}\frac{e^2}{m}u_{\nu_0}. \qquad (166\text{–}7)$$

167. Distribution of Energy in the Normal Radiation Spectrum.— Consider a cavity with perfectly reflecting walls. Inside the cavity we shall place a group of simple harmonic linear oscillators of all natural frequencies maintained at a temperature T. When equilibrium is reached between the oscillators and the radiation inside the cavity the mean rate of absorption of the former must equal their mean rate of emission. Hence

$$\frac{dU}{dt} = \frac{dR}{dt}$$

and from (166–7) and (166–3)

$$u_\nu = \frac{8\pi\nu^2}{c^3}U. \qquad (167\text{–}1)$$

On the principle of equipartition of energy of the classical theory

$$U = kT$$

from (98–6). Therefore

$$u_\nu = \frac{8\pi\nu^2 kT}{c^3}. \qquad (167\text{–}2)$$

This is known as the *Rayleigh-Jeans law*, and agrees well with experiment for long wave lengths or high temperatures. It cannot be right, however, for it implies an ever-increasing energy density as the frequency is increased, and an infinite total energy density u since

$$u = \int_0^\infty u_\nu d\nu = \frac{8\pi kT}{c^3}\int_0^\infty \nu^2 d\nu = \infty .$$

On the principle of partition of energy of the quantum theory

$$U = \frac{h\nu}{e^{h\nu/kT} - 1}$$

from (99–4) and

$$u_\nu = \frac{\dfrac{8\pi h\nu^3}{c^3}}{e^{h\nu/kT} - 1}. \qquad (167\text{–}3)$$

This law, proposed by Planck, fits the experimental curve over the whole range of frequencies. It reduces to the Rayleigh-Jeans law for $h\nu/(kT) << 1$, for then the denominator becomes approximately

$$e^{h\nu/kT} - 1 = 1 + \frac{h\nu}{kT} \ldots - 1 = \frac{h\nu}{kT}$$

and (167–3) reverts to (167–2).

As both the Rayleigh-Jeans law and Planck's law contain no reference to the mechanism of the oscillators with which the radiation is in equilibrium, the energy density of the radiation is independent of the nature of the matter with which it has been brought into equilibrium by the processes of absorption and emission. Such radiation is called *black radiation*, the curve showing the energy density per unit range of frequencies at any specified temperature plotted against the frequency being known as the *normal radiation spectrum*.

To find the total energy density from Planck's law we have

$$u = \int_0^\infty u_\nu d\nu = \frac{8\pi}{c^3}\int_0^\infty \frac{h\nu^3 d\nu}{e^{h\nu/kT} - 1}.$$

Put

$$x \equiv \frac{h\nu}{kT}, \quad dx = \frac{h}{kT}d\nu.$$

Then

$$u = \frac{8\pi k^4}{c^3 h^3} T^4 \int_0^\infty \frac{x^3 dx}{e^x - 1}.$$

Now

$$\int_0^\infty \frac{x^3 dx}{e^x - 1} = \int_0^\infty \frac{x^3 e^{-x} dx}{1 - e^{-x}} = \int_0^\infty x^3 dx (e^{-x} + e^{-2x} + e^{-3x} \ldots).$$

But, if we integrate by parts,

$$\int_0^\infty e^{-nx} x^3 dx = \left| -\frac{x^3}{n} e^{-nx} - \frac{3x^2}{n^2} e^{-nx} - \frac{6x}{n^3} e^{-nx} - \frac{6}{n^4} e^{-nx} \right|_0^\infty = \frac{6}{n^4}.$$

Consequently

$$\int_0^\infty \frac{x^3 dx}{e^x - 1} = 6\left(1 + \frac{1}{2^4} + \frac{1}{3^4} + \frac{1}{4^4} \ldots\right) = 6 \times 1.0823 \ldots = 6\left(\frac{\pi^4}{90}\right).$$

Therefore

$$u = aT^4 \tag{167–4}$$

where

$$a \equiv \frac{48 \times 1.0823\pi k^4}{c^3 h^3}. \tag{167–5}$$

This is the *Stefan-Boltzmann law*, which states that the total energy density of radiation in equilibrium with matter is proportional to the fourth power of the absolute temperature.

If we consider a range of wave lengths from λ to $\lambda + d\lambda$ corresponding to the range of frequencies from ν to $\nu + d\nu$, we have

$$\nu = \frac{c}{\lambda}, \qquad d\nu = -\frac{c}{\lambda^2} d\lambda,$$

and the energy density of radiation of wave lengths between λ and $\lambda + d\lambda$ is

$$u_\lambda d\lambda = -u_\nu d\nu = \frac{\dfrac{8\pi ch}{\lambda^5} d\lambda}{e^{ch/k\lambda T} - 1}.$$

Therefore the energy density per unit range of wave lengths is

$$u_\lambda = \frac{\dfrac{8\pi ch}{\lambda^5}}{e^{ch/k\lambda T} - 1}, \tag{167–6}$$

which is Planck's law expressed in terms of the wave length of the radiation instead of the frequency.

Let λ_m be the wave length for which u_λ is a maximum. Putting the derivative of u_λ with respect to λ equal to zero we find

$$e^{-\beta} + \frac{\beta}{5} - 1 = 0,$$

where β has been put for $ch/(k\lambda_m T)$. The solution of this equation is $\beta = 4.9651$. Therefore

$$\lambda_m T = b, \tag{167–7}$$

where

$$b \equiv \frac{ch}{4.9651k}, \tag{167–8}$$

This is known as *Wien's displacement law*. It shows that the wave length for which u_λ is a maximum becomes displaced toward the region of shorter wave lengths as the temperature is raised.

Experiment gives for the constants a and b appearing in the Stefan-Boltzmann law and Wien's displacement law respectively

$$a = 7.568(10)^{-15} \text{ erg/cm}^3 \ (1° \text{ C.})^4,$$

$$b = 0.2897 \text{ cm } 1° \text{ C.}$$

Solving (167–5) and (167–8) for h and k

$$h = 6.624(10)^{-27} \text{ erg sec},$$

$$k = 1.380(10)^{-16} \text{ erg}/1° \text{ C.}$$

From the latter we can calculate Avogadro's and Loschmidt's constants. For

$$pV = kNT$$

in the case of an ideal gas, from which it follows that one cubic centimeter of gas contains $2.687(10)^{19}$ molecules at 0° C. and one atmosphere pressure. As one gram molecule of gas occupies $2.241(10)^4$ cm^3 at 0° C. and one atmosphere pressure, Avogadro's constant is $6.023(10)^{23}$ molecules per gram molecule.

When a monovalent salt is ionized the charge carried by the ions of one sign per gram molecule of the salt is Faraday's constant 96490 coulombs. Hence the charge on a monovalent ion or electron is

$$e = \frac{96490}{6.023(10)^{23}} \text{ coulomb} = 4.803(10)^{-10} \text{e.s.u.}$$

in agreement with the value obtained by the oil drop method.

Problem 167a. Show that the energy density of black radiation of a specified range of wave lengths is greater at a given temperature T than at any lower temperature.

Problem 167b. Find the temperatures for which λ_m falls in the red [$7(10)^{-5}$ cm] and in the blue [$4.5(10)^{-5}$ cm] portions of the visible spectrum. *Ans.* 4100°, 6400°.

Problem 167c. Find the total energy density of black radiation of temperature 5000°. *Ans.* 4.8 erg/cm³.

REFERENCES

MAXWELL, J. CLERK: *A Treatise on Electricity and Magnetism*, Clarendon Press, Oxford.

ABRAHAM AND BECKER: *Electricity and Magnetism*, Blackie & Son, London.

PAGE AND ADAMS: *Electrodynamics*, D. Van Nostrand Co., New York.

LORENTZ, H. A.: *The Theory of Electrons*, B. G. Teubner, Leipzig.

RICHARDSON, O. W.: *The Electron Theory of Matter*, Cambridge University Press, Cambridge.

RICE, J.: *Relativity*, Longmans, Green & Co., London.

EDDINGTON, A. S.: *The Mathematical Theory of Relativity*, Cambridge University Press, Cambridge.

PART V

OPTICS AND SPECTROSCOPY

CHAPTER XIII

GEOMETRICAL OPTICS

168. Refraction at a Plane Surface. — About 1680 Huygens enunciated the principle that each point on a wave front may be considered as a new center of disturbance from which spherical wavelets spread out. Let MN (Fig. 163) be the trace of the plane interface between two media of indices of refraction n_1 and n_2. Let AB be a wave-front passing from the first into the second of these media. Considering the points A and B as secondary sources a wavelet from B reaches D in the time required for a wavelet from A to reach C, where

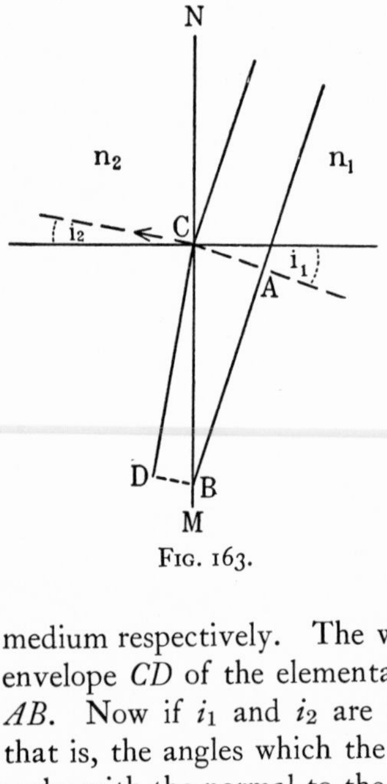

Fig. 163.

$$\frac{AC}{BD} = \frac{v_1}{v_2} = \frac{n_2}{n_1},$$

v_1 and v_2 being the velocities of propagation in the first and second medium respectively. The wave-front in the second medium is the envelope CD of the elementary wavelets proceeding from points on AB. Now if i_1 and i_2 are the angles of incidence and refraction, that is, the angles which the incident and refracted ray respectively make with the normal to the surface,

$$\frac{AC}{BD} = \frac{BC \sin i_1}{BC \sin i_2} = \frac{\sin i_1}{\sin i_2}.$$

Therefore we have *Snell's law*

$$n_1 \sin i_1 = n_2 \sin i_2, \qquad (168\text{–}1)$$

which was known empirically before it was deduced from theory. It should be noted that Huygens' principle, in the form in which it was originally stated, is only a partial representation of the facts, for it fails to explain why the secondary centers of disturbance do not in all cases give rise to waves traveling backwards as well as forwards.

We shall consider a couple of applications of Snell's law to refraction at plane surfaces. First consider a slab of thickness t (Fig. 164) with parallel faces in a medium of index of refraction n_1. If n_2 is the index of refraction of the slab,

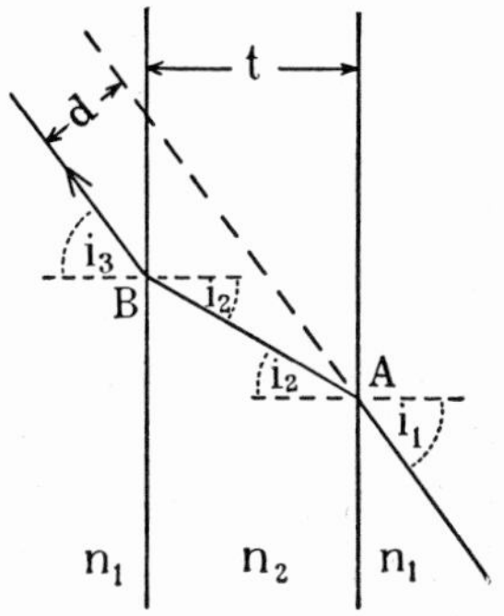

FIG. 164.

$$n_1 \sin i_1 = n_2 \sin i_2$$

for the first refraction, and

$$n_2 \sin i_2 = n_1 \sin i_3$$

for the second. Therefore the angle of emergence i_3 is equal to the angle of incidence i_1 and the emergent ray is parallel to the incident ray. It is, however, displaced a distance

$$d = AB \sin (i_1 - i_2) = t \frac{\sin (i_1 - i_2)}{\cos i_2}. \qquad (168\text{–}2)$$

Next consider radiation originating in the medium of greater index of refraction. As

$$\sin i_2 = \frac{n_1}{n_2} \sin i_1$$

by Snell's law, $\sin i_2$ becomes unity for a value of $\sin i_1$ less than unity if $n_1 > n_2$ and the refracted ray lies parallel to the interface. For angles of incidence greater than the critical angle $\sin^{-1} (n_2/n_1)$ transmission cannot occur and the radiation is totally reflected. If, for instance, one's eye is located under water at E (Fig. 165) one sees the region outside compressed inside the cone AEB. Outside this cone one receives light from below which has been totally reflected at the surface.

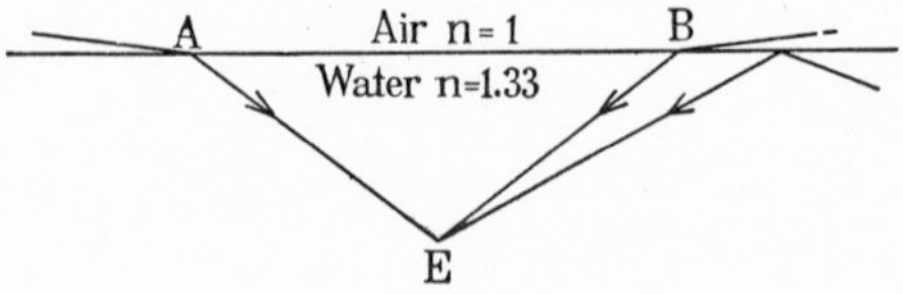

FIG. 165.

169. Refraction at a Spherical Surface. — Let OB (Fig. 166) be the trace of a spherical surface separating a medium of index of refraction n_1 on the right from one of index of refraction n_2 on the left. We shall take the radius of curvature r of the surface to be positive if the center of curvature C is to the right of the vertex O. Light coming from a point object P on the axis is refracted at the

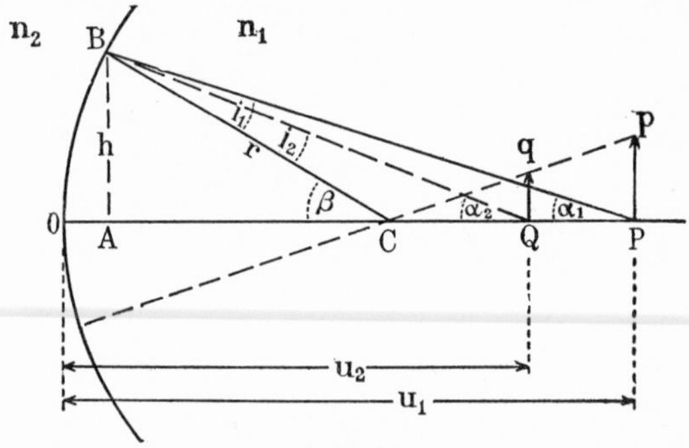

FIG. 166.

surface so as to appear to come from the image Q. We shall take the object distance u_1 or the image distance u_2 to be positive when the object or image respectively lies to the right of the refracting surface. Then a positive image distance signifies that the image is *virtual*, that is, to an observer at the left of the surface rays of light proceeding from P are so modified as to appear to come from Q although they do not actually pass through Q. On the other hand a negative image distance indicates that the image lies to the left of the refracting surface. Such an image is called a *real image*, as the rays of light actually pass through it after refraction.

If i_1 and i_2 are the angles of incidence and refraction of a ray passing through the surface at B

$$n_1 \sin i_1 = n_2 \sin i_2$$

from Snell's law (168–1). As $i_2 = -i_1$ at a reflecting surface the theory of reflecting surfaces is obtained from the more general theory of refracting surfaces by making $n_2 = -n_1$.

First we shall consider the simple case where the radius H of the aperture of the surface is small compared with r, u_1 and u_2. Then i_1 and i_2 are small angles and we can write Snell's law in the approximate form

$$n_1 i_1 = n_2 i_2.$$

Therefore

$$n_1(\beta - \alpha_1) = n_2(\beta - \alpha_2),$$

or

$$n_2\alpha_2 - n_1\alpha_1 = \beta(n_2 - n_1).$$

But

$$\alpha_2 \doteqdot \frac{OB}{u_2}, \quad \alpha_1 \doteqdot \frac{OB}{u_1}, \quad \beta = \frac{OB}{r}.$$

Consequently

$$\frac{n_2}{u_2} - \frac{n_1}{u_1} = \frac{n_2 - n_1}{r}. \qquad (169\text{–}1)$$

The focal length f_2 of the image space is the value of u_2 when $u_1 = \infty$, that is, the image distance for an infinitely distant object. Similarly the focal length f_1 of the object space is the value of u_1 when $u_2 = \infty$. Hence

$$\frac{f_2}{n_2} = -\frac{f_1}{n_1} = \frac{r}{n_2 - n_1},$$

and (169–1) may be written

$$\frac{n_2}{u_2} - \frac{n_1}{u_1} = \frac{n_2}{f_2} = -\frac{n_1}{f_1}. \qquad (169\text{–}2)$$

If instead of a point object we have an object Pp of finite size we can find the transverse magnification by taking a ray from p through the center of curvature C. Such a ray strikes the surface normally and therefore suffers no deviation on refraction. Consequently the image q of p lies on the line pC and the magnification is

$$M = \frac{Qq}{Pp} = \frac{u_2 - r}{u_1 - r} = \frac{u_2\left(\frac{1}{u_2} - \frac{1}{r}\right)}{u_1\left(\frac{1}{u_1} - \frac{1}{r}\right)} = \frac{n_1 u_2}{n_2 u_1} \qquad (169\text{–}3)$$

from (169–1).

Now we shall deduce a relation between image distance and object distance more exact than (169–1). From Snell's law and the geometry of Fig. 166 we have

$$\frac{n_2}{n_1} = \frac{\sin i_1}{\sin i_2} = \frac{\dfrac{\sin i_1}{\sin(\pi - \beta)}}{\dfrac{\sin i_2}{\sin(\pi - \beta)}} = \frac{\dfrac{CP}{BP}}{\dfrac{CQ}{BQ}} = \frac{CP}{CQ}\cdot\frac{BQ}{BP} = \frac{u_1 - r}{u_2 - r}\cdot\frac{BQ}{BP},$$

and therefore

$$n_2\left(\frac{1}{r} - \frac{1}{u_2}\right)\frac{u_2}{BQ} = n_1\left(\frac{1}{r} - \frac{1}{u_1}\right)\frac{u_1}{BP}. \tag{169–4}$$

If we approximate by putting $BQ = u_2$ and $BP = u_1$ we are led to (169–1) again. But exactly

$$\begin{aligned} \overline{BP}^2 &= r^2 + (u_1 - r)^2 + 2r(u_1 - r)\cos\beta \\ &= u_1^2 - 2r(u_1 - r)(1 - \cos\beta) \\ &= u_1^2\left\{1 - 4\frac{r}{u_1}\left(1 - \frac{r}{u_1}\right)\sin^2\frac{\beta}{2}\right\}, \end{aligned} \tag{169–5}$$

and

$$\overline{BQ}^2 = u_2^2\left\{1 - 4\frac{r}{u_2}\left(1 - \frac{r}{u_2}\right)\sin^2\frac{\beta}{2}\right\}. \tag{169–6}$$

Except for the trivial case where the object is placed at the center of curvature,

$$\frac{BP}{BQ} = \frac{u_1}{u_2}$$

for all values of β only when

$$\frac{r}{u_1} + \frac{r}{u_2} = 1. \tag{169–7}$$

Only for this one position of the object is (169–1) exact. The object distance for this position, found by eliminating u_2 from (169–7) and (169–1), is

$$u_1 = \frac{n_1 + n_2}{n_1}\,r \tag{169–8}$$

and the image distance

$$u_2 = \frac{n_1 + n_2}{n_2}\,r. \tag{169–9}$$

Therefore the magnification is

$$M = \frac{u_2 - r}{u_1 - r} = \left(\frac{n_1}{n_2}\right)^2. \tag{169–10}$$

In general we can obtain a second approximation by putting $h/(2r)$ for $\sin \beta/2$ in (169–5) and (169–6). Then

$$\frac{u_1}{BP} = 1 + \left(\frac{1}{r} - \frac{1}{u_1}\right)\frac{h^2}{2u_1},$$

$$\frac{u_2}{BQ} = 1 + \left(\frac{1}{r} - \frac{1}{u_2}\right)\frac{h^2}{2u_2},$$

and (169–4) becomes

$$n_2\left(\frac{1}{r} - \frac{1}{u_2}\right) + n_2\left(\frac{1}{r} - \frac{1}{u_2}\right)^2\frac{h^2}{2u_2} = n_1\left(\frac{1}{r} - \frac{1}{u_1}\right) + n_1\left(\frac{1}{r} - \frac{1}{u_1}\right)^2\frac{h^2}{2u_1}$$

or

$$\frac{n_2}{u_2} - \frac{n_1}{u_1} = \frac{n_2 - n_1}{r} + \frac{h^2}{2}\left\{\frac{n_2}{u_2}\left(\frac{1}{r} - \frac{1}{u_2}\right)^2 - \frac{n_1}{u_1}\left(\frac{1}{r} - \frac{1}{u_1}\right)^2\right\}.$$

Eliminating u_2 from the right-hand side by means of the first approximation (169–1) we get

$$\frac{n_2}{u_2} - \frac{n_1}{u_1} = \frac{n_2 - n_1}{r} + \frac{h^2}{2}\frac{n_2 - n_1}{n_2^2}\left\{\frac{n_1^2}{r} - \frac{n_1(n_2+n_1)}{u_1}\right\}\left(\frac{1}{r} - \frac{1}{u_1}\right)^2. \tag{169–11}$$

Consequently the image of a point source is not a point but a short line parallel to the axis. Its ends are given by making h equal to 0 and H in (169–11). This phenomenon is known as *longitudinal spherical aberration*. Spherical aberration is measured quantitatively by the difference between the focal length f' for the marginal ray and the focal length f for the axial ray.

Problem 169a. Write down formulae (169–1) and (169–11) for a spherical mirror. A concave mirror has a radius of curvature of 20 cm and an aperture of 10 cm diameter. Find its focal length and spherical aberration, and plot u_2 and M against u_1. *Ans.* $f = 10$ cm, $f' - f = -0.31$ cm.

170. The Thin Lens. — In this article we shall confine our attention to a lens so thin that the vertices of the two surfaces may be considered to be practically coincident. Denote by n the index of refraction of the lens relative to the medium outside, that is, the ratio of the index of refraction of the material of the lens to that of the air surrounding it. Let P_1 (Fig. 167) be the object, P' the image formed by the first refraction which serves as object for the second refraction, and P_2 the image of P' due to the second refraction. Then if r_1 is the radius of curvature of the first refracting surface we have

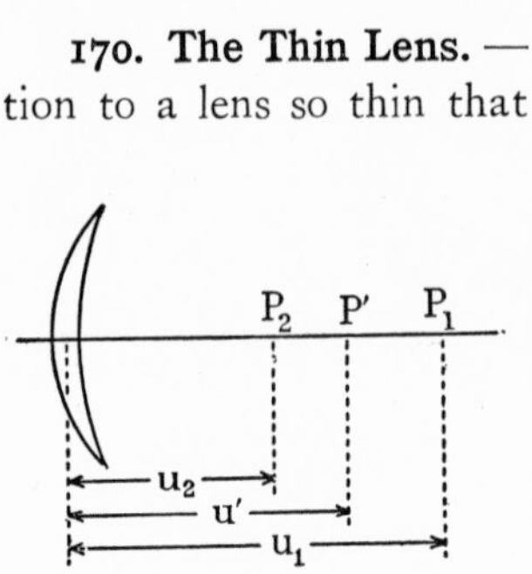

FIG. 167.

$$\frac{n}{u'} - \frac{1}{u_1} = \frac{n-1}{r_1}$$

from (169–1) as $n_2/n_1 = n$. Similarly if r_2 is the radius of curvature of the second surface

$$\frac{1}{u_2} - \frac{n}{u'} = \frac{1-n}{r_2}.$$

Adding

$$\frac{1}{u_2} - \frac{1}{u_1} = (n-1)\left(\frac{1}{r_1} - \frac{1}{r_2}\right). \qquad (170\text{–}1)$$

The focal length f of the image space obtained by putting $u_1 = \infty$ is given by

$$\frac{1}{f} = (n-1)\left(\frac{1}{r_1} - \frac{1}{r_2}\right), \qquad (170\text{–}2)$$

and (170–1) may be written

$$\frac{1}{u_2} - \frac{1}{u_1} = \frac{1}{f}. \qquad (170\text{–}3)$$

The reciprocal of the focal length is known as the *power* of the lens.

Denote the heights of object, intermediate and final images by y_1, y' and y_2 respectively. From (169–3) the magnification for the first refraction is

$$M_1 = \frac{y'}{y_1} = \frac{1}{n}\frac{u'}{u_1}$$

and that for the second

$$M_2 = \frac{y_2}{y'} = n\frac{u_2}{u'}.$$

Therefore the magnification of the lens is

$$M = \frac{y_2}{y_1} = \frac{u_2}{u_1}. \qquad (170\text{–}4)$$

We have the following types of lens.

I. *Divergent Lens.*—The focal length is positive. This occurs whenever the lens is thinner at the center than at the edge. Writing (170–3) in the form

$$\frac{1}{u_2} = \frac{1}{u_1} + \frac{1}{f}$$

we see that, as u_1 is essentially positive, u_2 is always positive. The image is always on the right-hand side of the lens and hence virtual. As the magnification is positive the image is erect.

II. *Convergent Lens.*—The focal length is negative. The condition for this is that the lens should be thicker at the center than at the edge. Putting f_0 for $-f$, (170–3) becomes

$$\frac{1}{u_2} = \frac{1}{u_1} - \frac{1}{f_0}.$$

So u_2 is positive if $u_1 < f_0$ and negative if $u_1 > f_0$. In the first case M is positive and the image is virtual and erect; in the second case M is negative and the image is real and inverted.

If we develop the preceding theory over again, taking account of spherical aberration, we must replace the equation for the first refraction by

$$\frac{n}{u'} - \frac{1}{u_1} = \frac{n-1}{r_1} + \frac{h^2}{2}\frac{n-1}{n^2}\left\{\frac{1}{r_1} - \frac{n+1}{u_1}\right\}\left(\frac{1}{r_1} - \frac{1}{u_1}\right)^2$$

from (169–11), and that for the second refraction by

$$\frac{1}{u_2} - \frac{n}{u'} = -\frac{n-1}{r_2} - \frac{h^2}{2}\frac{n-1}{1}\left\{\frac{n^2}{r_2} - \frac{n(n+1)}{u'}\right\}\left(\frac{1}{r_2} - \frac{1}{u'}\right)^2$$

$$= -\frac{n-1}{r_2} - \frac{h^2}{2}\frac{n-1}{n^2}\left\{\frac{1}{r_2} - \frac{n+1}{u_2}\right\}\left(\frac{1}{r_2} - \frac{1}{u_2}\right)^2.$$

Adding

$$\frac{1}{u_2}-\frac{1}{u_1}=(n-1)\left(\frac{1}{r_1}-\frac{1}{r_2}\right)+\frac{h^2}{2}\frac{n-1}{n^2}\left\{\left(\frac{1}{r_1}-\frac{n+1}{u_1}\right)\left(\frac{1}{r_1}-\frac{1}{u_1}\right)^2\right.$$
$$\left.-\left(\frac{1}{r_2}-\frac{n+1}{u_2}\right)\left(\frac{1}{r_2}-\frac{1}{u_2}\right)^2\right\}. \qquad (170\text{–}5)$$

Making $u_1=\infty$ to find the focal length we have

$$\frac{1}{f}=(n-1)\left(\frac{1}{r_1}-\frac{1}{r_2}\right)+\frac{h^2}{2}\frac{n-1}{n^2}\left\{\frac{1}{r_1{}^3}-\left(\frac{1}{r_2}-\frac{n+1}{f}\right)\left(\frac{1}{r_2}-\frac{1}{f}\right)^2\right\}, \qquad (170\text{–}6)$$

and the difference between the focal length f' for the marginal ray and the focal length f for the axial ray is

$$f'-f=\left(\frac{1}{f}-\frac{1}{f'}\right)ff'=-\frac{H^2f^2}{2}\frac{n-1}{n^2}\left\{\frac{1}{r_1{}^3}-\left(\frac{1}{r_2}-\frac{n+1}{f}\right)\left(\frac{1}{r_2}-\frac{1}{f}\right)^2\right\}. \qquad (170\text{–}7)$$

This is the measure of the spherical aberration of the lens. By means of a combination of lenses spherical aberration can be elimi-

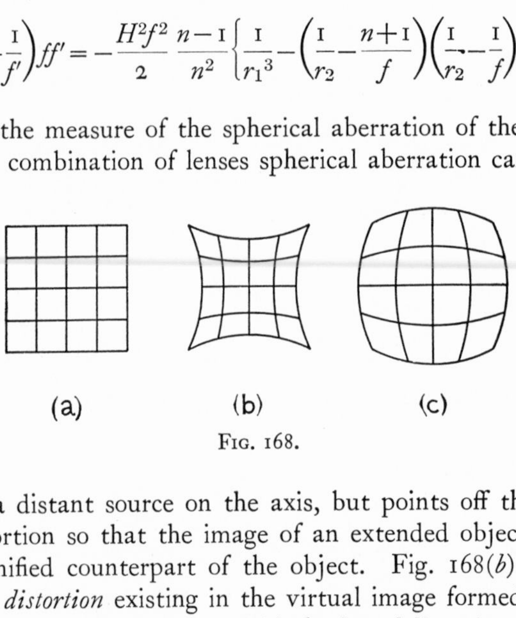

FIG. 168.

nated for a distant source on the axis, but points off the axis still suffer distortion so that the image of an extended object is not an exact magnified counterpart of the object. Fig. 168(*b*) shows the *pincushion distortion* existing in the virtual image formed by a convergent lens of the object (*a*), and (*c*) the *barrel distortion* produced in the real image of (*a*) formed by a convergent lens.

Let us investigate the design of a single lens so as to reduce spherical aberration to a minimum. If we put

$$C_1\equiv\frac{1}{r_1},\quad C_2\equiv\frac{1}{r_2},\quad \phi\equiv\frac{1}{f}$$

or the curvatures of the two faces of the lens and for its power espectively, (170–2) becomes

$$\phi = (n - 1)(C_1 - C_2), \tag{170-8}$$

and (170–7) for the spherical aberration

$$f' - f = -\frac{H^2 f^2}{2}\frac{n-1}{n^2}[C_1^3 - \{C_2 - (n+1)\phi\}(C_2 - \phi)^2]. \tag{170-9}$$

Put

$$J \equiv C_1^3 - \{C_2 - (n+1)\phi\}(C_2 - \phi)^2.$$

Eliminating C_1 by (170–8)

$$J = \left(C_2 + \frac{\phi}{n-1}\right)^3 - \{C_2 - (n+1)\phi\}(C_2 - \phi)^2$$

$$= C_2^2\phi\left\{\frac{n(n+2)}{n-1}\right\} - C_2\phi^2\left\{\frac{n(2n^2-n-4)}{(n-1)^2}\right\} + \phi^3\left\{\frac{n(n^3-2n^2+2)}{(n-1)^3}\right\}.$$

The discriminant of the quadratic in C_2 obtained by equating J to zero is $n^2(1 - 4n)$. As n for actual lenses is always greater han unity J cannot be made to vanish and therefore spherical berration cannot be eliminated in a single lens. To find the condiion for minimum spherical aberration we differentiate J with respect o C_2 and equate to zero getting

$$2C_2\phi\left\{\frac{n(n+2)}{n-1}\right\} - \phi^2\left\{\frac{n(2n^2-n-4)}{(n-1)^2}\right\} = 0.$$

Therefore

$$C_2 = \frac{\phi}{2}\frac{2n^2 - n - 4}{(n+2)(n-1)},$$

$$C_1 = C_2 + \frac{\phi}{n-1} = \frac{\phi}{2}\frac{2n^2 + n}{(n+2)(n-1)},$$

nd the radii of curvature are

$$\left.\begin{aligned} r_1 &= 2f\frac{(n+2)(n-1)}{2n^2+n}, \\ r_2 &= 2f\frac{(n+2)(n-1)}{2n^2-n-4}. \end{aligned}\right\} \tag{170-10}$$

If $n > 1$, r_1 must have the same sign as f, and if $n = 1.5$ (glass) r_2 must have the opposite sign to f. If the lens is convergent, then it should be double convex. As

$$\frac{r_2}{r_1} = \frac{n(2n + 1)}{2n^2 - n - 4}$$

it follows that $r_2 = -6r_1$ for glass. Therefore a glass lens used to form an image of a distant object should be nearly plano-convex for minimum spherical aberration, with the convex face toward the distant source.

Problem 170a. A thin double convex glass lens ($n = 1.5$) has radii of curvature of 20 cm and 30 cm. Find the focal length and plot u_2 and M against u_1. The object moves away from the lens along the axis at the rate of 100 cm/sec. Plot the velocity of the image against u_1 and note that the image always moves in the same direction as the object. *Ans.* $f = -24$ cm

Problem 170b. Each face of a thin double convex glass lens ($n = 1.5$) has a radius of curvature of 10 cm. The aperture of the lens is 8 cm in diameter. Find the focal length and the spherical aberration. *Ans.* -10 cm, 2.67 cm.

171. Helmholtz's Law. — Turning back to Fig. 166 we get from the law of sines

$$\frac{\sin i_1}{\sin \alpha_1} = \frac{CP}{CB}, \quad \frac{\sin i_2}{\sin \alpha_2} = \frac{CQ}{CB}.$$

Therefore

$$\frac{CP \sin \alpha_1}{\sin i_1} = \frac{CQ \sin \alpha_2}{\sin i_2}.$$

Multiplying by the equation (168–1) representing Snell's law

$$n_1 CP \sin \alpha_1 = n_2 CQ \sin \alpha_2. \qquad (171\text{–}1)$$

If we designate the heights Pp and Qq of object and image respectively by y_1 and y_2 we have

$$\frac{y_1}{CP} = \frac{y_2}{CQ}. \qquad (171\text{–}2)$$

Multiplying by (171–1) we get

$$n_1 y_1 \sin \alpha_1 = n_2 y_2 \sin \alpha_2. \qquad (171\text{–}3)$$

Consider $k - 1$ centered spherical refracting surfaces, that is, spherical surfaces with centers on a common axis. Then

$$n_1 y_1 \sin \alpha_1 = n_2 y_2 \sin \alpha_2,$$

$$n_2 y_2 \sin \alpha_2 = n_3 y_3 \sin \alpha_3,$$

$$\cdots\cdots\cdots$$

$$n_{k-1} y_{k-1} \sin \alpha_{k-1} = n_k y_k \sin \alpha_k.$$

Consequently

$$n_1 y_1 \sin \alpha_1 = n_k y_k \sin \alpha_k. \qquad (171\text{–}4)$$

This is Helmholtz's law. If the angles $\alpha_1 \ldots \alpha_k$ are small we can write

$$n_1 y_1 \alpha_1 = n_k y_k \alpha_k. \qquad (171\text{–}5)$$

172. Centered System of Spherical Refracting Surfaces. — Consider a centered system of $k - 1$ spherical refracting surfaces as illustrated in Fig. 169. Denote the radii of curvature of the surfaces

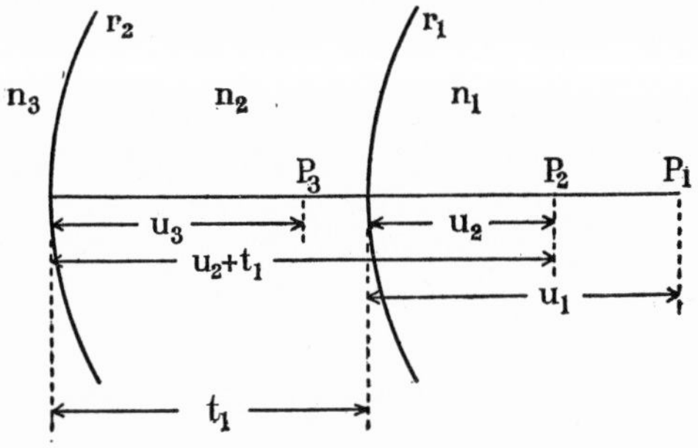

FIG. 169.

by r_1, $r_2 \ldots r_{k-1}$, the distances between successive surfaces by t_1, $t_2 \ldots t_{k-2}$, and the indices of refraction of the successive media by n_1, $n_2 \ldots n_k$. Let P_1 be a point object, P_2 its image formed by the first refraction, P_3 that due to the second refraction, and so on to the final image P_k. As indicated in the diagram we shall designate the distances of P_1 and P_2 from the vertex of the first surface by u_1 and u_2, the distance of P_3 from the vertex of the second surface by u_3

and so forth. As usual all distances are measured positive to the right. Then if we neglect spherical aberration, we have from (169–1)

$$\left.\begin{aligned} \frac{n_2}{u_2} - \frac{n_1}{u_1} &= \frac{n_2 - n_1}{r_1}, \\ \frac{n_3}{u_3} - \frac{n_2}{u_2 + t_1} &= \frac{n_3 - n_2}{r_2}, \\ \cdots\cdots & \\ \frac{n_k}{u_k} - \frac{n_{k-1}}{u_{k-1} + t_{k-2}} &= \frac{n_k - n_{k-1}}{r_{k-1}}. \end{aligned}\right\} \quad (172\text{–}1)$$

If we clear of fractions each of these equations is of the form

$$u_{p+1}u_p + au_{p+1} + bu_p + c = 0.$$

Now consider two successive equations of this form, such as

$$u_3u_2 + a_2u_3 + b_2u_2 + c_2 = 0,$$

$$u_4u_3 + a_3u_4 + b_3u_3 + c_3 = 0.$$

If we eliminate u_3 we get

$$\frac{b_2u_2 + c_2}{u_2 + a_2} = \frac{a_3u_4 + c_3}{u_4 + b_3}.$$

When we clear of fractions this equation has the same form

$$u_4u_2 + au_4 + bu_2 + c = 0$$

as the equations with which we started. So if we eliminate $u_2 \ldots u_{k-1}$ from the $k - 1$ equations (172–1) we get a relation between u_k and u_1 of the form

$$u_ku_1 + au_k + bu_1 + c = 0. \quad (172\text{–}2)$$

If we differentiate the equation describing a single refraction, such as the first of (172–1), we get

$$\frac{du_2}{du_1} = \frac{n_1u_2^2}{n_2u_1^2}.$$

As the right-hand side is always positive, any displacement of the object results in a displacement of its image in the same direction. As the image produced by one refraction serves as object for the next refraction, the same relation must hold between displacements f the final image P_k formed by the system of centered spherical efracting surfaces and the initial object P_1. From (172–2)

$$\frac{du_k}{du_1} = -\frac{u_k + b}{u_1 + a} = \frac{c - ab}{(u_1 + a)^2},$$

nd as the derivative is positive, $c - ab > 0$. So if we write (172–2) 1 the form

$$u_k u_1 + a u_k + b u_1 + ab = -(c - ab)$$

he expression inside parentheses on the right is positive.

As we shall have no further occasion to refer to the regions etween successive refracting surfaces we shall change our notation o the extent of employing the subscript 2 in place of k to refer to the nal image space. Then, putting $a \equiv - v_1$, $b \equiv - v_2$, $c - ab \equiv e^2$, ve have

$$(u_2 - v_2)(u_1 - v_1) = - e^2. \qquad (172\text{–}3)$$

When $u_1 = \infty$, $u_2 = v_2$. Therefore v_2 is the distance of the oint where parallel light converges after passing through the lens ystem from the vertex of the last refracting surface. This point is nown as the *principal focus* of the image space, and the plane through t perpendicular to the axis as the *focal plane*. Similarly the principal ocus of the object space is distant v_1 from the vertex of the first efracting surface.

Let F_1 and F_2 (Fig. 170) be the principal foci of object space and mage space respectively. Let H_1 be a point on the axis of the lens

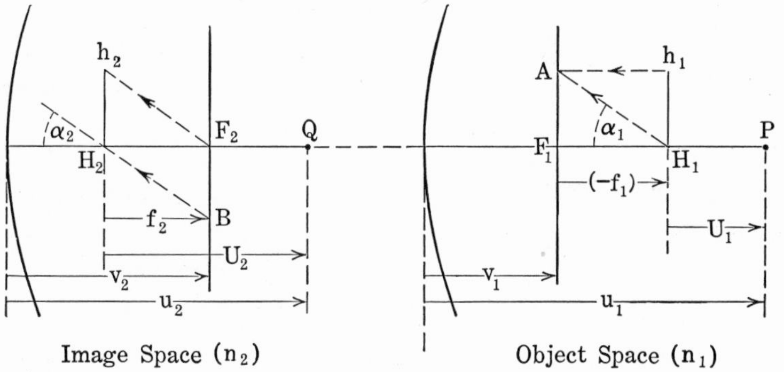

FIG. 170.

ystem and H_2 its final image. Instead of measuring focal lengths, bject and image distances from the first and last refracting surface, we shall measure the distances of points in the object space from H and those in the image space from H_2. If f_1 and f_2 are the distance of F_1 and F_2 from H_1 and H_2 respectively, and U_1 and U_2 the dis tances of a point P and its image Q from H_1 and H_2, we see from th figure that $u_2 - v_2 = U_2 - f_2$ and $u_1 - v_1 = U_1 + (-f_1)$. Henc (172–3) becomes

$$(U_2 - f_2)(U_1 - f_1) = - e^2. \qquad (172\text{–}4$$

Now if P coincides with H_1, Q coincides with the image H_2 of H and $U_1 = U_2 = 0$. Consequently $f_1 f_2 = - e^2$, showing that f_1 an f_2 are always of opposite sign, as represented on the figure. Replac ing $-e^2$ by $f_1 f_2$, the relation between image distance and objec distance becomes

$$(U_2 - f_2)(U_1 - f_1) = f_1 f_2$$

or

$$\frac{f_2}{U_2} + \frac{f_1}{U_1} = 1. \qquad (172\text{–}5$$

So far we have taken H_1 as an arbitrary point. Now let us plac it in such a position that the image $H_2 h_2$ of the extended objec $H_1 h_1$ has the same size as the object itself, that is, the magnificatio is unity. If then BH_2 is the course in the image space of the ra $H_1 A$, it follows from Helmholtz's law (171–5) that

$$n_1 \alpha_1 = n_2 \alpha_2,$$

where we have used n_1 and n_2 for the indices of refraction in the objec and image spaces respectively. Consider the ray $h_1 A$. As it i parallel to the axis it must pass through F_2 in the image space. Als as it goes through h_1 it must pass through the image h_2 of h_1. There fore it has the course $F_2 h_2$ in the image space. Now since the ray $H_1 A$ and $h_1 A$ proceed from a point A in the focal plane of the objec space their paths BH_2 and $F_2 h_2$ in the image space are paralle Consequently

$$f_2 \alpha_2 = H_2 h_2 = H_1 h_1 = (-f_1)\alpha_1.$$

Comparing with the last equation we get

$$n_2 f_1 = - n_1 f_2. \qquad (172\text{–}6$$

The points H_1 and H_2 are called the *principal points* of the syster of centered refracting surfaces, or, on account of the unit magnifica tion, *unit points*.

If the index of refraction of the image space is the same as that of ıe object space, as is generally the case, $f_1 = -f_2$ and (172–5) reduces) the same formula

$$\frac{1}{U_2} - \frac{1}{U_1} = \frac{1}{f_2} \tag{172-7}$$

s (170–3) for a thin lens. The focal length f_2 in this case is known s the *equivalent focal length* of the lens system.

To find the magnification consider a ray from P passing through ı. The angle α_1' which it makes with the axis is H_1h_1/U_1. This ıy, after refraction, passes through Q and h_2, since these points are ıe images of P and h_1 respectively, and the angle α_2' which it makes ith the axis is H_2h_2/U_2. So as $H_2h_2 = H_1h_1$ it follows that

$$\frac{\alpha_1'}{\alpha_2'} = \frac{U_2}{U_1}.$$

Therefore the magnification is

$$M = \frac{y_2}{y_1} = \frac{n_1\alpha_1'}{n_2\alpha_2'} = \frac{n_1U_2}{n_2U_1} \tag{172-8}$$

om Helmholtz's law (171–5). If $n_2 = n_1$ this reduces to the same ormula

$$M = \frac{U_2}{U_1} \tag{172-9}$$

s (170–4) for a thin lens.

Let $U_1 = f_1 + f_2$. Then $U_2 = f_1 + f_2$ from (172–5) and the ıagnification is

$$M = \frac{n_1\alpha_1'}{n_2\alpha_2'} = \frac{n_1}{n_2}$$

om (172–8). Therefore $\alpha_1' = \alpha_2'$. The points so defined are alled *nodal points*. One is the image of the other, and a ray of light ırough the one at an angle α with the axis passes through the other ne at the same angle. If $n_1 = n_2$, $f_1 = -f_2$ and the nodal points oincide with the principal points.

The principal points, principal foci and nodal points are known s the *cardinal points* of the centered optical system. The planes ırough these points perpendicular to the axis are called *principal lanes* or *unit planes*, *focal planes* and *nodal planes* respectively.

The existence of the cardinal points of a lens system was first pointe out by Gauss.

To locate the cardinal points of a lens system in which $n_2 = n$ we may proceed as follows. By finding the image of a distant objec first with one end of the lens system turned toward it and then wit the other, we locate the principal foci F_1 and F_2. To find the equiv alent focal length $f = f_2 = -f_1$, form an image of a nearby objec and then displace the lens system a distance d until an image is forme again in the same plane. Measure the magnification in each case Then if letters without primes refer to the first case and with prime to the second,

$$\frac{1}{U_2} - \frac{1}{U_1} = \frac{1}{f}, \qquad M = \frac{U_2}{U_1};$$

$$\frac{1}{U_2'} - \frac{1}{U_1'} = \frac{1}{f}, \qquad M' = \frac{U_2'}{U_1'};$$

$$d = U_2' - U_2.$$

Therefore

$$U_2 = f(1 - M), \quad U_2' = f(1 - M'),$$

and

$$f = \frac{d}{M - M'}.$$

As the principal points H_1 and H_2 are at distances f and $-$ from the principal foci F_1 and F_2 they are located once the equivalen focal length and the positions of the principal foci are known.

To construct the image Qq of an extended object Pp after th principal points H_1, H_2 and principal foci F_1, F_2 have been locate

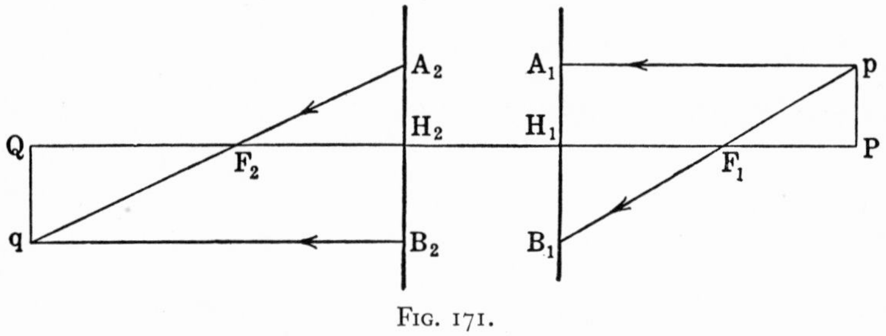

FIG. 171.

we proceed as indicated in Fig. 171. The ray pA_1 parallel to the axis passes through the image A_2 of A_1 at a height H_2A_2 above the axis equal to H_1A_1 since the magnification of objects in a unit plane is unity. It also passes through F_2 since pA_1 is parallel to the axis. Similarly a ray pF_1 emerges in the image space parallel to the axis at a distance $H_2B_2 = H_1B_1$ from it. The image q of p lies at the intersection of A_2F_2 and B_2q.

Problem 172a. A rigid lens system in air ($n_2 = n_1$) of equivalent focal length $f = -f_1$ (f_1 positive) is used to form a real image Q of an object P at a distance L from P. If D ($D < L$) is the distance between the principal points, show that there are two possible positions of the lens system (conjugate foci) if $L > D + 4f_1$, and none if $L < D + 4f_1$, and find U_1 for each. Show that the magnification in the one position is the reciprocal of that in the other.

$$Ans.\ U_1 = \tfrac{1}{2}(L - D)\left[1 \pm \sqrt{1 - 4\frac{f_1}{L - D}}\right]$$

173. The Thick Lens.—Let P_1 (Fig. 172) be the object, P' the

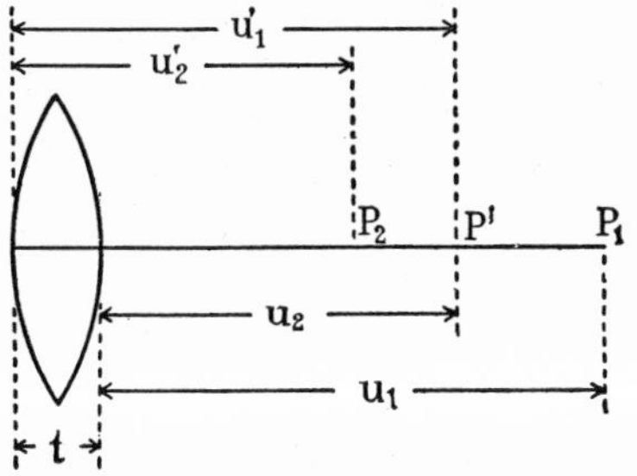

FIG. 172.

image formed by the first refraction, P_2 the final image, and t the thickness of the lens. For the first refraction

$$\frac{n}{u_2} - \frac{1}{u_1} = \frac{n - 1}{r_1}, \tag{173-1}$$

if $n \equiv n_2/n_1$. Similarly for the second

$$\frac{1}{u_2'} - \frac{n}{u_1'} = \frac{1 - n}{r_2}, \tag{173-2}$$

where

$$u_1' = u_2 + t.$$

To locate F_1 put $u_2' = \infty$. Then

$$u_1' = \frac{n}{n - 1} r_2$$

and

$$u_2 = u_1' - t = \frac{nr_2 - (n-1)t}{n-1}.$$

Therefore

$$\frac{1}{u_1} = \frac{n}{u_2} - \frac{n-1}{r_1} = \frac{(n-1)\{n(r_1 - r_2) + (n-1)t\}}{r_1\{nr_2 - (n-1)t\}}$$

and the distance of the principal focus F_1 of the object space from the vertex of the right-hand surface of the lens is

$$(u_1)_{F_1} = \frac{r_1\{nr_2 - (n-1)t\}}{(n-1)\{n(r_1 - r_2) + (n-1)t\}}. \qquad (173\text{–}3)$$

Similarly the distance of the principal focus F_2 of the image space from the vertex of the left-hand surface of the lens is

$$(u_2')_{F_2} = \frac{-r_2\{nr_1 + (n-1)t\}}{(n-1)\{n(r_1 - r_2) + (n-1)t\}}. \qquad (173\text{–}4)$$

The magnification due to the first refraction is

$$M_1 = \frac{1}{n}\frac{u_2}{u_1}$$

from (169–3), and that due to the second refraction

$$M_2 = n\frac{u_2'}{u_1'}.$$

Therefore the total magnification is

$$M = M_1 M_2 = \frac{u_2'}{u_1'}\frac{u_2}{u_1}.$$

To find the principal points we put $M = 1$. Then

$$\frac{1}{u_1} = \frac{u_1'}{u_2}\frac{1}{u_2'} = \frac{1}{u_2}\left\{n - (n-1)\frac{t}{r_2}\right\} - \frac{n-1}{r_2}$$

$$= \frac{1}{u_1}\left\{1 - \frac{n-1}{n}\frac{t}{r_2}\right\} + (n-1)\left(\frac{1}{r_1} - \frac{1}{r_2}\right) - \frac{(n-1)^2}{n}\frac{t}{r_1 r_2};$$

and the distance of the principal point H_1 from the vertex of the right-hand surface of the lens is

$$(u_1)_{H_1} = \frac{tr_1}{n(r_2 - r_1) - (n-1)t}. \qquad (173\text{–}5)$$

Similarly the distance of H_2 from the left-hand surface is

$$(u_2')_{H_2} = \frac{tr_2}{n(r_2 - r_1) - (n - 1)t}. \qquad (173\text{–}6)$$

The focal lengths f_1 and f_2 are

$$f_1 = (u_1)_{F_1} - (u_1)_{H_1}, \quad f_2 = (u_2')_{F_2} - (u_2')_{H_2}.$$

Hence the equivalent focal length is

$$f = f_2 = -f_1 = \frac{nr_1r_2}{(n-1)\{n(r_2 - r_1) - (n-1)t\}}. \qquad (173\text{–}7)$$

If the thickness of the lens is small compared with the radius of urvature, (173–5) and (173–6) become

$$\left.\begin{aligned} (u_1)_{H_1} &= \frac{tr_1}{n(r_2 - r_1)}, \\ (u_2')_{H_2} &= \frac{tr_2}{n(r_2 - r_1)}, \end{aligned}\right\} \qquad (173\text{–}8)$$

nd the focal length is given by the same expression (170–2) as for a hin lens.

As an example consider a symmetrical double convex lens made f glass having an index of refraction $n = 1.5$. Then $r_1 = -r$, $_2 = r$, and using the approximate formulae (173–8) we find that

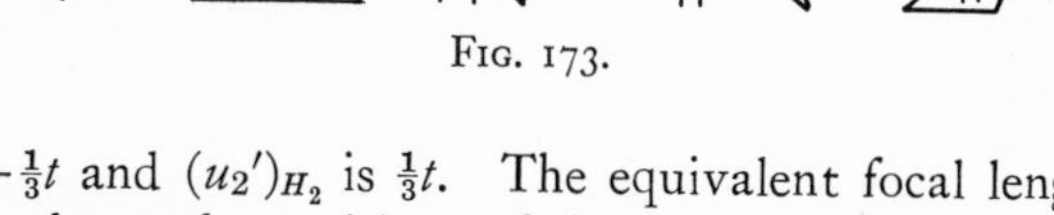

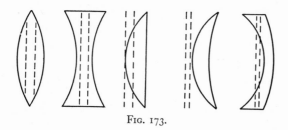

FIG. 173.

$u_1)_{H_1}$ is $-\frac{1}{3}t$ and $(u_2')_{H_2}$ is $\frac{1}{3}t$. The equivalent focal length is $-r$. igure 173 shows the positions of the principal planes for a number f different forms of lens.

Problem 173a. A spherical lens made of glass ($n = 1.5$) has a radius of o cm. Find the distances of the principal planes from the center and the quivalent focal length. *Ans.* 0, 0, -15 cm.

174. Two Thin Lenses. — Let f_1 be the focal length of the firs lens, f_2 that of the second, and t the distance between them. Thei for the first lens

$$\frac{1}{u_2} - \frac{1}{u_1} = \frac{1}{f_1} \qquad (174\text{–}1$$

from (170–3), and for the second

$$\frac{1}{u_2'} - \frac{1}{u_1'} = \frac{1}{f_2} \qquad (174\text{–}2$$

where

$$u_1' = u_2 + t.$$

To find the position of the principal focus F_1 put $u_2' = \infty$ anc solve for u_1. This gives

$$(u_1)_{F_1} = -\frac{f_1(f_2 + t)}{f_1 + f_2 + t}, \qquad (174\text{–}3$$

and similarly

$$(u_2')_{F_2} = \frac{f_2(f_1 + t)}{f_1 + f_2 + t}. \qquad (174\text{–}4$$

To locate the principal points we proceed from the expression fo the magnification precisely as in the previous article, getting

$$(u_1)_{H_1} = -\frac{tf_1}{f_1 + f_2 + t}, \qquad (174\text{–}5$$

$$(u_2')_{H_2} = \frac{tf_2}{f_1 + f_2 + t}. \qquad (174\text{–}6$$

The equivalent focal length is

$$f = (u_2')_{F_2} - (u_2')_{H_2} = \frac{f_1 f_2}{f_1 + f_2 + t},$$

or

$$\frac{1}{f} = \frac{1}{f_1} + \frac{1}{f_2} + \frac{t}{f_1 f_2}. \qquad (174\text{–}7$$

Problem 174a. Two thin lenses have focal lengths −30 cm and −10 cm Locate the principal points and the principal foci on diagrams and calculat the equivalent focal length if the distance between the lenses is (*a*) 5 cm (*b*) 15 cm, (*c*) 25 cm, (*d*) 40 cm, (*e*) 55 cm, (*f*) 70 cm. *Ans.* (*a*) −8.54 cm (*b*) −12.0 cm, (*c*) −20.0 cm, (*d*) ∞, (*e*) 20.0 cm, (*f*) 10.0 cm.

Problem 174b. Two thin lenses a fixed distance t apart are used to form n image Q of a point P. As U_1 is varied, show that the distance L of Q rom P assumes a stationary value for $U_2 = \pm U_1$, which is a maximum or a ninimum according as M/f is negative or positive. Calculate the magnifica-ion for each case, and the values of U_1, U_2 and L. Note that in one case P and Q coincide with the principal points.

Ans. $M = 1$, $U_1 = 0$, $U_2 = 0$; $M = -1$, $U_1 = -2f$, $U_2 = 2f$.

175. Chromatic Aberration. — As the index of refraction increases vith decrease in wave length in the region of normal dispersion as hown in article 163 the focal length (170–2) of a thin lens is shorter or violet light than for red light. Let n_C be the index of refraction of the material of which the lens is made for the red C Fraunhofer ine ($\lambda = 6.563(10)^{-5}$ cm) and n_F that for the blue F line $\lambda = 4.862(10)^{-5}$ cm). Then the focal lengths for these two wave engths are given by

$$\frac{1}{f_C} = (n_C - 1)\left(\frac{1}{r_1} - \frac{1}{r_2}\right),$$

$$\frac{1}{f_F} = (n_F - 1)\left(\frac{1}{r_1} - \frac{1}{r_2}\right),$$

espectively. Therefore

$$\frac{f_C - f_F}{f_C f_F} = \frac{1}{f_F} - \frac{1}{f_C} = (n_F - n_C)\left(\frac{1}{r_1} - \frac{1}{r_2}\right) = \frac{n_F - n_C}{(n-1)f},$$

where n is the mean index of refraction (more customarily the index of refraction for the intermediate D line) and f the mean focal length. Hence, as $f_C f_F = f^2$,

$$\frac{f_C - f_F}{f} = \frac{n_F - n_C}{n - 1} \equiv \omega, \qquad (175\text{–}1)$$

where ω is known as the *dispersive power* of the material.

Let us investigate the design of an achromatic lens constructed of two lenses of different glasses placed in contact. Denote the focal lengths of the two lenses by f and f' and that of the combination by F. Then as t is negligible it follows from (174–7) that

$$\frac{1}{F_C} = \frac{1}{f_C} + \frac{1}{f_C'},$$

$$\frac{1}{F_F} = \frac{1}{f_F} + \frac{1}{f_F'}.$$

Subtracting, and putting $F^2 = F_C F_F$, etc.,

$$\frac{F_C - F_F}{F^2} = \frac{f_C - f_F}{f^2} + \frac{f_C' - f_F'}{f'^2} = \frac{\omega}{f} + \frac{\omega'}{f'}.$$

So if

$$\frac{\omega}{f} + \frac{\omega'}{f'} = 0 \qquad (175\text{–}2$$

the combination is achromatic for the two wave lengths under con sideration and nearly achromatic for the whole range of the visibl spectrum.

Problem 175a. An achromatic plano-convex lens of 35 cm focal lengt is to be made from glasses of the following characteristics with the flint len plane on the outside.

	n	ω
Hard Crown................	1.517	0.0165
Dense Flint................	1.621	0.0277

Find the radii of curvature of the two component lenses. *Ans.* Flint r $= \infty$, $r_2 = -$ 14.8 cm, Crown $r_1 = -$ 14.8 cm, $r_2 =$ 14.6 cm.

176. Astronomical Telescope. — The astronomical telescope con sists of an *object glass O* (Fig. 174) and *eyepiece* or *ocular E*. Th

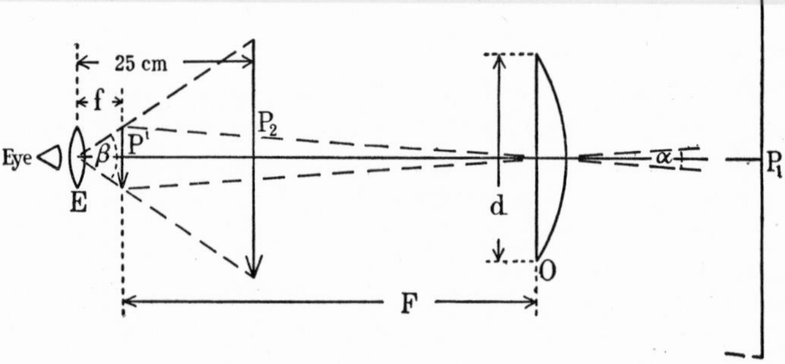

FIG. 174.

object glass is a convergent lens of large diameter d and long foca length F. To reduce spherical aberration to a minimum it is nearl plano-convex, as illustrated in the figure. The object glass forms real image P' close to its principal focus of the distant object P_1 This real image is magnified by the convergent eyepiece E whic forms a virtual image of it at P_2. The eyepiece is placed so as t bring the final image P_2 at the nearest distance of distinct vision from the eye, that is, about 25 cm. As the focal length f of the eyepiece is small compared with this distance, P' falls just to the left of its principal focus. In this article and the next we shall use F and f to designate the *positive* magnitudes of the focal lengths of object glass and eyepiece respectively.

The magnification M of the telescope is defined as the ratio of the angle β subtended at the eye by the image P_2 to the angle α that would be subtended by the object P_1 if the telescope were absent. Therefore

$$M = \frac{\beta}{\alpha} = \frac{F}{f}. \tag{176–1}$$

If cross wires are used, they must be placed in the plane of the real image P' formed by the object glass. A two-lens eyepiece is often used to diminish chromatic aberration.

On account of diffraction the image P' of a point source is a disk surrounded by alternate dark and bright rings. As will be shown in article 181 the distance of the first dark ring from the center of the disk is

$$1.22 \frac{F\lambda}{d}$$

for a wave length λ, where d is the diameter of the object glass. The least angular separation of two stars which can be recognized as distinct is that existing when the center of the diffraction disk of one falls on the first dark ring of the other. The angle between the two stars in this case is defined as the *resolving power* R of the telescope. Therefore

$$R = \frac{1.22 \dfrac{F\lambda}{d}}{F} = \frac{1.22\lambda}{d} = \frac{5.0''}{d\text{ (inches)}} \tag{176–2}$$

for a wave length of $2(10)^{-5}$ inches. So the resolving power is not improved by making the focal length longer but depends on the diameter of the object glass alone.

For the Yerkes telescope, the most powerful refractor yet built, $d = 40$ inches and $F = 65$ feet. Therefore

$$R = \frac{5.0''}{40} = \frac{1''}{8}.$$

In order that as much light as possible may enter the eye, the eye should be placed at the point where the rays come nearest together, that is, at the real image of the object glass formed by the eyepiece. This image is known as the *eye ring*. Let us denote its diameter by D and its distance from the eyepiece by u_2. Then from (170–3)

$$\frac{1}{u_2} - \frac{1}{F+f} = \frac{1}{-f}$$

since the focal length of the eyepiece is negative. Therefore

$$u_2 = -\frac{f}{F}(F+f),$$

and

$$\frac{d}{D} = \frac{u_1}{-u_2} = \frac{F}{f} \tag{176–3}$$

from (170–4). But this is just the magnification (176–1) of the telescope. So the magnification can be determined easily by measuring the diameters of the eye ring and of the object glass.

The eye ring must be smaller than the pupil of the eye, that is, $D < \frac{1}{5}$ inch, in order to insure that all the light reaches the retina. On the other hand vision is sensibly impaired by diffraction if $D < \frac{1}{30}$ inch. So the focal length of the eyepiece must satisfy the inequality

$$\frac{F}{d}\frac{1}{30}\text{ inch} < f < \frac{F}{d}\frac{1}{5}\text{ inch.} \tag{176–4}$$

As the resolving power r of the eye is about $1.5' = 90''$, the focal length of the eyepiece need be no less than that specified by the equation

$$90'' = \frac{1.22\dfrac{F\lambda}{d}}{f} = \frac{F}{f}\frac{1.22\dfrac{F\lambda}{d}}{F} = \frac{F}{f}\frac{5.0''}{d\text{ (inches)}} = M\frac{5.0''}{d\text{ (inches)}} = MR$$

in order to bring out the full detail of the real image P' produced by the object glass. Consequently the magnification of the telescope should be

$$M = \frac{r}{R} = 18 \times d\text{ (inches).} \tag{176–5}$$

A greater magnification than this will further enlarge the real image P' but cannot reveal any more detail since no more exists in the image formed by the object glass. For the Yerkes telescope

$$M = 18 \times 40 = 720$$

and the focal length of the eyepiece should be

$$f = \frac{F}{720} = 1.1 \text{ inch},$$

which lies well within the limits 0.65 inch and 3.9 inch imposed by (176–4). It is clear from the last equation that the object glass must have a long focal length in order that the focal length f of the eyepiece should not be impracticably small.

Problem 176a. The Galilean telescope or opera glass uses a divergent lens for eyepiece. Draw a sketch showing the positions of object and images and the course of the rays of light through the instrument. Calculate its magnification.

Ans. $M = \frac{F}{f}$.

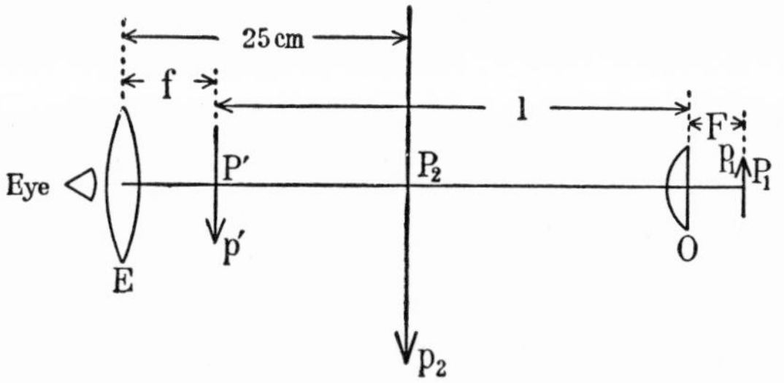

FIG. 175.

177. Compound Microscope. — The compound microscope constructed of two or more lenses is used in preference to the simple microscope consisting of a single lens in order to reduce aberration when a high magnification is desired. The instrument resembles an astronomical telescope in that it consists of an object glass O (Fig. 175) which forms a real image P' of the nearby object P_1 and an eyepiece E which produces an enlarged virtual image P_2 of P'.

The magnification M of the microscope is defined as the ratio of the angle subtended at the eye by the image P_2 to that which would be subtended by the object P_1 if placed 25 cm away from the naked eye. Hence

$$M = \frac{P_2p_2}{P_1p_1} = \frac{l}{F} \times \frac{25 \text{ cm}}{f}$$

$$= \frac{25 \text{ cm} \times l}{Ff}. \qquad (177\text{–}1)$$

The resolving power of the microscope is limited by diffraction in much the same way as that of the telescope. As with the latter, the resolving power is proportional to the wave length. For the wave length of the middle of the visible spectrum, a detailed calculation shows that the nearest distance of two points in the object which can be resolved by the best practicable instrument is $1.7\,(10)^{-5}$ cm. As the resolving power of the eye is $1.5'$, which subtends a length of $1.1(10)^{-2}$ cm at 25 cm, the magnification necessary to utilize the full resolving power of the object glass is, in accord with (176–5),

$$M = \frac{r}{R} = \frac{1.1(10)^{-2}}{1.7(10)^{-5}} = 650.$$

This, then, is the limiting useful magnification obtainable with the compound microscope for visible light. By using ultra-violet light and a photographic plate the resolving power can be somewhat increased. In the electron microscope a much higher resolving power is achieved by using very much shorter waves.

To eliminate spherical aberration as far as possible the objective of a high-powered microscope is constructed as illustrated in Fig. 176. The object P_1 is immersed in cedar oil directly below the hemispherical lens L_1, the fluid having the same index of refraction as the glass of which the lens is made. The position of the object is the critical position (169–8) for no spherical aberration on refraction at the upper surface of L_1. A virtual image P' magnified n^2 times is formed by this refraction. Then the convergent lens L_2 makes the light coming from P' nearly parallel. The lens L_2 is nearly plano-convex so as to minimize spherical aberration, and is made of two different kinds of glass so as to reduce chromatic aberration. The mage P', which acts as object for L_2, is located just below its principal focus so as to form a real image far above L_2. The two lenses L_1 and L_2 together take the place of the object glass of Fig. 175.

178. The Prism. — Light passing through a prism (Fig. 177) is always deviated away from the refracting edge A if the index of

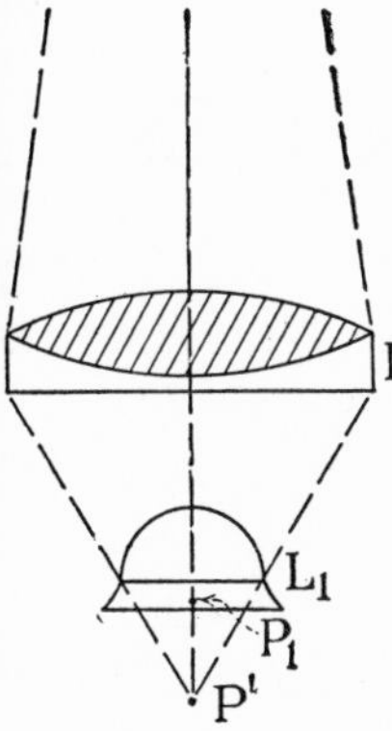

FIG. 176.

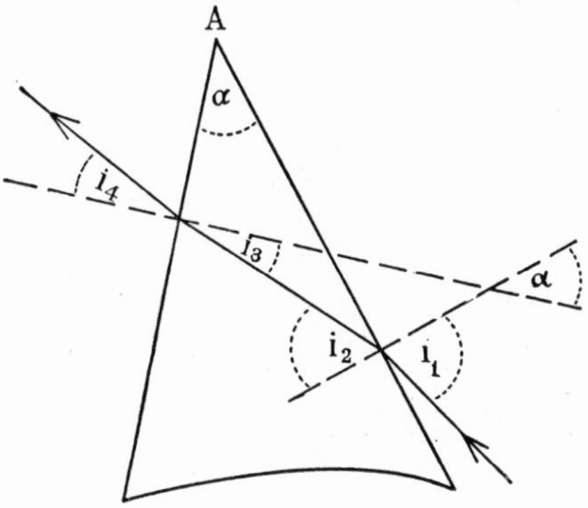

FIG. 177.

refraction n of the prism relative to the air outside is greater than unity. If we denote the angle of the prism by α and the deviation of the ray by δ we have

$$\sin i_1 = n \sin i_2,$$

$$\sin i_4 = n \sin i_3,$$

from Snell's law, and

$$i_2 - i_3 = \alpha,$$

$$\left.\begin{aligned} \delta &= (i_1 - i_2) + (i_3 - i_4) \\ &= i_1 - i_4 - \alpha, \end{aligned}\right\} \qquad (178\text{–}1)$$

from the geometry of the figure. To find the condition for minimum deviation we have

$$d\delta = di_1 - di_4 = 0.$$

Now

$$di_1 = n\frac{\cos i_2}{\cos i_1}di_2, \quad di_4 = n\frac{\cos i_3}{\cos i_4}di_3 = n\frac{\cos i_3}{\cos i_4}di_2.$$

Therefore

$$d\delta = n\left\{\frac{\cos i_2}{\sqrt{1 - n^2 \sin^2 i_2}} - \frac{\cos (\alpha - i_2)}{\sqrt{1 - n^2 \sin^2 (\alpha - i_2)}}\right\} di_2 = 0.$$

Clearing of radicals

$$\cos^2 i_2\{1 - n^2 \sin^2 (\alpha - i_2)\} = \cos^2 (\alpha - i_2)\{1 - n^2 \sin^2 i_2\}$$

or

$$\cos^2 i_2 = \cos^2 (\alpha - i_2),$$

and

$$i_2 = \frac{\alpha}{2}, \quad i_3 = -\frac{\alpha}{2}, \quad i_4 = -i_1. \tag{178-2}$$

If we proceed to the second derivative we find that this stationary value is a minimum. Therefore symmetric passage through the prism corresponds to minimum deviation. To find the deviation under these circumstances we have from (178–1) and (178–2)

$$\delta = 2i_1 - \alpha$$

or

$$i_1 = \frac{\delta + \alpha}{2}.$$

Consequently

$$n = \frac{\sin i_1}{\sin i_2} = \frac{\sin \frac{\delta + \alpha}{2}}{\sin \frac{\alpha}{2}}. \tag{178-3}$$

This formula provides us with a convenient method for measuring the index of refraction of the glass of which the prism is made. As the index of refraction varies with the wave length, different wave lengths are deviated different amounts. All the radiation being incident at the same angle, the *dispersion D* of the prism is

$$D = \frac{d\delta}{d\lambda} = -\frac{di_4}{d\lambda} = -\frac{di_4}{dn}\frac{dn}{d\lambda}, \quad i_1 \text{ constant.}$$

Differentiating the first three equations of this article, holding i_1 constant, we get

$$0 = \sin i_2 dn + n \cos i_2 di_2,$$

$$\cos i_4 di_4 = \sin i_3 dn + n \cos i_3 di_3,$$

$$di_2 = di_3.$$

Therefore

$$-\cos i_2 \cos i_4 di_4 = \sin (i_2 - i_3) dn = \sin \alpha dn,$$

and

$$D = \frac{\sin \alpha}{\cos i_2 \cos i_4} \frac{dn}{d\lambda}. \qquad (178\text{–}4)$$

In the region of normal dispersion ω^2 is small compared to k^2 and we have from (163–6) the approximate expression

$$n^2 = 1 + \frac{\frac{Ne^2}{m}}{k^2 - \omega^2} = 1 + \frac{Ne^2}{mk^2}\left(1 + \frac{4\pi^2 c^2}{\lambda^2 k^2}\right),$$

$$n = A + \frac{B}{\lambda^2}, \qquad (178\text{–}5)$$

for the index of refraction. This is known as *Cauchy's formula* and fits the experimental curve with a fair degree of accuracy over a limited range. Consequently

$$\frac{dn}{d\lambda} = -\frac{2B}{\lambda^3},$$

and

$$D = -\frac{2B \sin \alpha}{\lambda^3 \cos i_2 \cos i_4}. \qquad (178\text{–}6)$$

At minimum deviation $i_2 = \alpha/2$ and $i_4 = -i_1$. Hence

$$D = -\frac{4B \sin \alpha/2}{\lambda^3 \cos i_1}. \qquad (178\text{–}7)$$

Problem 178a. If a prism has a small angle α, show that all rays incident on the prism at a small angle with the normal suffer approximately the same deviation $(n - 1)\alpha$, and therefore a laterally displaced image is formed of a point source.

REFERENCES

Southall, J. P. C.: *The Principles and Methods of Geometrical Optics*, The Macmillan Co., New York.

Hastings, C. S.: *New Methods in Geometrical Optics*, The Macmillan Co., New York.

CHAPTER XIV

PHYSICAL OPTICS

179. Diffraction Equation. — Consider a screen coincident with the XY plane (Fig. 178) in which there is a small hole P. We want to find the disturbance at a point O below the screen due to radiation proceeding from the point source S' above. If v denotes the velocity of propagation the disturbance $d\Phi$ over an area dS of the aperture at P at a time τ may be written

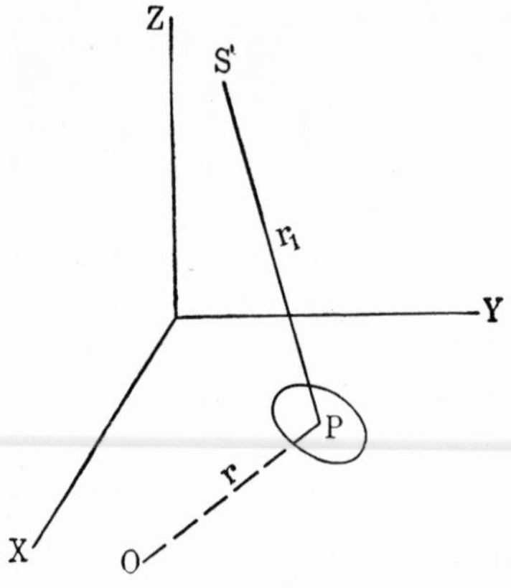

FIG. 178.

$$d\Phi_P = k' \sin \frac{2\pi}{\lambda} (r_1 - v\tau)dS.$$

According to Huygens' principle each point on the portion of the wave front passing through the aperture acts as a secondary source of disturbance. Therefore the disturbance at O at a time t due to the element of area dS is proportional to that existing at P at the time $\tau = t - r/v$, that is,

$$d\Phi_0 = k \sin \frac{2\pi}{\lambda} (r_1 + r - vt)dS,$$

and the total disturbance at O is

$$\Phi_0 = k \int \sin \frac{2\pi}{\lambda} (r_1 + r - vt)dS \qquad (179\text{–}1)$$

integrated over the area of the aperture, provided the dimensions of the hole are so small compared with r_1 and r that we can treat k as a constant.

The defect of this deduction from Huygens' principle is that it fails to explain why radiation does not proceed upward from the aperture to the same extent as downward. We shall now take up a more rigorous treatment of diffraction, following the theory of Kirchhoff as modified by Voigt.

Our problem is as follows: Given a scalar function $\Phi(x, y, z, \tau)$ of the coordinates and the time τ which satisfies the wave equation

$$\frac{\partial^2\Phi}{\partial x^2} + \frac{\partial^2\Phi}{\partial y^2} + \frac{\partial^2\Phi}{\partial z^2} - \frac{1}{v^2}\frac{\partial^2\Phi}{\partial \tau^2} = 0, \qquad (179\text{–}2)$$

we wish to find the value of the disturbance Φ at O (Fig. 179) at the time t in terms of the disturbance at points P on the closed surface S surrounding O at the time $t - r/v$.

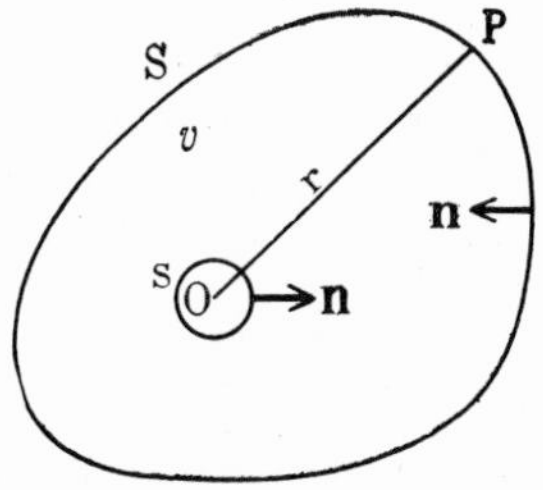

FIG. 179.

Consider a function $U(x, y, z, r, t)$ such that U and its derivatives are finite and continuous at the origin O. We shall designate true partial derivatives by the usual notation, for example,

$$\frac{\partial U}{\partial x}$$

is the derivative of U with respect to x when y, z, r, and t are held constant. On the other hand we shall denote by

$$\frac{dU}{dx} \equiv \frac{\partial U}{\partial x} + \frac{\partial U}{\partial r}\frac{\partial r}{\partial x}$$

the change in U per unit change in explicit x and in the x contained implicitly in $r = \sqrt{x^2 + y^2 + z^2}$, when y, z and t are held constant. The gradient of U, then, is

$$\nabla U = \mathbf{i}\frac{dU}{dx} + \mathbf{j}\frac{dU}{dy} + \mathbf{k}\frac{dU}{dz}$$

in our present notation. We shall have occasion to use also the vector

$$\nabla' U = \mathbf{i}\frac{\partial U}{\partial x} + \mathbf{j}\frac{\partial U}{\partial y} + \mathbf{k}\frac{\partial U}{\partial z}$$

which is not the true gradient. Evidently

$$\nabla U = \nabla' U + \mathbf{r}_1 \frac{\partial U}{\partial r}$$

where $\mathbf{r}_1$ is a unit vector in the direction of increasing r. We also have

$$\frac{dU}{dr} \equiv \mathbf{r}_1 \cdot \nabla U = \mathbf{r}_1 \cdot \nabla' U + \frac{\partial U}{\partial r}.$$

Now, since $\dfrac{\partial \mathbf{r}_1}{\partial r} = 0$ by (79–4), we have the identity

$$\begin{aligned}
\nabla \cdot \left(\frac{1}{r} \nabla' U\right) &= \left(\nabla' + \mathbf{r}_1 \frac{\partial}{\partial r}\right) \cdot \left(\frac{1}{r} \nabla' U\right) \\
&= \frac{1}{r} \nabla' \cdot \nabla' U + \mathbf{r}_1 \cdot \frac{\partial}{\partial r} \left\{ \frac{1}{r} \left(\nabla U - \mathbf{r}_1 \frac{\partial U}{\partial r} \right) \right\} \\
&= \frac{1}{r} \nabla' \cdot \nabla' U - \frac{1}{r^2} \left(\frac{dU}{dr} - \frac{\partial U}{\partial r} \right) + \frac{1}{r} \frac{\partial}{\partial r} \frac{dU}{dr} - \frac{1}{r} \frac{\partial^2 U}{\partial r^2} \\
&= \frac{1}{r} \left(\nabla' \cdot \nabla' U - \frac{\partial^2 U}{\partial r^2} \right) + \frac{1}{r^2} \frac{d}{dr} \left(r \frac{\partial U}{\partial r} - U \right).
\end{aligned}$$

Let us integrate this expression over the volume v (Fig. 179) included between the infinitesimal sphere s of radius r_0 surrounding the origin and the closed surface S. The integral of the expression on the left can be expressed as a surface integral by Gauss' theorem, and in this case we shall find it convenient to take the *inward* drawn normal as positive. Hence we have

$$\left.\begin{aligned}
&-\int_S \frac{1}{r} \nabla' U \cdot d\mathbf{S} - \int_s \frac{1}{r} \nabla' U \cdot d\mathbf{s} \\
&\quad = \int_v \frac{1}{r} \left(\nabla' \cdot \nabla' U - \frac{\partial^2 U}{\partial r^2} \right) dv + \int_v \frac{1}{r^2} \frac{d}{dr} \left(r \frac{\partial U}{\partial r} - U \right) dv.
\end{aligned}\right\} \qquad (179\text{–}3)$$

Now

$$-\int_S \frac{1}{r} \nabla' U \cdot d\mathbf{S} = -\int_S \frac{1}{r} \frac{\partial U}{\partial n} dS \qquad (179\text{–}4)$$

where dn is along the normal to the surface;

$$-\int_s \frac{1}{r}\nabla' U\cdot ds = -\int_s \frac{1}{r}\frac{\partial U}{\partial n}ds = -\overline{\left(\frac{\partial U}{\partial n}\right)}_0\int_s \frac{ds}{r_0} = -4\pi r_0\overline{\left(\frac{\partial U}{\partial n}\right)}_0 = 0 \tag{179-5}$$

since the mean value $\overline{\left(\frac{\partial U}{\partial n}\right)}_0$ of the derivative over s remains finite as r_0 approaches zero; and if we denote an element of solid angle described about the origin by $d\omega$,

$$\int_v \frac{1}{r^2}\frac{d}{dr}\left(r\frac{\partial U}{\partial r} - U\right)dv = \int_v \frac{d}{dr}\left(r\frac{\partial U}{\partial r} - U\right)dr\,d\omega$$
$$= \int_S \left(r\frac{\partial U}{\partial r} - U\right)d\omega - \int_s \left(r\frac{\partial U}{\partial r} - U\right)d\omega. \tag{179-6}$$

On the outer surface S

$$d\omega = -\frac{\cos \widehat{rn}\, dS}{r^2}$$

where $\widehat{rn}$ is the angle between the radius vector and the inward drawn normal. Therefore

$$\int_S \left(r\frac{\partial U}{\partial r} - U\right)d\omega = -\int_S \frac{\partial}{\partial r}\left(\frac{U}{r}\right)\cos \widehat{rn}\, dS. \tag{179-7}$$

The second term on the right of (179–6) becomes

$$-\int_s \left(r\frac{\partial U}{\partial r} - U\right)d\omega = -4\pi r_0\overline{\left(\frac{\partial U}{\partial r}\right)}_0 + 4\pi U_0 = 4\pi U_0. \tag{179-8}$$

Putting (179–7) and (179–8) in (179–6), and substituting (179–4), (179–5) and (179–6) in (179–3) the latter equation becomes

$$\left.\begin{aligned} 4\pi U_0 = &-\int_S\left\{\frac{1}{r}\frac{\partial U}{\partial n} - \cos \widehat{rn}\frac{\partial}{\partial r}\left(\frac{U}{r}\right)\right\}dS \\ &-\int_v \frac{1}{r}\left\{\frac{\partial^2 U}{\partial x^2} + \frac{\partial^2 U}{\partial y^2} + \frac{\partial^2 U}{\partial z^2} - \frac{\partial^2 U}{\partial r^2}\right\}dv. \end{aligned}\right\} \tag{179-9}$$

This is a purely mathematical relation and is true provided U and its derivatives are finite and continuous at the point O selected as origin. Now suppose we replace τ by $t - r/v$ in the function Φ satisfying the wave equation (179–2) and put

$$U \equiv \Phi\left(x, y, z, t - \frac{r}{v}\right)$$

As

$$\frac{\partial \Phi}{\partial r} = -\frac{1}{v}\frac{\partial \Phi}{\partial \tau}, \quad \frac{\partial^2 \Phi}{\partial r^2} = \frac{1}{v^2}\frac{\partial^2 \Phi}{\partial \tau^2},$$

the wave equation (179–2) may be written

$$\frac{\partial^2 \Phi}{\partial x^2} + \frac{\partial^2 \Phi}{\partial y^2} + \frac{\partial^2 \Phi}{\partial z^2} - \frac{\partial^2 \Phi}{\partial r^2} = 0. \qquad (179\text{–}10)$$

Hence, if we replace U by Φ, equation (179–9) becomes

$$\Phi_0 = -\frac{1}{4\pi}\int_S \left\{\frac{1}{r}\frac{\partial \Phi}{\partial n} - \cos \widehat{rn}\,\frac{\partial}{\partial r}\left(\frac{\Phi}{r}\right)\right\} dS \qquad (179\text{–}11)$$

since the integrand of the volume integral vanishes by virtue of (179–10).

This fundamental equation forms the basis for the solution of all problems in diffraction. Let us apply it to simple harmonic waves proceeding from a point source S′ (Fig. 180). Assuming that Φ is a function of the distance r_1 from the source and the time τ only, we have from (164–4)

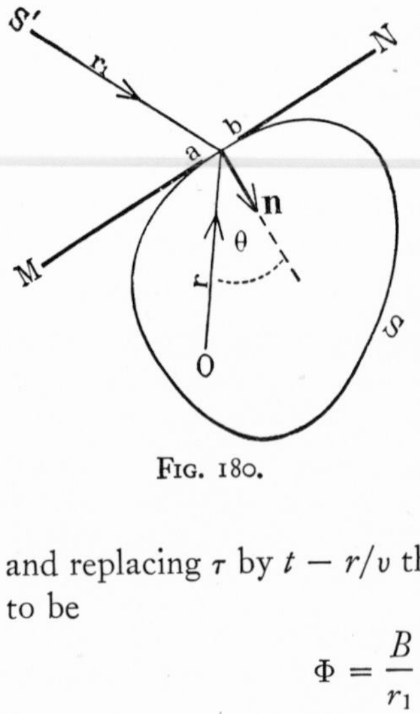

FIG. 180.

$$\Phi = \frac{B}{r_1}\cos\frac{2\pi}{\lambda}(r_1 - v\tau),$$

and replacing τ by $t - r/v$ the function appearing in (179–11) is seen to be

$$\Phi = \frac{B}{r_1}\cos\frac{2\pi}{\lambda}(r_1 + r - vt).$$

Now r_1 is a function of explicit x, y, z. So

$$\frac{\partial \Phi}{\partial n} = \frac{\partial \Phi}{\partial r_1}\cos \widehat{r_1 n}$$

$$= \left\{ - \frac{B}{r_1^2} \cos \frac{2\pi}{\lambda} (r_1 + r - vt) - \frac{2\pi B}{\lambda r_1} \sin \frac{2\pi}{\lambda} (r_1 + r - vt) \right\} \cos \widehat{r_1 n}$$

$$= - \frac{2\pi B}{\lambda r_1} \cos \widehat{r_1 n} \sin \frac{2\pi}{\lambda} (r_1 + r - vt)$$

if, as we shall assume to be the case, r_1 is large compared with λ and therefore the cosine term is negligible compared with the sine term. Similarly

$$\frac{\partial}{\partial r}\left(\frac{\Phi}{r}\right) = - \frac{B}{r_1 r^2} \cos \frac{2\pi}{\lambda} (r_1 + r - vt) - \frac{2\pi B}{\lambda r_1 r} \sin \frac{2\pi}{\lambda} (r_1 + r - vt)$$

$$= - \frac{2\pi B}{\lambda r_1 r} \sin \frac{2\pi}{\lambda} (r_1 + r - vt)$$

if r as well as r_1 is large compared with λ. Therefore the diffraction equation (179–11) for this case becomes

$$\Phi_0 = \frac{B}{2\lambda} \int_S \frac{1}{r_1 r} (\cos \widehat{r_1 n} - \cos \widehat{rn}) \sin \frac{2\pi}{\lambda} (r_1 + r - vt)\, dS. \quad (179\text{–}12)$$

If a screen MN with an opening ab is interposed between the source S' and the point O at which we wish to find the disturbance, we need integrate over only that portion of the closed surface S contained in the aperture, for the integrand vanishes over the rest of the surface. Furthermore, if the dimensions of the hole are small compared with the distances from it of S' and O, it follows that r_1, r and the cosines appearing in (179–12) are sensibly constant over the surface of the aperture and we may write

$$\Phi_0 = \frac{B}{2\lambda r_1 r} (\cos \widehat{r_1 n} - \cos \widehat{rn}) \int_S \sin \frac{2\pi}{\lambda} (r_1 + r - vt)\, dS. \quad (179\text{–}13)$$

To find the disturbance $d\Phi_0$ due to an element of a wave front we must consider a surface element dS perpendicular to r_1. Then $\cos \widehat{r_1 n} = 1$ and if we put $\cos \theta \equiv - \cos \widehat{rn}$,

$$d\Phi_0 = \frac{B}{2\lambda r_1 r} (1 + \cos \theta) \sin \frac{2\pi}{\lambda} (r_1 + r - vt)\, dS.$$

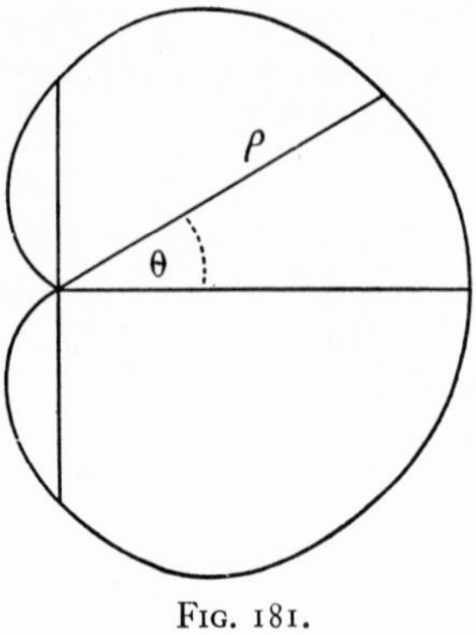

Fig. 181.

We can consider, therefore, that each element of a wave front acts as a secondary source of radiation, emitting wavelets of amplitude proportional to $1 + \cos\theta$. The maximum amplitude A_m occurs for $\theta = 0$, that is, in the direction of propagation of the primary wave, and the ratio ρ of the amplitude A for any angle θ to A_m is

$$\rho = \frac{A}{A_m} = \frac{1 + \cos\theta}{2} = \cos^2\frac{\theta}{2}. \qquad (179\text{–}14)$$

Plotting ρ against θ in polar coordinates we get the cardioid of Fig. 181. No radiation proceeds directly backwards from the secondary source as was implied in the earlier statement of Huygens' principle.

180. Single Slit. — Let AB (Fig. 182) be a slit of width a with its axis perpendicular to the plane of the paper. The source S is placed at the principal focus of a convergent lens L_1 so that the light waves striking the slit are plane. This device is equivalent to placing the source at an infinite distance from the slit. The lens L_2 on the other side of the slit is placed so that its principal focus lies on the screen DE, thus effectively removing the point O to infinity. Then from (179–13)

$$\Phi_0 = k\int_S \sin\frac{2\pi}{\lambda}(r_1 + r - vt)\,dS \qquad (180\text{–}1)$$

integrated over the slit, since

$$k \equiv \frac{B}{2\lambda r_1 r}(\cos \widehat{r_1 n} - \cos \widehat{rn})$$

is practically constant if only small ranges of angles of incidence i_1

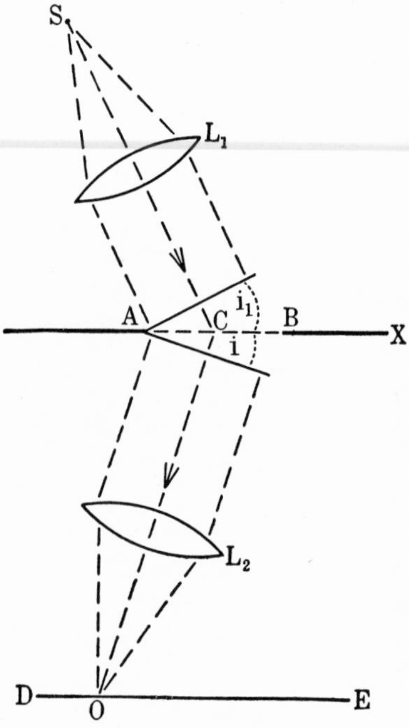

Fig. 182.

and angles of diffraction i are considered. Note that this formula is identical with (179–1) obtained directly from Huygens' principle.

Take the plane of the slit as the XY coordinate plane, with origin at the mid-point C of the slit and Y axis parallel to it. Then $dS = dx\,dy$, and as r_1 and r are not functions of y we can integrate with respect to y getting

$$\Phi_0 = c\int_{-a/2}^{a/2} \sin\frac{2\pi}{\lambda}(r_1 + r - vt)dx. \qquad (180\text{–}2)$$

If $\lambda\delta$ is the value of $r_1 + r$ for C, its value for any other point on the line AB is

$$r_1 + r = \lambda\delta + x(\sin i_1 + \sin i),$$

and if we put

$$\theta \equiv \frac{\sin i_1 + \sin i}{\lambda}, \quad \frac{v}{\lambda} = \frac{1}{P}, \qquad (180\text{–}3)$$

where P is the period of vibration, then

$$\left.\begin{aligned}\Phi_0 &= c\int_{-a/2}^{a/2} \sin 2\pi\left(\theta x - \frac{t}{P} + \delta\right)dx \\ &= c\left\{\cos 2\pi\left(\frac{t}{P} - \delta\right)\int_{-a/2}^{a/2} \sin 2\pi\theta x\cdot dx\right. \\ &\quad \left. - \sin 2\pi\left(\frac{t}{P} - \delta\right)\int_{-a/2}^{a/2} \cos 2\pi\theta x\cdot dx\right\} \\ &= -\,ca\frac{\sin \pi a\theta}{\pi a\theta}\sin 2\pi\left(\frac{t}{P} - \delta\right).\end{aligned}\right\} \qquad (180\text{–}4)$$

So the intensity of the radiation at O, being proportional to the square of the amplitude of Φ_0, is

$$I = C\left\{\frac{\sin \pi a\theta}{\pi a\theta}\right\}^2 = C\left\{\frac{\sin u}{u}\right\}^2 \qquad (180\text{–}5)$$

if we put u for $\pi a\theta$.

The zeros of intensity come at $\theta = m/a$, where m is any positive or negative integer except 0. As

$$\left[\frac{\sin u}{u}\right]_{u=0}^{t} = \left[\frac{u - \frac{u^3}{3!} + \ldots}{u}\right]_{u=0}^{t} = 1$$

the intensity is equal to C when $\theta = 0$, that is, when $i = -\,i_1$.

To find the maxima of intensity differentiate (180–5) with respect to u and equate to zero. This gives

$$u = \tan u. \qquad (180\text{–}6)$$

Plotting $\tan u$ against u we get the graph shown by the curves in Fig. 183. These are cut by the broken line representing the graph of u at the origin O, M_1, M_2, etc. The first of these points represents the maximum for u or θ equal to zero discussed above, the others represent maxima at values of u a little less than $\frac{3}{2}\pi$, $\frac{5}{2}\pi$, etc., respectively. It is not necessary to show that the second derivative of (180–5) is negative for these values of u, since it is quite clear from the form of this expression that the stationary points under consideration are maxima. The intensity at the maxima is given by

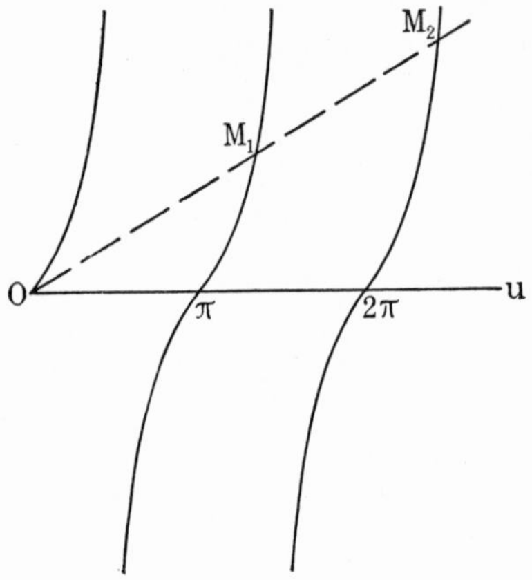

FIG. 183.

$$I_m = C\left\{\frac{\sin u_m}{u_m}\right\}^2 = C\left\{\frac{\sin u_m}{\tan u_m}\right\}^2 = C\cos^2 u_m$$

from (180–5), where u_m is a value of u satisfying (180–6). If I_0 is the intensity of the central maximum,

$$\frac{I_m}{I_0} = \cos^2 u_m. \qquad (180\text{–}7)$$

Figure 184 is a graph of the intensity plotted against u. The central maximum lies where the undeviated incident ray strikes the screen DE of Fig. 182, and the width of the central line, measured from the zero on one side to that on the other, is twice the width of any other line.

Since θ is $-1/a$ and $1/a$ at the zeros of intensity on the two sides of the central line, the width of the central line represents an increment $\Delta\theta = 2/a$ in θ. Therefore, from (180–3), the corresponding increment in sin i is Δ (sin i) $= 2\lambda/a$, or the angular width, subtended at the slit, of the central line is

$$\Delta i = \frac{2\lambda}{a \cos i} = \frac{2\lambda}{a \cos i_1}, \tag{180-8}$$

since $i = -i_1$ at the central maximum. If the radiation is incident normally on the slit, i_1 is zero and this expression takes the simpler form

$$\Delta i = \frac{2\lambda}{a}. \tag{180-9}$$

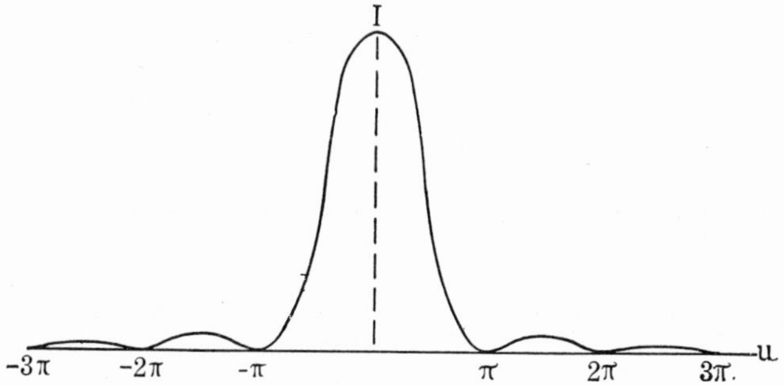

FIG. 184.

Two point sources, viewed through the slit, are said to be *resolved* when the central maximum of the one falls on the first minimum of the diffraction pattern of the other. Since the central maximum lies on the undeviated ray, the angular separation of the central maxima of the two diffraction patterns is the same as the angle Δi_1 between the sources. For resolution, then, Δi_1 must be half the angular width of the central line. If the angles of incidence are small, this requires that

$$\Delta i_1 = \frac{\lambda}{a} \tag{180-10}$$

from (180–9). Assuming the two sources to be of equal strength, the ratio of the intensity half way between the two maxima to that at either maximum is

$$\left.\frac{2C\left\{\dfrac{\sin\dfrac{\pi}{2}}{\dfrac{\pi}{2}}\right\}^2}{C} = \frac{8}{\pi^2} = 0.81057.\right\} \tag{180-11}$$

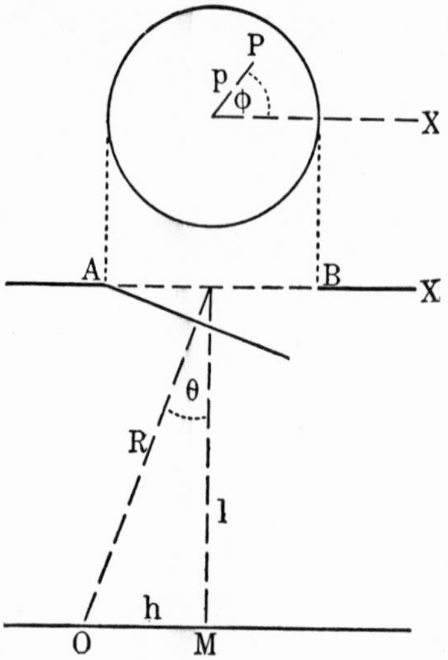

FIG. 185.

Problem 180a. The resolving power of the eye being 1.5′ find the largest width of slit such that the diffraction pattern may be perceived visually for a wave length of $5(10)^{-5}$ cm. *Ans.* 1.1 mm.

Problem 180b. For the central, first and second maxima in the diffraction pattern of a single slit calculate u as a multiple of π and the ratio of the intensity to that of the central maximum. If light falls normally on a slit of 0.1 cm width, find the width of the central line on a screen at a distance of 100 cm for a wave length of $5(10)^{-5}$ cm. *Ans.* 0, 1.430π, 2.459π; 1, 0.0465, 0.0165; 0.1 cm.

Problem 180c. Prove that

$$\int_0^{2\pi} \cos^n\phi d\phi = \begin{cases} \dfrac{1\cdot 3\cdot 5 \ldots (n-1)}{2\cdot 4\cdot 6 \ldots n}(2\pi) = \dfrac{n!}{2^2\cdot 4^2\cdot 6^2 \ldots n^2}(2\pi) \text{ for } n \text{ even,} \\ 0 \text{ for } n \text{ odd.} \end{cases}$$

181. Circular Aperture. — We shall confine our attention to the case where the incident waves are plane and parallel to the circular aperture AB (Fig. 185) of radius a which is shown in plan in the upper portion of the figure. From (179–13)

$$\Phi_0 = k\int_S \sin\frac{2\pi}{\lambda}(r_1 + r - vt)dS$$

provided we consider only a small range of values of the angle θ which the diffracted radiation makes with the normal to the slit. As r_1 has the same value for all points on the aperture we can write

$$\Phi_0 = k\int_S \sin\frac{2\pi}{\lambda}(r - vt)dS \qquad (181\text{–}1)$$

by taking a new zero of time.

Consider a point P on the aperture. Its distance r from the point

O on the screen OM at which we wish to find the intensity of the diffracted radiation is

$$r^2 = (h + p \cos \phi)^2 + l^2 + p^2 \sin^2 \phi$$
$$= R^2 + 2Rp \sin \theta \cos \phi + p^2.$$

As p is very small compared with R

$$r = R + p \sin \theta \cos \phi + \ldots$$

if we expand by the binomial theorem. Putting $1/P$ for v/λ equation (181–1) becomes

$$\left.\begin{aligned}\Phi_0 = &- k \sin 2\pi\left(\frac{t}{P} - \frac{R}{\lambda}\right)\iint \cos\frac{2\pi}{\lambda}(p \sin\theta\cos\phi)\, pdpd\phi \\ &+ k \cos 2\pi\left(\frac{t}{P} - \frac{R}{\lambda}\right)\iint \sin\frac{2\pi}{\lambda}(p \sin\theta\cos\phi)\, pdpd\phi,\end{aligned}\right\} \quad (181\text{–}2)$$

since $dS = pdpd\phi$, where ϕ goes from 0 to 2π and p from 0 to a.

Put

$$b \equiv \frac{2\pi}{\lambda}\sin\theta.$$

Then

$$\left.\begin{aligned}\iint e^{ibp\cos\phi}pdpd\phi = &\iint \cos\frac{2\pi}{\lambda}(p\sin\theta\cos\phi)\, pdpd\phi \\ &+ i\iint \sin\frac{2\pi}{\lambda}(p\sin\theta\cos\phi)pdpd\phi.\end{aligned}\right\} \quad (181\text{–}3)$$

But

$$e^{ibp\cos\phi} = 1 + ibp\cos\phi + \frac{(ibp\cos\phi)^2}{2!} + \ldots$$

Making use of the formulae proved in problem 180c

$$\int_0^{2\pi} e^{ibp\cos\phi}d\phi = 2\pi\left\{1 - \frac{(bp)^2}{2^2} + \frac{(bp)^4}{2^2\cdot 4^2} - \frac{(bp)^6}{2^2\cdot 4^2\cdot 6^2} + \ldots\right\},$$

and

$$\int_0^a\int_0^{2\pi} e^{ibp\cos\phi}d\phi pdp$$
$$= \pi a^2\left\{1 - \frac{(ba)^2}{2\cdot 2^2} + \frac{(ba)^4}{3\cdot 2^2\cdot 4^2} - \frac{(ba)^6}{4\cdot 2^2\cdot 4^2\cdot 6^2} + \ldots\right\}.$$

The last two series are known as Bessel's functions of the 0th and 1st order respectively. Comparing the last equation with (181–3)

$$\left.\begin{aligned} &\int_0^{2\pi}\int_0^a \cos\frac{2\pi}{\lambda}(p\sin\theta\cos\phi)\,pdpd\phi \\ &\qquad = \pi a^2\left\{1-\frac{x^2}{2\cdot 2^2}+\frac{x^4}{3\cdot 2^2\cdot 4^2}-\frac{x^6}{4\cdot 2^2\cdot 4^2\cdot 6^2}+\ldots\right\}, \\ &\int_0^{2\pi}\int_0^a \sin\frac{2\pi}{\lambda}(p\sin\theta\cos\phi)\,pdpd\phi = 0, \end{aligned}\right\} \quad (181\text{–}4)$$

where we have put

$$x \equiv ba = \frac{2\pi a}{\lambda}\sin\theta. \qquad (181\text{–}5)$$

Therefore

$$\left.\begin{aligned} \Phi_0 = -\pi k a^2\Big\{1-\frac{x^2}{2\cdot 2^2}+\frac{x^4}{3\cdot 2^2\cdot 4^2} \\ -\frac{x^6}{4\cdot 2^2\cdot 4^2\cdot 6^2}+\ldots\Big\}\sin 2\pi\left(\frac{t}{P}-\frac{R}{\lambda}\right). \end{aligned}\right\} \quad (181\text{–}6)$$

The function represented by the infinite series in the braces has, like the cosine function, an infinite number of zeros. The first of these comes for $x = 3.831706$. As x depends on θ only, the diffraction pattern consists of a central bright disk surrounded by bright rings.

The object glass of a telescope acts as a circular aperture delimiting the wave front entering the instrument, and at the same time plays the part of the lens L_2 of Fig. 182 in effectively removing the point O to infinity. In this case the approximate expression used for r in evaluating (181–1) becomes exact since R is infinite. Consequently the angular half-width of the central disk of the diffraction pattern is the angle θ, which is effectively equal to $\sin\theta$, obtained from (181–5) by putting 3.83 for x, and the radius of the image formed in the focal plane of the object glass is

$$F\theta = 3.83\frac{F\lambda}{2\pi a} = 1.22\frac{F\lambda}{d} \qquad (181\text{–}7)$$

where F is the focal length and $d = 2a$ the diameter of the object glass. This is the expression used in article 176.

Problem 181a. Find the first zero of (181–6) to three significant figures by the method of successive approximations.

Problem 181b. Retaining terms in p^2, show that the intensity at a point on the axis ($i = 0$) of the circular aperture of Fig. 185 vanishes for $R = a^2/2m\lambda$ and is maximum for $R = a^2/(2m + 1)\lambda$, where m is an integer. Also show that the maximum intensity is four times that which would exist if no screen were present.

182. Double Slit. — Let us replace the single slit of Fig. 182 by a pair of parallel slits of width a. Let b be the distance between the centers of the two slits. Then if we take origin half way between the two slits we must integrate (180–4) from $\frac{-b-a}{2}$ to $\frac{-b+a}{2}$ and again from $\frac{b-a}{2}$ to $\frac{b+a}{2}$. This gives for the disturbance at O

$$\begin{aligned}
\Phi_0 = &-\frac{c}{2\pi\theta}\Big[\cos 2\pi\left(\frac{t}{P}-\delta\right)\{\cos\pi\theta(-b+a) - \cos\pi\theta(-b-a) \\
&+ \cos\pi\theta(b+a) - \cos\pi\theta(b-a)\} \\
&+ \sin 2\pi\left(\frac{t}{P}-\delta\right)\{\sin\pi\theta(-b+a) - \sin\pi\theta(-b-a) \\
&+ \sin\pi\theta(b+a) - \sin\pi\theta(b-a)\}\Big] \\
= &-\frac{c}{\pi\theta}\{\sin\pi\theta(b+a) - \sin\pi\theta(b-a)\}\sin 2\pi\left(\frac{t}{P}-\delta\right) \\
= &-2ca\frac{\sin\pi a\theta}{\pi a\theta}\cos\pi b\theta\sin 2\pi\left(\frac{t}{P}-\delta\right),
\end{aligned}$$

and the intensity is

$$I = C\left\{\frac{\sin\pi a\theta}{\pi a\theta}\right\}^2(\cos\pi b\theta)^2 = C\left\{\frac{\sin u}{u}\right\}^2\cos^2 v \qquad (182\text{–}1)$$

if we put u for $\pi a\theta$ and v for $\pi b\theta$.

The zeros of intensity come at $\theta = m/a$ on account of the sine factor, where m is any integer except 0, and at $\theta = (k + \frac{1}{2})/b$ on account of the cosine factor, where k is any integer. So we have the same diffraction pattern as in the case of a single slit, except that the intensity is quadrupled, and superposed on this we have a new pattern which, if b is large compared with a, is of much finer structure.

The double slit diffraction pattern is shown by the full-line curve in Fig. 186, the enveloping single slit pattern being indicated by the broken line. All the lines are of the same width, corresponding to the increment $\Delta\theta = 1/b$ in θ. Therefore, from (180–3), the angular width of a line is

$$\Delta i = \frac{\lambda}{b \cos i}. \tag{182–2}$$

Consider two nearby sources of approximately the same strength lying close to the normal to the plane of the slits. If the distance b between the two slits is adjusted so that the double slit fringes disappear on account of the coincidence of the maxima of the pattern due to the one source with the minima of the pattern due to the other,

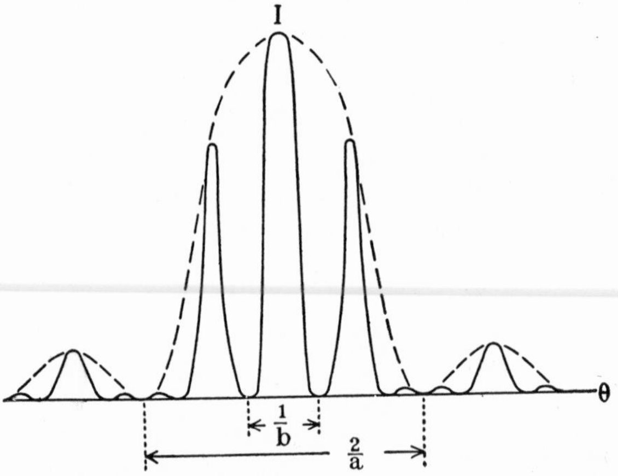

FIG. 186.

the angle Δi_1 between the sources must be half the angular width (182–2) of a line. As i is small this gives

$$\Delta i_1 = \frac{\lambda}{2b}. \tag{182–3}$$

If b is made large, the resolving power of such an arrangement is very great. Comparison with (176–2) shows that a telescope whose object glass is provided with a diaphragm containing two slits the distance between which is adjustable can resolve stars only half as far apart as can be resolved without the diaphragm, although at the xpense of the light reaching the image. An equivalent method, used n the Mt. Wilson stellar interferometer by Michelson, employs the iirrors *M*, *M* . . . (Fig. 187) above the object glass *O*. By means of his instrument Michelson made the first direct measurement of a tellar diameter in 1921 hen, by making b = 121 nches, he found that the ringes from the two halves f α Orionis (Betelgeuse) isappeared, indicating an ngular diameter of 0.047″ or this star. To obtain his resolving power without the mirrors an object glass of over 200 inch diameter would have een needed.

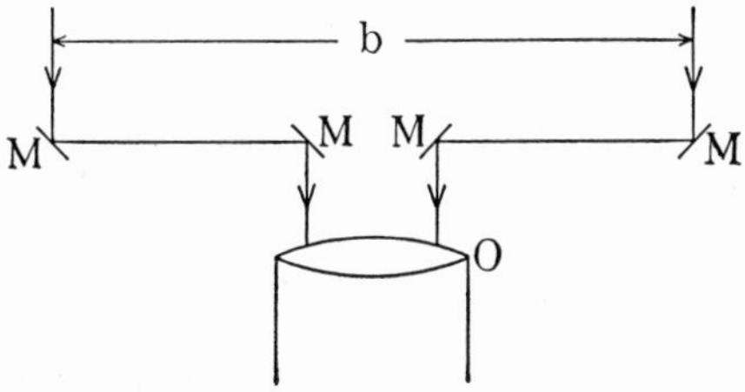

FIG. 187.

Problem 182a. Prove that

$$1 + \cos x + \cos 2x \ldots + \cos (N - 1)x = \frac{\sin N\dfrac{x}{2}}{\sin\dfrac{x}{2}} \cos (N - 1)\frac{x}{2},$$

$$\sin x + \sin 2x \ldots + \sin (N - 1)x = \frac{\sin N\dfrac{x}{2}}{\sin\dfrac{x}{2}} \sin (N - 1)\frac{x}{2}.$$

183. *N* Evenly Spaced Slits. — We shall consider now the type of diffraction exhibited by the diffraction grating. In this case we have N evenly spaced parallel slits all of the same width a. Denote by b the distance between the centers of consecutive slits. Taking origin at the center of the first slit equation (180–4) must be integrated from $-a/2$ to $a/2$, $b - a/2$ to $b + a/2$, $2b - a/2$ to $2b + a/2$ and so forth ending with the interval $(N - 1)b - a/2$ to $(N - 1)b + a/2$. Therefore

$$\Phi_0 = -\frac{c}{2\pi\theta}\left[\cos 2\pi\left(\frac{t}{P} - \delta\right)\{\cos \pi\theta a - \cos(-\pi\theta a) + \cos \pi\theta(2b + a)\right.$$

$$- \cos \pi\theta(2b - a) \ldots + \cos \pi\theta(2(N - 1)b + a)$$

$$- \cos \pi\theta(2(N-1)b-a)\} + \sin 2\pi\left(\frac{t}{P}-\delta\right)\{\sin \pi\theta a$$

$$- \sin(-\pi\theta a) + \sin \pi\theta(2b+a) - \sin \pi\theta(2b-a)\ldots$$

$$+ \sin \pi\theta(2(N-1)b+a) - \sin \pi\theta(2(N-1)b-a)\}\Big]$$

$$= - ca\frac{\sin \pi a\theta}{\pi a\theta}\left[\sin 2\pi\left(\frac{t}{P}-\delta\right)\{1+\cos 2\pi b\theta \ldots + \cos 2\pi(N-1)b\right.$$

$$\left.- \cos 2\pi\left(\frac{t}{P}-\delta\right)\{\sin 2\pi b\theta \ldots + \sin 2\pi(N-1)b\theta\}\right]$$

$$= - ca\frac{\sin \pi a\theta}{\pi a\theta}\frac{\sin \pi Nb\theta}{\sin \pi b\theta}\left[\sin 2\pi\left(\frac{t}{P}-\delta\right)\cos \pi(N-1)b\theta\right.$$

$$\left.- \cos 2\pi\left(\frac{t}{P}-\delta\right)\sin \pi(N-1)b\theta\right]$$

$$= - ca\frac{\sin \pi a\theta}{\pi a\theta}\frac{\sin \pi Nb\theta}{\sin \pi b\theta}\sin 2\pi\left\{\frac{t}{P}-\delta-\frac{N-1}{2}b\theta\right\}$$

from the result of problem 182*a*.

The intensity of the radiation is

$$I = C\left\{\frac{\sin \pi a\theta}{\pi a\theta}\frac{\sin \pi Nb\theta}{\sin \pi b\theta}\right\}^2 = C\left\{\frac{\sin u}{u}\frac{\sin Nv}{\sin v}\right\}^2 \qquad (183-$$

if we put u for $\pi a\theta$ and v for $\pi b\theta$. If $N = 2$, $\sin Nv = 2 \sin v$ cos and (183–1) reduces to the formula (182–1) for the double slit.

We have, then, superposed on the single slit diffraction patter a finer pattern due to the multiplicity of slits. As we have alreac discussed the single slit pattern we need consider now only the slit pattern. The zeros of intensity come where $Nb\theta = k$, where is any integer not an integral multiple of N. For $k = mN$, whe m is an integer, $b\theta = m$ and the denominator of (183–1) vanishe As

$$\Big|^{t}_{v=m\pi}\frac{\sin Nv}{\sin v} = \left(\frac{N \cos Nv}{\cos\ v}\right)_{v=m\pi} = \pm N$$

the intensity does not vanish for such a value of k.

Differentiating the second factor in (183–1) to find the maxima of ntensity we get

$$N \tan v = \tan Nv. \tag{183–2}$$

If v_m is a solution of this equation and u_m the corresponding value f u, the intensity at the maxima is given by

$$I_m = C\left\{\frac{\sin u_m}{u_m}\frac{\sin Nv_m}{\sin v_m}\right\}^2 = CN^2\left\{\frac{\sin u_m}{u_m}\frac{\cos Nv_m}{\cos v_m}\right\}^2$$

nd the ratio of I_m to the intensity I_0 of the central maximum is

$$\frac{I_m}{I_0} = \left\{\frac{\sin u_m}{u_m}\frac{\cos Nv_m}{\cos v_m}\right\}^2. \tag{183–3}$$

Equation (183–2) is satisfied for $v = m\pi$ or $b\theta = m$. In this case he second factor of (183–3) becomes unity. These maxima are nown as the *principal maxima.* 'he remaining solutions occur or Nv_m nearly equal to $(k + \frac{1}{2})\pi$, nd the intensity at these *subidiary maxima* is very small ompared with that at the principal maxima. In Fig. 188 the ntensity is plotted against θ for wo, four and an infinite number f slits. Although the lines are nfinitely sharp in the last case, certain amount of background emains due to the infinitely close ubsidiary maxima. The broken ne represents the enveloping ingle slit diffraction pattern.

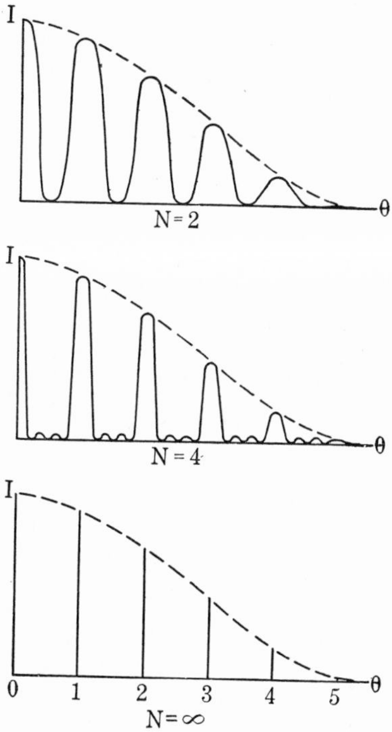

FIG. 188.

These sketches are for monohromatic radiation. If the incient light consists of more than ne wave length, the diffraction attern consists of the superposiion of a number of differently paced patterns of the type illusrated in the figure. The aggreate of first principal maxima to the right of the central maximum onstitute the *first order spectrum*, the aggregate of second principal maxima the *second order spectrum* and so on. The angle i of diffractio of the line of wave length λ in the mth order spectrum is obtaine by putting $b\theta = m$. Restoring the value of θ in accord with (180–3

$$\sin i = \frac{m\lambda}{b} - \sin i_1, \qquad (183\text{–}4$$

from which the wave length may be calculated.

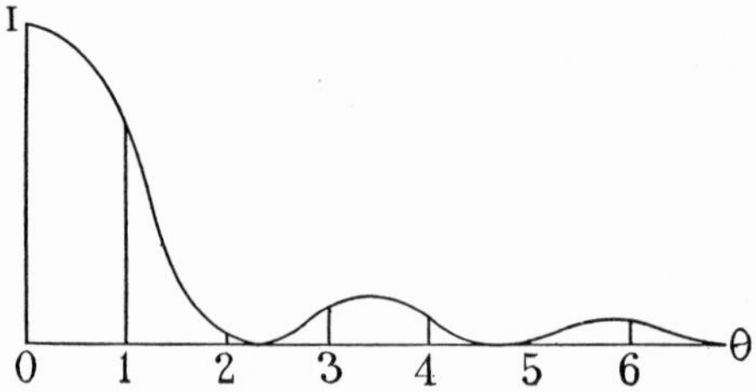

FIG. 189.

If a is comparabl with b the diffractio pattern may be influ enced appreciably by th enveloping single sli pattern even in spectr of low order, as indi cated in Fig. 189. I the case illustrated th second order spectrum is very weak, although the third order appears in considerable in tensity.

The *dispersion* D of a grating is the change in the angle of diffrac tion i per unit change in wave length. From (183–4)

$$D = \frac{m}{b \cos i}. \qquad (183\text{–}5$$

The dispersion, then, is greater the higher the order of the spec trum and varies inversely with the *grating space* b. It is independen of the number of slits N. If the diffracted light is viewed at righ angles to the surface of the grating $i = 0$ and

$$D = \frac{m}{b}$$

is practically constant over a considerable range of wave lengths.

There is a certain angle of incidence for which the deviation produced by a grating has a minimum value. For $\delta = i_1 + i$ an by (183–4)

$$\frac{m\lambda}{b} = \sin i_1 + \sin i = 2 \sin \frac{i_1 + i}{2} \cos \frac{i_1 - i}{2},$$

and

$$\sin \frac{\delta}{2} = \frac{m\lambda}{2b} \sec \frac{i_1 - i}{2}. \qquad (183\text{–}6$$

So the deviation is least when $i_1 = i$, a condition analogous to 178–2) for the prism.

If i_{θ_1} and i_{θ_2} are the angles of diffraction corresponding to the zeros f intensity on either side of a principal maximum, the angular width f a spectral line is

$$\Delta i_m = i_{\theta_2} - i_{\theta_1}$$

here, from (180–3),

$$\sin i_{\theta_1} = \lambda\theta_1 - \sin i_1, \quad \sin i_{\theta_2} = \lambda\theta_2 - \sin i_1,$$

nd

$$\theta_1 = \frac{k_1}{Nb} = \frac{k-1}{Nb}, \quad \theta_2 = \frac{k_2}{Nb} = \frac{k+1}{Nb},$$

here $k = mN$. Therefore

$$\sin i_{\theta_2} - \sin i_{\theta_1} = \lambda(\theta_2 - \theta_1) = \frac{2\lambda}{Nb},$$

r

$$\sin\frac{i_{\theta_2} - i_{\theta_1}}{2}\cos\frac{i_{\theta_2} + i_{\theta_1}}{2} = \frac{\lambda}{Nb}.$$

As $i_{\theta_2} - i_{\theta_1}$ is a small angle

$$i_{\theta_2} - i_{\theta_1} = \frac{2\lambda}{Nb\cos i},$$

here i has been put for the mean of i_{θ_1} and i_{θ_2}, and

$$\Delta i_m = \frac{2\lambda}{Nb\cos i}. \tag{183–7}$$

Two lines of equal intensity in the spectrum are said to be resolved f a principal maximum of the one falls on a first minimum of the other. f $\Delta\lambda$ is the difference in wave length of the two, the ratio $\lambda/\Delta\lambda$ is efined as the *spectroscopic resolving power* R of the grating. Now the ngular separation of two lines in the mth order spectrum which differ n wave length by $\Delta\lambda$ is $(m\Delta\lambda)/(b\cos i)$ from (183–4). Equating this o half the width Δi_m of a line as given by (183–7) we find

$$R = \frac{\lambda}{\Delta\lambda} = Nm. \tag{183–8}$$

So the resolving power is proportional to the total number of slits N and to the order m of the spectrum. Unlike the dispersion i is independent of the grating space b.

A transmission grating consists of a large number of parallel slit separated by opaque strips. A reflection grating, on the other hand is made by ruling parallel scratches on a metallic surface. In th first case the periodicity of the slits and in the second the periodicit of the scratches gives rise t the diffraction characteristi of the grating.

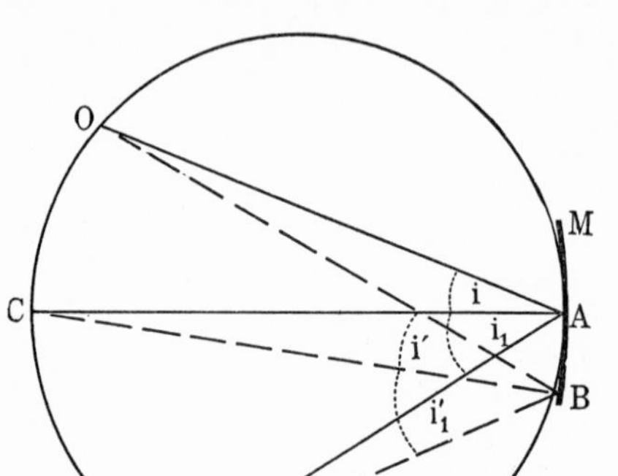

FIG. 190.

The use of glass lenses i conjunction with a gratin precludes work in the ultra violet on account of th absorption of glass in thi region. To avoid this diffi culty and to eliminate chro matic aberration Rowlan dispensed entirely with lense by ruling gratings on a con cave spherical mirror M (Fig 190) of speculum metal. Le C be the center of curvature of the grating, supposed to have a radiu of curvature large compared with its linear dimensions. The source and point of observation O are on the circumference of a circle o diameter CA. If we draw rays SAO and SBO, $i'_1 = i_1$ since bot angles are subtended by the same arc SC, and $i' = i$ since both ar subtended by CO. Hence all the light which is incident on the grat ing at the angle i_1 and diffracted at the angle i converges at O and n lenses are required. In the Rowland mounting O is placed at C s as to make $i = 0$. Then (183–4) reduces to

$$\sin i_1 = \frac{m\lambda}{b}. \qquad (183\text{–}9$$

Problem 183a. A grating of 4 cm width has 20,000 lines. Find th resolving power, and the difference in wave length of two lines which ar just resolved in the region of 5000 Å in the first order spectrum. Find th minimum deviation for this order and wave length, and the dispersion fo minimum deviation. *Ans.* 20,000m, 0.25Å, 14.4°, 0.173′ per Å.

Problem 183b. For a grating with very large N, show that the ratio o the intensity of the closest subsidiary maximum to that of a principal maxi mum is 4.7%.

184. Echelon. — We saw in the last article that the resolving power f a grating is proportional to the rder m of the spectrum as well as he number of lines N. The echelon, nvented by Michelson, obtains a igh resolving power by making the rder m very great. It consists of pile of N glass plates (Fig. 191) of hickness d, each of which is a little horter than the preceding one. Consider a plane wave incident ormally on the top of the echelon. After passing through the echelon he wave front AB is made up of ections Aa, ab, bc, . . . eB which ave passed through different thicknesses of glass and therefore are out of phase with one another. Going ack to formula (180–2), that is,

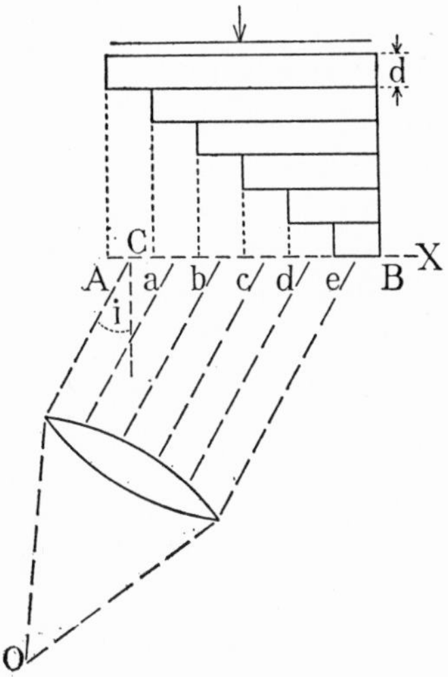

FIG. 191.

$$\Phi_0 = c\int \sin 2\pi\left(\frac{r_1}{\lambda} + \frac{r}{\lambda} - \frac{t}{P}\right)dx,$$

ve have for Aa

$$\frac{r_1}{\lambda} = \frac{d}{\lambda'} + \frac{(N-1)d}{\lambda} = \frac{Nd + (n-1)d}{\lambda}$$

ince the ratio of the wave length λ in air to the wave length λ' in glass is equal to the index of refraction n of glass relative to air. Similarly for ab

$$\frac{r_1'}{\lambda} = \frac{2d}{\lambda'} + \frac{(N-2)d}{\lambda} = \frac{Nd + 2(n-1)d}{\lambda},$$

and so forth. Also

$$\frac{r}{\lambda} = \text{Constant} + \frac{x \sin i}{\lambda}.$$

So if we take origin at the center C of Aa and denote $Aa = ab = bc \dots = eB$ by b,

$$\left.\begin{aligned}
\Phi_0 &= c\int \sin 2\pi\left(\frac{x\sin i}{\lambda}+\frac{r_1}{\lambda}-\frac{t}{P}\right)dx\\
&= -\frac{c\lambda}{2\pi\sin i}\left\{\left|\cos 2\pi\left(\frac{x\sin i}{\lambda}+\frac{r_1}{\lambda}-\frac{t}{P}\right)\right|_{-b/2}^{b/2}\right.\\
&\quad\left.+\left|\cos 2\pi\left(\frac{x\sin i}{\lambda}+\frac{r_1'}{\lambda}-\frac{t}{P}\right)\right|_{b/2}^{3b/2}+\dots\right\}\\
&= -\frac{c\lambda}{2\pi\sin i}\left\{\cos 2\pi\left(\frac{b\sin i}{2\lambda}+\frac{r_1}{\lambda}-\frac{t}{P}\right)\right.\\
&\quad-\cos 2\pi\left(-\frac{b\sin i}{2\lambda}+\frac{r_1}{\lambda}-\frac{t}{P}\right)\\
&\quad+\cos 2\pi\left(\frac{3b\sin i}{2\lambda}+\frac{r_1'}{\lambda}-\frac{t}{P}\right)\\
&\quad\left.-\cos 2\pi\left(\frac{b\sin i}{2\lambda}+\frac{r_1'}{\lambda}-\frac{t}{P}\right)+\dots\right\}\\
&= -bc\frac{\sin 2\pi\left(\frac{b\sin i}{2\lambda}\right)}{2\pi\left(\frac{b\sin i}{2\lambda}\right)}\left\{\sin 2\pi\left(\frac{t}{P}-\frac{r_1}{\lambda}\right)\right.\\
&\quad\left.+\sin 2\pi\left(\frac{t}{P}-\frac{r_1'}{\lambda}-\frac{b\sin i}{\lambda}\right)+\dots\right\}.
\end{aligned}\right\}\quad(184\text{–}1)$$

Put

$$\alpha \equiv \frac{(n-1)d+b\sin i}{\lambda},\quad \beta \equiv \frac{(N+n-1)d}{\lambda}. \qquad (184\text{–}2)$$

Then

$$\frac{r_1}{\lambda}=\beta,\quad \frac{r_1'}{\lambda}+\frac{b\sin i}{\lambda}=\alpha+\beta,\ \text{etc.,}$$

and

$$
\left.\begin{aligned}
&\sin 2\pi\left(\frac{t}{P}-\frac{r_1}{\lambda}\right)+\sin 2\pi\left(\frac{t}{P}-\frac{r_1'}{\lambda}-\frac{b\sin i}{\lambda}\right)+\dots\\
&=\sin 2\pi\left(\frac{t}{P}-\beta\right)+\sin 2\pi\left(\frac{t}{P}-\beta-\alpha\right)\\
&\qquad\qquad+\sin 2\pi\left(\frac{t}{P}-\beta-2\alpha\right)+\dots\\
&=\sin 2\pi\left(\frac{t}{P}-\beta\right)\{1+\cos 2\pi\alpha+\cos 4\pi\alpha+\cos 6\pi\alpha+\dots\}\\
&-\cos 2\pi\left(\frac{t}{P}-\beta\right)\{\sin 2\pi\alpha+\sin 4\pi\alpha+\sin 6\pi\alpha+\dots\}\\
&=\frac{\sin\pi N\alpha}{\sin\pi\alpha}\sin 2\pi\left(\frac{t}{P}-\beta-\frac{N-1}{2}\alpha\right)
\end{aligned}\right\}\quad(184\text{–}3)
$$

from the result of problem 182*a*. Substituting in (184–1)

$$
\Phi_0=-bc\frac{\sin 2\pi\left(\dfrac{b\sin i}{2\lambda}\right)}{2\pi\left(\dfrac{b\sin i}{2\lambda}\right)}\frac{\sin\pi N\alpha}{\sin\pi\alpha}\sin 2\pi\left(\frac{t}{P}-\beta-\frac{N-1}{2}\alpha\right).
$$

Therefore the intensity of the radiation is

$$
I=C\left\{\frac{\sin 2\pi\left(\dfrac{b\sin i}{2\lambda}\right)}{2\pi\left(\dfrac{b\sin i}{2\lambda}\right)}\frac{\sin\pi N\alpha}{\sin\pi\alpha}\right\}^2. \quad(184\text{–}4)
$$

This formula is of the same form as (183–1) for the grating. Therefore the principal maxima are given by $\alpha = m$ or

$$
\sin i=\frac{m\lambda-(n-1)d}{b} \quad(184\text{–}5)
$$

from (184–2). On account of the first factor inside the braces in (184–4), which corresponds to that responsible for the enveloping single slit diffraction pattern in the case of the grating, the intensity is considerable only for small values of i. But small values of i

correspond to spectra of orders comparable with the large numb $(n - 1)d/\lambda$. Hence practically all the light is thrown into spect of very high orders for which the resolving power, given by the san formula (183–8) as for a grating, is very large. The chief defect the echelon is that spectra of many orders overlap, causing confusic in the identification of new lines.

Problem 184a. An echelon consists of 30 glass plates each of which 1 cm thick. The index of refraction of the glass is 1.52. For yellow lig of wave length $\lambda = 5.896(10)^{-5}$ cm find the order of greatest intensity, t resolving power, and the wave length difference between two lines which a just resolved. Could the grating of problem 183*a* be used so as to obtain great a resolving power? *Ans.* 8800, 264,000, 0.023 Å, No.

185. Prism Spectrometer. — The prism spectrometer consists of collimator C (Fig. 192) and a telescope T placed on opposite sides

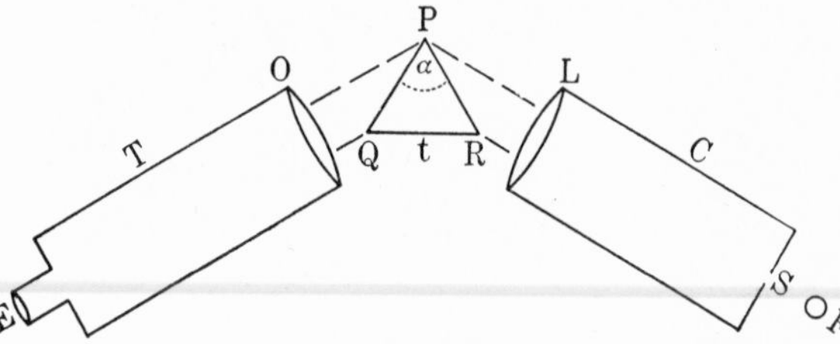

FIG. 192.

the prism P. The narrow slit S illuminated by the flame F ac as a line source consisting of the central line of its diffraction patter The lens L at the other end of the collimator is placed at a distanc from the slit equal to its focal length, so that the light incident c the prism shall consist of plane waves. The object glass O of th telescope forms an image of the slit in its focal plane, which is viewe through the eyepiece E. The prism and the telescope may b rotated independently about an axis perpendicular to the plane c the figure through the center of the table which carries the prism.

We found the dispersion of a prism in article 178. To find i resolving power we can consider the face PQ from which the radiatio emerges as a slit limiting the width of the beam which passes into th telescope. Then the angle i_4 of emergence of Fig. 177 is the angle of incidence of the plane waves on the slit, and, for two lines to b esolved, their angular separation must be half the width (180–8) of ither. Hence, putting i_4 for i_1 in (180–8),

$$\frac{di_4}{d\lambda}\Delta\lambda = \frac{\lambda}{a\cos i_4},$$

nd the resolving power of the prism is

$$R = \frac{\lambda}{\Delta\lambda} = a\cos i_4\frac{di_4}{d\lambda} = -\,aD\cos i_4 \qquad (185\text{–}1)$$

n terms of the dispersion D of the prism. Putting in the value of the lispersion given by (178–4) we find

$$R = -\,\frac{a\sin\alpha}{\cos i_2}\frac{dn}{d\lambda} \qquad (185\text{–}2)$$

vhere α is the angle of the prism. The spectrometer is generally ised at minimum deviation. For this arrangement $i_2 = \alpha/2$ and

$$R = -\,2a\sin\frac{\alpha}{2}\frac{dn}{d\lambda} = -\,t\frac{dn}{d\lambda}, \qquad (185\text{–}3)$$

vhere t is the length of the base of the triangle PQR. The resolving ower of a prism is greater the larger the prism, much as that of a elescope is greater the larger the object glass. Using the Cauchy ormula (178–5) for the index of refraction

$$R = \frac{2Bt}{\lambda^3}. \qquad (185\text{–}4)$$

Hence the resolving power as well as the dispersion varies inversely s the cube of the wave length. Consequently a prism spectrometer s especially useful in the ultra-violet region of the spectrum. Here, owever, a quartz prism must be used ince glass is opaque.

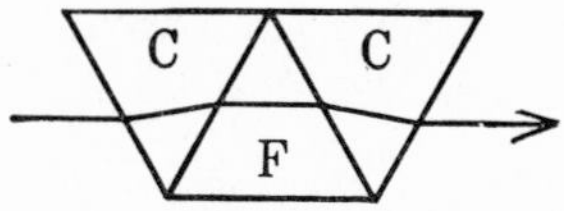

FIG. 193.

As a portable instrument for use in he hand it is convenient to have a spec- roscope which produces dispersion with- ut deviation of the central portion of he visible spectrum. An instrument having this property may be nade by cementing together two crown glass prisms C (Fig. 193) nd one flint glass prism F, since the latter has a dispersion more han double that of the former.

Problem 185a. How many 60° prisms 5 cm on a side are needed to resolve two lines 0.5Å apart in the neighborhood of 6000Å? The prisms are made of flint glass for which $B = 0.984(10)^{-10}$ cm². *Ans.* Three prisms.

186. Interference. — A source of visible light intense enough to produce perceptible effects contains a vast number of vibrating electrons whose phases are distributed at random. Hence we cannot expect to observe interference between trains of light waves originating in separate sources as we can between sound waves from two tuning forks. Not only must two beams of light originate in a single source in order that interference may be observed, but if there is a considerable difference in path between the two beams the source must be monochromatic. We shall consider two simple devices for producing interference.

I. *Fresnel Mirrors.* — Consider a monochromatic line source S (Fig. 194) at right angles to the plane of the paper placed in front

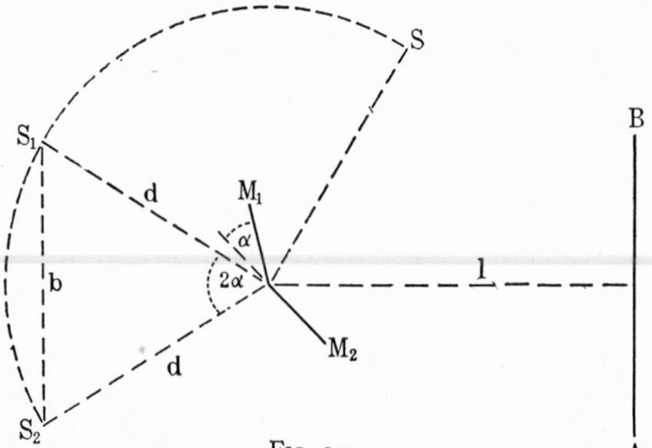

FIG. 194.

of two mirrors M_1 and M_2 which are inclined to each other at a small angle α. The effect on the screen AB is that of two virtual line sources S_1 and S_2 situated at the images of the source S in the mirrors M_1 and M_2.

The interference pattern is therefore the same in its essential features as the diffraction pattern of the double slit discussed in article 182 for the case where $i_1 = 0$. Consequently, as indicated by Fig. 186, the fringes on the screen are parallel to the slit S and at angular distances from one another equal to

$$\Delta i = \frac{\lambda}{b}$$

where b is the distance between the effective line sources S_1 and S_2. Since α is a small angle $b = 2\alpha d$ and

$$\Delta i = \frac{\lambda}{2\alpha d}.$$

If l is the distance of the screen AB from the mirrors and s the linear distance on the screen between consecutive fringes,

$$\Delta i = \frac{s}{l + d}. \qquad (186\text{–}1)$$

Therefore

$$\lambda = \frac{2\alpha s}{1 + \frac{l}{d}}. \qquad (186\text{–}2)$$

If the incident light is made parallel by a convergent lens placed between the source and the mirrors, d is effectively infinite and

$$\lambda = 2\alpha s. \qquad (186\text{–}3)$$

By measuring α and s the wave length λ can be computed from this formula.

II. *Fresnel Bi-prism.* — Here we have a line source S (Fig. 195) at right angles to the plane of the paper placed at a distance d behind

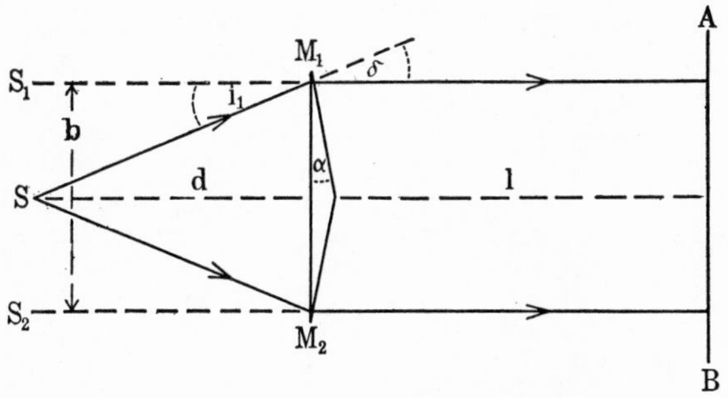

FIG. 195.

the bi-prism M_1M_2 of small angle α. As the angles of incidence and refraction are small we can write Snell's law in the form

$$i_1 = ni_2, \quad i_4 = ni_3,$$

and therefore the deviation δ is

$$\delta = i_1 - i_4 - \alpha = (n - 1)\alpha$$

from (178–1). As this is independent of the angle of incidence i_1 all rays from S striking the upper prism are deviated by the same amount and appear to come from S_1, where

$$SS_1 = \delta d = (n - 1)\alpha d.$$

Similarly rays from S striking the lower prism are deviated so as to appear to come from S_2, where $SS_2 = SS_1$. Hence the interference pattern on the screen AB is that due to two effective line sources S_1 and S_2 a distance b apart, where

$$b = 2SS_1 = 2(n - 1)\alpha d.$$

We have then for the angular separation of consecutive fringes

$$\Delta i = \frac{\lambda}{b} = \frac{\lambda}{2(n - 1)\alpha d}$$

just as in the case of Fresnel's mirrors. If l is the distance of the screen from the prism (186–1) gives Δi in terms of the linear distance between fringes. Consequently

$$\lambda = \frac{2(n - 1)\alpha s}{1 + \dfrac{l}{d}}, \qquad (186\text{–}4)$$

and if the incident light is made parallel by a lens interposed between the source and the bi-prism

$$\lambda = 2(n - 1)\alpha s. \qquad (186\text{–}5)$$

187. Michelson Interferometer. — This instrument contains a half-silvered mirror M (Fig. 196) which partially transmits and partially reflects parallel light coming through the lens L from the source S. The transmitted light is reflected by the mirror M_2 and again by M, ultimately reaching the eye at E. Similarly the reflected light is turned back by the mirror M_1 through M to E. The compensating plate of unsilvered glass C is placed in the path of the light reflected by M so that this ray shall pass through the same thickness of glass as the transmitted ray.

The observer at E sees the mirror M_1 and the image in M of the mirror M_2. So the actual arrangement is equivalent to two parallel mirrors M_1 and M_2 (Fig. 197) through which the two interfering beams come to the observer's eye from the images S_1 and S_2 of the

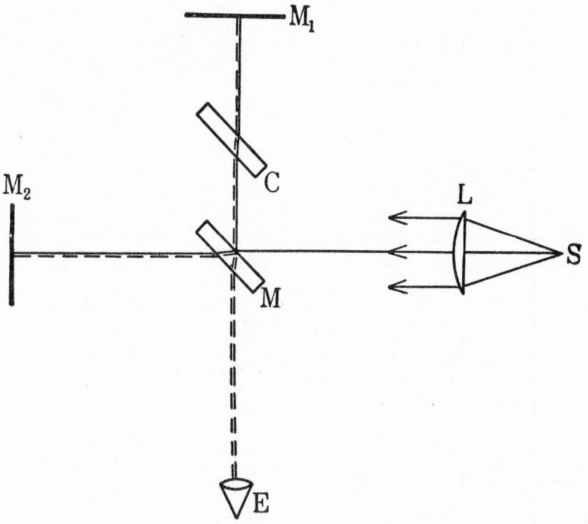

FIG. 196.

source S, supposed, for the moment, not to have been effectively removed to infinity by interposition of the lens L. If M_2 is at a distance from M greater than M_1 by t the radiation from the effective source S_2 has to travel a distance $2t \cos i$ greater than that from S_1 in order to reach O. Furthermore a phase difference between the two beams of a fraction ϵ of a wave length is introduced by the fact that one is reflected externally at M and the other internally. Consequently the interference pattern due to a point source consists of bright rings produced by reinforcement of the two trains of waves at angles given by

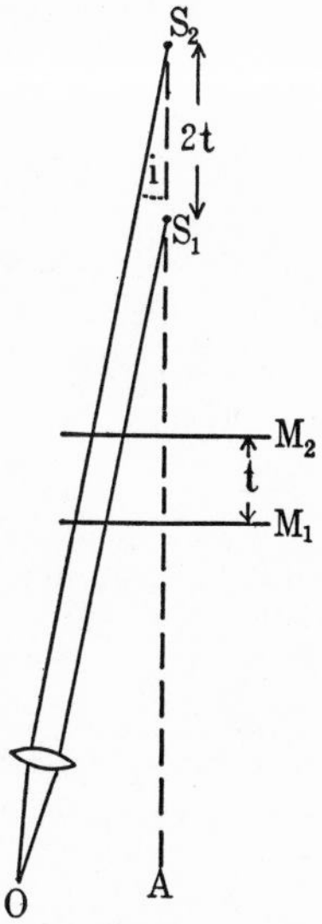

FIG. 197.

$$2t \cos i = (m - \epsilon)\lambda, \qquad (187\text{–}1)$$

where m is an integer, separated by dark rings produced by interference. At the center A of the field we have a bright spot if $2t = (m - \epsilon)\lambda$ and darkness if $2t = (m + \frac{1}{2} - \epsilon)\lambda$. If the source S is effectively removed to infinity by interposition of the lens L of Fig. 196 the central spot spreads out so as to occupy the whole field of view.

If, now, the mirror M_2 is moved slowly away from M while the mirror M_1 is kept fixed, the fringes spread out and a new fringe appears at A for every displacement of half a wave length of the mirror M_2. Therefore if N new fringes appear for a displacement Δt of this mirror, the wave length of the monochromatic light emitted by the source is

$$\lambda = \frac{2\Delta t}{N}. \qquad (187\text{–}2)$$

As generally used the images M_1 and M_2 (Fig. 197) of the mirrors are not quite parallel. If ϕ (Fig. 198) is the angle between them and we employ the rectangular axes indicated in the figure, the coordinates of S_1 are 0, $-h\phi$, $2h$ and those of S_2 are 0, $(h+t)\phi$, $2(h+t)$ since ϕ is a small angle. Suppose we wish to find the illumination at a point P in the XY plane whose coordinates are x, y, 0. If l_1 is the length of the path S_1P and l_2 that of S_2P, then, for small x and y

$$l_1^2 = x^2 + \{y + h\phi\}^2 + 4h^2 = 4h^2(1 + \tfrac{1}{4}\phi^2)\{1 + \frac{y}{2h}\phi + \ldots\},$$

$$l_2^2 = x^2 + \{y - (h+t)\phi\}^2 + 4(h+t)^2$$

$$= 4(h+t)^2(1 + \tfrac{1}{4}\phi^2)\{1 - \frac{y}{2(h+t)}\phi + \ldots\},$$

to a first approximation. Therefore

$$l_1 = 2h\sqrt{1 + \tfrac{1}{4}\phi^2}\{1 + \frac{y}{4h}\phi + \ldots\} = 2h\sqrt{1 + \tfrac{1}{4}\phi^2} + \tfrac{1}{2}y\phi + \ldots$$

$$l_2 = 2(h+t)\sqrt{1 + \tfrac{1}{4}\phi^2}\{1 - \frac{y}{4(h+t)}\phi + \ldots\}$$

$$= 2(h+t)\sqrt{1 + \tfrac{1}{4}\phi^2} - \tfrac{1}{2}y\phi + \ldots,$$

and the difference of the two paths is

$$\Delta l = l_2 - l_1 = 2t\sqrt{1 + \tfrac{1}{4}\phi^2} - y\phi.$$

The regions of brightness are given by

$$2t\sqrt{1 + \tfrac{1}{4}\phi^2} - y\phi = (m - \epsilon)\lambda, \qquad (187\text{–}3)$$

where m is an integer. This equation indicates that the fringes are straight lines parallel to the X axis. A closer approximation shows that they are slightly curved, except that the fringe corresponding to zero effective path difference is perfectly straight and achromatic in white light. This fringe is called the *central fringe*.

If one of the mirrors is displaced, the other remaining fixed, the fringes move across the field of view, the number of fringes crossing the center of the field being related to the displacement by the same formula (187–2) as for the number of new fringes appearing when the images of the mirrors are accurately parallel. From this relation the wave length of a monochromatic source can be measured with a high degree of precision, or a distance Δt can be determined in terms of a known wave length. In this way Michelson has found that the standard meter at 15° C. and normal pressure has a length of 1,553,163.5 red cadmium waves, 1,966,249.7 green cadmium waves, or 2,083,372.1 blue cadmium waves. He has also been able to detect interference for a path difference of half a million wave lengths, indicating that coherent wave trains of a length greater than this are emitted by radiating atoms.

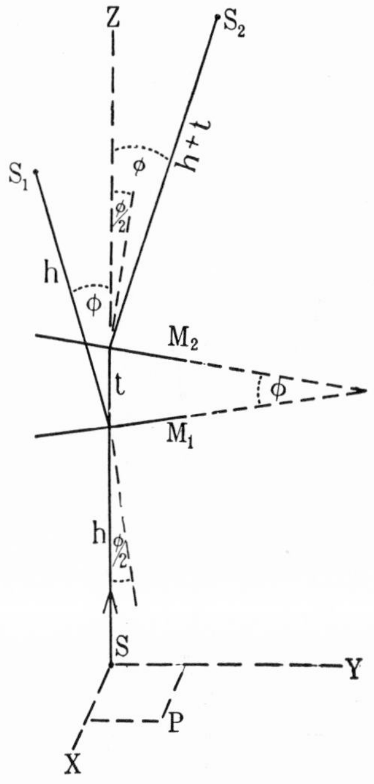

FIG. 198.

If a source is not quite monochromatic, but gives off, say, two monochromatic radiations of slightly different wave lengths, the fringes due to the one radiation will fall between those due to the other after the path difference has been increased by a certain amount. Further increase of path difference will bring the fringes into phase again, and so forth. If we define the *visibility* V of the fringes as the ratio of the difference of the maximum and minimum intensities to their sum, the visibility will fluctuate as the distance t is increased in case the source consists of a close doublet instead of a strictly monochromatic line. In the case of the H_α line of hydrogen Michelson found the visibility curve shown in Fig. 199*a* the analysis of which revealed the doublet indicated in Fig. 199*b*.

Problem 187a. Newton's rings are formed when light falls on a plano-convex lens placed on a flat piece of glass by interference between the light reflected from the under convex surface of the lens and that reflected from the upper surface of the flat glass. Find the relation between the radii ρ of the nth and $(n + s)$th rings, the radius of curvature R of the lower surface of the lens, the angle of incidence θ, and the wave length λ.

$$Ans.\ \lambda = \frac{\rho_{n+s}{}^2 - \rho_n{}^2}{sR} \cos \theta.$$

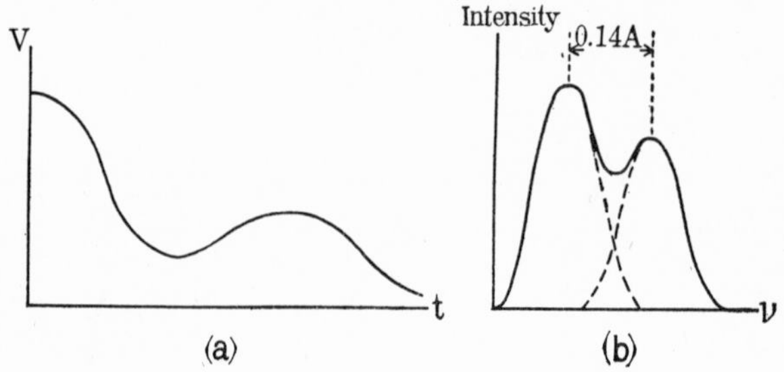

FIG. 199.

Problem 187b. Prove that, if ρ is less than unity,

$$1 + \rho \cos x + \rho^2 \cos 2x + \ldots = \frac{1 - \rho \cos x}{1 - 2\rho \cos x + \rho^2},$$

$$\rho \sin x + \rho^2 \sin 2x + \ldots = \frac{\rho \sin x}{1 - 2\rho \cos x + \rho^2}.$$

188. Fabry and Perot Interferometer. — This interferometer consists of two flat plates of glass, A and B (Fig. 200), partially silvered on their adjacent sides. Light coming from a point source S is partially transmitted and partially reflected at the silvered surfaces, so that the illumination to the right of the interferometer is that which would be produced by regularly spaced effective sources S, S_1, S_2 . . . of constantly diminishing strength at distances from one another double the distance d between the two mirror surfaces.

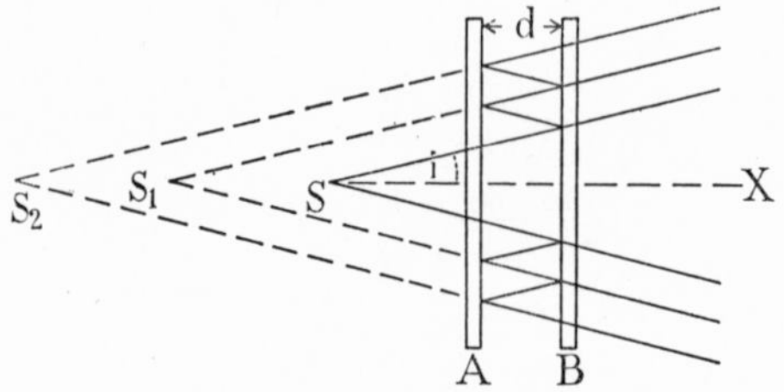

FIG. 200.

If the disturbance at a distance l from S due to the directly transmitted radiation proceeding in a direction making an angle i with the normal to the plates is

$$\Phi_0 = c \sin 2\pi\left\{\frac{l}{\lambda} - \frac{t}{P}\right\},$$

then that due to S_1 is

$$\Phi_1 = \rho c \sin 2\pi\left\{\frac{l + 2d\cos i + \epsilon\lambda}{\lambda} - \frac{t}{P}\right\},$$

where the factor ρ is introduced to take account of the loss of intensity and the term in ϵ to take account of the phase changes at the two reflections, and that due to S_2 is

$$\Phi_2 = \rho^2 c \sin 2\pi\left\{\frac{l + 4d\cos i + 2\epsilon\lambda}{\lambda} - \frac{t}{P}\right\},$$

and so forth. The resultant disturbance, then, is given by the infinite series

$$\Phi = \Phi_0 + \Phi_1 + \Phi_2 + \ldots$$

Put

$$\alpha \equiv 2\pi\left\{\frac{l}{\lambda} - \frac{t}{P}\right\}, \quad \beta \equiv 2\pi\left(\frac{2d\cos i}{\lambda} + \epsilon\right).$$

Then

$$\begin{aligned}\Phi &= c\{\sin\alpha + \rho\sin(\alpha+\beta) + \rho^2\sin(\alpha+2\beta) + \ldots\}\\ &= c\sin\alpha\,\{1 + \rho\cos\beta + \rho^2\cos 2\beta + \ldots\}\\ &\quad + c\cos\alpha\{\rho\sin\beta + \rho^2\sin 2\beta + \ldots\}\\ &= \frac{c}{1 - 2\rho\cos\beta + \rho^2}\{(1 - \rho\cos\beta)\sin\alpha + \rho\sin\beta\cos\alpha\}\end{aligned}$$

by the result of problem 187*b*. Therefore

$$\Phi = \frac{c}{\sqrt{1 - 2\rho\cos\beta + \rho^2}}\sin 2\pi\left\{\frac{l}{\lambda} - \frac{t}{P} + \delta\right\}, \tag{188–1}$$

where

$$\tan 2\pi\delta \equiv \frac{\rho\sin\beta}{1 - \rho\cos\beta},$$

and the intensity is

$$I = \frac{C}{1 - 2\rho\cos\beta + \rho^2} = \frac{C}{(1-\rho)^2 + 4\rho\sin^2(\beta/2)}. \tag{188–2}$$

The intensity has no zeros, but is a maximum for $\beta = 2k\pi$ and a minimum for $\beta = (2k + 1)\pi$, where k is an integer. Therefore the fringes on a screen parallel to the interferometer plates are concentric circles.

Let us now consider the fluctuations in intensity along the axis SX as the distance d between the plates is gradually increased. As $i = 0$, $\beta = 2\pi(2d/\lambda + \epsilon)$, and the intensity of the radiation proceeding in this direction has the maximum value

$$I_m = \frac{C}{(1 - \rho)^2}, \tag{188-3}$$

when

$$d = \tfrac{1}{2}(k - \epsilon)\lambda. \tag{188-4}$$

If Δd is the increase in d necessary to reduce the intensity to half its maximum value, we can take the ratio of Δd to the distance $\frac{1}{2}\lambda$ necessary to pass from one maximum to the next as a measure of the sharpness of the fringes. The smaller this ratio the sharper are the fringes. If, then, we put (188–2) equal to half (188–3) and solve for β we get

$$\sin\frac{\beta}{2} = \frac{1 - \rho}{2\sqrt{\rho}}$$

or, since $\sin(\beta/2)$ is zero at the maximum,

$$\sin 2\pi\frac{\Delta d}{\lambda} = \frac{1 - \rho}{2\sqrt{\rho}}.$$

Therefore

$$\frac{\Delta d}{\frac{1}{2}\lambda} = \frac{1}{\pi}\sin^{-1}\frac{1 - \rho}{2\sqrt{\rho}}. \tag{188-5}$$

If we put

$$F \equiv \frac{4\rho}{(1 - \rho)^2}$$

(188–5) becomes

$$\frac{\Delta d}{\frac{1}{2}\lambda} = \frac{1}{\pi}\sin^{-1}\frac{1}{\sqrt{F}} \tag{188-6}$$

and the ratio of the minimum to the maximum intensity is

$$\frac{I_{\min}}{I_{\max}} = \frac{(1 - \rho)^2}{(1 - \rho)^2 + 4\rho} = \frac{1}{1 + F}. \tag{188-7}$$

As ρ, which is equal to the reflecting power of the silvered surfaces, may be given various values between 0 and 1 depending upon the density of the silvering, the sharpness of the fringes and the ratio of the minimum to the maximum intensity may be given values best suited to the work for which the interferometer is to be used. As the following table shows, the fringes can be made very sharp by making the reflecting power large, and at the same time the ratio of minimum to maximum intensity becomes very small. These advantages, however, are obtained at the expense of brightness.

ρ	F	$I_{\min}/I_{\max}$	$\Delta d/\frac{1}{2}\lambda$
0.0	0.00	1.000	
0.2	1.25	0.445	0.352
0.4	4.44	0.184	0.158
0.6	14.40	0.065	0.086
0.8	80.00	0.012	0.036
1.0	∞	0.000	0.000

REFERENCES

Wood, R. W.: *Physical Optics*, The Macmillan Co., New York.
Drude, Paul: *The Theory of Optics*, Longmans, Green & Co., New York.
Schuster and Nicholson: *An Introduction to the Theory of Optics*, Edward Arnold & Co., London.

CHAPTER XV

ORIGIN OF SPECTRA

189. Doppler Effect. — When a source of light S (Fig. 201) is moving toward or away from an observer P, the measured frequency ν_1 of the waves emitted is not the same as the frequency ν determined when the source is stationary. Let α be the angle between the velocity **v** of the source relative to the observer and the line of sight SP. In a time dt the source moves a distance vdt to S_1. During this time it emits νdt waves. If we denote the distance SP by l and the velocity of light relative to the observer by v, the first of these waves reaches P at the time $t + l/v$. As the distance S_1P is $l - vdt \cos \alpha$, the last wave in the train under consideration, emitted by the source at S_1, reaches P at the time

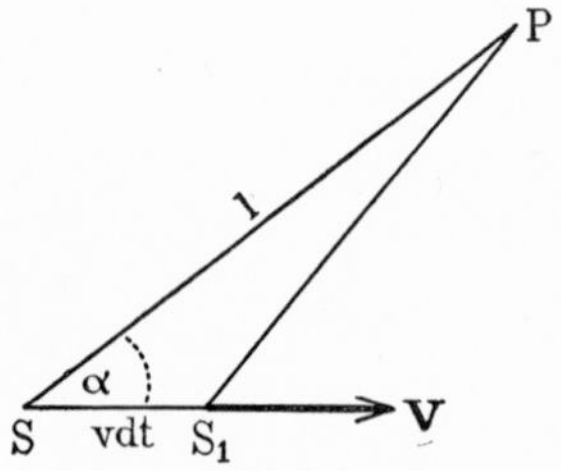

FIG. 201.

$$t + dt + (l - vdt \cos \alpha)/v.$$

Therefore νdt waves arrive at P in a time

$$dt_1 = t + dt + \frac{l - vdt \cos \alpha}{v} - \left(t + \frac{l}{v}\right) = dt\left(1 - \frac{v}{v} \cos \alpha\right),$$

and the apparent frequency measured at P is

$$\nu_1 = \frac{\nu dt}{dt_1} = \frac{\nu}{1 - \dfrac{v}{v} \cos \alpha}. \tag{189–1}$$

If v is small compared with v, as is nearly always the case,

$$\nu_1 = \nu\left(1 + \frac{v}{v} \cos \alpha\right) \tag{189–2}$$

to a sufficient degree of approximation. By measuring the wave length of a known line in the spectrum of a star and comparing with the wave length of the same line as determined in the laboratory, the component of the velocity of the star along the line of sight may be computed from this formula.

Problem 189a. Deduce the formula for the Doppler effect on the relativity theory, and show that it reduces to (189–2) as a first approximation.

$$Ans.\ \nu_1 = \frac{\nu\sqrt{1-\beta^2}}{1-\beta\cos\alpha}.$$

190. Aberration. — Astronomical aberration is the change in the measured angular position of a source of light due to a change in the velocity of the observer. Let the rectangular axes XYZ (Fig. 202) be fixed in the inertial system in which the earth E is at rest at the time t_1. At this time light coming from the distant star S makes an angle α_1 with the X axis to an observer stationed on the earth. Now consider a later time t_2 when the earth has acquired a velocity **v** in the X direction relative to the axes XYZ. In order that a ray of light coming from S may pass through a telescope T moving with the earth the telescope must be tilted forward at an angle α_2, where

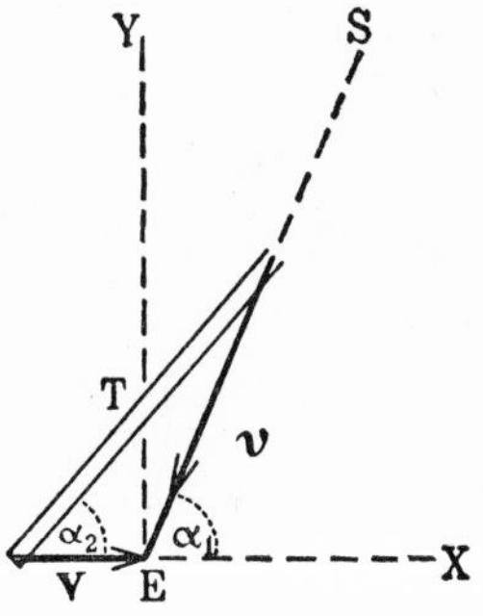

FIG. 202.

$$\frac{v}{\sin\alpha_2} = \frac{V}{\sin(\alpha_1-\alpha_2)},$$

or

$$\sin(\alpha_1-\alpha_2) = \frac{V}{v}\sin\alpha_2. \qquad (190\text{–}1)$$

As $\alpha_1 - \alpha_2$ is very small we may write this

$$\alpha_1-\alpha_2 = \frac{V}{v}\sin\alpha_2. \qquad (190\text{–}2)$$

The angle $\alpha_1 - \alpha_2$ is known as the *angle of aberration.* If it is measured, the velocity of light v may be computed from the formula (190–2). Bradley determined the velocity of light by this method in 1727.

Problem 190a. Deduce the formula for aberration on the relativity theory.

$$\textit{Ans. } \sin \tfrac{1}{2}(\alpha_1 - \alpha_2) = \frac{1}{\beta}\left\{1 - \sqrt{1 - \beta^2}\right\} \sin \tfrac{1}{2}(\alpha_1 + \alpha_2).$$

191. Determination of the Velocity of Light. — The velocity of light was first measured by the astronomical methods of Roemer and Bradley. Later Fizeau and Foucault devised terrestrial methods of determining this important constant. The most accurate determination was made by Michelson in 1926 by the modified Foucault method described below.

Light from the source S (Fig. 203) is reflected by one face of the octagonal mirror M to the 45° prism P_1, thence to P_2 and from

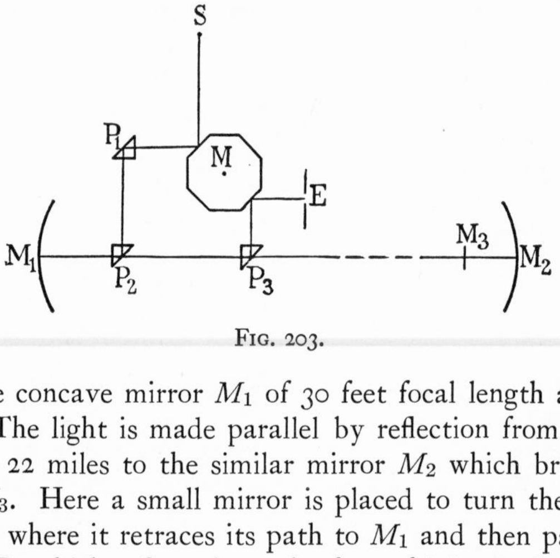

FIG. 203.

there to the concave mirror M_1 of 30 feet focal length and 24 inch aperture. The light is made parallel by reflection from this mirror and travels 22 miles to the similar mirror M_2 which brings it to a focus at M_3. Here a small mirror is placed to turn the light back to M_2 from where it retraces its path to M_1 and then passes to the 45° prism P_3 which reflects it to the face of M opposite to that on which it was originally incident. From here the light passes through the slit E. If, now, the mirror M is rotated about an axis perpendicular to the plane of the diagram, the returning beam will not enter the slit E until the mirror has attained a velocity sufficient to turn it through an eighth of a revolution in the time taken by light to travel from M_1 to M_2 and back.

The mirror M may be rated by an electrically driven tuning fork. The velocity of light is computed by dividing twice the distance M_1M_2 by one-eighth the period of rotation of M when the returning light passes through the slit E. The velocity thus found is the group velocity. If the medium has appreciable dispersion, (75–2) must be used to determine the phase velocity, and in any case the latter must be multiplied by the index of refraction in order to obtain the velocity c of light *in vacuo*. Michelson finds

$$c = 299{,}796 \text{ km/sec}$$

with a probable error of 4 km/sec.

Problem 191a. Monochromatic light of frequency ν is incident at an angle i on a plane mirror which is approaching with velocity v in a direction normal to its surface. Using Huygens' principle, find the angle of reflection i_1 and the frequency ν_1 of the reflected light.

Ans. $$\sin\frac{i - i_1}{2} = \beta \sin \alpha,$$

$$\frac{\nu_1}{\nu} = 1 + 2\beta \cos \alpha \frac{\sqrt{1 - \beta^2 \sin^2 \alpha} + \beta \cos \alpha}{1 - \beta^2},$$

where $$\alpha \equiv \frac{i + i_1}{2}, \quad \beta \equiv \frac{v}{c}.$$

Problem 191b. Michelson found that the velocity of light in carbon bisulphide is 1/1.76 that in air, whereas optical measurements of the index of refraction give 1.6547 for $\lambda = 4.861(10)^{-5}$ cm and 1.6168 for $\lambda = 6.708(10)^{-5}$ cm. Assuming that Michelson used a wave length half-way between those cited, explain the discrepancy quantitatively.

192. Types of Spectra. — Spectra are classified as line spectra, band spectra and continuous spectra. The first are due to gaseous atoms, the second to gaseous molecules, and the third to solids or liquids and in particular cases to gases. Each type of spectrum may exist as an emission spectrum or an absorption spectrum. The former consists of bright lines such as are emitted by an incandescent gas. In the case of the latter continuous radiation is passed through a cool gas or liquid, which absorbs certain wave lengths. Therefore the resulting spectrum consists of a bright background crossed by dark lines such as the Fraunhofer lines in the solar spectrum. In general absorption frequencies appear as emission frequencies under suitable conditions and *vice versa.*

Wave lengths are measured in Å (Ångström units) or $m\mu$ in the visible region, in μ in the infra-red, and in X. U. in the X-ray region. These units are defined as follows:

$$1 \text{ Å} = (10)^{-10} \text{ meter} = (10)^{-8} \text{ cm},$$
$$1\ \mu = (10)^{-6} \text{ meter} = (10)^{-4} \text{ cm} = (10)^{4} \text{ Å},$$
$$1\ m\mu = (10)^{-3}\ \mu = (10)^{-9} \text{ meter} = (10)^{-7} \text{ cm} = 10 \text{ Å},$$
$$1 \text{ X.U.} = (10)^{-3} \text{ Å} = (10)^{-13} \text{ meter} = (10)^{-11} \text{ cm}.$$

The visible region covers a single octave, extending from about 4000 Å to about 7500 Å.

In many cases the lines of a line spectrum may be grouped into *series* on account of common characteristics and regularity of spacing. A typical series is the *Balmer series* of hydrogen depicted in Fig. 204.

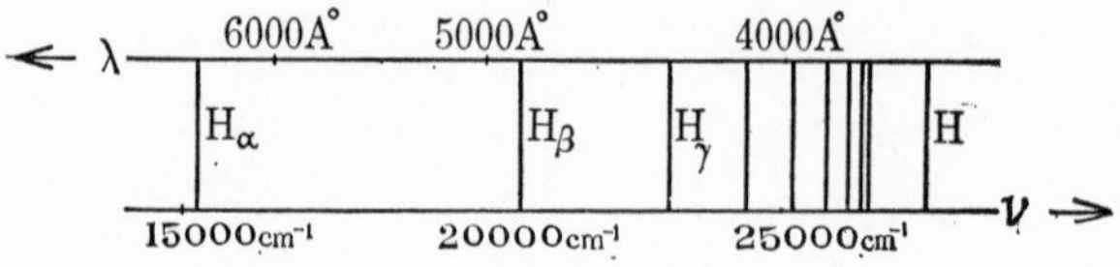

FIG. 204.

The strongest line is the red line H_α, the lines weakening in intensity and crowding closer together as we proceed toward the shorter wave lengths. The series ends at the *convergence frequency* H, the total number of lines being infinite. The lower scale on the diagram is given in *reciprocal wave lengths* instead of true frequencies. This is the general practice for the reason that wave lengths and not frequencies are the quantities directly measured by the spectroscopist, and so long as we are interested in relative frequencies alone nothing is gained and precision is sacrificed by multiplying the reciprocal wave length by the less accurately known velocity of light to obtain the true frequency.

Band spectra consist of groups of bands as illustrated in Fig. 205.

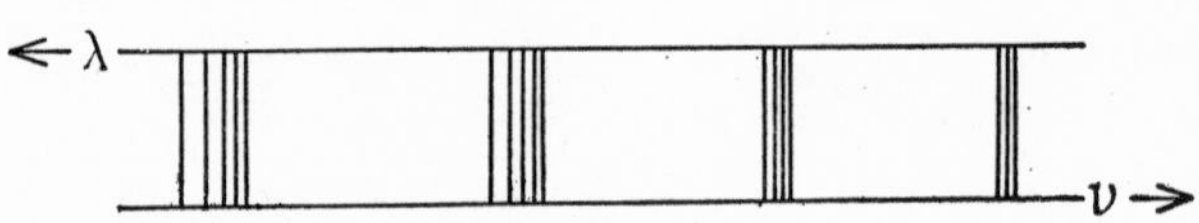

FIG. 205.

Under high resolution each band, depicted by a single line in Fig. 205, is found to consist of a number of fine lines as shown in Fig. 206.

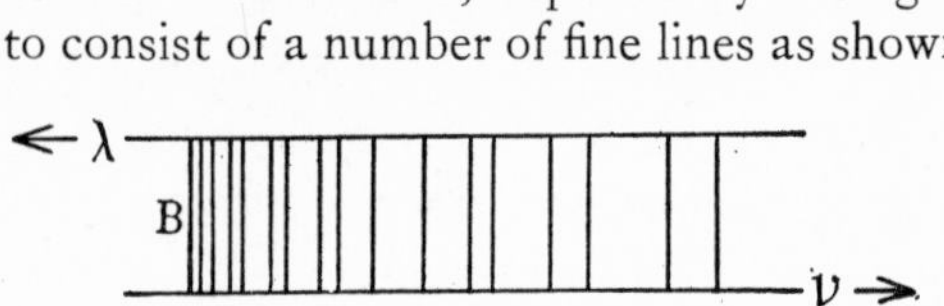

FIG. 206.

The lines end with the line B, which is known as the *head of the band*. The lines, however, are not infinitely dense at the head of a band as they are at the convergence frequency of a line series.

193. Bohr Theory of Line Spectra. — Rutherford's work on the single scattering of alpha particles has shown that the atom is made up of a massive positively charged nucleus of comparatively small dimensions surrounded by electrons. The nucleus itself is a closely packed group of protons and neutrons. In the normal uncharged atom the number of electrons in the outer atom, which determines its chemical properties, is equal to the number of oppositely charged protons in the nucleus. Each of these equal numbers is equal to the *atomic number* of the element under consideration, that is, the ordinal number specifying the position of the element in the periodic table. Thus hydrogen has one electron in the outer atom, helium two, lithium three, . . . sodium eleven, . . . chlorine seventeen, and so on.

As the mass of the electron is negligible compared with the mass of the proton, practically the entire mass of the atom is concentrated in the nucleus and is roughly proportional to the number of protons and neutrons present, since these particles have approximately equal masses. The hydrogen nucleus consists of a single proton, and therefore the number of protons plus neutrons in the nucleus of any other atom is equal to its atomic weight. When the atomic weight is not an integer the element exists in two or more forms each of which has an integral atomic weight.* These different forms of the same element, having practically identical physical and chemical properties with the single exception of atomic weight, are called *isotopes*. Thus chlorine with an atomic weight of 35.43 consists of two isotopes of weights 35 and 37, the former of which predominates. The atomic number, which determines all the properties of the element except weight, is the same for both. Therefore the first contains 17 protons and 18 neutrons in the nucleus, and the second 17 protons and 20 neutrons. Both have 17 electrons in the outer atom. They are designated by the symbols ${}_{17}Cl^{35}$ and ${}_{17}Cl^{37}$ respectively, the atomic number appearing as a subscript before the symbol for the element and the atomic weight as a superscript after it.

According to the theory proposed by Bohr in 1913 the electrons

* On the oxygen scale the atomic weights of hydrogen (1.0081) and of some of the heavier elements differ slightly from integers. The proposed explanation of these discrepancies will not be taken up here.

in the outer atom move in orbits about the nucleus without radiating energy, and only when a transition takes place from one orbit to another does emission or absorption of radiation take place. The orbits in which an electron can revolve about the nucleus without radiating are known as *stationary orbits*, and the corresponding states of the atom as *stationary states*. We shall confine our attention for the present to atoms containing only a single electron outside the nucleus, such as the normal hydrogen atom H and the positively ionized helium atom He^+.

The postulates of the Bohr theory are:

I. The stationary states of an atom are those for which each of the phase integrals defined in article 61 is equal to an integral multiple of Planck's constant $h = 6.624(10)^{-27}$ erg sec.

II. If an atom passes from a stationary state of energy U' to one of smaller energy U'', the frequency ν of the radiation emitted is given by

$$h\nu = U' - U''.$$

If the transition is in the opposite direction this equation gives the frequency of the radiation absorbed.

Let us consider a nucleus of atomic number Z about which a single electron is revolving. For the present we shall confine ourselves to circular orbits. Then if a is the radius of the orbit, ω the angular velocity of the electron, e its charge in electrostatic units, and m its mass, the second law of motion requires that

$$ma\omega^2 = \frac{e^2Z}{a^2} \tag{193-1}$$

if we neglect the motion of the comparatively massive nucleus.

By limiting our consideration to circular orbits we have reduced the atom to a mechanism of one degree of freedom. The single generalized coordinate is the azimuth θ of the electron and the conjugate momentum its constant angular momentum $ma^2\omega$ about the nucleus. Therefore the phase integral is

$$J_\theta = \int_0^{2\pi} ma^2\omega d\theta = 2\pi ma^2\omega,$$

and the first postulate of the Bohr theory gives us the relation

$$2\pi ma^2\omega = nh \tag{193-2}$$

where the integer n is known as the *quantum number* of the orbit. Solving (193–1) and (193–2) in turn for a, $a\omega$, and ω we find the radius, linear velocity, and angular velocity of a stationary orbit. Thus:

$$a = \left(\frac{h^2}{4\pi^2 me^2}\right)\frac{n^2}{Z} = 0.532(10)^{-8}\frac{n^2}{Z}\text{ cm,} \qquad (193\text{–}3)$$

$$\beta = \frac{a\omega}{c} = \left(\frac{2\pi e^2}{hc}\right)\frac{Z}{n} = 7.29(10)^{-3}\frac{Z}{n}, \qquad (193\text{–}4)$$

$$\omega = \left(\frac{8\pi^3 me^4}{h^3}\right)\frac{Z^2}{n^3} = 4.12(10)^{16}\frac{Z^2}{n^3}\text{ rad/sec.} \qquad (193\text{–}5)$$

From (193–3) it appears that the radii of the first ($n = 1$), second ($n = 2$), third ($n = 3$), etc., orbits are in the ratio 1 : 4 : 9 : etc., and that for $Z = 2$ (ionized helium) corresponding orbits are only half as large as for $Z = 1$ (hydrogen). From (193–4) it is seen that the linear velocity decreases with increase in quantum number n and increases with increase in atomic number Z. The same is true of the angular velocity as is shown by (193–5).

To get the energy of the stationary states we have

$$U = T + V = \tfrac{1}{2}ma^2\omega^2 - \frac{e^2Z}{a},$$

and, from (193–1),

$$U = \frac{e^2Z}{2a} - \frac{e^2Z}{a} = -\frac{e^2Z}{2a}.$$

Eliminating a by (193–3)

$$U = -Nh\frac{Z^2}{n^2} \qquad (193\text{–}6)$$

where

$$N \equiv \frac{2\pi^2 me^4}{h^3} = 3.29(10)^{15}/\text{sec}$$

is known as the *Rydberg constant.*

Consequently the second postulate of the Bohr theory gives for the frequency of the radiation emitted or absorbed,

$$\nu = \frac{U' - U''}{h} = NZ^2\left\{\frac{1}{n''^2} - \frac{1}{n'^2}\right\}. \qquad (193\text{–}7)$$

In 1885 Balmer showed that a formula of this form, in which n'' is made equal to 2 and n' given successive integral values starting with 3, describes very accurately the hydrogen lines in the visible region. The great achievement of Bohr lay in the theoretical calculation of the Rydberg constant N in terms of e, m and h.

Since the nucleus of the atom attracts the electron revolving around it with a force which varies inversely with the square of the distance we should expect from the results of article 30 that the most general form of orbit would be an ellipse described about the nucleus as one focus. This type of motion of two degrees of freedom has already been treated in articles 60 and 61. If we put $J_\theta = n_\theta h$, $J_r = n_r h$, in accord with the first postulate of the Bohr theory, where the integer n_θ is known as the *azimuthal quantum number* and the integer n_r as the *radial quantum number*, equation (61–17) gives us for the energy of a stationary state

$$U = -Nh\frac{Z^2}{(n_\theta + n_r)^2}. \qquad (193\text{–}8)$$

This expression is identical in form with (193–6), for the sum of two integers is an integer itself. If, then, we call $n = n_\theta + n_r$ the *total* or *principal quantum number*, we see that the energy of a stationary orbit depends on its total quantum number alone. For instance, the energy associated with an elliptical orbit of azimuthal quantum number 1 and radial quantum number 2 is the same as that associated with an elliptical orbit of azimuthal quantum number 2 and radial quantum number 1 or with a circular orbit of azimuthal quantum number 3. All orbits of the same total quantum number have equal major axes, as is evident from (61–20).

If we should replace the classical dynamics by the relativity dynamics, taking account of the variation with velocity of the mass of the electron as specified (161–8) and (161–9), we would find slight differences between the energies of elliptical and circular orbits of the same total quantum number. In this way Sommerfeld has accounted for the fine structure of spectral lines, such as that which was noted for the H_α line of hydrogen in article 187.

194. Hydrogen Atom Spectrum. — As Z is unity for hydrogen (193-7) becomes

$$\nu = N\left\{\frac{1}{n''^2} - \frac{1}{n'^2}\right\}. \qquad (194\text{–}1)$$

A series is the group of lines obtained by assigning a fixed integral value to n'' and then giving n' successive integral values starting with the integer one unit larger than n''. The series farthest in the ultra-violet is the *Lyman series* obtained by making $n'' = 1$ and giving n' the values 2, 3, 4, etc. It is given by the formula

$$\nu = N\left\{1 - \frac{1}{n'^2}\right\}, \quad n' = 2, 3, 4, \ldots. \qquad (194\text{-}2)$$

The first line in this series has a wave length $\lambda_1 = 4c/3N = 1216\text{Å}$, and the convergence wave length obtained by making n' infinite is $\lambda_\infty = c/N = 912$ Å. The spacing of the lines is similar to that of the Balmer series illustrated in Fig. 204. Evidently the entire series lies in the ultra-violet.

The next series, obtained by putting $n'' = 2$, is given by

$$\nu = N\left\{\frac{1}{4} - \frac{1}{n'^2}\right\}, \quad n' = 3, 4, 5 \ldots. \qquad (194\text{-}3)$$

This is the *Balmer series*. It lies in the visible region, the first line coming in the red at $\lambda_1 = 36c/5N = 6563$ Å and the convergence wave length in the violet at $\lambda_\infty = 4c/N = 3646$ Å. Some forty lines of this series have been observed.

Finally the *Paschen series*, obtained by making $n'' = 3$, is given by the formula

$$\nu = N\left\{\frac{1}{9} - \frac{1}{n'^2}\right\}, \quad n' = 4, 5, 6 \ldots. \qquad (194\text{-}4)$$

This series lies in the infra-red, the first line being at 18,751 Å and the convergence wave length at 8205 Å. Other series farther in the infra-red correspond to transitions from outer orbits to orbits of quantum numbers 4, 5, etc.

If we designate the energy levels of the atom corresponding to the stationary states of quantum numbers 1, 2, 3, etc., by horizontal lines drawn as in Fig. 207 at vertical distances from one another proportional to the differences of energy between successive levels, we can indicate the transitions corresponding to the various lines in the spectrum by vertical arrows. Since the frequency is proportional to the drop in energy the length of each arrow measures the frequency of the line emitted. In the diagram Lyman lines are denoted by L_α, L_β, L_γ, Balmer lines by H_α, H_β, H_γ, and Paschen lines by P_α, P_β, P_γ.

The electron in the normal hydrogen atom is in a one-quantum orbit. Therefore the normal atom can absorb only the Lyman series. If, however, the atom is excited so as to remove the electron to the two-quantum orbit before absorption takes place, the lines in the Balmer series appear in the absorption spectrum.

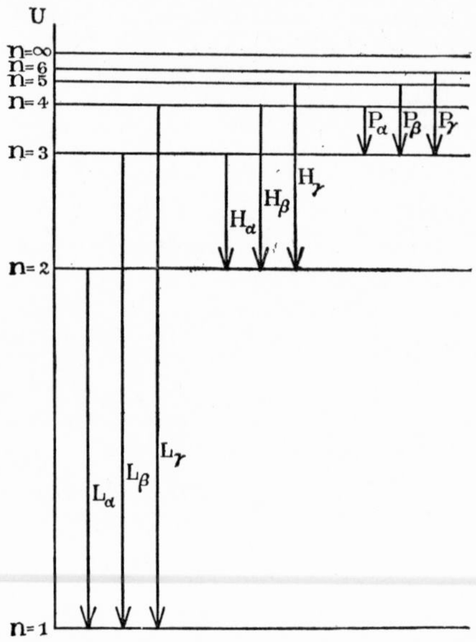

FIG. 207.

195. Helium Ion Spectrum. — In deducing the formula (193–7) for the frequency of a line emitted by an atom containing only one electron outside the nucleus we have assumed that the nucleus remains immobile. More precisely, however, electron and nucleus revolve together about the center of mass of the atom. Therefore, if M is the mass of the nucleus, we must replace the mass of the electron in the formulae of article 193 by the reduced mass μ, where

$$\frac{1}{\mu} = \frac{1}{m} + \frac{1}{M}$$

in accord with (30–20). This changes the value of the Rydberg constant to

$$N = \frac{2\pi^2 \mu e^4}{h^3},$$

and if we denote the former value of N for a nucleus of infinite mass by N_∞ we have

$$N = \frac{\mu}{m} N_\infty = \frac{N_\infty}{1 + \frac{m}{M}}. \qquad (195\text{–}1)$$

As the ratio of the mass M_{He} of the helium nucleus to the mass M_H of the hydrogen nucleus is

$$\frac{M_{He}}{M_H} = \frac{4.0039}{1.0081} = 3.9717$$

the Rydberg constant N_{He} pertaining to the helium ion spectrum is slightly different from the constant N_H involved in the hydrogen atom spectrum.

The spectrum of the neutral atom is called the *arc spectrum*, and that of an ion which has lost one electron the *spark spectrum*. We are interested here in the spectrum of a helium atom from which one electron has been completely detached, and which therefore possesses only a single electron in the outer atom. As $Z = 2$ formula (193–7) becomes

$$\nu = 4N_{He}\left\{\frac{1}{n''^2} - \frac{1}{n'^2}\right\}. \qquad (195\text{–}2)$$

The series in the visible region is that for which $n'' = 4$ and n' takes on the values 5, 6, 7 . . . . We shall split the series into two parts. If n' is even we can put $n' = 2k$ where k is an integer, and get

$$\nu = 4N_{He}\left\{\frac{1}{16} - \frac{1}{4k^2}\right\} = N_{He}\left\{\frac{1}{4} - \frac{1}{k^2}\right\}, \quad k = 3, 4, 5 \ldots . \qquad (195\text{–}3)$$

But for the slight difference between N_{He} and N_H these lines would coincide with the Balmer lines (194–3) of hydrogen.

If n' is odd we put $n' = 2k + 1$ and get

$$\left.\begin{aligned}\nu = 4N_{He}\left\{\frac{1}{16} - \frac{1}{4(k+\frac{1}{2})^2}\right\} = N_{He}\left\{\frac{1}{4} - \frac{1}{(k+\frac{1}{2})^2}\right\},\\ k = 2, 3, 4 \ldots .\end{aligned}\right\} \qquad (195\text{–}4)$$

These lines alternate with those given by (195–3). Until the advent of the Bohr theory both of these sets of lines were attributed to hydrogen. The theory, however, assigned them to the helium ion and careful purification of the gases whose spectra were to be examined completely confirmed the prediction of the theory. In addition to the series discussed above other series due to the helium ion exist in the ultra-violet and in the infra-red.

From accurate measurements of the wave lengths of the arc

spectrum of hydrogen and the spark spectrum of helium

$$N_H = 109{,}677.581c$$

$$N_{He} = 109{,}722.263c$$

are found for the Rydberg constants for the hydrogen atom and the helium ion respectively. Now from (195–1)

$$N_H\left(1 + \frac{m}{M_H}\right) = N_{He}\left(1 + \frac{m}{M_{He}}\right)$$

$$= N_{He}\left(1 + \frac{m}{3.9717M_H}\right),$$

whence

$$\frac{M_H}{m} = \frac{N_H - \dfrac{1}{3.9717}N_{He}}{N_{He} - N_H}.$$

Putting in the values given above, we get

$$\frac{M_H}{m} = 1836, \tag{195–5}$$

that is, the proton has a mass 1836 times that of the electron. Further, from (203–1),

$$N_\infty = N_H\left(1 + \frac{m}{M_H}\right) = 109{,}737.303c. \tag{195–6}$$

Now

$$\frac{M_H}{m} = \frac{\dfrac{e}{m}}{\dfrac{e}{M_H}} = -\frac{\dfrac{e}{m}}{96{,}490 \text{ coulombs}/1.0081}$$

since the denominator is the accurately known Faraday constant divided by the atomic weight of hydrogen.

Consequently the ratio of charge to mass of the electron is

$$\frac{e}{m} = -5.269(10)^{17}\text{e.s.u./gm.} \tag{195–7}$$

This value, obtained from spectroscopic data, agrees well with that found by the deflection method of article 138.

Problem 195a. Show from first principles that in the case of circular orbits the Rydberg constant of formula (193–7) must be replaced by (195–1) when account is taken of the motion of the nucleus.

195.1 Bohr's Correspondence Principle. — In many spectra it is found that the lines corresponding to the transitions between certain energy levels are missing. Evidently selection rules are needed to specify which transitions may occur and which are forbidden. Such rules are provided by Bohr's correspondence principle.

We have seen in article 61 that if $\bar{H}(J_1 \dots J_f)$ is the energy of a conservative dynamical system executing periodic motions, the fundamental frequencies are

$$\omega_s = \frac{\partial \bar{H}}{\partial J_s}, \quad s = 1, 2, 3 \dots f. \tag{195.1–1}$$

In addition to these frequencies themselves we may have appearing in the description of the motion the overtones $p_1\omega_1, p_2\omega_2, \dots p_f\omega_f$ and the combinational tones $p_1\omega_1 + p_2\omega_2 \dots + p_f\omega_f$, where $p_1, p_2 \dots p_f$ are integers. Therefore, in the most general case, the coordinate q_s is given in terms of the angle variables $w_s = \omega_s t + \delta_s$ by

$$q_s = \sum_{p_1 \dots p_f = 0}^{\infty} \Big[A^s_{p_1 \dots p_f} \cos 2\pi (p_1 w_1 + p_2 w_2 \dots + p_f w_f) + B^s_{p_1 \dots p_f} \sin 2\pi (p_1 w_1 + p_2 w_2 \dots + p_f w_f) \Big]$$

$$= \sum_{p_1 \dots p_f = 0}^{\infty} \Big[\tfrac{1}{2}(A^s_{p_1 \dots p_f} - iB^s_{p_1 \dots p_f}) e^{2\pi i (p_1 w_1 + p_2 w_2 \dots + p_f w_f)} + \tfrac{1}{2}(A^s_{p_1 \dots p_f} + iB^s_{p_1 \dots p_f}) e^{-2\pi i (p_1 w_1 + p_2 w_2 \dots + p_f w_f)} \Big].$$

This may be written in the form

$$q_s = \sum_{p_1 \dots p_f = -\infty}^{\infty} C^s_{p_1 \dots p_f} e^{2\pi i (p_1 w_1 + p_2 w_2 \dots + p_f w_f)}$$

$$= \sum_{p_1 \dots p_f = -\infty}^{\infty} D^s_{p_1 \dots p_f} e^{2\pi i (p_1 \omega_1 + p_2 \omega_2 \dots + p_f \omega_f) t} \tag{195.1–2}$$

where the coefficients C and D may be complex. If some of the fundamental frequencies are commensurable, the motion can be described in terms of a number of frequencies less than the number f of degrees of freedom. In that case the dynamical system is said to be *degenerate*.

On classical electromagnetic theory the frequency ν_c of the radiation emitted by a vibrating charged particle is identical with the dynamical frequency of its oscillations, that is, equal to ω in the case of a fundamental, $p\omega$ in the case of an overtone, $p_1\omega_1 + p_2\omega_2 \ldots + p_f\omega_f$ in the case of a combinational tone.

On quantum theory, however, the frequency ν_q of the emitted radiation is equal to the change $\Delta\bar{H}$ in energy of the whole atomic or molecular structure divided by h. Suppose that the transition under consideration is one in which a single phase integral J_s changes. As $J_s = n_s h$ in a stationary state, the change in J_s is

$$\Delta J_s = (n'_s - n''_s)h = p_s h$$

where the integer $p_s = n'_s - n''_s$. Consequently

$$\nu_q = \frac{\Delta\bar{H}}{h} = p_s \frac{\Delta\bar{H}}{\Delta J_s}. \qquad (195.1\text{–}3)$$

Similarly, if more than one phase integral changes during a transition,

$$\nu_q = \sum_s p_s \frac{\Delta\bar{H}}{\Delta J_s}. \qquad (195.1\text{–}4)$$

By analogy with (195.1–1) we say that (195.1–3) represents a quantum fundamental when the quantum jump $p_s = 1$, a quantum first overtone when $p_s = 2$, and so on. It must be noted, however, that the frequency of a quantum overtone is an integral multiple of the frequency of the quantum fundamental only when $\bar{H}$ is a linear function of J_s. Similarly (195.1–4) is called a quantum combinational tone. In all, then, we have the following correspondence:

	Classical Theory	Quantum Theory
Fundamental Frequencies.....	$\nu_c = \dfrac{\partial\bar{H}}{\partial J_s}$	$\nu_q = \dfrac{\Delta\bar{H}}{\Delta J_s}$
Overtones..................	$\nu_c = p_s \dfrac{\partial\bar{H}}{\partial J_s}$	$\nu_q = p_s \dfrac{\Delta\bar{H}}{\Delta J_s}$
Combinational Tones........	$\nu_c = \sum_s p_s \dfrac{\partial\bar{H}}{\partial J_s}$	$\nu_q = \sum_s p_s \dfrac{\Delta\bar{H}}{\Delta J_s}$

It is well known that electromagnetic theory gives results in agreement with experimental observation in the region of long wave lengths or low frequencies. It is only when dealing with short wave lengths or high frequencies that resort must be had to quantum theory. This is well illustrated by the fact that Planck's radiation law reduces to the Rayleigh-Jeans law for small ν, as shown in article 167. Therefore quantum theory must yield the same frequencies as classical theory in the region of long wave lengths. As $J_s \gg \Delta J_s$ in this region, the difference quotient $\frac{\Delta \bar{H}}{\Delta J_s}$ approaches the differential quotient $\frac{\partial \bar{H}}{\partial J_s}$. Consequently, in the region of long wave lengths quantum theory must predict only those overtones or combinational tones which are found in the classical description of at least one of the energy states between which the quantum transition occurs. The correspondence principle extrapolates the last statement to the region of short wave lengths. In effect it prohibits any transition which represents a quantum overtone or combinational tone to which there corresponds no overtone or combinational tone in the classical description of either of the two energy states between which the transition occurs. Thus, in the case of the linear simple harmonic oscillator, the motion of which is described classically entirely in terms of a fundamental frequency, only the quantum fundamental may appear, that is, only those transitions in which the quantum number changes by unity. Again, if the electron in the hydrogen atom is limited to circular orbits, only one-quantum jumps are permitted, because the coordinates of the electron are described classically in terms of a fundamental frequency alone. If, however, the electron describes an elliptical orbit in one of the stationary states involved, the classical description of the motion along the radius vector involves a fundamental and all its overtones. Consequently the radial quantum number n_r may change by any integer. The probability of a specified quantum transition is determined by the average magnitude of the coefficients of the corresponding classical overtone or combinational tone in the two states between which the transition occurs. If these classical coefficients are both zero, then the quantum transition is forbidden, in accord with our previous statement. Finally, since classical theory gives the correct polarization in the region of long wave lengths, the polarization of the radiation emitted during a quantum transition is that of the corresponding classical tone.

The most important application of the correspondence principle is to the case of a cyclic coordinate θ measuring an azimuth, which does not appear explicitly in the Hamilton-Jacobi equation. Let $q_1 = \theta$ in (59–5). Then we can perform one separation of variables at once, getting

$$\frac{\partial S}{\partial \theta} = f_1\left(\frac{\partial S}{\partial q_2} \cdots \frac{\partial S}{\partial q_f}, q_2 \cdots q_f, \alpha_1\right) = \alpha_2$$

and

$$S = \alpha_2\theta + f_2(q_2 \ldots q_f, \alpha_1, \alpha_2, \ldots \alpha_f).$$

But

$$J_\theta = \int_0^{2\pi} \frac{\partial S}{\partial \theta} d\theta = 2\pi\alpha_2$$

and therefore

$$S = \frac{1}{2\pi} J_\theta \theta + f_3 (q_2 \ldots q_f, J_\theta, J_2 \ldots J_f). \qquad (195.1\text{–}5)$$

Hence the integrated equations of motion (61–6) are

$$\frac{\theta}{2\pi} + \frac{\partial f_3}{\partial J_\theta} = \omega_\theta t + \delta_\theta, \qquad (195.1\text{–}6)$$

$$\frac{\partial f_3}{\partial J_s} = \omega_s t + \delta_s, \quad s = 2, 3 \ldots f. \qquad (195.1\text{–}7)$$

As the f–1 equations (195.1–7) do not contain $q_1 = \theta$, we can solve them for $q_2 \ldots q_f$, getting

$$q_s = \sum_{-\infty}^{\infty} E^s_{p_2 \ldots p_f} e^{2\pi i(p_2\omega_2 \ldots + p_f\omega_f)t}, \quad s = 2, 3 \ldots f, \qquad (195.1\text{–}8)$$

whereas (195.1–6) gives

$$\theta = 2\pi\omega_\theta t + f_4(q_2 \ldots q_f, J_\theta, J_2 \ldots J_f)$$

or

$$e^{i\theta} = e^{2\pi i\omega_\theta t} \sum_{-\infty}^{\infty} F^s_{p_2 \ldots p_f} e^{2\pi i(p_2\omega_2 \ldots + p_f\omega_f)t}. \qquad (195.1\text{–}9)$$

Let the XY plane be that in which the azimuth θ is measured, the origin coinciding with the center of mass of the atomic or molecular structure. Take a set of axes $X'Y'Z'$ which are rotating about the Z axis at the same rate as θ is increasing. Then the coordinates x', y', z' of each charged particle are functions of $q_2, q_3 \ldots q_f$ only, and their Fourier expansions involve only the frequencies $\omega_2, \omega_3 \ldots \omega_f$. Hence the coordinates of the kth particle relative to $X'Y'Z'$ are given by

$$\left.\begin{aligned} x'_k + iy'_k &= \sum_{-\infty}^{\infty} A^k_{p_2 \ldots p_f} e^{2\pi i(p_2\omega_2 \ldots + p_f\omega_f)t}, \\ z'_k &= \sum_{-\infty}^{\infty} B^k_{p_2 \ldots p_f} e^{2\pi i(p_2\omega_2 \ldots + p_f\omega_f)t}. \end{aligned}\right\} \qquad (195.1\text{–}10)$$

Now, as

$$\begin{aligned} x + iy &= (x' \cos\theta - y' \sin\theta) + i(y' \cos\theta + x' \sin\theta) \\ &= (x' + iy')e^{i\theta} \end{aligned}$$

the coordinates of this particle relative to XYZ are

$$\left.\begin{aligned} x_k + iy_k &= e^{2\pi i\omega_\theta t}\sum_{-\infty}^{\infty} C^k{}_{p_2\ldots p_f}\, e^{2\pi i(p_2\omega_2\ldots+p_f\omega_f)t}, \\ z_k &= \sum_{-\infty}^{\infty} B^k{}_{p_2\ldots p_f}\, e^{2\pi i(p_2\omega_2\ldots+p_f\omega_f)t}, \end{aligned}\right\} \qquad (195.1\text{–}11)$$

from (195.1–9) and (195.1–10).

The classical description of the motion of the particle in the XY plane given by the first of the two equations (195.1–11) contains only the fundamental of the frequency ω_θ associated with the azimuth θ. Consequently in the corresponding quantum transition the quantum number n_θ can change by only one unit. When this does occur, the polarization of the radiation emitted is that predicted by electromagnetic theory for a charged particle executing an orbit in the XY plane in accord with the first equation of (195.1–11). For transverse observation, that is, for radiation proceeding in a direction at right angles to the Z axis, the waves are plane polarized with the electric vector perpendicular (s) to the Z axis.

On the other hand the classical description of the motion of the particle along the Z axis given by the second of the two equations (195.1–11) does not contain ω_θ at all. Hence in the corresponding quantum transition the quantum number n_θ cannot change. In this case the polarization of the radiation emitted is that for a classical charged particle vibrating along the Z axis. For transverse observation, then, the waves proceeding from the particle are plane polarized with the electric vector parallel (p) to the Z axis.

To summarize, we have the following selection rules for an azimuthal quantum number n_θ:

(1) $n_\theta \begin{smallmatrix}\nearrow n_\theta + 1 \\ \searrow n_\theta - 1\end{smallmatrix}$ Polarization s for transverse observation,

(2) $n_\theta \rightarrow n_\theta$ Polarization p for transverse observation.

Of course the quantum numbers associated with other degrees of freedom may change during a transition by any integers found among the p's in the combinational tones $p_2\omega_2 \ldots + p_f\omega_f$ appearing in (195.1–11). If, however, the motion is confined to the XY plane, $z_k = 0$, and the transition for which $n_\theta \rightarrow n_\theta$ is excluded. For this structure the azimuthal quantum number must change by unity.

In contradistinction to the correspondence emphasized in this article we must note one important difference between the emission of radiation on the classical theory and emission on the quantum theory even in the region of long wave lengths where the two may be expected to lead to the same frequencies. On the classical theory all the overtones are emitted simultaneously with the fundamental frequency, whereas on the quantum theory only a single frequency is emitted as the result of a single atomic transition. Hence it is only in the statistical sense that we can maintain that classical theory and quantum theory are equivalent in the region of long wave lengths.

196. Spectra of Atoms with a Single Valence Electron. — As the atoms of the inert gases helium, neon, argon, krypton, xenon and radon do not combine with other atoms to form molecules it is generally supposed that in these atoms the outermost ring or shell of electrons is complete and no valence electron is present. The elements following the inert gases in the periodic table, that is, the alkalis lithium, sodium, potassium, rubidium and cesium, have each one more electron in the outer atom than the preceding inert gas. This additional electron, then, must revolve alone outside an atom core similar in structure to the completed shell configuration of the preceding inert gas. Therefore the atoms of the alkalis differ from the hydrogen atom only in that the minute nucleus of the latter is replaced by an extended atom core. Hence the arc spectra of the alkalis should resemble the simple spectrum of the hydrogen atom. Furthermore the alkaline earths, following the alkalis in the periodic table, have two outer valence electrons in their normal un-ionized condition. If one of these electrons is detached, the positive alkaline earth ion has again a structure similar to the hydrogen atom, or more exactly to the helium ion since the effective atomic number Z is *two* instead of *one*. Therefore the spark spectra of the alkaline earths should be similar to the arc spectra of the alkalis.

The effect of the motion of the valence electron produced by replacing the approximately point nucleus of the hydrogen atom by an extended atom core is to cause the elliptical orbit existing in the case of the former to precess. To show that this is the case we shall suppose the potential energy function V to be expanded in a series of which the first two terms are

$$V = -\frac{e^2Z}{r} + \frac{e^2c}{r^2}.$$

The second term has been given the opposite sign to the first for the reason that the effect of the negatively charged electrons in the atom core is to diminish the attraction that would exist if these electrons were located in the nucleus. If, then, we put u for $1/r$ as in article 30 and write p_θ for the angular momentum mh of that article, the energy equation becomes

$$\frac{p_\theta^2}{2m}\left\{\left(\frac{du}{d\theta}\right)^2 + u^2\right\} - e^2Zu + e^2cu^2 = U.$$

Differentiating with respect to θ

$$\frac{d^2u}{d\theta^2} + \left(1 + \frac{2me^2c}{p_\theta^2}\right)u = \frac{me^2Z}{p_\theta^2}.$$

The integral is

$$u = \frac{me^2Z}{p_\theta^2\gamma^2} + A\cos\gamma(\theta + \delta), \qquad (196\text{–}1)$$

where

$$\gamma^2 \equiv 1 + \frac{2me^2c}{p_\theta^2}.$$

Equation (196–1) differs in form from (30–4) only in the presence of the factor γ in the argument of the cosine. To see that it represents a precessing elliptical orbit consider two successive perihelia. The radius vector r is a minimum when $\gamma(\theta + \delta) = 0$ and again when $\gamma(\theta + \delta) = 2\pi$. Therefore, as c is small, θ increases by

$$\frac{2\pi}{\gamma} = 2\pi\left(1 - \frac{me^2c}{p_\theta^2}\right)$$

as we pass from one perihelion to the next. During a period of revolution, then, the orbit precesses through the angle

$$\Delta\theta = \frac{2\pi}{\gamma} - 2\pi = -\frac{2\pi me^2c}{p_\theta^2}. \qquad (196\text{–}2)$$

We have here a non-degenerate system in which the two fundamental frequencies ω_r and ω_θ of article 61 are not the same. Now ω_r is the number of times per second that the valence electron passes through perihelion, that is, the number of times that θ increases by $2\pi + \Delta\theta$, while ω_θ is the number of times per second that θ increases by 2π. Hence $(2\pi + \Delta\theta)\omega_r = 2\pi\omega_\theta$, since either represents the total angle described per second. But the perihelion advances through an angle $\Delta\theta$ every time θ increases by $2\pi + \Delta\theta$, that is, ω_r times a second.

The angular advance of the perihelion per second is then $\omega_r\Delta\theta$, or its frequency σ is

$$\sigma = \frac{\omega_r\Delta\theta}{2\pi} = \omega_\theta - \omega_r,$$

and from (61–14)

$$d\bar{H} = \omega_r dJ_r + \omega_\theta dJ_\theta = \omega_r d(J_r + J_\theta) + \sigma dJ_\theta.$$

Putting J for the sum of the phase integrals J_r and J_θ and dropping the subscript r appended to the frequency ω_r of revolution in the precessing ellipse,

$$d\bar{H} = \omega dJ + \sigma dJ_\theta. \tag{196–3}$$

The frequency ω corresponds to the principal quantum number $n = n_r + n_\theta$ involved in $J = nh$, and σ to the azimuthal quantum number n_θ which we shall now designate by k involved in $J_\theta = kh$.

To find the energies of the stationary states let us write the Hamiltonian function in terms of the variables r and θ. It is

$$H = \frac{1}{2m}\left(p_r^2 + \frac{1}{r^2}p_\theta^2\right) - \frac{e^2Z}{r} + \frac{e^2c}{r^2}$$

$$= \frac{1}{2m}\left\{p_r^2 + \frac{1}{r^2}(p_\theta^2 + 2me^2c)\right\} - \frac{e^2Z}{r},$$

which differs from (60–3) only in that the square of the constant angular momentum p_θ is replaced by the constant $p_\theta^2 + 2me^2c$. Therefore the only change necessary in the subsequent treatment of articles 60 and 61 is to replace α_2^2 in equations (60–6) and (61–16) by $\alpha_2^2 + 2me^2c$. This gives us in place of (61–15) and (61–16) the two equations

$$J_\theta = 2\pi\alpha_2,$$

$$J_r = \frac{2\pi me^2Z}{\sqrt{-2m\alpha_1}} - 2\pi\sqrt{\alpha_2^2 + 2me^2c}.$$

Eliminating α_2 and solving for the energy α_1 we have

$$U = \alpha_1 = -\frac{2\pi^2me^4Z^2}{\{J_r + \sqrt{J_\theta^2 + 8\pi^2me^2c}\}^2}.$$

For a stationary state

$$J = J_r + J_\theta = nh, \quad J_\theta = kh.$$

Consequently

$$U = -Nh\frac{Z^2}{(n + \alpha_k)^2}, \qquad (196\text{–}4)$$

where α_k is a function of the azimuthal quantum number k alone. From the second postulate of the Bohr theory we have for the frequency of the radiation emitted or absorbed

$$\nu = \frac{U' - U''}{h} = NZ^2\left\{\frac{1}{(n'' + \alpha''_k)^2} - \frac{1}{(n' + \alpha')^2_k}\right\}. \qquad (196\text{–}5)$$

This formula was proposed by Rydberg on empirical grounds some time before the advent of the quantum theory. It represents the series of the alkalis with a fair degree of accuracy provided the constants α'_k and α''_k are adjusted so as to fit the measured wave lengths. Attempts to calculate these constants theoretically from suggested models of the atom have been only partially successful.

The energy levels for which the azimuthal quantum number is *one* are known as *s* levels, those for which it is *two p* levels, those for which it is *three d* levels and those for which it is *four f* levels.

Since the motion of the valence electron is confined to the plane in which the azimuth θ is measured, the correspondence principle permits only those transitions in which the azimuthal quantum number changes by unity. If, then, we plot on separate vertical lines the *s*, *p*, *d* and *f* energy levels, we obtain for sodium the diagram shown in Fig. 208. The transitions represented by full lines constitute the so-called *principal series*. The lowest *s* level is a three-quantum level rather than a one-

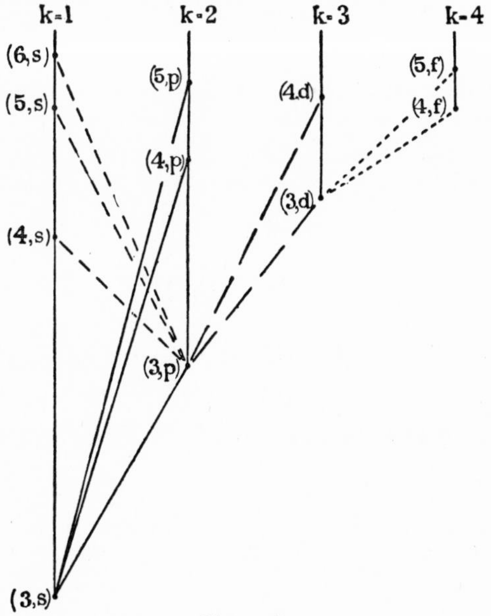

FIG. 208.

quantum level on account of the penetration of the atom core by the valence electron. In addition to the lines represented by the series above, *combination lines* due to other transitions between stationary states in adjacent columns in the diagram are found. In every case, however, the azimuthal quantum number k changes by *one* and *one* only as required by the correspondence principle.

In the arc spectra of the alkalis $Z = 1$ in (196–5), whereas in the spark spectra of the alkaline earths $Z = 2$. In both cases the s levels are single but each p level really consists of two levels very close together. Therefore the lines in the principal series are doublets. These doublets have received a quantum explanation based on the assignment to the valence electron of an angular momentum and an accompanying magnetic moment.

A formula which expresses the energy levels more precisely than the Rydberg formula (196–4) is obtained by taking more terms in the series for the potential energy. This formula, which was originally proposed by Ritz on grounds quite foreign to the quantum theory, is

$$U = -Nh\frac{Z^2}{\left(n + \alpha_k - \beta_k \dfrac{U}{h}\right)^2}, \tag{196–6}$$

where α_k and β_k are functions of the azimuthal quantum number k alone.

196.1. Evaluation of Phase Integrals. — Phase integrals can be evaluated more simply as contour integrals in the complex plane than by finding the indefinite integral and then substituting the appropriate limits. Take for instance the integral (61–16). This integral is of the form

$$J = \oint\sqrt{A + 2\frac{B}{r} + \frac{C}{r^2}}\,dr \tag{196.1–1}$$

where the positive sign is to be taken in front of the radical when dr is positive and the negative sign when dr is negative. As A and C are both negative, the integrand can be written

$$I \equiv \sqrt{A + 2\frac{B}{r} + \frac{C}{r^2}} = \frac{\sqrt{-A}}{r}\sqrt{(r_2 - r)(r - r_1)} \tag{196.1–2}$$

which is real only when $r_1 \leq r \leq r_2$.

Put $r = x + iy$. Then we want to integrate (196.1–1) along the real axis (Fig. 208.1) from Q to P with the negative sign in front of the integrand (196.1–2) and back again to Q with the positive sign. Suppose we follow the curve shown on the figure, going from Q to P just above the real axis, looping the branch point at P, and then returning to Q just below the real axis, with a final loop about the branch point Q to reach the starting point.

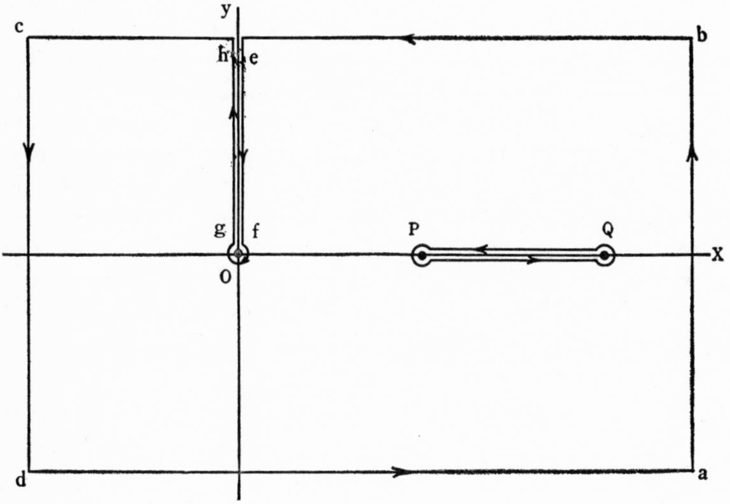

FIG. 208.1.

At P we may put $r - r_1 = \rho e^{i\theta}$ where ρ is the radius of the loop about P, and hence write

$$I = -\frac{\sqrt{-A}}{r_1}\sqrt{r_2 - r_1}\sqrt{\rho}\, e^{i\theta/2}, \qquad (196.1\text{–}3)$$

where the minus sign is taken so as to make I negative when $\theta = 0$. But when $\theta = 2\pi$, $e^{i\theta/2} = -1$ and the integrand becomes positive, as required, for the integration from P back to Q.

At Q we put $r - r_2 = \rho e^{i\theta}$, getting

$$I = i\frac{\sqrt{-A}}{r_2}\sqrt{r_2 - r_1}\sqrt{\rho}\, e^{i\theta/2}, \qquad (196.1\text{–}4)$$

which is real and positive for $\theta = -\pi$ and real and negative for $\theta = \pi$. Consequently, if we follow the indicated path of integration, the sign of the integrand changes at each libration limit, as required.

We note from (196.1–3) that I is a negative imaginary for $\theta = \pi$, that is, for points on the real axis to the left of P. Hence the value

$\sqrt{C}/r$ of the integrand in the neighborhood of the origin is a negative imaginary, indicating that $\sqrt{C}$ is a negative imaginary. Similarly, since (196.1–4) is a positive imaginary for $\theta = 0$, that is, for points on the real axis to the right of Q, $\sqrt{A}$ must be a positive imaginary.

We can distort the path of integration as much as we choose without affecting the value of the integral, provided we do not cross a singularity, such as the pole at the origin where I becomes infinite. Therefore we may replace the original path by the path *abefghcda*. But the integral along *gh* annuls that along *ef* since they are taken in opposite senses. Therefore we are left with the integral J_r around a small circle surrounding the origin and the integral J_s around the remote closed curve *abcda*.

The first of these is

$$J_r = \oint \sqrt{A + 2\frac{B}{r} + \frac{C}{r^2}}\, dr = \oint \frac{dr}{r}\sqrt{C + 2Br + Ar^2}$$

$$= \oint \frac{dr}{r}\sqrt{C}\{1 + \ldots\}.$$

Putting $r = \rho e^{i\theta}$, $dr = i\rho e^{i\theta} d\theta$, where ρ is the radius of the circle around O, and

$$\oint_0^{-2\pi} \frac{dr}{r^n} = \frac{i}{\rho^{n-1}} \int_0^{-2\pi} e^{-i(n-1)\theta}\, d\theta = \left| \begin{matrix} -2\pi i & \text{if } n = 1, \\ 0 & \text{if } n \neq 1. \end{matrix} \right. \qquad (196.1\text{–}5)$$

Therefore

$$J_r = -\, 2\pi i \sqrt{C}. \qquad (196.1\text{–}6)$$

To evaluate J_s we transform to the inverse $s = 1/r$ plane. Putting $s = x' + iy'$, we have $x' = x/(x^2 + y^2)$, $y' = -\, y/(x^2 + y^2)$. So in the s plane, the branch cut PQ and the curve *abcda* are located as in Fig. 208.2. Shrinking the path of integration down to a small circle surrounding the pole at the origin O' we have, since $dr = -\, ds/s^2$,

$$J_s = -\oint \frac{ds}{s^2}\sqrt{A + 2Bs + Cs^2} = -\oint \frac{ds}{s^2}\sqrt{A}\left\{1 + \frac{B}{A}s + \ldots\right\}.$$

Therefore, utilizing (196.1–5),

$$J_s = 2\pi i \frac{B}{\sqrt{A}}. \qquad (196.1\text{–}7)$$

As we have seen, $\sqrt{C}$ is a negative imaginary. Consequently, if we change the sign of J_r so as to make all imaginaries positive,

$$J = J_r + J_s = 2\pi i\left\{\frac{B}{\sqrt{A}} + \sqrt{C}\right\}. \qquad (196.1\text{–}8)$$

Problem 196.1a. With all imaginaries positive, show that

$$\oint \frac{r\,dr}{\sqrt{A + 2\dfrac{B}{r} + \dfrac{C}{r}}} = \frac{2\pi i}{\sqrt{A}}\left\{\frac{3}{2}\frac{B^2}{A^2} - \frac{1}{2}\frac{C}{A}\right\}.$$

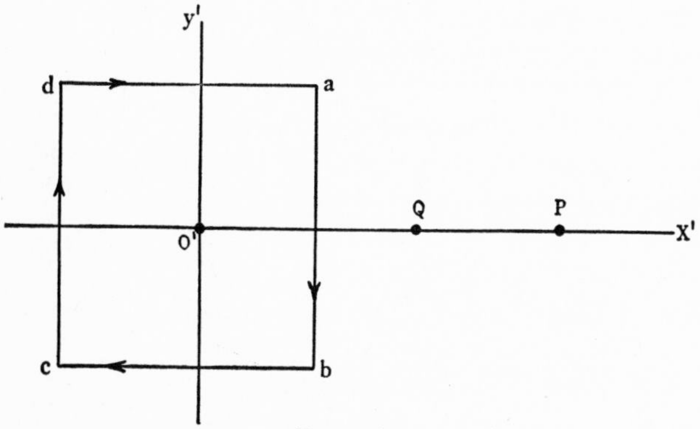

FIG. 208–2.

197. Stark Effect. — If a source of radiation is placed in a strong electric field the lines normally present are found to be broken up into a number of components in a manner somewhat similar to the splitting which occurs when a source is placed in a magnetic field. This phenomenon is known as the *Stark effect.* While the normal Zeeman effect finds a ready explanation on classical electromagnetic theory, this theory is quite unable to account for the Stark effect. One of the triumphs of quantum theory is the beautiful explanation of the Stark effect which it has afforded at the hands of Schwarzschild and Epstein in the case of a two-body atomic structure.

We shall confine our attention to an atom containing a point nucleus of charge eZ and a single electron. If we take origin at the nucleus with the X axis in the direction of the electric intensity $\mathbf{E}$ the potential energy of the electron is

$$V = -\frac{e^2Z}{r} + eEx. \qquad (197\text{–}1)$$

In order to separate the variables in the Hamilton-Jacobi partial differential equation (59–5) it is necessary to use as coordinate surfaces two families of confocal paraboloids of revolution about the X axis and a family of planes passing through this axis. Designating the two families of paraboloids by ξ = constant and η = constant, and putting $\rho^2 = y^2 + z^2$, the parameters ξ and η are related to x and ρ by the complex equation

$$x \pm i\rho = \tfrac{1}{2}(\xi \pm i\eta)^2, \qquad (197\text{–}2)$$

or the equivalent equations

$$x = \tfrac{1}{2}(\xi^2 - \eta^2), \quad \rho = \xi\eta. \qquad (197\text{–}3)$$

Eliminating in turn η and then ξ the equations of the two families of paraboloids are found to be

$$\frac{\rho^2}{\xi^2} + 2x = \xi^2, \quad \frac{\rho^2}{\eta^2} - 2x = \eta^2.$$

The traces of these paraboloids on a plane through the X axis are shown in Fig. 209. It may easily be shown that the two families intersect orthogonally.

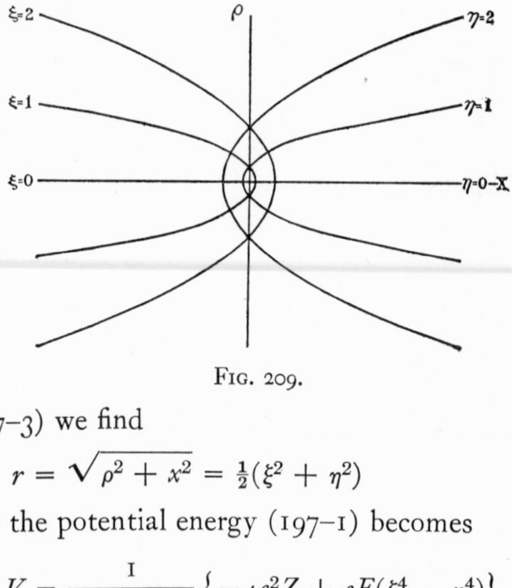

FIG. 209.

From (197–3) we find

$$r = \sqrt{\rho^2 + x^2} = \tfrac{1}{2}(\xi^2 + \eta^2)$$

and therefore the potential energy (197–1) becomes

$$V = \frac{1}{2(\xi^2 + \eta^2)}\left\{-4e^2Z + eE(\xi^4 - \eta^4)\right\}. \qquad (197\text{–}4)$$

To get the kinetic energy we have for an element of arc

$$ds^2 = dx^2 + d\rho^2 + \rho^2 d\phi^2,$$

where ϕ is the azimuth measured in the YZ plane. If we use first the upper sign and then the lower sign in (197–2) we get

$$dx + id\rho = (\xi + i\eta)(d\xi + id\eta),$$
$$dx - id\rho = (\xi - i\eta)(d\xi - id\eta),$$

and multiplying

$$dx^2 + d\rho^2 = (\xi^2 + \eta^2)(d\xi^2 + d\eta^2).$$

Therefore

$$ds^2 = (\xi^2 + \eta^2)(d\xi^2 + d\eta^2) + \xi^2\eta^2 d\phi^2,$$

and the kinetic energy is

$$T = \frac{1}{2} m \left(\frac{ds}{dt}\right)^2 = \frac{m}{2}\{(\xi^2 + \eta^2)(\dot{\xi}^2 + \dot{\eta}^2) + \xi^2\eta^2\dot{\phi}^2\}. \quad (197\text{–}5)$$

The momenta conjugate to ξ, η, ϕ are, respectively,

$$p_\xi = \frac{\partial T}{\partial \dot{\xi}} = m(\xi^2+\eta^2)\dot{\xi}, \quad p_\eta = \frac{\partial T}{\partial \dot{\eta}} = m(\xi^2+\eta^2)\dot{\eta}, \quad p_\phi = \frac{\partial T}{\partial \dot{\phi}} = m\xi^2\eta^2\dot{\phi}.$$

Writing the kinetic energy in terms of the momenta and adding the potential energy (197–4) the Hamiltonian function is found to be

$$H = \frac{1}{2m(\xi^2+\eta^2)}\left\{p_\xi^2 + p_\eta^2 + \left(\frac{1}{\xi^2}+\frac{1}{\eta^2}\right)p_\phi^2 - 4me^2Z + meE(\xi^4-\eta^4)\right\}. \quad (197\text{–}6)$$

The Hamilton-Jacobi partial differential equation is obtained from this by replacing p_ξ, p_η, and p_ϕ by the partial derivatives of the action S with respect to ξ, η, and ϕ, respectively, and equating to the constant α_1. As ϕ is a cyclic coordinate the conjugate momentum p_ϕ is equal to a constant p. So rearranging terms and multiplying through by $2m(\xi^2 + \eta^2)$ we have

$$\left.\begin{aligned} &\left(\frac{\partial S}{\partial \xi}\right)^2 + \frac{p^2}{\xi^2} - 2me^2Z + meE\xi^4 - 2m\alpha_1\xi^2 \\ &= -\left\{\left(\frac{\partial S}{\partial \eta}\right)^2 + \frac{p^2}{\eta^2} - 2me^2Z - meE\eta^4 - 2m\alpha_1\eta^2\right\}, \end{aligned}\right\} \quad (197\text{–}7)$$

in which we notice that the variables ξ and η are separated. Let us put each side of this equation equal to the constant $2m\gamma$. Then

$$\frac{\partial S}{\partial \phi} = p \text{ (a constant)},$$

$$\frac{\partial S}{\partial \xi} = \xi\sqrt{2m\alpha_1 + 2m(e^2Z + \gamma)\frac{1}{\xi^2} - \frac{p^2}{\xi^4} - meE\xi^2},$$

$$\frac{\partial S}{\partial \eta} = \eta\sqrt{2m\alpha_1 + 2m(e^2Z - \gamma)\frac{1}{\eta^2} - \frac{p^2}{\eta^4} + meE\eta^2},$$

and the phase integrals are

$$J_\phi = \oint p\,d\phi = 2\pi p, \tag{197–8}$$

$$J_\xi = \tfrac{1}{2}\oint \sqrt{A + 2\frac{B_1}{r} + \frac{C}{r^2} + D_1 r}\,dr, \tag{197–9}$$

$$J_\eta = \tfrac{1}{2}\oint \sqrt{A + 2\frac{B_2}{r} + \frac{C}{r^2} + D_2 r}\,dr, \tag{197–10}$$

where

$$A \equiv 2m\alpha_1, \quad B_1 \equiv m(e^2Z + \gamma), \quad B_2 \equiv m(e^2Z - \gamma), \quad C \equiv -p^2,$$

$$D_1 \equiv -\, meE, \quad D_2 \equiv meE,$$

and r has been put for ξ^2 in the integrand of J_ξ and for η^2 in that of J_η.

To integrate an expression of the form of J_ξ or J_η we can expand the radical by the binomial theorem since D_1 and D_2 are relatively small, getting

$$J = \tfrac{1}{2}\oint \sqrt{A + 2\frac{B}{r} + \frac{C}{r^2} + Dr}\,dr$$

$$= \tfrac{1}{2}\oint \sqrt{A + 2\frac{B}{r} + \frac{C}{r^2}}\,dr + \frac{D}{4}\oint \frac{r\,dr}{\sqrt{A + 2\frac{B}{r} + \frac{C}{r^2}}} + \ldots$$

The first integral is (196.1–8) and the second was evaluated in problem 196.1*a*. Therefore

$$J = \pi i\left\{\frac{B}{\sqrt{A}} + \sqrt{C}\right\} + \pi i\,\frac{D}{2\sqrt{A}}\left\{\frac{3}{2}\frac{B^2}{A^2} - \frac{1}{2}\frac{C}{A}\right\}. \tag{197–11}$$

Next it is necessary to eliminate p from J_ξ and J_η by (197–8) and then to eliminate γ, which occurs only in B_1 and B_2, from the resulting equations, and finally to solve for the energy α_1 as a function of the phase integrals. The elimination, which is somewhat tedious and will not be reproduced here, can best be done by successive approximations, remembering that the terms in D_1 and D_2 are small correction terms. The final result is

$$\alpha_1 = U = -\frac{2\pi^2 me^4 Z^2}{(J_\xi + J_\eta + J_\phi)^2} - \frac{3E}{8\pi^2 meZ}(J_\eta - J_\xi)(J_\xi + J_\eta + J_\phi). \quad (197\text{–}12)$$

To find the stationary states we put

$$J_\xi = n_1 h, \quad J_\eta = n_2 h, \quad J_\phi = n_3 h,$$

getting

$$U = -Nh\frac{Z^2}{(n_1+n_2+n_3)^2} - \frac{3Eh^2}{8\pi^2 meZ}(n_2 - n_1)(n_1+n_2+n_3), \quad (197\text{–}13)$$

where N is the Rydberg constant.

The first term in (197–13) is identical with the Balmer term (193–6). The second term represents the slight deviations of the energy levels produced by the electric field E. The quantum number n_3 associated with the azimuth ϕ corresponds to the azimuthal quantum number k of article 196 and the correspondence principle requires that it change by unity or zero during a transition, the first giving rise to s polarization and the second to p polarization in the radiation emitted at right angles to the electric field.

We shall apply (197–13) to the simplest line of all, the first line of the Lyman series of hydrogen, in which the transition is from a two-quantum level to the basic one-quantum level of the normal atom. The smallest value n_3 can assume is one, as the electron would strike the nucleus if n_3 were zero. Therefore $n_1 = n_2 = 0$ for the one-quantum level, and this level remains single even in the presence of the electric field. The two-quantum level, however, is split up into three levels which we shall denote by H_1, H_2, H_1', where for H_1, $n_1 = 1$, $n_2 = 0$, $n_3 = 1$; for H_2, $n_1 = 0$, $n_2 = 0$, $n_3 = 2$; for H_1', $n_1 = 0$, $n_2 = 1$, $n_3 = 1$. If the transition is from H_1 or H_1' to the one quantum level, the line is polarized p since n_3 remains unchanged, whereas if the transition is from H_2 the line is polarized s since n_3 changes by one unit. Therefore we get a triplet similar to the normal Zeeman triplet of Fig. 162 but with the polarizations reversed. The frequency separation of the components is

$$\Delta\nu = \frac{3h}{4\pi^2 meZ}E. \quad (197\text{–}14)$$

If the transition is between energy levels of higher quantum numbers the structure of the line is more complex, the number of components increasing with the quantum number. Measurement of the field strength shows that the formula is correct quantitatively as well as qualitatively.

Problem 197a. Show that the paraboloids of article 197 have a common focus at the origin, and that the two families intersect orthogonally.

Problem 197b. Plot the two and the three-quantum energy levels for the Stark effect in hydrogen, indicate by arrows the permissible transitions with specification of the polarization of each, and show both the p and the s components of the H_α line on frequency diagrams like that of Fig. 204.

Problem 197c. A particle is attracted by two fixed centers a distance l apart with forces varying inversely as the square of the distance. Show that if confocal ellipsoids and hyperboloids of revolution having their common foci at the two centers are used as coordinate surfaces the variables may be separated in the Hamilton-Jacobi partial differential equation.

197.1. Fine Structure. — In discussing the spectrum of a one-electron atom on the Newtonian dynamics (art. 193), we noted that the energies of elliptical orbits of the same total quantum number are the same, irrespective of eccentricity. If we use the relativity dynamics this degeneracy is removed and a fine structure is revealed which is well confirmed by experiment.

In accord with (161–10) the radial and angular momenta of the electron are

$$p_r = \frac{m\dot{r}}{\sqrt{1 - \beta^2}}, \qquad p_\theta = \frac{mr^2\dot{\theta}}{\sqrt{1 - \beta^2}}, \qquad (197.1\text{–}1)$$

where $\beta \equiv v/c$ and m is the rest mass. Solving for β we have

$$\frac{1}{1 - \beta^2} = 1 + \frac{1}{m^2c^2}\left(p_r^2 + \frac{1}{r^2}p_\theta^2\right),$$

and using (161–12) for the kinetic energy, the Hamiltonian is found to be

$$H = mc^2\sqrt{1 + \frac{1}{m^2c^2}\left(p_r^2 + \frac{1}{r^2}p_\theta^2\right)} - \frac{e^2Z}{r}. \qquad (197.1\text{–}2)$$

Putting this equal to a constant α_1 and separating the variables we get

$$p_\theta = \alpha_2, \quad p_r = \sqrt{A + 2\frac{B}{r} + \frac{C}{r^2}},$$

where

$$A \equiv -m^2c^2 + \frac{\alpha_1{}^2}{c^2}, \quad B \equiv \frac{e^2Z\alpha_1}{c^2}, \quad C \equiv -\alpha_2{}^2 + \frac{e^4Z^2}{c^2}.$$

These give for the phase integrals

$$J_\theta = 2\pi\alpha_2, \quad J_r = 2\pi i\left\{\frac{B}{\sqrt{A}} + \sqrt{C}\right\}. \qquad (197.1\text{–}3)$$

Eliminating α_2

$$2\pi i\frac{B}{\sqrt{A}} = J_r + \sqrt{J_\theta{}^2 - \alpha^2h^2Z^2}, \quad \alpha \equiv \frac{2\pi e^2}{hc},$$

where the dimensionless constant α, which has already appeared in (193–4), is known as the *fine structure constant.*

Solving for α_1, which is contained in both A and B, and putting $J_r = n_rh$ and $J_\theta = n_\theta h$ in accord with the first postulate of the Bohr theory, we have for the energy $U = \alpha_1$

$$U = \frac{2Nh}{\alpha^2}\left[1 + \frac{\alpha^2Z^2}{(n_r + \sqrt{n_\theta{}^2 - \alpha^2Z^2})^2}\right]^{-\frac{1}{2}}, \qquad (197.1\text{–}4)$$

where N is the Rydberg constant. This expression, first obtained by Sommerfeld, does not reduce to (197.1–8) when we neglect the term in α^2Z^2 because the zero of kinetic energy on the relativity theory is quite different from that of the Newtonian dynamics.

Expanding the exact expression (197.1–4) in powers of the small quantity α^2,

$$U = \frac{2Nh}{\alpha^2}\left[1 - \frac{\frac{1}{2}\alpha^2Z^2}{(n_r + \sqrt{n_\theta{}^2 - \alpha^2Z^2})^2} + \frac{\frac{3}{8}\alpha^4Z^4}{(n_r + \sqrt{n_\theta{}^2 - \alpha^2Z^2})^4} + \dots\right]. \qquad (197.1\text{–}5)$$

But, if we put $n \equiv n_r + n_\theta$ and $k \equiv n_\theta$,

$$(n_r + \sqrt{n_\theta{}^2 - \alpha^2Z^2})^2 = \left\{n_r + n_\theta\sqrt{1 - \frac{\alpha^2Z^2}{n_\theta{}^2}}\right\}^2$$

$$= \left\{n_r + n_\theta - \frac{\alpha^2Z^2}{2n_\theta} + \dots\right\}^2 = n^2\left\{1 - \frac{\alpha^2Z^2}{kn} + \dots\right\}.$$

Therefore

$$U = \frac{2Nh}{\alpha^2}\left[1 - \frac{1}{2}\frac{\alpha^2 Z^2}{n^2} - \frac{1}{2}\frac{\alpha^4 Z^4}{kn^3} + \frac{3}{8}\frac{\alpha^4 Z^4}{n^4} + \dots\right]$$

or

$$U - \frac{2Nh}{\alpha^2} = -Nh\frac{Z^2}{n^2} - Nh\frac{\alpha^2 Z^4}{n^4}\left(\frac{n}{k} - \frac{3}{4}\right) + \dots \qquad (197.1\text{–}6)$$

through terms in α^2. This expression is comparable with (193–8), to which it reduces if the term in α^2 is neglected. As k has its greatest value n for a circular orbit, we see that the energy level of the circular orbit is higher than that of any of the elliptical orbits of the same total quantum number n. In fact, the frequency difference of two levels of total quantum number n and azimuthal quantum numbers k and $k + 1$ is

$$\Delta\nu \equiv \frac{U(n,k+1) - U(n,k)}{h} = \frac{N\alpha^2 Z^4}{n^3}\left\{\frac{1}{k} - \frac{1}{k+1}\right\}. \qquad (197.1\text{–}7)$$

The fine structure is wider the larger Z and the smaller n, which is the reverse in both respects of the Stark effect. It is better observed for He^+ than for H because of larger Z and less broadening due to Doppler effect. Since the atom is a plane structure with no electric moment perpendicular to the plane in which θ is measured, the correspondence principle permits only those transitions in which k changes by unity.

Problem 197.1a. Plot the energy levels of hydrogen for $n = 1, 2, 3, 4$ and indicate by arrows the permissible transitions for the first two lines of the Balmer series.

198. Infra-Red Spectra. — In the case of atomic spectra the Bohr theory has scored a success only in the case of two-body atomic structures. So, too, in the case of molecular spectra it is only for the diatomic molecule that the theory is satisfactory.

To start with, we shall picture a diatomic molecule as a dumb-bell in form, the two component atoms being held rigidly at a fixed distance from each other. We shall confine our attention to a polar molecule, formed of a positive and a negative ion.

The only motion of such a molecule which can be quantized is that of rotation about an axis through the center of mass at right angles to the line joining the two atoms. If θ is the angle in the plane of rotation through which the axis of the molecule has turned and I the moment of inertia of the molecule, its kinetic energy is

$T = \frac{1}{2}I\dot{\theta}^2$ and the momentum conjugate to the coordinate θ is the constant angular momentum $p_\theta = I\dot{\theta}$ by (57–1). Hence

$$U = T = \frac{1}{2I}p_\theta^2. \tag{198–1}$$

Therefore the phase integral is

$$J = \int_0^{2\pi} p_\theta d\theta = 2\pi p_\theta. \tag{198–2}$$

The stationary states, given by equating the phase integral to the product of an integer j by Planck's constant, are specified by

$$2\pi p_\theta = jh. \tag{198–3}$$

Eliminating p_θ from (198–3) and (198–1) we find for the energy

$$U = \frac{h^2}{8\pi^2 I}j^2. \tag{198–4}$$

From the second postulate of the Bohr theory we get for the frequency of emission or absorption

$$\nu = \frac{U' - U''}{h} = \frac{h}{8\pi^2 I}(j'^2 - j''^2). \tag{198–5}$$

The correspondence principle requires that the quantum number j shall change by one unit during a transition. Since ν is essentially positive we must have $j' = j'' + 1$, and if we drop the accents on j'',

$$\nu = \frac{h}{8\pi^2 I}(2j + 1). \tag{198–6}$$

The lines are evenly spaced, the frequency interval between successive lines being

$$\Delta\nu = \frac{h}{4\pi^2 I}. \tag{198–7}$$

From it I can be calculated, and, as the masses of the atoms are known, the distance between them can be computed. The spectra under consideration are known as *pure rotation spectra* and are found in the far infra-red. They have been investigated in some detail for such polar molecules as HCl.

If, next, we take into account the possibility that the two atoms constituting a polar diatomic molecule may vibrate along the line joining them as well as rotate about a perpendicular axis through the center of mass, the theory predicts a more complicated spectrum known as the *rotation-vibration spectrum*. Let m_1 and m_2 be the masses of the two ions and r_1 and r_2 their distances from the center of mass. If $r \equiv r_1 + r_2$ and μ is the reduced mass as given by (30–20), $m_1 r_1 = m_2 r_2 = \mu r$ and $m_1 r_1^2 + m_2 r_2^2 = \mu r^2$. Therefore the kinetic energy due to the combined vibration and rotation is

$$T = \tfrac{1}{2}m_1(\dot{r}_1^2 + r_1^2\dot{\theta}^2) + \tfrac{1}{2}m_2(\dot{r}_2^2 + r_2^2\dot{\theta}^2) = \tfrac{1}{2}\mu(\dot{r}^2 + r^2\dot{\theta}^2). \quad (198\text{–}8)$$

We shall suppose that the inverse square force $-e^2/r^2$ of electrostatic attraction is opposed by an inverse cube force $e^2 r_0/r^3$ of repulsion. When $r = r_0$, the two forces are in balance; if $r < r_0$, the repulsion exceeds the attraction; whereas if $r > r_0$, the attraction exceeds the repulsion. Hence r_0 marks the separation for stable equilibrium when the molecule is not in rotation. For small oscillations about this equilibrium separation, we may take $-(e^2/r_0^3)(r - r_0)$ for the force, and, if we put $R \equiv r - r_0$, the equation of motion is

$$\mu\ddot{R} + \frac{e^2}{r_0^3}R = 0.$$

Hence the frequency ν_0 of these oscillations is

$$\nu_0 = \frac{1}{2\pi}\sqrt{\frac{e^2}{\mu r_0^3}} = \frac{1}{2\pi}\sqrt{\frac{e^2}{I r_0}} \quad (198\text{–}9)$$

where I is the equilibrium moment of inertia μr_0^2.

If we put $\rho \equiv r/r_0$ the potential energy associated with the two forces is

$$V = -\frac{e^2}{r} + \frac{e^2 r_0}{2r^2} = -4\pi^2 I\nu_0^2\left(\frac{1}{\rho} - \frac{1}{2\rho^2}\right), \quad (198\text{–}10)$$

and the kinetic energy (198–8) becomes

$$T = \tfrac{1}{2}I(\dot{\rho}^2 + \rho^2\dot{\theta}^2). \quad (198\text{–}11)$$

Therefore the generalized momenta are $p_\rho = I\dot{\rho}$ and $p_\theta = I\rho^2\dot{\theta}$, and the Hamiltonian is

$$H = \frac{1}{2I}\left(p_\rho^2 + \frac{1}{\rho^2}p_\theta^2\right) - 4\pi^2 I\nu_0^2\left(\frac{1}{\rho} - \frac{1}{2\rho^2}\right). \quad (198\text{–}12)$$

Equating this to α_1 and separating the variables we get

$$p_\theta = \alpha_2, \quad p_\rho = 2\pi I\nu_0\sqrt{A + 2\frac{B}{\rho} + \frac{C}{\rho^2}},$$

where

$$A \equiv \frac{\alpha_1}{2\pi^2 I\nu_0^2}, \quad B \equiv 1, \quad C \equiv -\left(1 + \frac{\alpha_2^2}{4\pi^2 I^2\nu_0^2}\right).$$

These give for the phase integrals

$$J_\theta = 2\pi\alpha_2, \quad J_\rho = 4\pi^2 iI\nu_0\left\{\frac{B}{\sqrt{A}} + \sqrt{C}\right\}. \qquad (198\text{–}13)$$

Eliminating α^2 and putting $J_\theta = jh$, $J_\rho = nh$, we have

$$\frac{i}{\sqrt{A}} = \frac{nh}{4\pi^2 I\nu_0} + \sqrt{1 + \frac{j^2h^2}{16\pi^4 I^2\nu_0^2}}. \qquad (198\text{–}14)$$

Since $\Delta\nu_r \equiv h/(4\pi^2 I)$, the frequency interval of the pure rotation spectrum, is very small compared with ν_0, the second term under the radical is small compared with unity. Therefore

$$\frac{i}{\sqrt{A}} = 1 + \frac{nh}{4\pi^2 I\nu_0} + \frac{j^2h^2}{32\pi^4 I^2\nu_0^2} + \ldots$$

and

$$A = -\left[1 - \frac{nh}{2\pi^2 I\nu_0} - \frac{j^2h^2}{16\pi^4 I^2\nu_0^2} + 3\left\{\frac{n^2h^2}{16\pi^4 I^2\nu_0^2} + \frac{nj^2h^3}{64\pi^6 I^3\nu_0^3}\right\} + \ldots\right]$$

where we have retained the term in nj^2 even while neglecting the term in n^3, since j often is a relatively large integer as compared with n.

The energy $U = \alpha_1$ is given by

$$U + 2\pi^2 I\nu_0^2 = nh\nu_0(1 - nx) + \frac{j^2h^2}{8\pi^2 I} - j^2 a_n h \qquad (198\text{–}15)$$

where

$$x \equiv \frac{3h}{8\pi^2 I\nu_0} = \frac{3}{2}\frac{\Delta\nu_r}{\nu_0}, \qquad a_n \equiv n\frac{3h^2}{32\pi^4 I^2\nu_0} = \frac{3}{2}n\nu_0\left(\frac{\Delta\nu_r}{\nu_0}\right)^2.$$

By the second postulate of the Bohr theory the frequency of the radiation emitted during a transition is

$$\nu = \nu_n + B(j'^2 - j''^2) - (a'_n j'^2 - a''_n j''^2), \qquad (198\text{–}16)$$

where

$$\nu_n = n'\nu_0(1 - n'x) - n''\nu_0(1 - n''x) \qquad (198\text{–}17)$$

and $B \equiv h/(8\pi^2 I)$, the single accent referring to the initial state and the double accent to the final state.

Let us consider the structure of a single band, that is, a group of lines for all of which ν_n is the same. If $n' = n'' = 0$ we have the pure rotation spectrum previously discussed. Otherwise, since $\nu_n \gg B$, we may have $j \to j + 1$ as well as $j \to j - 1$. The latter transition gives rise to the *positive* (R) *branch* of the band, the former to the *negative* (P) *branch*. Dropping the accents on j'' and putting $j' = j \pm 1$ to include both branches,

$$\nu = \nu_n + (B - a'_n)(\pm 2j + 1) - (a'_n - a''_n)j^2. \qquad (198\text{–}18)$$

The frequency interval between successive lines is

$$\Delta\nu_j = 2(B - a'_n) - (a'_n - a''_n)(\pm 2j + 1). \qquad (198\text{–}19)$$

Increasing j means increasing frequency for the positive branch and decreasing frequency for the negative branch. Hence, as $a'_n - a''_n$ is positive since $n' > n''$, it follows that the lines in both branches come nearer together as we proceed in the direction of increasing frequency, instead of being evenly spaced as in the pure rotation spectra. This is quite in accord with observation.

Next we study band systems, focusing our attention on the band center ν_n (even though it does not represent an actual line in the spectrum). From (198–17) we find for the frequency interval between the nth and the $n + 1$th energy level

$$\Delta\nu_n = \nu_0\{1 - (2n + 1)x\}, \qquad (198\text{–}20)$$

showing that the energy levels crowd together as the energy increases. This is in good agreement with the observed characteristics of bands in the near infra-red.

Finally we note that, since ν_0 involves the reduced mass μ, the band centers and therefore the whole band system will be shifted if one of the atoms of a diatomic molecule is replaced by an isotope. New isotopes have actually been discovered from the study of these spectra.

Problem 198a. Find the stationary states and the energy levels of a linear simple harmonic oscillator. Show by applying the correspondence principle that the frequency of the radiation emitted by such an oscillator on the Bohr theory is identical with its dynamical frequency of vibration.

199. Electronic Bands. — If, in addition to changes in the energies of vibration and of rotation of a diatomic molecule, there occurs at the same time a change in the energy of the electronic configuration of one or both atoms, the frequency of the emitted radiation, being proportional to the total change in energy, is much higher and the band spectrum produced may lie in the visible or even in the ultra-violet region. Such a band is called an *electronic band*. On account of the change in electronic configuration, the constants ν_0, x and I in this case are different in the initial and the final states.

We shall consider only the structure of a single band, writing ν_e for the contribution to the frequency due to the change in electronic energy and ν_n for that due to the change in vibrational energy. Then, designating the initial state by one accent and the final state by two as usual, we have from (198–15)

$$\nu = \nu_e + \nu_n + \left(\frac{h}{8\pi^2 I'} - a'_n\right)j'^2 - \left(\frac{h}{8\pi^2 I''} - a''_n\right)j''^2. \quad (199\text{–}1)$$

As there may be electric oscillations perpendicular to the plane of the rotation in the classical description of this motion on account of the changing electronic configuration, the correspondence principle permits the transition $j \rightarrow j$ (Zero Q branch) as well as that in which $j \rightarrow j - 1$ (Positive R branch) and that in which $j \rightarrow j + 1$ (Negative P branch). Furthermore, as the changing electric configuration by itself may supply all the necessary electric oscillations, these bands can be produced by non-polar as well as by polar molecules.

Putting $j'' = j$ and $j' = j \pm 1$ to include both the R and the P branches,

$$\nu = A \pm 2Bj + Cj^2 \quad (199\text{–}2)$$

where

$$A \equiv \nu_e + \nu_n + \left(\frac{h}{8\pi^2 I'} - a'_n\right), \quad B \equiv \frac{h}{8\pi^2 I'} - a'_n,$$

$$C \equiv \frac{h}{8\pi^2}\left(\frac{1}{I'} - \frac{1}{I''}\right) - (a'_n - a''_n),$$

whereas for the Q branch

$$\nu = A_0 + Cj^2, \quad A_0 \equiv \nu_e + \nu_n. \tag{199-3}$$

All three branches are represented by parabolas in j. The structure of the band is shown in the Fortrat diagram of Fig. 210 for the

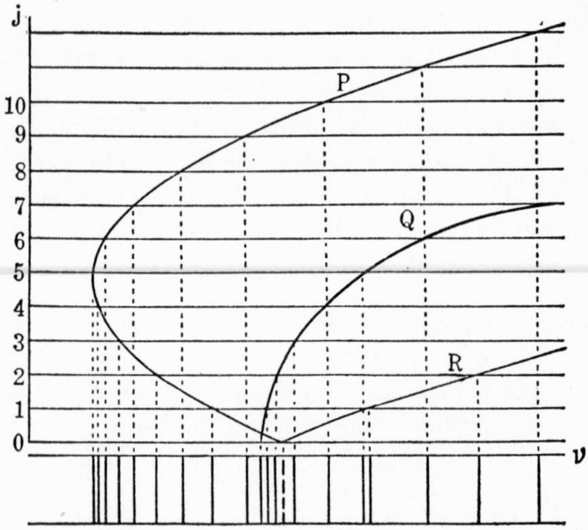

FIG. 210.

case $C > 0$. In the lower part of the figure is represented the spectrum corresponding to the various possible transitions. The head of the band is the line nearest to the vertex of the P parabola. It is obtained by setting the derivative of ν with respect to j equal to zero in the equation for the P branch, that is,

$$B - Cj = 0,$$

and taking the integral value of j which most nearly satisfies this equation. While the lines are most crowded near the head, they do not become infinitely dense as at the convergence frequency of an atomic spectrum. The band pictured is said to degrade toward the violet. If $C < 0$, the parabolas point in the opposite direction and the band degrades toward the red.

200. Wave Mechanics. — Although the Bohr theory has been successful in furnishing an algorithm whereby the frequencies of the radiation from two-body atomic or molecular structures may be calculated, it has been only through the introduction of an extraneous concept — the correspondence principle — that it has been able to provide a selection principle to determine what transitions can occur and to give a rather uncertain estimate of the intensity of the radiation emitted. Moreover the attempt to extend the Bohr concepts to as simple a structure as the normal helium atom containing but two electrons outside the nucleus has led to definitely erroneous results.

These limitations of the Bohr theory have led to the development of a new theory known as *wave mechanics*. Initiated by de Broglie in 1926, it was put into more serviceable form by Schrödinger and has been developed and extended by Heisenberg and Dirac. We shall confine our consideration of wave mechanics to conservative dynamical systems of three degrees of freedom, such as a hydrogen atom consisting of a fixed nucleus located at the origin and a single electron.

The wave mechanics interprets the conservation laws of classical physics as operator equations, replacing the three rectangular components of linear momentum in the classical expressions by the differential operators $(h/2\pi i)\dfrac{\partial}{\partial x}$, $(h/2\pi i)\dfrac{\partial}{\partial y}$, $(h/2\pi i)\dfrac{\partial}{\partial z}$ respectively, where h is Planck's constant and $i \equiv \sqrt{-1}$. For instance, if U is the constant energy of the hydrogen atom, the classical law of conservation of energy

$$\frac{1}{2m}(p_x^2 + p_y^2 + p_z^2) - \frac{e^2}{r} = U, \quad r \equiv \sqrt{x^2 + y^2 + z^2},$$

becomes

$$-\frac{h^2}{8\pi^2 m}\left(\frac{\partial^2}{\partial x^2} + \frac{\partial^2}{\partial y^2} + \frac{\partial^2}{\partial z^2}\right) - \frac{e^2}{r} = U. \qquad (200\text{–}1)$$

For this relation to have physical meaning, we must provide a function Ψ (x, y, z) for the operator to act upon. Applying both sides of the equation to this function we get the *Schrödinger equation*

$$-\frac{h^2}{8\pi^2 m}\left(\frac{\partial^2\Psi}{\partial x^2}+\frac{\partial^2\Psi}{\partial y^2}+\frac{\partial^2\Psi}{\partial z^2}\right)-\frac{e^2}{r}\Psi = U\Psi, \quad (200\text{–}2)$$

which is usually written

$$H\Psi = U\Psi, \quad (200\text{–}3)$$

where the energy operator H is obtained from the Hamiltonian of article 57 by replacing each p_x by $(h/2\pi i)\dfrac{\partial}{\partial x}$ etc.

The function Ψ (x, y, z) obtained by solving this differential equation is interpreted as representing the *physical state* of the atomic mechanism, the meaning of which will be explained in more detail later. As Ψ has physical significance it must be continuous, single-valued, everywhere finite, and vanish at infinity. Now the theory of differential equations teaches that (200–3) has solutions satisfying these requirements in the case of negative energy only for a discrete set of values of the parameter U. These values of U, which we shall designate by $U_1, U_2, \ldots U_n \ldots$ are known as the *eigenvalues* of the operator H, and the corresponding solutions $\Psi_1, \Psi_2, \ldots \Psi_n \ldots$ as its *eigenfunctions*. In the case of the hydrogen atom the eigenvalues of the energy operator H may be shown to be

$$U_n = -\frac{Nh}{n^2}, \quad n = 1, 2, 3 \ldots$$

agreeing with the energy levels (193–6) predicted by the Bohr theory.

While the energy operator H is of fundamental importance, the theory is not limited to considerations of energy. We might be interested in the Z component of the angular momentum of the electron. The classical law of conservation of this component of angular momentum is

$$xp_y - yp_x = \gamma \text{ (a constant)}$$

which yields the operator relation

$$\frac{h}{2\pi i}\left(x\frac{\partial}{\partial y} - y\frac{\partial}{\partial x}\right) = \gamma, \quad (200\text{–}4)$$

or the differential equation

$$\frac{h}{2\pi i}\left(x\frac{\partial\chi}{\partial y} - y\frac{\partial\chi}{\partial x}\right) = \gamma\chi, \qquad (200\text{–}5)$$

if we allow (200–4) to operate on the function $\chi\ (x, y, z)$. This is usually written

$$M_z\chi = \gamma\chi, \qquad (200\text{–}6)$$

where M_z is the operator formed from the classical expression for the component of angular momentum under consideration by replacing each p_x by $(h/2\pi i)\dfrac{\partial}{\partial x}$ etc.

If we write (200–5) in spherical coordinates r, θ, ϕ with polar axis along Z, it assumes the simple form

$$\frac{h}{2\pi i}\frac{\partial\chi}{\partial\phi} = \gamma\chi, \qquad (200\text{–}7)$$

of which the solution, to within an arbitrary constant factor, is

$$\chi = e^{(2\pi i/h)\gamma\phi} = \cos\frac{2\pi}{h}\gamma\phi + i\sin\frac{2\pi}{h}\gamma\phi.$$

For this solution to be single-valued, γ must be an integral multiple of $h/2\pi$. Hence the eigenvalues of (200–5) are $\gamma_m = mh/2\pi$ and the corresponding eigenfunctions are

$$\chi_m = e^{im\phi} \qquad (200\text{–}8)$$

where m in an integer.

With this introduction we are now ready to state the

First Principle of Wave Mechanics. — To every mechanical quantity a there corresponds an operator A obtained by replacing p_x by $(h/2\pi i)\dfrac{\partial}{\partial x}$ etc. in the classical expression for a. If we measure a experimentally, we will always find one of the eigenvalues of the operator A, that is, one of the values of the parameter α in the differential equation

$$A\Phi = \alpha\Phi \qquad (200\text{–}9)$$

for which the solution $\Phi\ (x, y, z)$ is everywhere finite, continuous and single-valued, and vanishes at infinity.

Although the eigenvalues of the energy and angular momentum operators discussed above form discrete sets and therefore the same is true of the possible energy levels and angular momentum values, the operators of many simple mechanical quantities have continuous sets of eigenvalues and therefore all values of these quantities are observable. We shall confine our attention, however, to cases where a discrete set exists.

The eigenfunctions of an operator A which has *real* eigenvalues, as the operators corresponding to physical quantities must, may be shown to be *orthogonal*. This means that, if we denote by Φ^*_k the complex conjugate of Φ_k formed by replacing i by $-i$, then

$$\int_{-\infty}^{\infty}\int_{-\infty}^{\infty}\int_{-\infty}^{\infty} \Phi_k^* \Phi_l \, dx\, dy\, dz = 0, \quad k \neq l. \qquad (200\text{–}10)$$

Furthermore, as the operator equation (200–9) is linear, the eigenfunctions are determined only to within an arbitrary constant factor. We may choose this constant coefficient so that

$$\int_{-\infty}^{\infty}\int_{-\infty}^{\infty}\int_{-\infty}^{\infty} \Phi_k^* \Phi_k \, dx\, dy\, dz = 1. \qquad (200\text{–}11)$$

Then the eigenfunctions are said to be *normalized* to unity. We shall suppose that all eigenfunctions are so normalized. Finally the eigenfunctions of an operator form a complete set, that is, any arbitrary function of x, y, z, which satisfies certain unimportant conditions can be expanded as a series in Φ_1, Φ_2, . . . with constant coefficients. If Ψ is such a function, then, we can put

$$\Psi = c_1\Phi_1 + c_2\Phi_2 \ldots + c_k\Phi_k \ldots \qquad (200\text{–}12)$$

Now suppose we consider two mechanical quantities a and b with operators A and B respectively. Their eigenfunctions Φ_k and Ψ_l are the allowable solutions, and their eigenvalues the corresponding parameters α_k and β_l, of the differential equations

$$A\Phi_k = \alpha_k\Phi_k, \quad B\Psi_l = \beta_l\Psi_l. \qquad (200\text{–}13)$$

Let us now measure experimentally the quantity b. According to the first principle we must find as a result of the measurement one of the eigenvalues of its operator, say β_m. Then the corresponding eigenfunction Ψ_m determines the physical state of the system so far as revealed by our measurement. We now ask ourselves this question:

what was the value of the quantity a when we made the measurement of b?. As the eigenfunctions of A constitute a complete set, we can express the state Ψ_m in terms of them by the series

$$\Psi_m = c_1\Phi_1 + c_2\Phi_2 \ldots + c_k\Phi_k \ldots \qquad (200\text{–}14)$$

as noted above. Now we can make use of the

Second Principle of Wave Mechanics. — If a state Ψ is expressed in terms of the eigenfunctions of an operator A by the series $\Psi = \sum_l c_l\Phi_l$, the probability that the quantity a of which A is the operator is equal to a specified eigenvalue α_n of A is $c^*{}_n c_n$. Consequently the measurement of b does not in general determine the value of a. The utmost information regarding a to be derived from the measurement of b is that the probability that a has the value α_1 is $c^*{}_1 c_1$, the probability that it has the value α_2 is $c^*{}_2 c_2$, etc. Only when the two operators have the *same* eigenfunctions and therefore $\Psi_m = \Phi_m$ can we say with certainty that a has the value α_m when it is known that b has the value β_m.

To show the consistency of this principle we must prove that the probability that a has the value of *some* one of its eigenvalues is unity, that is, that $\sum_n c^*{}_n c_n = 1$. This is easily done. Multiplying (200–14) by the conjugate equation

$$\Psi^*{}_m = c^*{}_1\Phi^*{}_1 + c^*{}_2\Phi^*{}_2 \ldots + c^*{}_l\Phi^*{}_l \ldots$$

and integrating over the three coordinates we have

$$1 = \sum_n c^*{}_n c_n, \qquad (200\text{–}15)$$

since both the Ψ_m's and the Φ_n's are normalized orthogonal functions.

We note that the wave mechanics is a purely statistical theory. It does not attempt, like the Bohr theory, to give a detailed picture of a microscopic mechanism, but contents itself with the specification of probabilities. In this respect it may be likened to the kinetic theory of gases.

If Ψ_m and Ψ_n are two eigenfunctions of the energy operator and U_m and U_n the corresponding eigenvalues it may be shown that the probability of a transition from the first of these states to the second, with emission of radiation such as would proceed from a classical electric dipole oscillating along the X axis with frequency $(U_m - U_n)/h$, is proportional to

$$X_{mn} = \int_{-\infty}^{\infty}\int_{-\infty}^{\infty}\int_{-\infty}^{\infty} \Psi_n^* x \Psi_m \, dx \, dy \, dz. \qquad (200\text{–}16)$$

By calculating these integrals definite selection rules are obtained without invoking extraneous principles, such as the correspondence principle of the Bohr theory. If $X_{mn} = 0$, the specified transition is prohibited. Note that the second postulate of the Bohr theory remains valid in wave mechanics, although the determination of the stationary states is made by a very different procedure.

As the solution of the Schrödinger equation for the hydrogen atom requires a greater knowledge of analysis than has been assumed of the reader of this book, we shall choose an even simpler mechanism for the purpose of applying the methods of wave mechanics, namely, the rigid diatomic molecule discussed in article 198. Furthermore we shall treat it as a system of only one degree of freedom by confining the motion to rotation in the XY plane. As there is no potential energy, the second term on the left of (200–2) drops out, and if we express the Laplacian in the parenthesis in spherical coordinates by (79–5) with $r = a$ and $\sin\theta = 1$ held constant, we obtain

$$\frac{\partial^2\Psi}{\partial\phi^2} + \frac{8\pi^2 I}{h^2} U\Psi = 0, \qquad (200\text{–}17)$$

where I is the moment of inertia of the molecule.

The single-valued normalized solutions of (200–17) are

$$\Psi_m = \frac{1}{\sqrt{2\pi}} e^{im\phi}, \qquad m^2 \equiv \frac{8\pi^2 I}{h^2} U,$$

where m is a positive or negative integer, and therefore the energy levels are

$$U = \frac{h^2}{8\pi^2 I} m^2 \qquad (200\text{–}18)$$

in agreement with (198–4). This agreement is spurious, however, as the physical mechanism is really of two degrees of freedom, and when investigated on that basis the Schrödinger equation leads to energy values proportional to $m(m + 1)$ instead of m^2. Consequently we must consider the example under consideration merely as illustrative of the methods of wave mechanics rather than as representative of the diatomic molecule. Actually the wave mechanical solution of the problem with $m(m + 1)$ replacing m^2 agrees better with observation than that given by the Bohr theory.

Since the eigenfunctions (200–8) of the angular momentum are identical with those of the energy, the measurement of either determines the other uniquely. When the energy has the value (200–18) the angular momentum is $mh/2\pi$.

To find the transition probabilities (200–16) we have $x \pm iy = ae^{\pm i\phi}$ and therefore

$$X_{mn} \pm iY_{mn} = \frac{a}{2\pi}\int_0^{2\pi} e^{i(m-n\pm 1)\phi}\, d\phi = \begin{vmatrix} a \text{ if } n = m \pm 1, \\ 0 \text{ if } n \neq m \pm 1. \end{vmatrix}$$

Hence only those transitions are allowed for which the quantum number decreases by one unit, a rule identical with that predicted by the correspondence principle.

Although in many simple cases the wave mechanics leads to the same energy levels as the Bohr theory, it frequently gives expressions such as $n(n + 1)$ where the Bohr theory leads to the square of the quantum number n. Finally, calculations indicate that the wave mechanics gives correct energy levels in the case of the normal helium atom and other more complicated atoms.

REFERENCES

BALY, E. C. C.: *Spectroscopy*, Longmans, Green & Co., London.

SOMMERFELD, ARNOLD: *Atomic Structure and Spectral Lines*, E. P. Dutton & Co., New York.

RICHTMYER, F. K.: *Introduction to Modern Physics*, McGraw-Hill Book Co., New York.

SLATER AND FRANK: *Introduction to Theoretical Physics*, McGraw-Hill Book Co., New York.

DEBROGLIE, LOUIS: *Théorie de la Quantification dans la nouvelle Mécanique*, Hermann et Cie, Paris.

PAULING AND WILSON: *Introduction to Quantum Mechanics*, McGraw-Hill Book Co., New York.

ROJANSKY, VLADIMIR: *Introductory Quantum Mechanics*, Prentice-Hall, New York.

INDEX

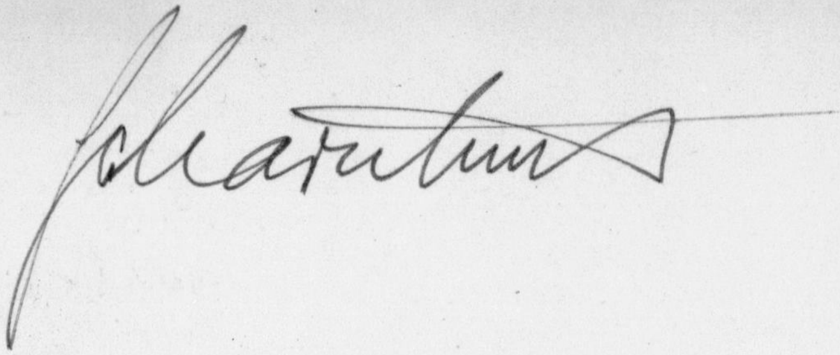